Additional copies of *Aviation Weather and Weather Services* are available from

Gleim Publications, Inc.
P.O. Box 12848 • University Station
Gainesville, Florida 32604
(352) 375-0772
(800) 87-GLEIM or (800) 874-5346
FAX: (352) 375-6940
Internet: www.gleim.com | Email: avmarketing@gleim.com

The price is $29.95 (subject to change without notice). Orders must be prepaid. Call us, order online, or use the order form on page 551. Shipping and handling charges apply to all orders. Add applicable sales tax to shipments within Florida.

Gleim Publications, Inc. guarantees the immediate refund of all resalable materials purchased directly from Gleim Publications, Inc. if they are returned within 30 days. Shipping and handling charges are nonrefundable. Returns of books purchased from bookstores and other resellers should be made to the respective bookstore or reseller.

REVIEWERS AND CONTRIBUTORS

Eric L. Crump, CMEL, CFII, AGI, B.S., Middle Tennessee State University, is our aviation editor. Mr. Crump researched changes, wrote and edited additions, and incorporated revisions into the text.

John F. Rebstock, B.S., Fisher School of Accounting, University of Florida, reviewed portions of the edition and composed the page layout.

The many FAA and NWS employees who helped, in person or by telephone, primarily in Gainesville, Orlando, Oklahoma City, and Washington, DC.

The CFIs who have worked with us throughout the years to develop and improve our pilot training materials.

A PERSONAL THANKS

This manual would not have been possible without the extraordinary effort and dedication of Jacob Brunny, Kyle Cadwallader, Julie Cutlip, Mumbi Ngugi, Eileen Nickl, Teresa Soard, and Joanne Strong, who typed the entire manuscript and all revisions and drafted and laid out the diagrams and illustrations in this book.

The authors also appreciate the production and editorial assistance of Christine Bertrand, Ellen Buhl, Katie Goodrich, James Harvin, Jean Marzullo, Shane Rapp, Victoria Rodriguez, and Martha Willis.

Finally, we appreciate the encouragement, support, and tolerance of our families throughout this project.

Groundwood Paper and Highlighters – This book is printed on high quality groundwood paper. It is lightweight and easy to recycle. We recommend that you purchase a highlighter specifically designed to be non-bleed-through (e.g., Avery Glidestick™) at your local office supply store.

FIFTH EDITION

AVIATION WEATHER AND WEATHER SERVICES

by

Irvin N. Gleim, Ph.D., CFII

and

Garrett W. Gleim, CFII

ABOUT THE AUTHORS

Irvin N. Gleim earned his private pilot certificate in 1965 from the Institute of Aviation at the University of Illinois, where he subsequently received his Ph.D. He is a commercial pilot and flight instructor (instrument) with multiengine and seaplane ratings and is a member of the Aircraft Owners and Pilots Association, American Bonanza Society, Civil Air Patrol, Experimental Aircraft Association, National Association of Flight Instructors, and Seaplane Pilots Association. He is the author of flight maneuvers and practical test prep books for the private, sport, instrument, commercial, and flight instructor certificates/ratings and the author of study guides for the private/recreational, sport, instrument, commercial, flight/ground instructor, fundamentals of instructing, airline transport pilot, and flight engineer FAA knowledge tests. Additional pilot training books are *Pilot Handbook* and *FAR/AIM*.

Dr. Gleim has also written articles for professional accounting and business law journals and is the author of widely used review manuals for the CIA (Certified Internal Auditor) exam, the CMA (Certified Management Accountant) exam, the CPA (Certified Public Accountant) exam, and the EA (IRS Enrolled Agent) exam. He is Professor Emeritus, Fisher School of Accounting, University of Florida, and is a CFM, CIA, CMA, and CPA.

Garrett W. Gleim earned his private pilot certificate in 1997 in a Piper Super Cub. He is a commercial pilot (single and multi-engine), ground instructor (advanced and instrument), and flight instructor (instrument and multi-engine), and he is a member of the Aircraft Owners and Pilots Association and the National Association of Flight Instructors. He is the author of study guides for the private/recreational, sport, instrument, commercial, flight/ground instructor, fundamentals of instructing, and airline transport pilot FAA knowledge tests. He received a Bachelor of Science in Economics from The Wharton School, University of Pennsylvania.

Gleim Publications, Inc.
P.O. Box 12848 · University Station
Gainesville, Florida 32604

(352) 375-0772
(800) 87-GLEIM or (800) 874-5346
FAX: (352) 375-6940

Internet: www.gleim.com
Email: admin@gleim.com

ISSN 1098-450X

ISBN 978-1-58194-680-2

First Printing: May 2008

This is the first printing of the fifth edition of *Aviation Weather and Weather Services*.

Please email update@gleim.com with **AWWS 5-1** in the subject or text. You will receive our current update as a reply. Updates are available until the next edition is published.

EXAMPLE:

To: update@gleim.com
From: *your email address*
Subject: **AWWS 5-1**

HELP!!

Please send any corrections and suggestions for subsequent editions to the authors, c/o Gleim Publications, Inc. The last page in this book has been reserved for you to make comments and suggestions. It can be torn out and mailed to Gleim Publications, Inc.

Please bring Gleim books to the attention of flight instructors, fixed base operators, and others with a potential interest in flying. Wide distribution of our books and increased interest in flying depend on your assistance and good word. Thank you.

NOTE: UPDATES

If necessary, we will develop an update for *Aviation Weather and Weather Services*. Send an email to update@gleim.com as described above and visit our website for the latest updates and information on all of our products. To continue providing our customers with first-rate service, we request that questions about our materials be sent to us via mail, email, or fax. The appropriate staff member will give each question thorough consideration and a prompt response. Questions concerning orders, prices, shipments, or payments will be handled via telephone by our competent and courteous customer service staff.

TABLE OF CONTENTS

PREFACE

The purpose of this book is to provide an up-to-date compilation of all the FAA's weather publications in one easy-to-understand and easy-to-use book. This book is largely a reformation of *Aviation Weather* (AC 00-6A) and *Aviation Weather Services* (AC 00-45F -- October 2007), but other ACs are covered as well.

Parts I and II contain 16 study units, which are a restatement and amplification of each of the 16 chapters in AC 00-6A: *Aviation Weather*. We have broken *Aviation Weather* into Parts I and II to differentiate the advanced topics in Part II from the more basic topics in Part I.

The FAA's AC 00-6A: *Aviation Weather* is 219 pages in length. After editing the material in *Aviation Weather* and presenting it in larger type and in outline format, our outline is 208 pages in length. Our outline is much easier to read and study. We explain how to study each study unit, including the material to be scanned vs. the important material to be studied.

More importantly, you learn more from our outline. Your mind is not a word processor. It does not deal in terms of sentences and paragraphs. Your mind works with concepts, and our outline presents concepts and their relationship to other concepts.

Similarly, the FAA's AC 00-45F: *Aviation Weather Services* (AWS) is 390 pages in length. Our Part III of this book, which outlines AWS, is 290 pages in length. Our outline includes the necessary and useful tables, diagrams, weather maps, charts, etc., that appear in AWS.

The images used throughout this book are taken directly from the FAA Advisory Circulars on which the book is based (AC 00-6A and AC 00-45F). You may notice that the images in Parts I and II look different than the images in Part III. This is because of the difference in image type between the two ACs. You also may note a difference in the quality of the images presented throughout the book. This disparity is merely a reflection of the quality of the images provided in the original FAA texts. Where possible, Gleim has improved the quality of the images to provide you with the best reference material available based on the FAA's weather-related ACs.

NOTE: We provide guidance on topics that are important and need to be studied vs. topics that are not necessary for most pilots to study. We also have 100% coverage of all material in the FAA's AC 00-6A and AC 00-45F. Our index (beginning on page 543) is very thorough so you can research any topic, concept, etc., you desire.

Enjoy Flying Safely!

Irvin N. Gleim
Garrett W. Gleim

May 2008

PART I:
AVIATION WEATHER

(2 pages of outline)

Aviation Weather was published jointly by the FAA and National Weather Service (NWS) in 1975. The book had previously included weather services (e.g., then available reports and forecasts); however, these prior editions quickly went out of date. In 1975, *Aviation Weather* was accompanied by *Aviation Weather Services* (AC 00-45A). Subsequent editions of *Aviation Weather Services* were published in 1979, 1985, 1995, and 1999. AC 00-45F was published in October 2007.

NOTE: Gleim Publications, Inc. does not have the FAA's problem in staying up to date, since we revise and reprint our books frequently. Thus, we can and will provide pilots with all current relevant weather information in one book.

Aviation Weather (AC 00-6A) contains 16 chapters, which are outlined on pages 3 through 208 of this book. Most figures in *Aviation Weather* are reproduced. Only those that do not add to or facilitate understanding of the topics explained in the outline are omitted. Because the images were created in 1975, you will notice that they are not as rich in color as the images in Part III of this book, which were produced much more recently. We expect the FAA to revise and refresh this book in the near future. When new and updated images are available from the FAA, we will incorporate them into our text.

Additional information and explanations have been added to our outline where they facilitate learning and understanding of weather by pilots. You, as a pilot, should learn and understand aviation weather as presented in Study Units 1 through 12 in Part I of this book.

Part I: Aviation Weather

1. The Earth's Atmosphere
2. Temperature
3. Atmospheric Pressure and Altimetry
4. Wind
5. Moisture, Cloud Formation, and Precipitation
6. Stable and Unstable Air
7. Clouds
8. Air Masses and Fronts
9. Turbulence
10. Icing
11. Thunderstorms
12. Common IFR Producers

Study Units 13 through 16, which are presented as Part II of this book, cover specialized topics that may be beyond your present interest.

Part II: Aviation Weather -- Over and Beyond

13. High Altitude Weather
14. Arctic Weather
15. Tropical Weather
16. Soaring Weather

You do **not** have to read the FAA's *Aviation Weather* (AC 00-6A) in conjunction with this outline. We have presented all of the information that is in *Aviation Weather*. Our contribution is to present the information in a format that will facilitate **knowledge transfer** to you. Our outline is easy to study because you seek a working knowledge of weather as it relates to flying.

Our outline is effective. Remember that human minds are not word processing computers that deal with sentences and paragraphs. Human minds deal with concepts and how they relate to other concepts -- which is exactly what our outline presentation facilitates for you.

Of the 16 chapters in *Aviation Weather*, the FAA has "In Closing" sections at the back of eight chapters. In addition to a summary, the FAA's "In Closing" sections provide additional comments on and insight into chapter discussion. We have provided an "In Closing" section at the end of each Gleim study unit, which is a summary of the FAA's "In Closing" section, if one exists, and our summary of the material.

HOW TO STUDY EACH GLEIM STUDY UNIT

1. Each study unit begins with a listing of the study unit's topics.

2. Before beginning to study (i.e., learn from) the outline, think about the subject of the study unit and how the study unit's topics relate to the overall subject of the outline. Anticipate what will be said in the outline about these topics (even if you have never studied the topics). This step should require only 3 to 5 minutes.

3. Study the outline. Studying differs from reading in that studying, by definition, results in understanding. In other words, by studying, you are internalizing weather information so you can use it as a pilot in the future.

4. In each study unit, ask yourself

    a. What each topic is about and how it affects your present and future flying,

    b. What was covered on each page as you complete each page,

    c. How well the "In Closing" section of the outline summarized and gave you further insight into the study unit, and

    d. How you would have improved the study unit if you had to explain the topics in the study unit to your flight instructor or another pilot.

5. Relate each study unit's coverage to the expected coverage in other study units by looking back to the Table of Contents on page v.

6. Make notes as appropriate on pages 553 and 554 to be sent to your author upon completion of your study of *Aviation Weather and Weather Services*.

STUDY UNIT ONE
THE EARTH'S ATMOSPHERE

(4 pages of outline)

Please take a few minutes to study each of the concepts listed above and anticipate/imagine what they are and how they relate to the other listed concepts.

1.1 INTRODUCTION

1. Our restless **atmosphere** is almost constantly in motion as it strives to reach equilibrium.

2. Because the sun heats the atmosphere unequally, differences in pressure result, which cause a series of never-ending air movements.

3. These air movements set up chain reactions which culminate in a continuing variety of weather.

4. Virtually all of our activities are affected by weather, but aviation is affected most of all.

1.2 COMPOSITION

1. Air is a mixture of several gases.

   a. When completely dry, it is about 78% nitrogen and 21% oxygen.

   b. The remaining 1% is other gases such as argon, carbon dioxide, neon, helium, and others.

   c. However, air is never completely dry. It always contains some water vapor in amounts varying from almost zero to about 5% by volume.

1.3 VERTICAL STRUCTURE

1.   The atmosphere is classified into layers, or spheres, by the characteristics exhibited in these layers. See Figure 2 below.

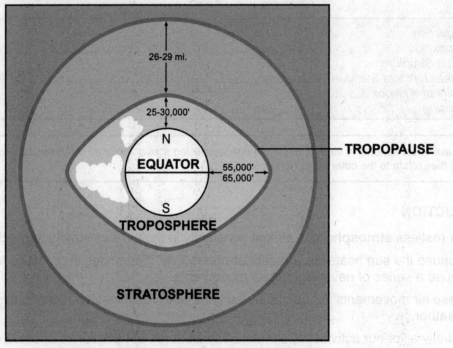

Figure 2. Earth's Atmosphere to 29 Miles High

a.   The **troposphere** is the layer from the surface to an average altitude of about 7 mi.

   1)   It is characterized by an overall decrease of temperature with increasing altitude.
   2)   The height of the troposphere varies with latitude and seasons.
   3)   It slopes from about 20,000 ft. over the poles to about 65,000 ft. over the Equator (4-12 mi.).
   4)   It is higher in summer than in winter.

b.   At the top of the troposphere is the **tropopause**, a transition zone marking the boundary between the troposphere and the layer above, the stratosphere.

   1)   The thickness of the tropopause varies from several discrete layers in some regions to entirely broken up in others.
   2)   The tropopause acts to trap most of the water vapor in the troposphere.
   3)   It is characterized by decreasing winds and constant temperatures with increases in altitude.

c.   Above the tropopause is the **stratosphere**, i.e., beginning at 4-12 mi.

   1)   This layer is characterized by relatively small changes in temperatures with height except for a warming trend near the top (26-29 mi.) and a near absence of water vapor.

1.4 THE INTERNATIONAL STANDARD ATMOSPHERE (ISA)

1. The International Standard Atmosphere (ISA) is a fixed standard of reference for engineers and meteorologists.

2. To arrive at a standard, the average conditions throughout the atmosphere for all latitudes, seasons, and altitudes have been used.

3. ISA consists of a specified sea-level temperature and pressure: 15°C (59°F) and 29.92 in. of mercury (Hg).

    a. It also consists of specific rates of decrease of temperature and pressure with height: 2°C per 1,000 ft. and 1 in. Hg per 1,000 ft.

4. These standards are used for calibrating pressure altimeters and developing aircraft performance data.

1.5 DENSITY AND HYPOXIA

1. Air is matter and has weight.

    a. Since it is a gas, it is compressible.
    b. Thus, as its pressure increases, its **density** also increases.

2. The pressure that the atmosphere exerts on a given surface is the result of the weight of the air above that surface.

    a. Thus, air near the surface of the Earth exerts more pressure and is more dense than air at high altitudes.
    b. There is a decrease of air density and pressure with height.

3. The rate at which the lungs absorb oxygen depends on the pressure exerted by oxygen in the air. Oxygen makes up about 20% of the atmosphere.

    a. Since air pressure decreases as altitude increases, the oxygen pressure also decreases.
    b. A pilot continuously gaining altitude or making a prolonged flight at high altitude without supplemental oxygen will likely suffer from a deficiency of oxygen.
    c. This deficiency of oxygen results in **hypoxia**, which may cause

        1) A feeling of exhaustion,
        2) Impairment of vision and judgment, and
        3) Unconsciousness.

4. FAR 91.211 requires you to use aviation breathing oxygen for any flight in excess of 30 min. at cabin pressure altitudes above 12,500 ft. MSL up to and including 14,000 ft. MSL.

    a. You are required to use oxygen continuously when piloting an airplane at cabin pressure altitudes above 14,000 ft. MSL.
    b. Your passengers are required to have continuous oxygen provided at cabin pressure altitudes above 15,000 ft. MSL.
    c. FARs concerning commercial flight require that supplemental oxygen be provided to pilots and used at even lower cabin pressure altitudes.
    d. Hypoxia may affect night vision adversely at altitudes as low as 5,000 ft. MSL.
    e. If you feel fatigued, drowsy, etc., descend and see if you begin to feel better.

1.6 IN CLOSING

1. The troposphere extends upward to an average altitude of about 7 mi.

   a. The tropopause is a transition zone between the troposphere and stratosphere.
   b. The stratosphere is next with small changes in temperature.

2. International Standard Atmosphere (ISA)

   a. Sea-level temperature and pressure is 59°F (15°C) and 29.92 in. Hg
   b. Average lapse rate (i.e., decrease of temperature and pressure with altitude) is 2°C per 1,000 ft. and 1 in. Hg per 1,000 ft.

3. Air pressure decreases with altitude, and insufficient oxygen is available to pilots beginning at about 10,000 to 12,000 ft. MSL.

   a. Oxygen deficiency is called hypoxia.

END OF STUDY UNIT

STUDY UNIT TWO
TEMPERATURE

(7 pages of outline)

Please take a few minutes to study each of the concepts listed above and anticipate/imagine what they are and how they relate to the other listed concepts.

2.1 INTRODUCTION

1.   Temperature affects every aspect of weather and aviation.
2.   Temperature variation is the cause of most weather phenomena.

   a.   It is a major factor in the determination of aircraft performance.

2.2 TEMPERATURE AND HEAT

1.   The temperature of a particular substance, such as air or water, is a measurement of the average kinetic energy of the molecules in that substance, relative to some set standard.

   a.   Heat is energy which is being transferred from one object to another because of the temperature difference between them.

   b.   After being transferred, this heat is stored as internal energy.

2.   A specific amount of heat absorbed by or removed from a substance raises or lowers its temperature a definite amount.

   a.   Each substance has its unique temperature change for the specific change in heat.

   b.   EXAMPLE: If a land surface and a water surface have the same temperature and an equal amount of heat is added, the land surface becomes hotter than the water surface. Conversely, with equal heat loss, the land becomes colder than the water.

3.   The Earth receives energy from the sun in the form of solar radiation.

   a.   The Earth, in turn, radiates energy, and this outgoing radiation is "terrestrial radiation."

   b.   The average heat gained from incoming solar radiation must equal heat lost through terrestrial radiation in order to keep the Earth from getting progressively hotter or colder.

      1)   This balance is world-wide; we must consider regional and local imbalances which create temperature variations.

2.3 TEMPERATURE SCALES

1.   Two commonly used temperature scales are Celsius (Centigrade) and Fahrenheit.

2.   The Celsius scale is used exclusively for upper air temperatures and is rapidly becoming the world standard for surface temperatures also.

   a.   Celsius is used to report the surface and dew point temperatures in the aviation routine weather report (METAR).

3.   Two common temperature references are the melting point of pure ice and the boiling point of pure water at sea level.

   a.   The boiling point of water is 100°C or 212°F.
   b.   The melting point of ice is 0°C or 32°F.

      1)   NOTE: Although 0°C (32°F) is generally the freezing point of water as well as the melting point of ice, this is not always so.

         a)   Under certain conditions, supercooled (not yet frozen) droplets of water can often be found in clouds at temperatures down to –15°C (5°F). This will be further explained in Part I, Study Unit 5, "Moisture, Cloud Formation, and Precipitation," beginning on page 45.

         b)   Supercooled water freezes on impact with an airplane.
   c.   Figure 3 below compares the two scales.

Figure 3. Fahrenheit vs. Celsius

4. The difference between the boiling point of water and the melting point of ice (the temperature range between which water is a liquid) is 100°C or 180°F.

  a. The ratio between degrees Celsius and Fahrenheit is 100/180 or 5/9.

  b. Since 0°F is 32 Fahrenheit degrees colder than 0°C, you must apply this difference when comparing temperatures on the two scales.

  c. Conversion formulae:

$$°C = \frac{5}{9}(F - 32) \quad or \quad °F = \frac{9}{5}C + 32$$

  d. EXAMPLES:

°Celsius	°Fahrenheit	°Fahrenheit	°Celsius
0	+ 32	0	−18
+ 10	50	+ 10	−12
20	68	20	−7
30	86	30	−1
40	104	40	+4
50	122	50	10
60	140	60	16
70	158	70	21
80	176	80	27
90	194	90	32
100	212	100	38

  e. Most flight computers provide for direct conversion of temperature from one scale to the other.

2.4 TEMPERATURE VARIATIONS

1. The amount of solar radiation received by any region varies with time of day, with seasons, with latitude, with differences in topographical surface, and with altitude.

2. These differences in solar radiation create temperature variations.

3. **Diurnal variation** is the change in temperature from day to night brought about by the daily rotation of the Earth.

  a. The Earth receives heat during the day by solar radiation and continuously dissipates heat by terrestrial radiation.

  b. During the day, solar radiation exceeds terrestrial radiation and the surface becomes warmer.

  c. At night, solar radiation ceases but terrestrial radiation continues and cools the surface.

    1) Cooling continues after sunrise until solar radiation again exceeds terrestrial radiation.

      a) Minimum temperature usually occurs after sunrise, sometimes by as much as 1 hr.

    2) The continued cooling after sunrise is one reason that fog sometimes forms shortly after the sun is above the horizon.

4. **Seasonal variation.** Since the axis of the Earth tilts to the plane of orbit, the sun is more nearly overhead in one hemisphere than in the other, depending upon the season.

    a. The Northern Hemisphere is warmer in June, July, and August because it receives more solar energy than does the Southern Hemisphere.

    b. The Southern Hemisphere receives more solar radiation and is warmer during December, January, and February.

    c. Figures 4 and 5 on page 11 show these seasonal surface temperature variations.

5. **Variation with latitude.** Since the Earth is essentially spherical, the sun is more nearly overhead in equatorial regions than at higher latitudes.

    a. Equatorial regions receive the most solar radiation and are warmest.

    b. Slanting rays of the sun at higher latitudes deliver less energy over a given area, with the least being received at the poles.

    c. Thus, temperature varies with latitude--from the warm Equator to the cold poles.

        1) You can see this average temperature variation in Figures 4 and 5 on page 11.

6. **Variations with topography.** Not related to the movement or shape of the Earth are temperature variations induced by water and terrain.

    a. Large, deep water bodies tend to minimize temperature changes, whereas continents favor large changes.

        1) Wet soil, such as in swamps and marshes, is almost as effective as water in suppressing temperature changes.

        2) Thick vegetation tends to control temperature changes since it contains some water and also insulates against heat transfer between the ground and the atmosphere.

        3) Arid, barren surfaces permit the greatest temperature changes.

    b. These topographical influences are both diurnal and seasonal.

        1) EXAMPLE: The difference between a daily maximum and minimum may be 10° or less over water, near a shore line, or over a swamp or marsh, while a difference of 50° or more is common over rocky or sandy deserts.

        2) Figures 4 and 5 on page 11 also show the seasonal topographical variation.

            a) Note that in the Northern Hemisphere in July, temperatures are warmer over continents than over oceans; in January, they are colder over continents than over oceans.

Figure 4. World-Wide Average Surface Temperatures (°F) in July

Figure 5. World-Wide Average Surface Temperatures (°F) in January

    c.   Abrupt temperature differences develop along lake and ocean shores. These variations generate pressure differences and local winds.

        1)   Figure 6 below illustrates a possible effect.

80°F

WARMED

98°F

79°F

Figure 6. Temperature Differences Create Weather

    d.   Prevailing wind is also a factor in temperature controls.

        1)   In an area where prevailing winds are from large water bodies, e.g., islands, temperature changes are rather small.

        2)   Temperature changes are more pronounced where prevailing wind is from dry, barren regions.

7.   **Variation with altitude.** Temperature normally decreases with increasing altitude throughout the troposphere. This is due primarily to solar radiation heating the surface and to the surface, in turn, warming the air above it by terrestrial radiation.

    a.   This decrease of temperature with altitude is defined as lapse rate.

        1)   The average decrease of temperature -- average lapse rate -- in the troposphere is 2°C per 1,000 ft.

    b.   An increase in temperature with altitude is defined as an inversion, i.e., the lapse rate is inverted.

1) An inversion often develops near the ground on clear, cool nights when wind is light.

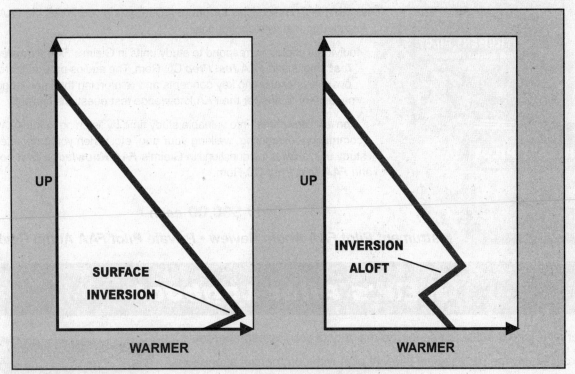

Figure 7. Temperature Inversion Graphs

    a) The ground radiates and cools much faster than the overlying air.

    b) Air in contact with the ground becomes cold, while the temperature a few hundred feet above changes very little.

    c) Thus, temperature increases with height.

2) Inversions may also occur at any altitude when conditions are favorable.

    a) EXAMPLE: A current of warm air aloft overrunning cold air near the surface produces an inversion aloft.

3) Inversions are common in the stratosphere.

2.5 IN CLOSING

1. The two commonly used scales for measuring temperature are Celsius and Fahrenheit.

2. Land absorbs and radiates heat much faster than water.

3. Variations in solar radiation create temperature variations which are the primary cause of weather.

    a. The amount of solar radiation received varies with

      1) Day-night
      2) Season
      3) Latitude
      4) Topography
      5) Altitude

END OF STUDY UNIT

STUDY UNIT THREE
ATMOSPHERIC PRESSURE AND ALTIMETRY

(13 pages of outline)

Please take a few minutes to study each of the concepts listed above and anticipate/imagine what they are and how they relate to the other listed concepts.

3.1 ATMOSPHERIC PRESSURE

1. **Atmospheric pressure** is the force per unit area exerted by the weight of the atmosphere.

2. The instrument designed for measuring pressure is the **barometer**.

   a. Weather services and the aviation community use two types of barometers in measuring pressure -- mercurial and aneroid.

3. The **mercurial barometer** diagramed in Figure 8 on page 16 consists of an open dish of mercury into which the open end of an evacuated glass tube is placed.

   a. Atmospheric pressure forces mercury to rise in the tube.
   b. Near sea level, the column of mercury rises on the average to a height of 29.92 in.
   c. The height of the mercury column is a measure of atmospheric pressure.

4. An **aneroid barometer** (illustrated in Figure 9 on page 16) uses a flexible metal cell and a registering mechanism.

   a. The cell is partially evacuated of air and contracts or expands as the pressure outside it changes.

      1) One end of the cell is fixed, while the other end moves the registering mechanism.
      2) This mechanism drives an indicator hand along a scale graduated in pressure units.

Figure 8. The Mercurial Barometer

Figure 9. The Aneroid Barometer

5.   Two commonly used pressure units are inches of mercury (in. Hg) and hectoPascal (hPa).

    a.   Inches of mercury refers to the height to which a column of mercury would be raised in the basic mercurial barometer.

    b.   In the metric system, the unit of measurement for pressure is the hectoPascal (hPa).

        1)   The hectoPascal will replace millibars (mb), which is currently in use.

            a)   The units are equivalent; i.e., 1013.2 mb is 1013.2 hPa.
            b)   1013.2 mb/hPa is the ISA sea level pressure.

        2)   In this book, both millibars and hectoPascals will be used.

    c.   Note the relationship between inches and millibars in Figure 9(a) below.

in. Hg	mb	
32.78	1110	
32.48	1100	
32.19	1090	
31.89	1080	← 1084 mb (32.01 in.) Highest recorded sea level pressure: Agata, Siberia (December, 1968)
31.60	1070	
31.30	1060	← 1064 mb (31.42 in.) Highest recorded sea level pressure in United States: Miles City, Montana (December, 1983)
31.00	1050	← Strong high pressure system
30.71	1040	
30.42	1030	
30.12	1020	
29.82	1010	← 1013.25 mb (29.92 in.) Average sea level pressure
29.53	1000	
29.24	990	
28.94	980	← Deep low pressure system
28.64	970	
28.35	960	
28.05	950	
27.76	940	
27.46	930	
27.17	920	← 922 mb (27.23 in.) Hurricane Andrew (August, 1992)
26.87	910	
26.58	900	
26.28	890	← 888 mb (26.22 in.) Hurricane Gilbert (September, 1988)
25.99	880	
25.69	870	← 870 mb (25.70 in.) Lowest recorded sea level pressure: typhoon Tip (October, 1979)
25.40	860	
25.10	850	

Figure 9(a). Atmospheric Pressure in Inches of Mercury and in Millibars

6.   The pressure measured at a station or airport is called the **station pressure** or the pressure at field elevation.

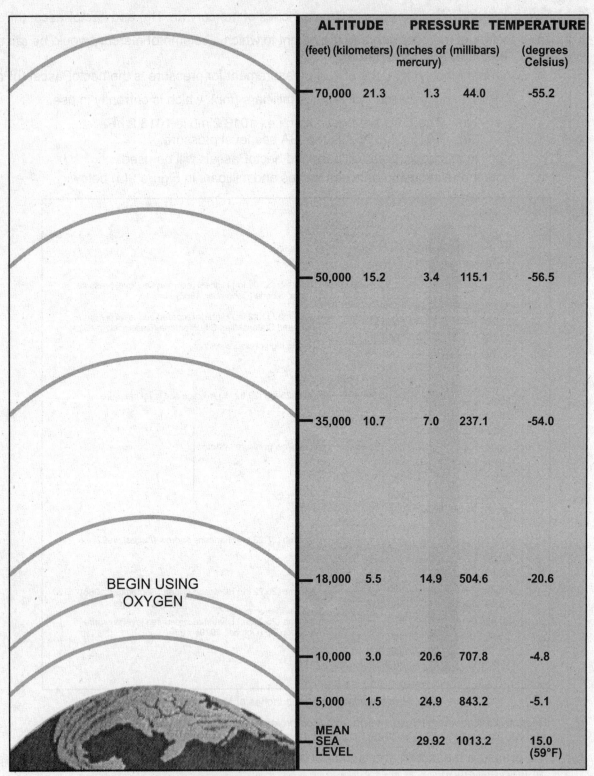

ALTITUDE		PRESSURE		TEMPERATURE
(feet)	(kilometers)	(inches of mercury)	(millibars)	(degrees Celsius)
70,000	21.3	1.3	44.0	-55.2
50,000	15.2	3.4	115.1	-56.5
35,000	10.7	7.0	237.1	-54.0
18,000	5.5	14.9	504.6	-20.6
10,000	3.0	20.6	707.8	-4.8
5,000	1.5	24.9	843.2	-5.1
MEAN SEA LEVEL		29.92	1013.2	15.0 (59°F)

BEGIN USING OXYGEN

Figure 10. The Standard Atmosphere -- Decrease in Pressure with Increasing Heights

3.2 PRESSURE VARIATION

1.   Pressure varies primarily with altitude and temperature of the air.

2.   **Altitude.** As we move upward through the atmosphere, the amount, and thus the weight, of the air above us becomes less and less.

   a.   If we carry a barometer with us, we can measure a decrease in pressure as weight of the air above decreases.

     1)   Within the lower few thousand feet of the troposphere, pressure decreases roughly 1 in. for each 1,000-ft. increase in altitude.

     2)   The higher we go, the slower is the rate of decrease with height.

   b.   Figure 10 on page 18 shows the pressure decrease with height in the standard atmosphere.

3.   **Temperature.** Like most substances, air expands as it becomes warmer and contracts as it cools.

   a.   Figure 11 below shows three equal columns of air -- one colder than standard, one at standard temperature, and one warmer than standard.

Figure 11. Effect of Temperature on Pressure

     1)   Because each column contains the same amount of air, pressure is equal at the bottom of each column and equal at the top of each column.

     2)   Thus, pressure decrease upward through each column is the same.

   b.   However, vertical expansion of the warm column has made it higher than the column at standard temperature.

     1)   Shrinkage of the cold column has made it shorter.

   c.   Thus, the rate of decrease of pressure with height in warm air is less than standard.

     1)   The rate of decrease of pressure with height in cold air is greater than standard.

4.   **Sea level pressure.** To readily compare pressure between stations at different altitudes, we must adjust them to some common level, i.e., mean sea level (MSL).

   a.   In Figure 12 below, pressure measured at a 5,000-ft. station is 25 in. Hg; pressure changes about 1 in. Hg for each 1,000 ft. or a total of 5 in. Hg. Sea level pressure at this station is thus approximately 25 + 5, or 30 in. Hg.

   1)   The weather observer takes temperature and other effects into account, but this simplified example explains the basic principle of sea level pressure.

A Pressure
at 5000' of
25 INCHES

When reduced to
sea-level is   **25+5=30 inches**

Figure 12. Reduction of Station Pressure to Sea Level

   b.   Sea level pressure is reported in hectoPascals in the remarks section of the aviation routine weather report (METAR) at designated stations.

   1)   See Part III, Study Unit 3, "Aviation Routine Weather Reports (METAR)," beginning on page 223.

5.   **Pressure analyses.** We plot sea level pressures on a map and draw lines connecting points of equal pressure.

   a.   These lines of equal pressure are **isobars**.

   1)   The surface map in Figure 13 on page 21 is an isobaric analysis showing identifiable, organized pressure patterns.

   a)   See Part III, Study Unit 8, "Surface Analysis Charts," beginning on page 275.

   2)   The five pressure systems shown are defined as follows:

   a)   **Low** -- an area of pressure surrounded on all sides by higher pressure, also called a cyclone. In the Northern Hemisphere, a cyclone is a mass of air which rotates counter-clockwise (i.e., a low-pressure system), viewed from above.

   b)   **High** -- a center of pressure surrounded on all sides by lower pressure, also called an anticyclone. In the Northern Hemisphere, an anticyclone is a mass of air which rotates clockwise (i.e., a high-pressure system), viewed from above.

   c)   **Trough** -- an elongated area of low pressure with the lowest pressure along a line marking maximum cyclonic curvature.

   d)   **Ridge** -- an elongated area of high pressure with the highest pressure along a line marking maximum anticyclonic curvature.

   e)   **Col** -- the neutral area between two highs or two lows. It also is the intersection of a trough and a ridge. The col on a pressure surface is analogous to a mountain pass on a topographic surface.

Figure 13. Pressure Systems

b. Upper air weather maps reveal these same types of pressure patterns aloft for several levels.

1) They also show temperature, moisture, and wind at each level.

c. An upper air map is a **constant pressure analysis**. Constant pressure simply refers to a specific pressure (e.g., 700 mb/hPa).

1) Everywhere above the Earth's surface, pressure decreases with height. At some height, it decreases to this constant pressure of 700 mb/hPa (about 10,000 ft. MSL, depending upon temperature).

a) Thus, there is a "surface" throughout the atmosphere at which pressure is 700 mb/hPa.

b) This is called the 700-mb/hPa constant pressure surface.

c) However, the height of this surface is **not** constant.

i) Rising pressure pushes the surface upward into highs and ridges.

ii) Falling pressure lowers the height of the surface into lows and troughs.

iii) These systems migrate continuously as "waves" on the pressure surface.

    2)   The National Weather Service (NWS) and military weather services take routinely scheduled upper-air observations, sometimes called soundings.

        a)   A balloon carries aloft an instrument (called a radiosonde) which transmits data such as wind, temperature, moisture, and height at selected pressure surfaces.

        b)   These observations are used to plot the heights of a desired constant pressure surface (e.g., 700 mb/hPa).

            i)   Variations in these heights are small, and for all practical purposes, you may regard the 700-mb/hPa chart as a weather map at approximately 10,000 ft. MSL.

        c)   A contour analysis of this chart shows highs, ridges, lows, and troughs aloft just as the isobaric analysis shows such systems at the surface.

    3)   See Part III, Study Unit 9, "Constant Pressure Charts," beginning on page 281.

    4)   These charts, when tied together, present a three-dimensional picture of atmospheric pressure patterns.

  d.   Low-pressure systems quite often are regions of poor flying weather, and high-pressure systems predominantly are regions of favorable flying weather.

    1)   However, this rough general rule should appropriately be supplanted with a complete weather briefing.

    2)   Pressure patterns also bear a direct relationship to wind.

3.3 ALTIMETRY

1.   The altimeter is essentially an aneroid barometer.

  a.   The altimeter is graduated to read increments of height rather than units of pressure.

  b.   The standard for graduating the altimeter is the standard atmosphere.

2.   Altitude seems like a simple term; it means height. But in aviation, it can have many meanings.

3.   **True altitude** is the actual or exact altitude above mean sea level.

  a.   Since existing conditions in a real atmosphere are seldom standard, altitude indications on the altimeter are seldom actual or true altitudes.

4.   **Indicated altitude** is the altitude above mean sea level indicated on the altimeter when set at the local altimeter setting.

  a.   The height indicated on the altimeter changes with changes in surface pressure.

    1)   Figure 15 on page 23 shows this effect.

    2)   A movable scale on the altimeter permits you to adjust for variations in surface pressure.

    3)   **Altimeter setting** is the value to which the scale of the pressure altimeter is set so as to indicate true altitude at field elevation.

        a)   This value is the atmospheric pressure adjusted to sea level in the region in which you are flying.

    4)   You must keep your altimeter setting current by adjusting it frequently in flight to the setting reported by the nearest tower or weather reporting station.

    5)   If an altimeter setting is not available before takeoff, you can set the altimeter to read field elevation, i.e., true altitude.

994mb

When Pressure **LOWERS**
Enroute - **YOU ARE LOWER**
THAN YOUR ALTIMETER
INDICATES

998mb

1002mb

1006mb

1010mb

29.84"
(1010.5mb)

29.96"
(1014.6mb)

Figure 15. Effect of Pressure on Indicated Altitude

b.   Unfortunately, you have no means for adjusting the altimeter for changes in temperature.

1)   Look again at Figure 11 on page 19 showing the effect of mean temperature on the height of the three columns of air.

a)   Pressures are equal at the bottoms and the tops of the three layers.

b)   Since the altimeter is essentially a barometer, altitude indicated by the altimeter at the top of each column would be the same.

2)   To see this effect more clearly, study Figure 14 below.

Figure 14. Effect of Temperature on Indicated
Altitude

a)   Note that in the warm air, true altitude is higher than indicated.
b)   In the cold air, true altitude is lower than indicated.

5.   **Corrected (approximately true) altitude** is indicated altitude corrected for the temperature of the air column below the aircraft.

a.   If it were possible for a pilot to determine mean temperature of the column of air between the aircraft and the surface, flight computers would be designed to use this mean temperature in computing true altitude.

1)   However, the only guide a pilot has to temperature below him/her is the outside air temperature at his/her altitude.

2)   Thus, the flight computer uses outside air temperature to correct indicated altitude to approximate true altitude.

a)   It is close enough to true altitude to be used for terrain clearance provided you have your altimeter set to the value reported from a nearby reporting station.

b)   Pilots have met with disaster because they failed to allow for the difference between indicated and true altitude. In cold weather when you must clear high terrain, take time to compute true altitude.

b.   EXAMPLE: If you are flying at an indicated altitude of 5,000 ft. MSL with an altimeter setting of 29.92 (standard pressure), your pressure altitude is also 5,000 ft. Once you determine pressure altitude and know the outside air temperature (OAT), use your flight computer to determine the corrected altitude.

1)   If your OAT is +5°C (standard temperature at 5,000 ft. MSL), your corrected altitude is 5,000 ft. MSL.

2)   However, if your OAT is −15°C (20° below standard), your corrected altitude is only 4,640 ft. MSL.

6. **Pressure altitude** is the altitude in the standard atmosphere where pressure is the same as where you are currently flying.

   a. In the standard atmosphere, pressure at sea level is 29.92 in. Hg and decreases approximately 1 in. per 1,000 ft. of altitude.

   b. Thus, for example, if the pressure at your altitude of flight is 27.92 in. Hg, you are flying at a pressure altitude of approximately 2,000 ft. higher than your indicated altitude.

   c. You can determine pressure altitude by setting your altimeter to the standard altimeter setting of 29.92 in.

   d. All flights at and above 18,000 ft. MSL, i.e., in Class A airspace, are flown at pressure altitudes.

7. **Density altitude** is the altitude in the standard atmosphere where air density is the same as where you are.

   a. Pressure, temperature, and to a lesser extent, humidity determine air density.

      1) On a hot day, the air becomes "thinner" or lighter, and its density where you are is equivalent to a higher altitude in the standard atmosphere -- thus the term "high density altitude."

      2) On a cold day, the air becomes heavy; its density is the same as that at an altitude in the standard atmosphere lower than your altitude -- "low density altitude."

   b. Density altitude is not a height reference; rather, it is an index to aircraft performance.

      1) Low density altitude increases performance.

      2) High density altitude is a real hazard since it reduces aircraft performance. It affects performance in three ways.

         a) It reduces power because the engine takes in less air to support combustion.

         b) It reduces thrust because the propeller gets less grip on the light air or a jet has less mass of gases to spit out the exhaust.

         c) It reduces lift because the light air exerts less force on the airfoils.

   c. You cannot detect the effect of high density altitude on your airspeed indicator. Your aircraft lifts off, climbs, cruises, glides, and lands at the prescribed indicated airspeeds.

      1) But at a specified indicated airspeed, your true airspeed and your groundspeed increase proportionally as density altitude becomes higher.

   d. The net results are that high density altitude lengthens your takeoff and landing rolls and reduces your rate of climb.

      1) Before liftoff, you must attain a faster groundspeed, and therefore, you need more runway; your reduced power and thrust add a need for still more runway.

      2) You land at a faster groundspeed and, therefore, need more room to stop.

      3) At a prescribed indicated airspeed, you are flying at a faster true airspeed, and therefore, you cover more distance in a given time, which means climbing at a more shallow angle.

         a) Add to this the problems of reduced power and rate of climb, and you are in double jeopardy in your climb.

         b) Figure 17 on page 26 shows the effect of density altitude on takeoff distance and rate of climb.

            i) It shows the takeoff roll increasing from 1,300 ft. to 1,800 ft. and the rate of climb decreasing from 1,300 fpm to less than 1,000 fpm.

e. High density altitude also can be a problem at cruising altitudes. When air is abnormally warm, the high density altitude lowers your service ceiling.

Figure 17. Effect of Density Altitude on Takeoff and Climb

f. To compute density altitude:

   1) Set your altimeter at 29.92 in. and read pressure altitude from your altimeter.

      a) Read outside air temperature, and then use your flight computer or a graph to get density altitude.

      b) EXAMPLE: If temperature at 10,000 ft. pressure altitude is 20°C, density altitude is 12,700 ft. (Check this on your flight computer.) Your aircraft will perform as though it were at 12,700 ft. MSL indicated with a standard temperature of –8°C.

   2) At an airport served by a weather observing station, you usually can get density altitude for the airport from the weather observer.

   3) A graph for computing density altitude is in Part III, Study Unit 36, "Other Weather Related Information," beginning on page 457.

3.4 IN CLOSING

1. Pressure patterns (highs, lows, etc.) can be a clue to weather causes and movement of weather systems. Pressure decreases with increasing altitude.

2. The altimeter is an aneroid barometer graduated in increments of altitude in the standard atmosphere instead of units of pressure.

3. There are several types of altitude: true, indicated, pressure, corrected, and density.

4. Temperature greatly affects the rate of pressure decrease with height; therefore, it influences altimeter readings.

   a. Temperature also determines the density of air at a given pressure (density altitude).

5. Density altitude is an index to aircraft performance.

   a. Always be alert for departures of pressure and temperature from normals and compensate for these abnormalities.

6. Here are a few operational reminders:

   a. Beware of the low pressure-bad weather, high pressure-good weather rule of thumb. It frequently fails. Always get the **complete** weather picture.

   b. When flying from high pressure to low pressure at constant indicated altitude and without adjusting the altimeter, you are losing true altitude.

   c. When temperature is colder than standard, you are at an altitude **lower** than your altimeter indicates. When temperature is warmer than standard, you are **higher** than your altimeter indicates.

   d. When flying cross country, keep your altimeter setting current. This procedure assures more positive altitude separation from other aircraft.

   e. When flying over high terrain in cold weather, compute your corrected altitude to ensure terrain clearance.

   f. When your aircraft is heavily loaded, the temperature is abnormally warm, and/or the pressure is abnormally low, compute density altitude.

      1) Then check your aircraft manual to ensure that you can become airborne from the available runway.

      2) Check further to determine that your rate of climb permits clearance of obstacles beyond the end of the runway.

      3) This procedure is advisable for any airport regardless of altitude.

   g. When planning takeoff or landing at a high altitude airport regardless of load, determine density altitude.

      1) The procedure is especially critical when temperature is abnormally warm or pressure abnormally low.

      2) Make certain you have sufficient runway for takeoff or landing roll.

      3) Make sure you can clear obstacles beyond the end of the runway after takeoff or in event of a go-around.

END OF STUDY UNIT

STUDY UNIT FOUR
WIND

(16 pages of outline)

Please take a few minutes to study each of the concepts listed above and anticipate/imagine what they are and how they relate to the other listed concepts.

4.1 INTRODUCTION

1. Differences in temperature create differences in pressure. These pressure differences drive a complex system of winds in a never-ending attempt to reach equilibrium.

4.2 CONVECTION

1. When two surfaces are heated unequally, they heat the overlying air unevenly, resulting in a circulatory motion called convection. Figure 18 on page 30 shows the convective process.

   a. The warmer air expands and becomes lighter or less dense than the cooler air.

   b. The dense, cooler air sinks to the ground by its greater mass, forcing the warmer air upward.

   c. The rising air spreads and cools, eventually descending to complete the convective process.

   d. As long as the uneven heating persists, a continuous convective current is maintained.

2. The horizontal air flow in a convective current is wind. Convection of both large and small scales accounts for systems ranging from hemispheric circulations down to local eddies.

   a. This horizontal flow, wind, is sometimes called **advection**.

   b. However, the term advection more commonly applies to the transport of atmospheric properties by the wind, i.e., warm advection, cold advection, advection of water vapor, etc.

Figure 18. The Convective Process

4.3 PRESSURE GRADIENT FORCE

1.   Whenever a pressure difference (or gradient) develops over an area, the air begins to move directly from the higher pressure to the lower pressure.

   a.   The pressure gradient is the rate of decrease of pressure per unit of distance at a fixed time.

   b.   The force that causes the air to move is called the pressure gradient force.

2.   Recall that areas of high and low pressure are encircled by isobars, or lines of equal pressure. (See Figure 13 on page 21.)

   a.   The pressure gradient force moves the air directly across the isobars.

   b.   Closely spaced isobars indicate a strong pressure gradient or a sharp change in pressure over a short distance.

      1)   Thus, the pressure gradient force is also strong.

   c.   The stronger the pressure gradient force, the stronger the wind

   d.   From a pressure analysis, you can get a general idea of wind speed from the isobar spacing.

      1)   Closely spaced isobars mean strong winds.
      2)   Widely spaced isobars mean lighter winds.

3.   Because of uneven heating of the Earth, surface pressure is low in warm equatorial regions and high in cold polar regions.

    a.   A pressure gradient develops from the poles to the Equator.

    b.   If the Earth did not rotate, this pressure gradient force would be the only force acting on the wind.

        1)   Circulation would be two giant hemispheric convective currents as shown in Figure 19 below.

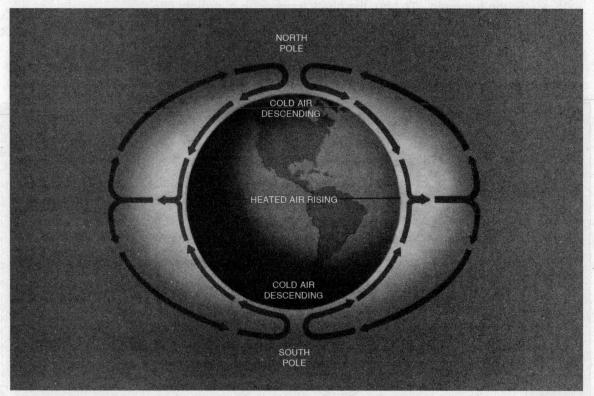

Figure 19. Circulation Pattern of a Nonrotating Earth

        2)   Cold air would sink at the poles, wind would blow straight from the poles to the Equator, warm air at the Equator would be forced upward, and high level winds would blow directly toward the poles.

    c.   However, the Earth does rotate, and because of its rotation, this simple circulation is greatly distorted.

4.4 CORIOLIS FORCE

1. A moving mass (e.g., air) travels in a straight line until acted upon by some outside force (Newton's First Law of Motion).

    a. However, if you viewed the moving mass from a rotating platform, the path of the moving mass relative to your platform would appear to be deflected or curved.

    b. EXAMPLE: Imagine the turntable of a record player rotating counterclockwise. Use a piece of chalk and a ruler to draw a "straight" line from the center to the outer edge of the turntable. To you, the chalk traveled in a straight line.

        1) Now stop the turntable. The line you have drawn spirals outward from the center as shown in Figure 20 below.

        2) To a viewer on the turntable, some apparent force deflected the chalk to the right.

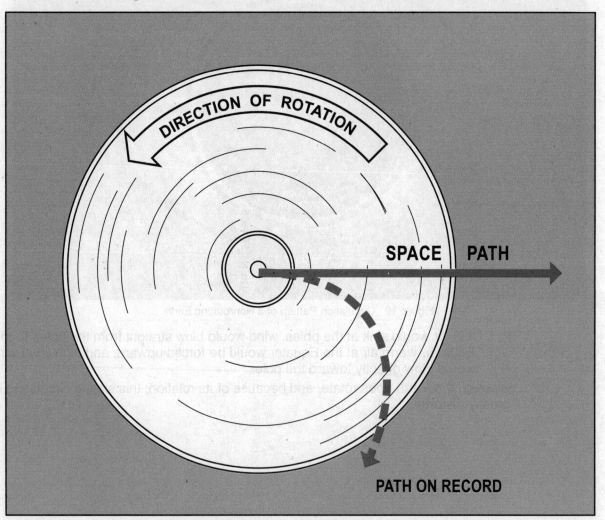

Figure 20. Apparent Deflective Force Due to Rotation of a Horizontal Platform

2. Similarly, air moving across the surface of the Earth seems to us to be deflected by some force.

    a. This principle was first explained by a Frenchman, Gaspard Coriolis, and carries his name -- the Coriolis force.

    b. Because the Earth is spherical, the Coriolis force is much more complex than the simple turntable example.

3. The Coriolis force affects the paths of aircraft, missiles, flying birds, ocean currents, and most important to the study of weather, air currents.

    a. It deflects air to the right in the Northern Hemisphere and to the left in the Southern Hemisphere.

    b. This book concentrates on deflection to the right in the Northern Hemisphere.

4. The Coriolis force varies directly with wind speed and latitude.

    a. The stronger the wind speed, the greater the deflection.

    b. Coriolis force varies with latitude from zero at the Equator to maximum at the poles.

5. When a pressure gradient force is first established, wind begins to blow from higher to lower pressure directly across the isobars. In Figure 21 below, it would be from bottom to top.

    a. However, the instant the air begins moving from high pressure to low pressure, the Coriolis force deflects it to the right, curving its path.

    b. As the speed of this moving air increases, the Coriolis force increases, deflecting the wind more and more to the right.

    c. Eventually, the wind speed increases to a point where the Coriolis force balances the pressure gradient force, as shown in Figure 21 below.

        1) At this point, the wind has been deflected 90° and is now parallel to the isobars (depicted as "Resultant Wind" in Figure 21 below.

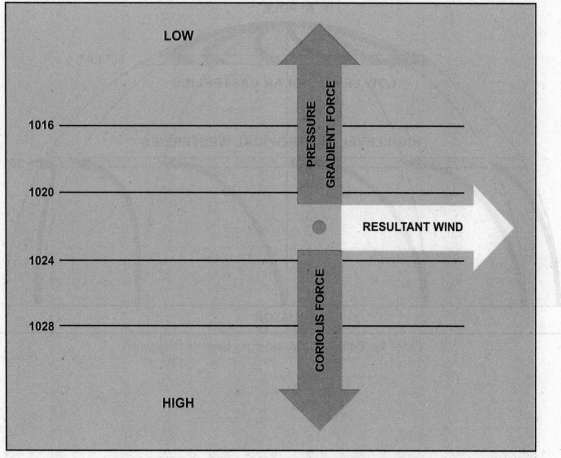

Figure 21. Effect of Coriolis Force on Wind Relative to Isobars

4.5 THE GENERAL CIRCULATION

1. As air is forced aloft at the Equator and begins its high-level trek northward, the Coriolis force turns it to the right or to the east as shown in Figure 22 below.

    a. Wind becomes westerly (i.e., moves from west to east) at about 30° latitude, temporarily blocking further northward movement as shown in Figure 22 below.

    b. Similarly, as air over the poles begins its low-level journey southward toward the Equator, it likewise is deflected to the right and becomes an east wind, halting for a while its southerly progress at about 60° latitude, also shown in Figure 22.

2. As a result, air piles up between 30° and 60° latitude in both hemispheres.

    a. The added weight of the air increases the pressure into semipermanent high pressure belts.

        1) Figures 23 and 24 on page 35 are maps of mean surface pressure for the months of July and January.

            a) The maps show clearly the subtropical high pressure belts near 30° latitude in both the Northern and Southern Hemispheres.

    b. These high pressure belts create a temporary impasse disrupting the simple convective transfer between the Equator and the poles.

Figure 22. General Circulation in the Northern Hemisphere

Figure 23. Mean World-Wide Surface Pressure Distribution in July

Figure 24. Mean World-Wide Surface Pressure Distribution in January

c.   Large masses of cold air break through the northern barrier (i.e., 60° latitude) plunging southward toward the Tropics.

    1)   Large mid-latitude storms develop between cold outbreaks and carry warm air northward.

    2)   The result is a mid-latitude band of migratory storms with ever-changing weather.

    3)   Figure 25 below is an attempt to standardize this chaotic circulation into an average general circulation.

3.   Since pressure differences cause wind, seasonal pressure variations determine to a great extent the areas of these cold air outbreaks and mid-latitude storms.

a.   Seasonal pressure variations are largely due to seasonal temperature changes.

    1)   At the surface, warm temperatures largely determine low pressure and cold temperatures, high pressure.

b.   During summer, warm continents tend to be areas of low pressure and the relatively cool oceans, high pressure.

    1)   In winter, the reverse is true -- high pressure over the cold continents and low pressure over the relatively warm oceans.

    2)   Figures 23 and 24 on page 35 show this seasonal pressure reversal.

Figure 25. General Average Circulation in the Northern Hemisphere

c.   Cold outbreaks are strongest in the winter and are predominantly from the colder continental areas.

    1)   Outbreaks are weaker in the summer, and more likely to originate from the cooler water surfaces.

    2)   Since these outbreaks are masses of cool, dense air, they characteristically are high-pressure areas.

4. As the air moves outward from high pressure, it is deflected to the right by the Coriolis force.

    a. Thus, the wind around a high moves clockwise.

        1) The high pressure with its associated wind system is called an **anticyclone**.

    b. The storms that develop between high pressure systems are characterized by low pressure.

        1) As wind moves inward toward low pressure, it is also deflected to the right.
        2) Thus, the wind around a low is counterclockwise.
        3) The low pressure and its wind system are called a **cyclone**.

    c. Figure 26 below shows winds moving parallel to isobars (called contours on upper level charts). The winds are clockwise around highs and counterclockwise around lows.

Figure 26. Airflow around Pressure Systems

5. The high pressure belt between 30° and 60° latitude forces air outward to the north and to the south, resulting in three major wind belts, as shown in Figure 25 on page 36.

    a. The southward moving air is deflected by the Coriolis force, becoming the well-known subtropical northeast trade winds (see Part II, Study Unit 15, "Tropical Weather," beginning on page 161).

        1) These winds carry tropical storms from east to west, e.g., hurricanes from the ocean off North Africa west into the Caribbean.

    b. The northbound air becomes entrained into the mid-latitude storms.

        1) High-level winds are deflected to the right and are known as the prevailing westerlies.
        2) These westerlies drive mid-latitude storms generally from west to east.

    c. Polar easterlies dominate low-level circulation north of about 60° latitude where few major storm systems develop.

4.6 FRICTION

1. Friction between the wind and the terrain surface slows the wind.

    a. The rougher the terrain, the greater the frictional force.
    b. The stronger the wind speed, the greater the friction.
    c. Frictional force always acts in opposition to the wind direction.

2. When the wind is within approximately 3,000 ft. of the surface, friction reduces the wind speed, which in turn reduces the Coriolis force.

    a. Recall that in the absence of surface friction, the Coriolis force turns the wind 90° to the right to parallel the isobars.
    b. Surface friction slows the wind, which reduces the Coriolis force, causing the wind to turn to the left, across the isobars at an angle, toward the area of lower pressure.

    NOTE: Surface winds generally flow slightly to the left of winds aloft, e.g., a 270° wind aloft may be accompanied by surface winds of 240°.

3. Thus, in the Northern Hemisphere, friction causes the surface winds that are moving in a clockwise direction around a high pressure area to cross the isobars at an angle and flow toward an area of low pressure, as shown in Figure 28 below.

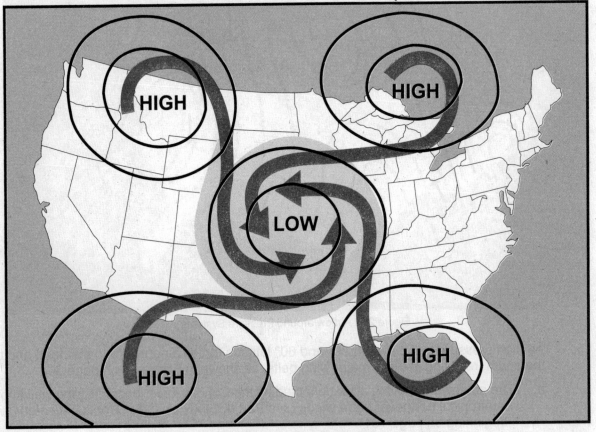

Figure 28. Circulation around Pressure Systems at the Surface

4. The angle of surface wind to isobars is about 10° over water, increasing with roughness of terrain.

   a. In mountainous regions, one often has difficulty relating surface wind to pressure gradient because of immense friction and also because local terrain effects on pressure could cause the angle to be 40° or more.

   b. The average angle across the isobars is about 30° for all surfaces.

   c. The speed of the wind will also affect this angle.

      1) Normally, the angle is smaller for high winds (i.e., due to a stronger Coriolis force) and large for slower winds (i.e., weaker Coriolis force).

4.7 JET STREAM

1. A discussion of the general circulation is incomplete when it does not mention the **jet stream**.

   a. Winds on the average increase with height throughout the troposphere, culminating in a maximum near the level of the tropopause.

   b. These maximum winds tend to be further concentrated in narrow bands.

2. A jet stream, then, is a narrow band of strong winds meandering through the atmosphere at a level near the tropopause.

   a. Since it is of interest primarily to high-level flight, further discussion of the jet stream is reserved for Part II, Study Unit 13, "High Altitude Weather," beginning on page 143.

4.8 LOCAL AND SMALL-SCALE WINDS

1. The previous discussion has dealt only with the general circulation and major wind systems. Local terrain features such as mountains and shore lines influence local winds and weather.

2. **Mountain and Valley Winds**

   a. In the daytime, air next to a mountain slope is heated by contact with the ground as the ground receives radiation from the sun.

      1) This air usually becomes warmer than air at the same altitude but farther from the slope.

      2) Colder, denser air in the surroundings settles downward and forces the warmer air near the ground up the mountain slope.

         a) This wind is a "valley wind," so called because the air is flowing up out of the valley.

   b. At night, the air in contact with the mountain slope is cooled by terrestrial radiation and becomes heavier than the surrounding air.

      1) It sinks along the slope, producing the "mountain wind" which flows like water down the mountain slope.

   c. Mountain winds are usually stronger than valley winds, especially in winter.

      1) The mountain wind often continues down the more gentle slopes of canyons and valleys, and in such cases takes the name "drainage wind."

      2) It can become quite strong over some terrain conditions and in extreme cases can become hazardous when flowing through canyon restrictions as discussed in Part I, Study Unit 9, "Turbulence," beginning on page 91.

3.   **Katabatic Wind**

a.   A **katabatic wind** is any wind blowing down an incline when the incline is influential in causing the wind.

1)   Thus, the mountain wind is a katabatic wind.

b.   Any katabatic wind originates because cold, heavy air spills down sloping terrain displacing warmer, less dense air ahead of it.

1)   Air is heated and dried as it flows down slope.
2)   Sometimes the descending air becomes warmer than the air it replaces.

c.   Many katabatic winds recurring in local areas have been given colorful names to highlight their dramatic local effect.

1)   Some of these include

a)   Bora, a cold northerly wind blowing from the Alps to the Mediterranean coast;

b)   The Chinook, a warm wind down the east slope of the Rocky Mountains often reaching hundreds of miles into the high plains;

c)   The Taku, a cold wind in Alaska blowing off the Taku glacier; and

d)   The Santa Ana, a warm wind descending from the Sierras into the Santa Ana Valley of California.

4.   **Land and Sea Breezes**

a.   As frequently stated earlier, land surfaces warm and cool more rapidly than do water surfaces.

b.   Land is warmer than the sea during the day.

1)   Wind blows from the cool water to warm land -- the "sea breeze," so called because it blows from the sea.

2)   At night, the wind reverses, blows from cool land to warmer water, and creates a "land breeze."

c.   Figure 30 below diagrams land and sea breezes.

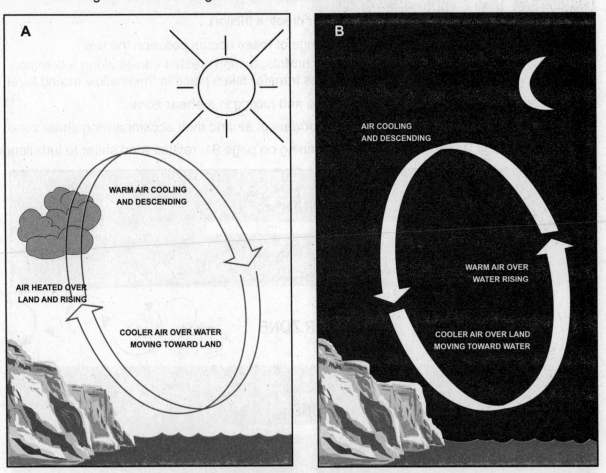

Figure 30. Land and Sea Breezes

d.   Land and sea breezes develop only when the overall pressure gradient is weak.

1)   Wind occurring as a result of a strong pressure gradient mixes the air so rapidly that local temperature and pressure gradients do not develop along the shore line.

4.9 WIND SHEAR

1. Rubbing two objects against each other creates friction.

    a. If the objects are solid, no exchange of mass occurs between the two.

    b. However, if the objects are fluid currents, friction creates eddies along a common shallow mixing zone, and a mass transfer takes place in the shallow mixing layer.

        1) This zone of induced eddies and mixing is a **shear zone**.

2. Figure 31 below shows two adjacent currents of air and their accompanying shear zone.

3. Part I, Study Unit 9, "Turbulence," beginning on page 91, relates wind shear to turbulence.

Figure 31. Wind Shear

4. Basically, there are two potentially hazardous shear situations.

    a. First, a tailwind may shear to either a calm or headwind component.

        1) In this instance, initially the airspeed increases, the aircraft pitches up, and the altitude increases.

    b. Second, a headwind may shear to a calm or tailwind component.

        1) In this instance, initially the airspeed decreases, the aircraft pitches down, and the altitude decreases.

5. Aircraft speed, aerodynamic characteristics, power-to-weight ratio, powerplant response time, and pilot reactions along with other factors have a bearing on wind shear effects.

6. Remember that wind shear can cause problems for any aircraft and pilot.

4.10 IN CLOSING

1. The horizontal air flow in a convective current is wind.

    a. Wind speed is proportional to the spacing of isobars or contours on a weather map.

        1) However, with the same spacing, wind speed at the surface will be less than aloft because of surface friction.

    b. You can also determine wind direction from a weather map.

        1) If you visualize standing with the wind aloft at your back (Northern Hemisphere), low pressure should be on your left and high pressure on your right.

            a) If you visualize standing with the surface wind to your back, then turn clockwise about 30°, low pressure should be on your left and high pressure on your right.

        2) On a surface map, wind will cross the isobar at an angle toward lower pressure; on an upper air chart, it will be nearly parallel to the contour.

2. As the pressure gradient force drives the wind from high- to low-pressure areas, the Coriolis force deflects the wind to the right (in the Northern Hemisphere), resulting in the general circulation around high- and low-pressure systems.

    a. In the Northern Hemisphere, wind blows counterclockwise around a low and clockwise around a high.

        1) At the surface where winds cross the isobars at an angle, you can see a transport of air from high to low pressure.

        2) Although winds are virtually parallel to contours on an upper air chart, there still is a slow transport of air from high to low pressure.

3. At the surface when air converges into a low, it cannot go outward against the pressure gradient, nor can it go downward into the ground; it must go upward.

    a. Thus, a low or trough is an area of rising air.

        1) Rising air is conducive to cloudiness and precipitation; thus, we have the general association of low pressure and bad weather.

    b. By similar reasoning, air moving out of a high or ridge depletes the quantity of air. Highs and ridges, therefore, are areas of descending air.

        1) Descending air favors dissipation of cloudiness; hence the association of high pressure and good weather.

4. Three exceptions to the low pressure -- bad weather, high pressure -- good weather rule:

    a. Many times weather is more closely associated with an upper air pattern than with features shown by the surface map. Although features on the two charts are related, they seldom are identical.

        1) A weak surface system often loses its identity in the upper air pattern, while another system may be more evident on the upper air chart than on the surface map.

        2) Widespread cloudiness and precipitation often develop in advance of an upper trough or low.

            a) A line of showers and thunderstorms is not uncommon with a trough aloft even though the surface pressure pattern shows little or no cause for the development.

   b.   Downward motion in a high or ridge places a "cap" on convection, preventing any upward motion.

      1)   Air may become stagnant in a high, trap moisture and contamination in low levels, and restrict ceiling and visibility.

         a)   Low stratus, fog, haze, and smoke are not uncommon in high pressure areas.

      2)   However, a high or ridge aloft with moderate surface winds most often produces good flying weather.

   c.   A dry, sunny region becomes quite warm from intense surface heating, thus generating a surface low pressure area, called a thermal low.

      1)   The warm air is carried to high levels by convection, but cloudiness is scant because of lack of moisture.

         a)   Since in warm air, pressure decreases slowly with altitude, the warm surface low is not evident at upper levels.

      2)   The thermal low is relatively shallow with weak pressure gradients and no well-defined cyclonic circulation.

         a)   It generally supports good flying weather.

         b)   However, during the heat of the day, one must be alert for high density altitude and convective turbulence.

5.   Due to surface friction, highs and lows tend to lean from the surface into the upper atmosphere, i.e., the upper portion moves faster than the lower portion, which is slowed by friction with the surface.

   a.   Winds aloft often flow across the associated surface systems.

   b.   Upper winds tend to steer surface systems in the general direction of the upper wind flow.

   c.   An intense, cold, low pressure vortex leans less than does a weaker system.

      1)   The intense low becomes oriented almost vertically and is clearly evident on both surface and upper air charts.

         a)   Upper winds encircle the surface low and do not blow across it.

         b)   Thus, the storm moves very slowly and usually causes an extensive and persistent area of clouds, precipitation, strong winds, and generally adverse flying weather.

6.   There are three major wind belts in the Northern Hemisphere:

   a.   Subtropical, northeasterly trade winds, which carry tropical storms from east to west

   b.   Midlatitude westerlies, which drive midlatitude storms generally from west to east (which encompasses the United States)

   c.   Polar easterlies, which primarily contribute to the development of midlatitude storms

7.   Local terrain features influence local winds and weather, e.g.,

   a.   Mountain and valley winds
   b.   Katabatic wind
   c.   Land and sea breezes

END OF STUDY UNIT

STUDY UNIT FIVE
MOISTURE, CLOUD FORMATION, AND PRECIPITATION

(10 pages of outline)

Please take a few minutes to study each of the concepts listed above and anticipate/imagine what they are and how they relate to the other listed concepts.

5.1 WATER VAPOR

1. Water evaporates into the air and becomes an ever-present but variable part of the atmosphere.

2. Water vapor is invisible, just as oxygen and other gases are invisible.

    a. We can readily measure water vapor and express the results in different ways. Two commonly used terms are

        1) Relative humidity and
        2) Dew point.

3. **Relative humidity** relates the actual water vapor present to that which could be present.

    a. Relative humidity is routinely expressed as a percentage.

    b. Temperature largely determines the maximum amount of water vapor a parcel of air can hold.

        1) As Figure 32 below shows, warm air can hold more water vapor than cool air.

Figure 32. Air Temperature and Water Vapor

    c.   Relative humidity expresses the degree of saturation. Air with 100% relative humidity is saturated; at less than 100%, unsaturated.

        1)   If a given volume of air is cooled to some specific temperature, it can hold no more water vapor than is actually present; relative humidity becomes 100%, and saturation occurs.

4.   **Dew point** is the temperature to which air must be cooled to become saturated by the water vapor already present in the air.

    a.   Aviation weather reports normally include the air temperature and dew point.

    b.   Comparing the dew point to the air temperature reveals how close the air is to saturation.

    c.   Figure 33 below relates water vapor, temperature, and relative humidity.

Figure 33. Relative Humidity and Dew Point

5. The difference between air temperature and dew point is commonly known as the **temperature-dew point spread**.

    a. As this spread becomes smaller, relative humidity increases, and it reaches 100% when temperature and dew point are the same.

    b. Surface temperature-dew point spread is important in anticipating fog, but has little bearing on precipitation.

        1) To support precipitation, air must be saturated through thick layers aloft.

    c. Sometimes the spread at ground level may be quite large, yet at higher altitudes the air is saturated and clouds form.

        1) Some rain may reach the ground, or it may evaporate as it falls into the drier air.

            a) Figure 34 below is a photograph of "virga" -- streamers of precipitation trailing beneath clouds but evaporating before reaching the ground.

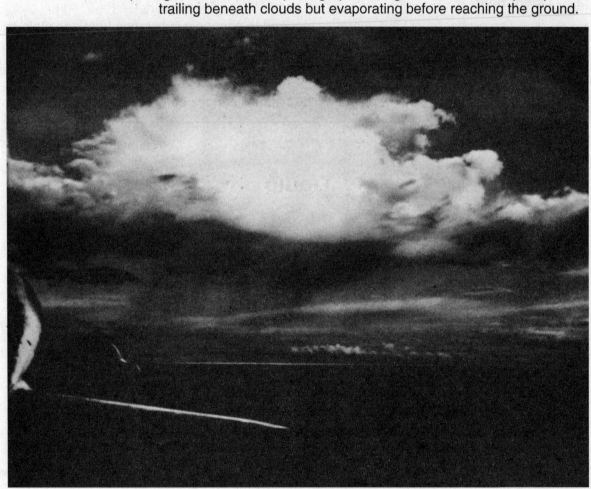

Figure 34. Virga

5.2　CHANGE OF STATE

1. Evaporation, condensation, freezing, melting, and sublimation are changes of state in water.

   a. Evaporation is the changing of liquid water to invisible water vapor.

      1) Condensation is the reverse process, i.e., water vapor into water.

   b. Freezing is the changing of liquid water into solid water, or ice.

      1) Melting is the reverse process, i.e., ice into water.

   c. Sublimation is the changing of ice directly to water vapor, or water vapor to ice, bypassing the liquid state in each process.

      1) Snow or ice crystals result from the sublimation of water vapor directly to the solid state.

2. **Latent Heat**

   a. The exchange of heat energy is required to change a substance from one state to another.

      1) This energy is called "latent heat" and is significant, as we will learn in later study units.

      2) Figure 35 below diagrams the heat exchanges between the different states.

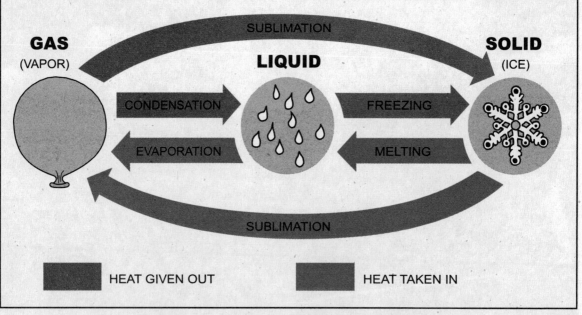

Figure 35.　Heat Transactions When Water Changes State

   b. Evaporation of water, for example, requires heat energy that may come from the water itself or from some other source, such as the surrounding air.

      1) This energy is known as the "latent heat of vaporization," and its transference to the water vapor cools the source it comes from.

         a) Evaporation is thus a cooling process.

         b) When you step out of the shower, the evaporation of water from your body removes heat from your skin, making you feel cold.

        2)   The heat energy is stored or hidden in the water vapor, thus the term "latent (hidden) heat."

            a)   It is considered hidden because the temperature of the evaporated water remains the same.

        3)   When the water vapor condenses back into liquid water, this energy is released to the atmosphere as the "latent heat of condensation."

            a)   Thus, condensation is a warming process.

    c.   Melting and freezing involve the exchange of "latent heat of fusion" in a similar manner.

        1)   The latent heat of fusion is much less than that of condensation and evaporation; however, each plays an important role in aviation weather.

3.   **Condensation nuclei.** As air becomes saturated, water vapor begins to condense on the nearest available surface.

    a.   The atmosphere is never completely clean; an abundance of microscopic solid particles suspended in the air are condensation surfaces.

        1)   These particles, such as salt, dust, and combustion by-products are condensation nuclei.

        2)   Some condensation nuclei have an affinity for water and can induce condensation or sublimation even when air is almost, but not completely, saturated.

    b.   As water vapor condenses or sublimates on condensation nuclei, liquid or ice particles begin to grow.

        1)   Whether the particles are liquid or ice does not depend entirely on temperature.

            a)   Liquid water may be present at temperatures well below freezing.

4.   **Supercooled Water**

    a.   Freezing is complex, and liquid water droplets often condense or persist at temperatures colder than 0°C because the molecular motion of the droplet remains large enough to weaken any formation of an ice crystal within the droplet.

        1)   Water droplets colder than 0°C are supercooled.
        2)   When they strike an exposed object, the impact induces freezing.
        3)   Impact freezing of supercooled water can result in aircraft icing.

    b.   Supercooled water drops very often are in abundance in clouds at temperatures between 0°C and –15°C, with decreasing amounts at colder temperatures.

        1)   Usually, at temperatures colder than –15°C, sublimation is prevalent, and clouds and fog may be mostly ice crystals with a lesser amount of supercooled water.

        2)   Strong vertical currents may carry supercooled water to great heights where temperatures are much colder than –15°C.

            a)   Supercooled water has been observed at temperatures colder than –40°C.

5.   **Dew and Frost**

    a.   During clear nights with little or no wind, vegetation often cools by radiation to a temperature at or below the dew point of the adjacent air.

        1)   Moisture then collects on the leaves just as it does on a pitcher of ice water in a warm room.

        2)   Heavy dew often collects on grass and plants while none collects on pavements or large solid objects.

            a)   These larger objects absorb abundant heat during the day, lose it slowly during the night, and cool below the dew point only in extreme cases.

    b.   Frost forms in much the same way as dew. The difference is that the dew point of surrounding air must be colder than freezing.

        1)   Water vapor then sublimates directly as ice crystals or frost rather than condensing as dew.

        2)   Sometimes dew forms and later freezes; however, frozen dew is easily distinguished from frost.

            a)   Frozen dew is hard and transparent while frost is white and opaque.

5.3 CLOUD FORMATION

1.   Normally, air must become saturated for condensation or sublimation to occur.

    a.   Saturation may result from cooling temperature, increasing dew point, or both.

        1)   Cooling is far more predominant.

2.   Three basic processes may cool air to saturation:

    a.   Air moving over a colder surface
    b.   Stagnant air overlying a cooling surface
    c.   Expansional (adiabatic) cooling in upward-moving air

        1)   Expansional cooling is the major cause of cloud formation.
        2)   See Part I, Study Unit 6, "Stable and Unstable Air," beginning on page 55.

3.   A cloud is a visible collection of minute water or ice particles suspended in air.

    a.   If the cloud is near the ground, it is called fog.
    b.   When entire layers of air cool to saturation, fog or sheet-like clouds result.
    c.   Saturation of a localized updraft produces a towering cloud.
    d.   A cloud may be composed entirely of liquid water, ice crystals, or a mixture of the two.

5.4 PRECIPITATION

1. Precipitation is an all-inclusive term denoting drizzle, rain, snow, ice pellets, hail, and ice crystals.

    a. Precipitation occurs when these particles grow in size and weight until the atmosphere no longer can suspend them and they fall.

2. These particles grow primarily in two ways.

    a. Once a water droplet or ice crystal forms, it continues to grow by added condensation or sublimation directly onto the particle.

        1) This is the slower of the two methods and usually results in drizzle or very light rain or snow.

    b. Cloud particles collide and merge into a larger drop in the more rapid growth process. This process produces larger precipitation particles and does so more rapidly than the simple condensation growth process.

        1) Upward currents enhance the growth rate and also support larger drops, as shown in Figure 36 below.

Figure 36. Growth of Raindrops by Collision of Cloud Droplets

        2) Precipitation formed by merging drops with mild upward currents can produce light to moderate rain and snow.

        3) Strong upward currents support the largest drops and build clouds to great heights.

            a) They can produce heavy rain, heavy snow, and hail.

3.   **Liquid, Freezing, and Frozen Precipitation**

    a.   Precipitation that forms and remains in a liquid state is either rain or drizzle.

    b.   Sublimation forms snowflakes, and they reach the ground as snow if temperatures remain below freezing.

    c.   Precipitation can change its state as the temperature of its environment changes.

        1)   Falling snow may melt in warmer layers of air at lower altitudes to form rain.

        2)   Rain falling through colder air may become supercooled, freezing on impact as freezing rain; or it may freeze during its descent, falling as ice pellets.

           a)   Ice pellets always indicate freezing rain at higher altitude.

    d.   Sometimes strong upward currents sustain large supercooled water drops until some freeze; subsequently, other drops freeze to them forming hailstones.

4.   To produce significant precipitation, clouds usually must be 4,000 ft. thick or more.

    a.   The thicker the clouds, the heavier the precipitation is likely to be.

    b.   When arriving at or departing from an airport reporting precipitation of light or greater intensity, expect clouds to be more than 4,000 ft. thick.

5.5   LAND AND WATER EFFECTS

1.   Land and water surfaces underlying the atmosphere greatly affect cloud and precipitation development.

    a.   Large bodies of water such as oceans and large lakes add water vapor to the air.

        1)   Expect the greatest frequency of low ceilings, fog, and precipitation in areas where prevailing winds have an over-water trajectory.

           a)   Be especially alert for these hazards when moist winds are blowing upslope.

2.   In winter, cold air frequently moves over relatively warm lakes.

    a.   The warm water adds heat and water vapor to the air, causing showers to the leeward side of the lakes.

    b.   In other seasons, the air may be warmer than the lakes.

        1)   When this occurs, the air may become saturated by evaporation from the water while also becoming cooler in the low levels by contact with the cool water.

           a)   Fog often becomes extensive and dense to the lee of a lake.

    c.   Figure 37 on page 53 illustrates movement of air over both warm and cold lakes.

    d.   Strong cold winds across the Great Lakes often carry precipitation to the Appalachians, as shown in Figure 38 on page 53.

3.   A lake only a few miles across can influence convection and cause a diurnal fluctuation in cloudiness.

    a.   During the day, cool air over the lake blows toward the land, and convective clouds form over the land.

    b.   At night, the pattern reverses; clouds tend to form over the lake as cool air from the land flows over the lake, creating convective clouds over the water.

Figure 37. Lake Effects

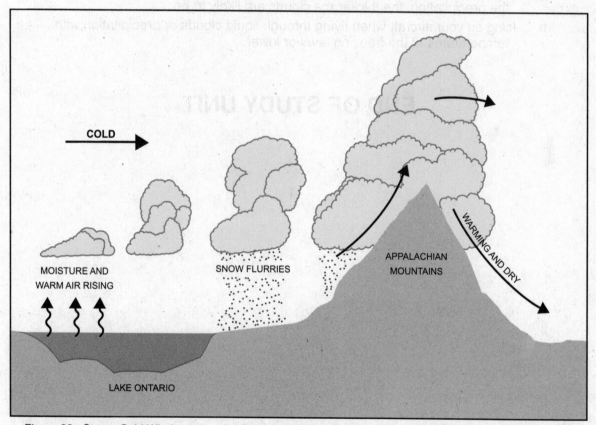

Figure 38. Strong Cold Winds across the Great Lakes Absorb Water Vapor and May Carry Showers as Far Eastward as the Appalachians.

5.6 IN CLOSING

1.   Water exists in three states -- solid, liquid, and gaseous.

   a.   Water vapor is an invisible gas. Condensation or sublimation of water vapor creates many common aviation weather hazards.

2.   You may anticipate

   a.   Fog when temperature-dew point spread is 3°C (5°F) or less and decreasing.

   b.   Lifting or clearing of low clouds and fog when temperature-dew point spread is increasing.

   c.   Frost on a clear night when temperature-dew point spread is 3°C (5°F) or less and is decreasing, and the dew point is lower than 0°C (32°F).

   d.   More cloudiness, fog, and precipitation when wind blows from water than when it blows from land.

   e.   Cloudiness, fog, and precipitation over higher terrain when moist winds are blowing uphill.

   f.   Showers to the lee of a lake when air is cold and the lake is warm. Expect fog to the lee of the lake when the air is warm and the lake is cold.

   g.   Clouds at least 4,000 ft. thick when significant precipitation is reported. The heavier the precipitation, the thicker the clouds are likely to be.

   h.   Icing on your aircraft when flying through liquid clouds or precipitation with temperatures at the freezing level or lower.

END OF STUDY UNIT

STUDY UNIT SIX
STABLE AND UNSTABLE AIR

(7 pages of outline)

Please take a few minutes to study each of the concepts listed above and anticipate/imagine what they are and how they relate to the other listed concepts.

6.1 DEFINITIONS

1. A **stable** atmosphere resists any upward or downward displacement.

2. An **unstable** atmosphere allows an upward or downward disturbance to grow into a vertical, or convective, current.

6.2 ADIABATIC COOLING AND HEATING

1. Anytime air moves upward, it expands because of decreasing atmospheric pressure.

   a. Conversely, downward-moving air is compressed by increasing pressure.
   b. But as pressure and volume change, temperature also changes.

2. When air expands, it cools, and when compressed, it warms.

   a. These changes are **adiabatic**, i.e., no heat is removed from or added to the air.
   b. We frequently use the terms **expansional (adiabatic) cooling** and **compressional (adiabatic) heating**.
   c. The adiabatic rate of change of temperature is constant in unsaturated air but varies with the amount of moisture in saturated air.

3. **Unsaturated air** moving upward and downward cools and warms at about 3°C per 1,000 ft. (5.4°F per 1,000 ft.).

   a. This rate is the dry adiabatic rate of temperature change and is independent of the temperature of the mass of air through which the vertical movements occur.
   b. Figure 41 on page 56 illustrates a "chinook wind," which is a warm wind blowing down the side of a mountain -- an excellent example of dry adiabatic warming.

      1) As the cold, relatively dry air moves, it sinks down the side of the mountain.
      2) As it is compressed by the increasing atmospheric pressure, it becomes warmer through adiabatic heating.

4. When **saturated air** moves upward and cools, condensation occurs.

   a. Latent heat released through condensation (see Part I, Study Unit 5, "Moisture, Cloud Formation, and Precipitation," beginning on page 45) partially offsets the expansional cooling.

      1) Thus, the saturated adiabatic rate of cooling is slower than the dry rate.
      2) The saturated cooling rate depends on saturation temperature (dew point) of the air, i.e., the relative humidity.

   b. Because warmer air can hold more water before becoming saturated, more latent heat is released through condensation in saturated warm air than in cold.

      1) Thus, the saturated adiabatic rate of cooling is less in warm air than in cold.

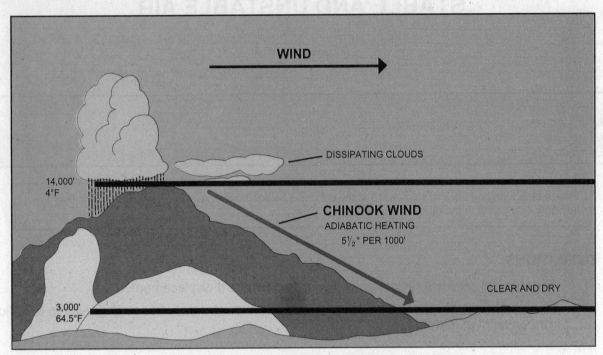

Figure 41. Adiabatic Warming of Downward Moving Air

    c.   When saturated air moves downward, it heats at the same rate as it cools on ascent provided liquid water evaporates rapidly enough to maintain saturation.

        1)   Minute water droplets in the air evaporate rapidly enough.

        2)   Larger drops evaporate more slowly and complicate the moist adiabatic process in downward-moving air.

5.   **Adiabatic Cooling and Vertical Air Movement**

    a.   At this point we should clarify the terms "ambient, or existing, lapse rate" and "adiabatic rates of cooling."

        1)   As you move upward through the atmosphere, the temperature of the air around you generally changes with altitude.

            a)   This change is the ambient (existing) lapse rate.

            b)   In the standard atmosphere, the lapse rate is 2°C per 1,000 ft. (see Part I, Study Unit 2, "Temperature," beginning on page 7).

        2)   As a parcel of air is forced upward, it expands, and therefore cools, at a given rate.

            a)   This is the adiabatic rate of cooling, or adiabatic lapse rate.

            b)   This rate depends on the amount of moisture present in the parcel of air that is forced upward.

    b.   If a parcel of air is forced upward into the atmosphere, we must consider two possibilities:

        1)   As the sample cools, it may become colder than the surrounding air, or

        2)   Even though it cools, the air may remain warmer than the surrounding air.

    c.   If the upward-moving air becomes colder than the surrounding air, the adiabatic lapse rate is greater than the ambient (existing) lapse rate, and the parcel of air sinks.

        1)   If it remains warmer, the adiabatic lapse rate is less than the ambient (existing) lapse rate, and the parcel of air continues to rise as a convective current.

6.3 STABILITY AND INSTABILITY

1.   EXAMPLE: The difference between the ambient (existing) lapse rate of a given mass of air and the adiabatic rates of cooling in upward-moving air determines whether the air is stable or unstable.

    a.   In Figure 42 below, for three situations, we filled a balloon at sea level with air at 31°C -- the same as the ambient temperature. We carried the balloon to 5,000 ft. In each situation, the air in the balloon expanded and cooled at the dry adiabatic rate of 3°C for each 1,000 ft. to a temperature of 16°C at 5,000 ft.

Figure 42. Stability Related to Temperatures Aloft and Adiabatic Cooling

      1)   In the first situation (left), air inside the balloon, even though cooled adiabatically, remained warmer than surrounding air.

         a)   Vertical motion was favored.
         b)   The colder, more dense surrounding air forced the balloon further upward.
         c)   The air was unstable, and a convective current developed.

      2)   In the second situation (center), the air aloft was warmer.

         a)   Air inside the balloon, cooled adiabatically, became colder than the surrounding air.

         b)   The balloon sank under its own weight, returning to its original position when the lifting force was removed.

         c)   The air was stable, and spontaneous convection was impossible.

      3)   In the third situation (right), the temperature of the air inside the balloon was the same as that of the surrounding air. The balloon remained at rest.

         a)   This condition was neutrally stable; that is, the air was neither stable nor unstable.

4)   Note that, in all three situations, temperature of air in the expanding balloon cooled at a fixed rate.

a)   The differences in the three conditions depend, therefore, on the temperature differences between the surface and 5,000 ft., that is, on the ambient (existing) lapse rates.

2.   Stability runs the gamut from absolutely stable to absolutely unstable, and the atmosphere usually is in a delicate balance somewhere in between.

a.   A change in ambient temperature lapse rate of an air mass can tip this balance.

1)   For example, surface heating or cooling aloft can make the air more unstable; on the other hand, surface cooling or warming aloft often tips the balance toward greater stability.

b.   Air may be stable or unstable in layers.

1)   A stable layer may overlie and cap unstable air; or
2)   Conversely, air near the surface may be stable with unstable layers above.

3.   **Stratiform Clouds**

a.   Since stable air resists convection, clouds in stable air form in horizontal, sheet-like layers or "strata."

1)   Thus, within a stable layer, clouds are **stratiform**.

b.   Recall that adiabatic cooling is the major cause of cloud formation.

1)   Adiabatic cooling may be caused by upslope flow, as illustrated in Figure 43 below, by lifting over cold, denser air, or by converging winds.

2)   Cooling by an underlying cold surface is also a stabilizing process and may produce fog.

c.   If clouds are to remain stratiform, the layer must remain stable after condensation has occurred.

STABLE AIR

UNSTABLE AIR

Figure 43. Stable and Unstable Air Forced Upward

4.   **Cumuliform Clouds**

   a.   Unstable air favors convection. A cumulus (heaping) cloud forms in a convective updraft and builds upward, also shown in Figure 43 on the previous page.

   1)   Thus, within an unstable layer, clouds are **cumuliform**, and the vertical extent of the cloud depends on the depth of the unstable layer.

   b.   Initial lifting to trigger a cumuliform cloud may be the same as that for lifting stable air.

   1)   In addition, convection may be set off by surface heating (see Part I, Study Unit 4, "Wind," beginning on page 29).

   c.   Air may be unstable or slightly stable before condensation occurs, but for convective cumuliform clouds to develop, it must be unstable after saturation.

   1)   Cooling in the updraft is now at the slower moist adiabatic rate because of the release of latent heat of condensation.

   a)   Temperature in the saturated updraft is warmer than ambient temperature, and convection is spontaneous.

   2)   Updrafts accelerate until temperature within the cloud cools below the ambient temperature.

   a)   This condition occurs where the unstable layer is capped by a stable layer, often marked by a temperature inversion.

   3)   Vertical heights range from the shallow fair weather cumulus to the giant thunderstorm cumulonimbus -- the ultimate in atmospheric instability capped by the tropopause.

   d.   You can estimate the heights of cumuliform cloud bases using surface temperature-dew point spread.

   1)   Unsaturated air in a convective current cools at about 3°C (5.4°F) per 1,000 ft.; dew point decreases at about 5/9°C (1°F).

   a)   Thus, in a convective current, temperature and dew point converge at about 2.5°C (4.4°F) per 1,000 ft., as illustrated in Figure 44 on page 60.

   b)   The point at which they converge is the base of the clouds.

   2)   We can get a quick estimate of a convective cloud base in thousands of feet by rounding these values and dividing into the spread.

   a)   When using Celsius, divide by 2; when using Fahrenheit, divide by 4.

   b)   This method of estimating is reliable only with instability clouds and during the warmer part of the day.

   c)   EXAMPLE: If the surface temperature is 30°C and the dew point is 10°C, the spread is 20°C. Dividing by 2 yields 10. Thus, the convective cloud base is approximately 10,000 ft.

   e.   When unstable air lies above stable air, convective currents aloft sometimes form middle- and high-level cumuliform clouds.

   1)   In relatively shallow layers, they occur as altocumulus and ice crystal cirrocumulus clouds.

   2)   Altocumulus castellanus clouds develop in deeper midlevel unstable layers.

Figure 44. Cloud Base Determination

5. **Merging Stratiform and Cumuliform**
    a. A layer of stratiform clouds may sometimes form in a mildly stable layer while a few ambitious convective clouds penetrate the layer, thus merging stratiform with cumuliform.
    b. Convective clouds may be almost or entirely embedded in a massive stratiform layer and pose an unseen threat to instrument flight.

6.4 IN CLOSING

1.   The usual convection in unstable air gives a bumpy ride; only at times is it violent enough to be hazardous.

    a.   In stable air, flying is usually smooth but sometimes can be plagued by low ceiling and visibility.

    b.   In preflight planning, you need to take into account stability or instability and any associated hazards.

2.   Certain observations you can make on your own:

    a.   Thunderstorms are sure signs of violently unstable air. Give these storms a wide berth.

    b.   Showers and clouds towering upward indicate strong updrafts and rough (turbulent) air. Stay clear of these clouds.

    c.   Fair weather cumulus clouds often indicate bumpy turbulence beneath and in the clouds. The cloud tops indicate the approximate upper limit of convection; flight above is usually smooth.

    d.   Dust devils are a sign of dry, unstable air, usually to considerable height. Your ride may be fairly rough unless you can get above the instability.

    e.   Stratiform clouds indicate stable air. Flight generally will be smooth, but low ceiling and visibility might require IFR.

    f.   Restricted visibility at or near the surface over large areas usually indicates stable air. Expect a smooth ride, but poor visibility may require IFR.

    g.   Thunderstorms may be embedded in stratiform clouds, posing an unseen threat to instrument flight.

    h.   Even in clear weather, you have some clues to stability, such as:

        1)   When temperature decreases uniformly and rapidly as you climb (approaching 3°C per 1,000 ft.), you have an indication of unstable air.

        2)   If temperature remains unchanged or decreases only slightly with altitude, the air tends to be stable.

        3)   If the temperature increases with altitude through a layer -- an inversion -- the layer is stable and convection is suppressed. Air may be unstable beneath the inversion.

        4)   When air near the surface is warm and moist, suspect instability. Surface heating, cooling aloft, converging or upslope winds, or an invading mass of colder air may lead to instability and cumuliform clouds.

END OF STUDY UNIT

STUDY UNIT SEVEN
CLOUDS

(10 pages of outline)

7.1 INTRODUCTION

1.   To you as a pilot, clouds are your weather "signposts in the sky."

    a.   They give you an indication of air motion, stability, and moisture.

    b.   Clouds help you visualize weather conditions and potential weather hazards you might encounter in flight.

2.   The photographs on pages 64 through 71 illustrate some of the basic cloud types discussed below.

    a.   The caption with each photograph describes the cloud type and its significance to flight.

    b.   Study the descriptions and potential hazards posed by each type.

7.2 CLASSIFICATION

1.   Clouds are classified according to the way they are formed.

2.   Clouds formed by vertical currents in unstable air are **cumulus**, meaning accumulation or heap.

    a.   They are characterized by their lumpy, billowy appearance.

3.   Clouds formed by the cooling of a stable layer are **stratus**, meaning stratified or layered.

    a.   They are characterized by their uniform, sheet-like appearance.

4.   In addition to the above, the prefix **nimbo** or the suffix **nimbus** means raincloud.

    a.   Thus, stratified clouds from which rain is falling are **nimbostratus**

    b.   A heavy, swelling cumulus type cloud which produces precipitation is a **cumulonimbus**.

5.   Clouds broken into fragments are often identified by adding the suffix **fractus**.

    a.   EXAMPLE: Fragmentary cumulus is **cumulus fractus**.

7.3 IDENTIFICATION

1.   For identification purposes, you must also be concerned with the four families of clouds.

2.   The **high cloud** family is cirriform and includes cirrus, cirrocumulus, and cirrostratus clouds.

    a.   They are composed almost entirely of ice crystals.

    b.   The height of the bases of these clouds ranges from about 16,500 to 45,000 ft. in middle latitudes.

    c.   Figures 45 through 47 on pages 64 and 65 are photographs of high clouds.

3.   In the **middle cloud** family are the altostratus, altocumulus, and nimbostratus clouds.

    a.   These clouds are primarily water, much of which may be supercooled.

    b.   The height of the bases of these clouds ranges from about 6,500 to 23,000 ft. in middle latitudes.

    c.   Figures 48 through 52 on pages 66 through 69 are photographs of middle clouds.

4.   In the **low cloud** family are the stratus, stratocumulus, and fair weather cumulus clouds.

    a.   Low clouds are almost entirely water, but at times the water may be supercooled.

        1)   Low clouds at subfreezing temperatures can also contain snow and ice particles.

    b.   The bases of these clouds range from near the surface to about 6,500 ft. in middle latitudes.

    c.   Figures 53 through 55 on pages 69 and 70 are photographs of low clouds.

5.   The **clouds with extensive vertical development** family includes towering cumulus and cumulonimbus.

    a.   These clouds usually contain supercooled water above the freezing level.

        1)   But when a cumulus grows to great heights, water in the upper part of the cloud freezes into ice crystals, forming a cumulonimbus.

    b.   The heights of cumuliform cloud bases range from 1,000 ft. or less to above 10,000 ft.

    c.   Figures 56 and 57 on page 71 are photographs of clouds with extensive vertical development.

Figure 45. CIRRUS. Cirrus are thin, feather-like ice crystal clouds in patches or narrow bands. Larger ice crystals often trail downward in well-defined wisps called "mares' tails." Wispy, cirrus-like, these contain no significant icing or turbulence. Dense, banded cirrus, which often are turbulent, are discussed in Study Unit 13.

Figure 46. CIRROCUMULUS. Cirrocumulus are thin clouds, the individual elements appearing as small white flakes or patches of cotton. May contain highly supercooled water droplets. Some turbulence and icing.

Figure 47. CIRROSTRATUS. Cirrostratus is a thin whitish cloud layer appearing like a sheet or veil. Cloud elements are diffuse, sometimes partially striated or fibrous. Due to their ice crystal makeup, these clouds are associated with halos–large luminous circles surrounding the sun or moon. No turbulence and little if any icing. The greatest problem flying in cirriform clouds is restriction to visibility. They can make the strict use of instruments mandatory.

Figure 48. ALTOCUMULUS. Altocumulus are composed of white or gray colored layers or patches of solid cloud. The cloud elements may have a waved or roll-like appearance. Some turbulence and small amounts of icing.

Figure 49. ALTOSTRATUS. Altostratus is a bluish veil or layer of clouds. It is often associated with altocumulus and sometimes gradually merges into cirrostratus. The sun may be dimly visible through it. Little or no turbulence with moderate amounts of ice.

Figure 50. ALTOCUMULUS CASTELLANUS. Altocumulus castellanus are middle level convective clouds. They are characterized by their billowing tops and comparatively high bases. They are a good indication of mid-level instability. Rough turbulence with some icing.

Figure 51. STANDING LENTICULAR ALTOCUMULUS CLOUDS. Standing lenticular altocumulus clouds are formed on the crests of waves created by barriers in the wind flow. The clouds show little movement, hence the name standing. Wind, however, can be quite strong blowing through such clouds. They are characterized by their smooth, polished edges. The presence of these clouds is a good indication of very strong turbulence and should be avoided. Study Unit 9, "Turbulence," further explains the significance of this cloud.

Figure 52. NIMBOSTRATUS. Nimbostratus is a gray or dark massive cloud layer, diffused by more or less continuous rain, snow, or ice pellets. This type is classified as a middle cloud although it may merge into very low stratus or stratocumulus. Very little turbulence, but can pose a serious icing problem if temperatures are near or below freezing.

Figure 53. STRATUS. Stratus is a gray, uniform, sheet-like cloud with relatively low bases. When associated with fog or precipitation, the combination can become troublesome for visual flying. Little or no turbulence, but temperatures near or below freezing can create hazardous icing conditions.

Figure 54. STRATOCUMULUS. Stratocumulus bases are globular masses or rolls unlike the flat, sometimes indefinite, bases of stratus. They usually form at the top of a layer mixed by moderate surface winds. Sometimes, they form the breaking up of stratus or the spreading out of cumulus. Some turbulence and possible icing at subfreezing temperatures. Ceiling and visibility usually better than with low stratus.

Figure 55. CUMULUS. Fair weather cumulus clouds form in connective currents and are characterized by relatively flat bases and dome-shaped tops. Fair weather cumulus do not show extensive vertical development and do not produce precipitation. More often, fair weather cumulus indicates a shallow layer of instability. Some turbulence and no significant icing.

Figure 56. TOWERING CUMULUS. Towering cumulus signifies a relatively deep layer of unstable air. It shows considerable vertical development and has billowing cauliflower tops. Showers can result from these clouds. Very strong turbulence; some clear icing above the freezing level.

Figure 57. CUMULONIMBUS. Cumulonimbus are the ultimate manifestation of instability. They are vertically developed clouds of large dimensions with dense boiling tops often crowned with thick veils of dense cirrus (the anvil). Nearly the entire spectrum of flying hazards are contained in these clouds including violent turbulence. They should be avoided at all times! This cloud is the thunderstorm cloud and is discussed in detail in Study Unit 11, "Thunderstorms."

7.4 IN CLOSING

1.   Clouds give an indication of weather conditions and weather hazards you may encounter. Remember that there are four families of clouds:

     a.   The high cloud family, including cirrus, cirrocumulus, and cirrostratus

     b.   The middle cloud family, including altostratus, altocumulus, and nimbostratus

     c.   The low cloud family, including stratus, stratocumulus, and fair weather cumulus clouds

     d.   The clouds with extensive vertical development family, including towering cumulus and cumulonimbus

2.   Study the photographs and descriptions on the preceding pages so you will be familiar with each cloud type and its potential hazards.

END OF STUDY UNIT

STUDY UNIT EIGHT
AIR MASSES AND FRONTS

(18 pages of outline)

8.1 AIR MASSES

1. When a body of air comes to rest or moves slowly over an extensive area that has fairly uniform properties of temperature and moisture, the body of air takes on those properties.

    a. Thus, the air over the area becomes a kind of entity as illustrated in Figure 58 below and has a fairly uniform horizontal distribution of its properties.

    b. The area over which the air mass acquires its identifying distribution of moisture and temperature is known as its **source region**.

Figure 58. Horizontal Uniformity of an Air Mass

2. Source regions are many and varied, but the best source regions for air masses are large snow- or ice-covered polar regions, cold northern oceans, tropical oceans, and large desert areas.

    a. Mid-latitudes are poor source regions because air movement is so constantly varied that air masses have little opportunity to stagnate and take on the properties of the underlying region.

3. Just as an air mass took on the properties of its source region, it will tend to take on properties of a new underlying surface when it moves away from its source region, thus becoming modified.

    a. The degree of modification depends on the speed with which the air mass moves, the nature of the region over which it moves, and the temperature difference between the new surface and the air mass.

    b. Some ways air masses are modified are

        1) Warming from below

            a) Cool air moving over a warm surface is heated from below, generating instability and increasing the possibility of showers.

        2) Cooling from below

            a) Warm air moving over a cool surface is cooled from below, increasing stability. If air is cooled to its dew point, stratus and/or fog forms.

        3) Addition of water vapor

            a) Evaporation from water surfaces and falling precipitation adds water vapor to the air. When the water is warmer than the air, evaporation can raise the dew point sufficiently to saturate the air and form stratus or fog.

        4) Subtraction of water vapor

            a) Water vapor is removed by condensation and precipitation.

4. The **stability** of an air mass determines its typical weather characteristics.

    a. Characteristics typical of an unstable and a stable air mass are as follows:

Unstable Air	**Stable Air**
Cumuliform Clouds	Stratiform clouds and fog
Showery precipitation	Continuous precipitation
Rough air (turbulence)	Smooth air
Good visibility, except in	Fair to poor visibility in haze
blowing obstructions	and smoke

8.2 FRONTS

1. As air masses move out of their source regions, they come in contact with other air masses of different properties. The zone between two different air masses is a **frontal zone**, or **front**.

    a. Across this zone, temperature, humidity, and wind often change rapidly over short distances.

2. **Discontinuities.** When you pass through a front, the change from the properties of one air mass to those of the other is sometimes quite abrupt. Abrupt changes indicate a narrow frontal zone. At other times, the change of properties is very gradual, indicating a broad and diffuse frontal zone.

    a. **Temperature** is one of the most easily recognized discontinuities across a front.

        1) At the surface, the passage of a front usually causes a noticeable temperature change.

        2) When flying through a front, you note a significant change in temperature, especially at low altitudes.

        3) Remember that the temperature change, even when gradual, is faster and more pronounced than a change during a flight wholly within one air mass.

            a) Thus, for safety, obtain a new altimeter setting after flying through a front.

   b.   **Dew point** and temperature-dew point spread usually differ across a front.

        1)   This difference helps identify the front and may give a clue to changes in cloudiness and/or fog.

   c.   **Wind** always changes across a front.

        1)   Wind discontinuity may be in direction, in speed, or in both.
        2)   Be alert for a wind shift when flying in the vicinity of a frontal surface.
        3)   The relatively sudden change in wind also creates wind shear.

   d.   **Pressure.** A front lies in a pressure trough, and pressure generally is higher in the cold air.

        1)   Thus, when you cross a front directly into colder air, pressure usually rises abruptly.
        2)   When you approach a front toward warm air, pressure generally falls until you cross the front and then remains steady or falls slightly in the warm air.
        3)   However, pressure patterns vary widely across fronts, and your course may not be directly across a front.
        4)   The important thing to remember is that when crossing a front, you will encounter a difference in the rate of pressure change; be especially alert in keeping your altimeter setting current.

3.   The three principal types of fronts are the **cold front**, the **warm front**, and the **stationary front**.

   a.   The leading edge of an advancing cold air mass is a **cold front**.

        1)   At the surface, cold air is overtaking and replacing warmer air.
        2)   Cold fronts move at about the speed of the wind component perpendicular to the front just above the frictional layer.
        3)   Figure 59 on page 76 shows the vertical cross section of a cold front and the symbol depicting it on a surface weather chart.

             a)   The vertical cross section in the top illustration shows the frontal slope.

                  i)   The frontal slope is steep near the leading edge as cold air replaces warm air.
                  ii)   The solid heavy arrow shows movement of the front.
                  iii) Warm air may descend over the front as indicated by the dashed arrows, but more commonly, the cold air forces warm air upward over the frontal surface as shown by the solid arrows.

             b)   The symbol in the bottom illustration is a line with barbs pointing in the direction of movement.

                  i)   If a map is in color, a blue line represents the cold front.

        4)   A shallow cold air mass or a slow moving cold front may have a frontal slope more like a warm front shown in Figure 60 on page 77.

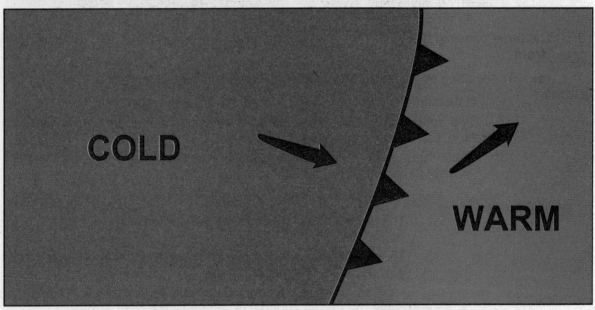

Figure 59. Cross Section and Weather Map Symbol of a Cold Front

   b.   The edge of an advancing warm air mass is a **warm front** -- warmer air is overtaking and replacing colder air.

       1)   Since the cold air is denser than the warm air, the cold air hugs the ground. The warm air slides up and over the cold air, leaving the cold air relatively undisturbed.

           a)   Thus, the cold air is slow to retreat in advance of the warm air.

           b)   This slowness of the cold air to retreat produces a frontal slope that is more gradual than the cold frontal slope, as shown in Figure 60 on page 77.

           c)   Consequently, warm fronts on the surface are seldom as well marked as cold fronts, and they usually move about half as fast when the general wind flow is the same in each case.

2)   Figure 60 shows the vertical cross section of a warm front and the symbol depicting it on a surface weather chart.

a)   In the top illustration, the slope of a warm front generally is more shallow than the slope of a cold front.

i)   Movement of a warm front, shown by the heavy black arrow, is slower than the wind in the warm air, represented by the light solid arrows.

ii)   The warm air gradually erodes the cold air.

b)   The symbol in the bottom illustration is a line with half circles aimed in the direction of movement.

i)   If a map is in color, a red line represents the warm front.

Figure 60. Cross Section and Weather Map Symbol of a Warm Front

c.   When neither air mass is replacing the other, the front is **stationary**.

1)   The opposing forces exerted by adjacent air masses of different densities are such that the frontal surface between them shows little or no movement.

a)   In such cases, the surface winds tend to blow parallel to the frontal zone.

b)   The slope of a stationary front is normally shallow, although it may be steeper, depending on wind distribution and density difference.

2)   Figure 61 on page 79 shows a cross section of a stationary front and its symbol on a surface chart.

a)   The top illustration shows the front has little or no movement and winds are nearly parallel to the front.

b)   The symbol in the bottom illustration is a line with alternating barbs and half circles on opposite sides of the line, the barbs aiming away from the cold air and the half circles away from the warm air.

i)   If a map is in color, a line of alternating red and blue segments represents the stationary front.

Figure 61. Cross Section and Weather Map Symbol of a Stationary Front

4.   **Frontal Waves and Occlusion**

    a.   Frontal waves and cyclones (areas of low pressure) usually form on slow-moving cold fronts or on stationary fronts.

        1)   The life cycle and movement of a cyclone are dictated to a great extent by the upper wind flow.

    b.   In the initial condition of a frontal wave development in Figure 62 on page 81, the winds on both sides of the front are blowing parallel to the stationary front (A).

        1)   Small disturbances then may start a wavelike bend in the front (B).

    c.   If this tendency persists and the wave increases in size, a cyclonic (counterclockwise) circulation develops.

        1)   One section of the front begins to move as a warm front, while the section next to it begins to move as a cold front (C).

        2)   This deformation is called a **frontal wave**.

    d.   The pressure at the peak of the frontal wave falls, and a low-pressure center forms.

        1)   The cyclonic circulation becomes stronger, and the surface winds are now strong enough to move the fronts; the cold front moves faster than the warm front (D).

    e.   When the cold front catches up with the warm front, the two of them **occlude** (close together).

        1)   The result is an **occluded front**, or an occlusion (E).

        2)   This is the time of maximum intensity for the wave cyclone.

        3)   Note that the symbol depicting the occlusion is a combination of the symbols for the warm and cold fronts.

    f.   As the occlusion continues to grow in length, the cyclonic circulation diminishes in intensity and the frontal movement slows down (F).

        1)   Sometimes a new frontal wave begins to form on the long westward-trailing portion of the cold front (F,G), or a secondary low pressure system forms at the apex where the cold front and warm front come together to form the occlusion.

    g.   In the final stage, the two fronts may have become a single stationary front again.

        1)   The low center with its remnant of the occlusion is disappearing (G).

Figure 62. The Life Cycle of a Frontal Wave

h. Figure 63 below indicates a warm-front occlusion in vertical cross section and the symbol depicting it on a surface weather chart.

1) In the warm front occlusion, air under the cold front is not as cold as air ahead of the warm front; and when the cold front overtakes the warm front, the less cold air rides over the colder air.

a) In a warm front occlusion, milder temperatures replace the colder air at the surface.

2) The symbol is a line with alternating barbs and half circles on the same side of the line aiming in the direction of movement.

a) Shown in color on a weather map, the line is purple.

Figure 63. Cross Section and Weather Map Symbol for a Warm-Front Occlusion

i.   Figure 64 below indicates a cold-front occlusion in vertical cross section.

   1)   In the cold-front occlusion, the coldest air is under the cold front.

   2)   When it overtakes the warm front, it lifts the warm front aloft; and cold air replaces cool air at the surface.

   3)   The weather map symbol is the same as used for a warm-front occlusion.

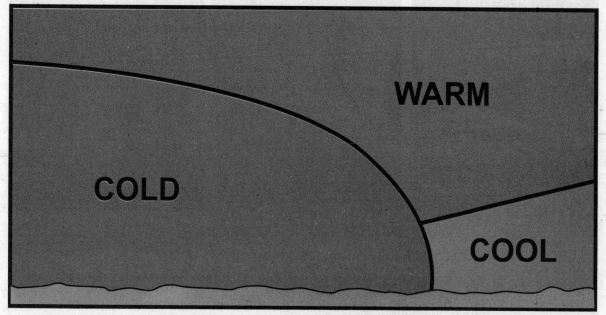

Figure 64. Cross Section of a Cold-Front Occlusion

5.   **Nonfrontal Lows**

   a.   As we have learned, fronts lie in troughs, or elongated areas of low pressure.

   1)   These frontal troughs mark the boundaries between air masses of different properties.

   2)   Low-pressure areas lying solely in a homogeneous air mass are called nonfrontal lows.

   b.   Nonfrontal lows are infrequent east of the Rocky Mountains in mid-latitudes but do occur occasionally during the warmer months.

   1)   Small nonfrontal lows over the western mountains are common, as is the semistationary thermal low in the extreme southwestern United States.

   c.   Tropical lows are also nonfrontal.

6.   **Frontolysis and Frontogenesis**

   a.   As adjacent air masses modify and as temperature and pressure differences equalize across a front, the front dissipates.

   1)   This process, frontolysis, is illustrated in Figure 65 below.

Figure 65. Frontolysis of a Stationary Front

   b.   Frontogenesis is the generation of a front.

   1)   It occurs when a relatively sharp zone of transition develops over an area between two air masses which have densities gradually becoming more and more in contrast with each other.

   a)   The necessary wind flow pattern develops at the same time.

   2)   Figure 66 below shows an example of frontogenesis with the symbol.

Figure 66. Frontogenesis of a Stationary Front

7. **Frontal Weather**

   a. In fronts, flying weather varies from virtually clear skies to extreme hazards including hail, turbulence, icing, low clouds, and poor visibility.

      1) Weather occurring with a front depends on the

         a) Amount of moisture available,
         b) Degree of stability of the air that is forced upward,
         c) Slope of the front,
         d) Speed of frontal movement, and
         e) Upper wind flow.

   b. Sufficient moisture must be available for clouds to form; otherwise, there will be no clouds.

      1) As an inactive front (i.e., no precipitation) comes into an area of moisture, clouds and precipitation may develop rapidly.

      2) A good example of this is a cold front moving eastward from the dry slopes of the Rocky Mountains into a tongue of moist air from the Gulf of Mexico over the Plains States.

         a) Thunderstorms may build rapidly and catch a pilot unaware.

   c. The degree of stability of the lifted air determines whether cloudiness will be predominately stratiform or cumuliform.

      1) If the warm air overriding the front is stable, stratiform clouds develop.

         a) Precipitation from stratiform clouds is usually steady, as illustrated in Figure 67 below, and there is little or no turbulence.

Figure 67. A Cold Front Underrunning Warm, Moist, Stable Air

2)   If the warm air is unstable, cumuliform clouds develop.

    a)   Precipitation from cumuliform clouds is showery, as in Figure 68 below, and the clouds are turbulent.

Figure 68. A Cold Front Underrunning Warm, Moist, Unstable Air

d.   Shallow frontal surfaces tend to cause extensive cloudiness with large precipitation areas, as shown in Figure 69 below.

1)   Widespread precipitation associated with a gradual sloping front often causes low stratus and fog.

    a)   In this case, the rain raises the humidity of the cold air to saturation.

    b)   This and related effects may produce low ceiling and poor visibility over thousands of square miles.

Figure 69. A Warm Front with Overrunning Moist, Stable Air

2) If temperature of the cold air near the surface is below freezing but the warmer air aloft is above freezing, precipitation falls as freezing rain or ice pellets.

   a) However, if temperature of the warmer air aloft is well below freezing, precipitation forms as snow.

e. When the warm air overriding a shallow front is moist and unstable, the usual widespread cloud mass forms; but embedded in the cloud mass are altocumulus, cumulus, and even thunderstorms as in Figures 70 and 71 below.

1) These embedded storms are more common with warm and stationary fronts but may occur with a slow-moving, shallow cold front.

   a) A good preflight briefing helps you to foresee the presence of these hidden thunderstorms.

   b) Radar also helps in this situation and is discussed in Part I, Study Unit 11, "Thunderstorms," beginning on page 113.

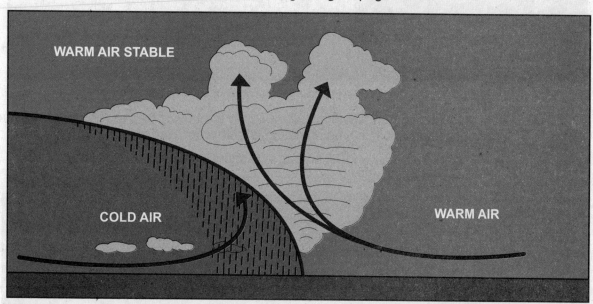

Figure 70. A Slow-Moving Cold Front Underrunning Warm, Moist, Unstable Air

Figure 71. Warm Front with Overrunning Warm, Moist, Unstable Air

f.   A fast-moving, steep cold front forces upward motion of the warm air along its leading edge.

   1)   If the warm air is moist, precipitation occurs immediately along the surface position of the front, as shown in Figure 72 below.

Figure 72. Fast-Moving Cold Front Underrunning Warm, Moist, Unstable Air

g.   Since an occluded front develops when a cold front overtakes a warm front, weather with an occluded front is a combination of both warm and cold frontal weather.

   1)   Figures 73 below and 74 on page 89 show warm and cold occlusions and associated weather.

Figure 73. Warm Front Occlusion Lifting Warm, Moist, Unstable Air

Figure 74. Cold Front Occlusion Lifting Warm, Moist, Stable Air

h. A front may have little or no cloudiness associated with it.

    1) **Dry fronts** occur when the warm air aloft is flowing down the frontal slope or the air is so dry that any cloudiness that occurs is at high levels.

i. The upper wind flow dictates to a great extent the amount of cloudiness and rain accompanying a frontal system as well as movement of the front itself.

    1) When winds aloft blow across a front, it tends to move with the wind.

        a) When winds aloft parallel a front, the front moves slowly, if at all.

    2) A deep, slow-moving trough aloft forms extensive cloudiness and precipitation, while a rapid-moving, minor trough more often restricts weather to a rather narrow band.

        a) However, the latter often breeds severe, fast-moving, turbulent spring weather.

8. **Instability Line**

a. An instability line is a narrow, nonfrontal line or band of convective activity.

    1) If the activity consists of fully developed thunderstorms, the line is a **squall line** (see Part I, Study Unit 11, "Thunderstorms," beginning on page 113).

b. Instability lines form in moist, unstable air.

    1) An instability line may develop far from any front.

    2) More often, it develops ahead of a cold front, and sometimes a series of these lines move out ahead of the front.

    3) A favored location for instability lines which frequently erupt into severe thunderstorms is a dew point front or dry line.

9. **Dew Point Front or Dry Line**

   a.   During a considerable part of the year, dew point fronts are common in western Texas and New Mexico northward over the Plains States.

      1)   Moist air flowing north from the Gulf of Mexico abuts the drier and therefore slightly denser air flowing from the southwest.

      2)   Except for moisture differences, there is seldom any significant air mass contrast across this front, and thus, it is commonly called a "dry line."

   b.   Nighttime and early morning fog and low-level clouds often prevail on the moist side of the line, while generally clear skies mark the dry side.

      1)   In the spring and early summer over Texas, Oklahoma, and Kansas, and for some distance eastward, the dry line is a favored spawning area for squall lines and tornadoes.

8.3 IN CLOSING

1.   An air mass is a body of air with fairly uniform properties of temperature and moisture.

   a.   Its stability determines its typical weather characteristics.

2.   A front is the zone between two different air masses.

   a.   There are three principal types of fronts: cold, warm, and stationary.

3.   Frontal waves usually form on slow-moving cold fronts or on stationary fronts.

   a.   One section of the front begins to move as a warm front, and the section beside it begins to move as a cold front.

   b.   The cold front moves faster than the warm front, and the two close together to form an occlusion.

4.   Nonfrontal lows are low-pressure areas lying solely in a homogeneous air mass.

5.   Frontolysis is the dissipation of a front.

6.   Frontogenesis is the development of a front.

7.   In fronts, flying weather varies from virtually clear skies to extremely hazardous conditions.

   a.   Surface weather charts pictorially portray fronts and, in conjunction with other forecast charts and special analyses, help you in determining expected weather conditions along your proposed route.

      1)   Knowing the locations of fronts and associated weather helps you determine whether you can proceed as planned.

      2)   Often you can change your route to avoid adverse weather.

   b.   Frontal weather may change rapidly.

      1)   For example, there may be only cloudiness associated with a cold front over northern Illinois during the morning but with a strong squall line forecast by afternoon.

   c.   A mental picture of what is happening and what is forecast should greatly help you in avoiding adverse weather conditions.

      1)   If unexpected adverse weather develops en route, your mental picture helps you in planning the best diversion.

      2)   **Always obtain a good preflight weather briefing.**

END OF STUDY UNIT

STUDY UNIT NINE
TURBULENCE

(12 pages of outline)

Please take a few minutes to study each of the concepts listed above and anticipate/imagine what they are and how they relate to the other listed concepts.

9.1 INTRODUCTION

A turbulent atmosphere is one in which air currents vary greatly over short distances.

1. These currents may range from rather mild eddies to strong currents of relatively large dimensions.

2. As an aircraft moves through these currents, it undergoes changing accelerations which jostle it from its smooth flight path.

    a. This jostling is turbulence.

        1) Turbulence ranges from bumpiness, which can annoy crew and passengers, to severe jolts, which can structurally damage the aircraft or injure passengers.

    b. Aircraft reaction to turbulence varies with the difference in wind speed in adjacent currents, size of the aircraft, wing loading, airspeed, and aircraft attitude.

        1) When an aircraft travels rapidly from one current to another, it undergoes abrupt changes in acceleration.

        2) Obviously, if the aircraft were to move more slowly, the changes in acceleration would be less.

        3) Thus, the first rule in flying through turbulence is to reduce airspeed.

            a) Your aircraft manual most likely lists recommended airspeed for penetrating turbulence.

3. The main causes of turbulence are

    a. Convective currents,
    b. Obstructions to wind flow, and
    c. Wind shear.

4. Turbulence also occurs in the wake of moving aircraft whenever the airfoils exert lift, i.e., wake turbulence.

5. Any combination of causes may occur at one time.

9.2 CONVECTIVE CURRENTS

1. Convective currents are a common cause of turbulence, especially at low altitudes. These currents are localized vertical air movements, both ascending and descending.

    a. For every rising current, there is a compensating downward current.

    b. The downward currents frequently occur over broader areas than do the upward currents. Therefore, they have a slower vertical speed than do the rising currents.

2.   Convective currents are most active on warm summer afternoons when winds are light.

   a.   Heated air at the surface creates a shallow, unstable layer because the warm air is forced upward.

      1)   Convection increases in strength and to greater heights as surface heating increases.

   b.   Barren surfaces, such as sandy or rocky wastelands and plowed fields, become hotter than open water or ground covered by vegetation.

      1)   Thus, air at and near the surface heats unevenly.

         a)   Because of this uneven heating, the strength of convective currents can vary considerably within short distances.

3.   When cold air moves over a warm surface, it becomes unstable in lower levels.

   a.   Convective currents may extend several thousand feet above the surface, resulting in rough, choppy turbulence when you are flying through the cold air.

      1)   This condition often occurs in any season after the passage of a cold front.

Figure 76. Effect of Convective Currents on Final Approach

b.   Figure 76 on page 92 illustrates the effect of low-level convective turbulence on an aircraft approaching a landing field.

   1)   Predominantly upward currents (top) tend to cause the aircraft to overshoot the intended touchdown point.

   2)   Predominantly downward currents (bottom) tend to cause the aircraft to undershoot the intended touchdown point.

4.   Turbulence on approach can cause abrupt changes in airspeed and may even result in a stall at a dangerously low altitude.

   a.   To guard against this danger, increase airspeed slightly over normal approach speed.

   1)   This procedure may appear to conflict with the rule of reducing airspeed for turbulence penetration, but remember, the approach speed for your aircraft is well below the recommended turbulence penetration speed.

5.   As air moves upward, it cools by expansion.

   a.   A convective current continues upward until it reaches a level where its temperature cools to that of the surrounding air.

   1)   If it cools to saturation, a cloud forms.

   b.   Billowy fair weather cumulus clouds, usually seen on sunny afternoons, are signposts in the sky indicating convective turbulence.

   1)   The cloud top usually marks the approximate upper limit of the convective current.

   2)   You can expect to encounter turbulence beneath or in the clouds. While above the clouds, air generally is smooth.

   3)   You will find flight more comfortable above the cumulus clouds, as illustrated in Figure 77 below.

Figure 77. Avoiding Turbulence by Flying above Convective Clouds

c.   When convection extends to greater heights, it develops larger towering cumulus clouds and cumulonimbus with anvil-like tops.

    1)   The cumulonimbus (i.e., thunderstorm) provides visual warning of violent convective turbulence. See Part I, Study Unit 11, "Thunderstorms," beginning on page 113.

d.   You should also know that when air is too dry for cumulus clouds to form, convective currents still can be active.

    1)   There is little indication of their presence until you encounter turbulence.
    2)   This is sometimes referred to as clear air turbulence (CAT).

9.3 OBSTRUCTIONS TO WIND FLOW

1.   Obstructions, such as buildings, trees, and rough or mountainous terrain, disrupt smooth wind flow into a complex snarl of eddies, as diagramed in Figure 78 below.

a.   An aircraft flying through these eddies experiences turbulence.

b.   This turbulence is classified as "mechanical" since it results from mechanical disruption of the ambient wind flow.

Figure 78. Mechanical Turbulence

2.   The degree of mechanical turbulence depends on wind speed and roughness of the obstructions.

   a.   The higher the speed and/or the rougher the surface, the greater the turbulence.

   b.   The wind carries the turbulent eddies downstream -- how far depends on wind speed and stability of the air.

      1)   Unstable air allows larger eddies to form than those that form in stable air.

      2)   However, the instability breaks up the eddies quickly, whereas in stable air, they dissipate slowly.

3.   Mechanical turbulence can cause cloudiness near the top of the mechanically disturbed layer, just as convective turbulence can.

   a.   The type of cloudiness tells you whether it is from mechanical or convective mixing.

      1)   Mechanical mixing produces stratocumulus clouds in rows or bands, while convective clouds form a random pattern.

      2)   The cloud rows developed by mechanical mixing may be parallel to or perpendicular to the wind depending on meteorological factors, which we do not discuss here.

4.   The airport area is especially vulnerable to mechanical turbulence, which invariably causes gusty surface winds.

   a.   When an aircraft is in a low-level approach or a climb, airspeed fluctuates in the gusts, and the aircraft may even stall.

      1)   During extremely gusty conditions, maintain a margin of airspeed above normal approach or climb speed to allow for changes in airspeed.

   b.   When landing with a gusty crosswind, be alert for control problems in mechanical turbulence caused by airport structures upwind.

      1)   Surface gusts can also create taxi problems.

5.   Mechanical turbulence can affect low-level cross-country flight almost anywhere.

   a.   When flying over rolling hills, you may experience mechanical turbulence.

      1)   Generally, such turbulence is not hazardous, but it may be annoying or uncomfortable.

      2)   A climb to higher altitude should reduce the turbulence.

   b.   When flying over rugged hills or mountains, however, you may have some real turbulence problems.

      1)   When wind speed across a mountain exceeds about 40 kt., you can anticipate turbulence. Where and to what extent depends largely on air stability.

      2)   If the air crossing the mountains is unstable, turbulence on the windward side is almost certain.

         a)   If sufficient moisture is present, convective clouds form, intensifying the turbulence.

         b)   Convective clouds over a mountain or along a ridge are a sure sign of unstable air and turbulence on the windward side and over the mountain crest.

3) As the unstable air crosses the barrier, it spills down the leeward slope, often as a violent downdraft.

a) Sometimes the downward speed exceeds the maximum climb rate for your aircraft and may drive the craft into the mountainside, as shown in Figure 80 below.

Figure 80. Wind Flow in Mountain Areas

4) In the process of crossing the mountains, mixing reduces the instability to some extent.

a) Thus, hazardous turbulence in unstable air generally does not extend a great distance downwind from the barrier.

6. **Mountain Wave**

a. When stable air crosses a mountain barrier, the turbulent situation is somewhat reversed.

1) Air flowing up the windward side is relatively smooth.
2) Wind flow across the barrier is laminar -- that is, it tends to flow in layers.

b. The barrier may set up waves in these layers much as waves develop on a disturbed water surface.

1) The waves remain nearly stationary while the wind blows rapidly through them.
2) The wave pattern, diagramed in Figure 81 on the next page, is a "standing" or "mountain" wave, so named because it remains essentially stationary and is associated with the mountains.

c. Wave crests extend well above the highest mountains, sometimes into the lower stratosphere.

1) Under each wave crest is a rotary circulation, also diagramed in Figure 81.

a) The "rotor" forms below the elevation of the mountain peaks.
b) One of the most dangerous features of a mountain wave is the turbulent areas in and below rotor clouds.

2) Updrafts and downdrafts in the waves can also create violent turbulence.

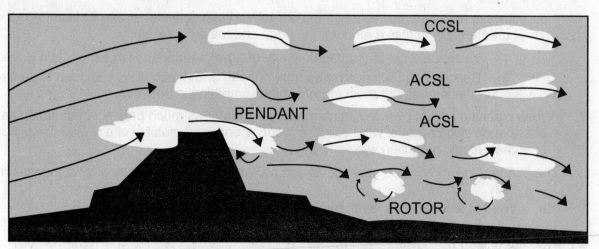

Figure 81. Cross Section of a Mountain Wave

d. Figure 81 above further illustrates clouds often associated with a mountain wave.

1) When moisture is sufficient to produce clouds on the windward side, they are stratified.

2) Crests of the standing waves may be marked by stationary, lens-shaped clouds known as "standing lenticular" clouds. (See Figure 51 on page 68.)

a) They form in the updraft and dissipate in the downdraft, so they do not move as the wind blows through them.

3) The rotor may also be marked by a "rotor" cloud.

a) Figure 83 below is a photograph of a series of rotor clouds, each under the crest of a wave.

Figure 83. Standing Wave Rotor Clouds

e.   Always anticipate possible mountain wave turbulence when strong winds of 40 kt. or greater blow across a mountain or ridge and the air is stable.

1)   You should not be surprised at any degree of turbulence in a mountain wave.

2)   Reports of turbulence range from none to turbulence violent enough to damage the aircraft, but most reports show something in between.

7.   When planning a flight over mountainous terrain, gather as much preflight information as possible on cloud reports, wind direction, wind speed, and stability of air. Satellite pictures often help locate mountain waves.

a.   Adequate information may not always be available, so remain alert for signposts in the sky.

b.   Wind at mountain top level in excess of 25 kt. suggests some turbulence.

1)   Wind in excess of 40 kt. across a mountain barrier dictates caution.

c.   Stratified clouds mean stable air.

1)   Standing lenticular and/or rotor clouds suggest a mountain wave.

a)   Expect turbulence many miles to the lee of mountains and relatively smooth flight on the windward side.

d.   Convective clouds on the windward side of mountains mean unstable air.

1)   Expect turbulence in close proximity to and on either side of the mountain.

e.   When approaching mountains from the leeward side during strong winds, begin your climb well away from the mountains -- 100 miles in a mountain wave and 30 to 50 miles otherwise.

1)   Climb to an altitude 3,000 to 5,000 ft. above mountain tops before attempting to cross.

2)   It is recommended that you approach a ridge at a 45° angle to enable a rapid retreat to calmer air.

a)   If unable to make good on your first attempt and you have higher altitude capabilities, you may choose to back off and make another attempt at higher altitude.

b)   Sometimes you may have to choose between turning back or detouring the area.

f.   Flying through mountain passes and valleys is not a safe procedure in high winds.

1)   The mountains funnel the wind into passes and valleys, thus increasing wind speed and intensifying turbulence.

2)   If winds at mountain top level are strong, go high or go around.

g.   Surface wind may be relatively calm in a valley surrounded by mountains when wind aloft is strong.

1)   If taking off in the valley, climb above mountain top level before leaving the valley.

2)   Maintain lateral clearance from the mountains sufficient to allow recovery if caught in a downdraft.

9.4 WIND SHEAR

1.   Wind shear generates eddies between two wind currents of differing velocities.

a.   The differences may be in wind speed, wind direction, or both.

1)   Wind shear may be associated with either a wind shift or a wind speed gradient at any level in the atmosphere.

b. Three conditions are of special interest:

1) Wind shear with a low-level temperature inversion,

2) Wind shear in a frontal zone, and

3) Clear air turbulence (CAT) at high levels associated with a jet stream or strong circulation.

   a) High-level CAT is discussed in detail in Part II, Study Unit 13, "High Altitude Weather," beginning on page 143.

2. Wind shear with a low-level temperature inversion

a. A temperature inversion forms near the surface on a clear night with calm or light surface wind.

b. Wind just above the inversion may be relatively strong.

1) As illustrated in Figure 86 below, a wind shear zone develops between the calm and the stronger winds above.

Figure 86. Wind Shear in a Low-level Temperature Inversion

c. Eddies in the shear zone cause airspeed fluctuations as an aircraft climbs or descends through the inversion.

1) An aircraft most likely is either climbing from takeoff or approaching to land when passing through the inversion; therefore, airspeed is relatively slow -- perhaps only a few knots greater than stall speed.

2) The fluctuation in airspeed can induce a stall precariously close to the ground.

d. Since surface wind is calm or very light, takeoff or landing can be in any direction.

1) Takeoff may be in the direction of the wind above the inversion.

   a) If so, the aircraft encounters a sudden tailwind and a corresponding loss of airspeed when climbing through the inversion. Stall is possible.

2) If the landing approach is into the wind above the inversion, the headwind is suddenly lost when descending through the inversion. Again, a sudden loss in airspeed may induce a stall.

e. When taking off or landing in calm wind under clear skies within a few hours before or after sunrise, be prepared for a temperature inversion near the ground.

1) You can be relatively certain of a shear zone in the inversion if you know the wind at 2,000 to 4,000 ft. is 25 kt. or more.

2) Allow a margin of airspeed above normal climb or approach speed to alleviate danger of stall in event of turbulence or sudden change in wind velocity.

3. Wind shear in a frontal zone

    a. While wind changes abruptly in the frontal zone, not all fronts have associated wind shear.

    b. The following is a method of determining the approximate height of a front above an airport, with the consideration that wind shear is most critical when it occurs close to the ground.

        1) A cold front wind shear occurs just after the front passes the airport and for a short period afterward.

            a) If the front is moving 30 kt. or more, the frontal surface (wind shear zone) will usually be 5,000 ft. above the airport about 3 hr. after the frontal passage.

        2) With a warm front, the most critical period is approximately 6 hr. before the front passes the airport. Warm front shear may exist from the surface to 5,000 ft. AGL.

            a) Wind shear conditions cease after the front passes the airport.

    c. Turbulence may or may not exist in wind shear conditions.

        1) If the surface wind under the front is strong and gusty, there will be some turbulence associated with wind shear.

    d. When turbulence is expected in a frontal zone, follow turbulence penetration procedures recommended in your aircraft manual.

9.5 WAKE TURBULENCE

1. An aircraft generates lift due, in part, to relatively high pressure beneath its wings and relatively low pressure above.

    a. This causes air spillage at the wingtips from the underside, up and over the wings.

    b. Thus, whenever the wings are producing lift, they generate rotary motions or vortices off the wingtips.

2. When the landing gear bears the entire weight of the aircraft, no wingtip vortices develop.

    a. But the instant the aircraft rotates on takeoff, these vortices begin.

        1) Figure 87 below illustrates how they might appear if visible behind the plane as it breaks ground.

Figure 87. Wingtip Vortices

    b. These vortices continue throughout the flight until the craft again settles firmly on its landing gear (i.e., no lift is produced).

3. These vortices spread downward and outward from the flight path. They also drift with the wind. Avoid flying through these vortices.

    a. The strength of the vortices is proportional to the weight of the aircraft as well as other factors.

        1) Therefore, wake turbulence is more intense behind large, transport category aircraft than behind small aircraft.

        2) Generally, it is a problem only when following the larger aircraft.

4. The turbulence persists several minutes and may linger after the aircraft is out of sight.

    a. Most jets when taking off lift the nose wheel about midpoint in the takeoff roll; therefore, vortices begin at approximately the middle of the takeoff roll.

    b. Vortices behind propeller aircraft begin only a short distance behind liftoff.

    c. Following a landing of either type of aircraft, vortices end at approximately the point where the nose wheel touches down.

5. Follow these guidelines when using the same runway as a heavier aircraft:

    a. If landing behind another aircraft, keep your approach above its approach and keep your touchdown beyond the point where its nose wheel touched the runway, as in Figure 88 (A);

    b. If landing behind a departing aircraft, land only if you can complete your landing roll before reaching the midpoint of its takeoff roll, as in Figure 88 (B);

    c. If departing behind another departing aircraft, take off only if you can become airborne before reaching the midpoint of its takeoff roll and only if you can climb fast enough to stay above its flight path, as in Figure 88 (C); and

    d. Do not depart behind a landing aircraft unless you can taxi onto the runway beyond the point at which its nosewheel touched down and have sufficient runway left for safe takeoff, as in Figure 88 (D).

Figure 88. Planning Landing or Takeoff to Avoid Wake Turbulence

e.   If parallel runways are available and the heavier aircraft takes off with a crosswind on the downwind runway, you may safely use the upwind runway.

f.   Never land or take off downwind from the heavier aircraft.

g.   When using a runway crossing the heavier aircraft's runway, you may safely use the upwind portion of your runway.

h.   You may cross behind a departing aircraft behind the midpoint of its takeoff roll.

i.   If none of these procedures is possible, wait 5 minutes or so for the vortices to dissipate or to blow off the runway.

6.   The problem of wake turbulence is more operational than meteorological.

9.6   IN CLOSING

1.   The main causes of turbulence are

    a.   Convective currents,
    b.   Obstructions to wind flow, and
    c.   Wind shear.

2.   Turbulence also occurs in the wake of moving aircraft whenever the airfoils are producing lift.   It is called wake turbulence.

    a.   You need to avoid flying through these wingtip vortices.

3.   Occurrences of turbulence are local in extent and transient in character.

    a.   A forecast of turbulence will generally specify a volume of airspace that is relatively large compared to the localized extent of the hazard.

    b.   Although general forecasts of turbulence are quite good, forecasting precise locations is, at present, impossible.

4.   Generally, when you receive a forecast of turbulence, you should plan your flight to avoid areas of **most probable turbulence**.

    a.   Since no instruments are currently available for directly observing turbulence, the weather briefer can only confirm its existence or absence via pilot reports.

    b.   Help your fellow pilot and the weather service -- send pilot reports.

5.   To make reports and forecasts meaningful, turbulence is classified into intensities based on the effects it has on the aircraft and passengers.

    a.   These intensities are listed and described in Part III, Study Unit 4, "Pilot Weather Reports (PIREP)," on page 245.   Use this guide in reporting your turbulence encounters.

END OF STUDY UNIT

STUDY UNIT TEN
ICING

(10 pages of outline)

Please take a few minutes to study each of the concepts listed above and anticipate/imagine what they are and how they relate to the other listed concepts.

10.1 INTRODUCTION

Aircraft icing is one of the major weather hazards to aviation. It is a cumulative hazard.

1. Icing reduces aircraft efficiency by increasing weight, reducing lift, decreasing thrust, and increasing drag.

    a. As shown in Figure 89 below, each effect tends either to slow the aircraft or to force it downward.

Figure 89. Effects of Structural Icing

2. Icing also seriously impairs aircraft engine performance.

3. Other icing effects include false indications on flight instruments, loss of radio communications, and loss of operation of control surfaces, brakes, and landing gear.

4. In this study unit, we discuss the principles of structural, induction system, and instrument icing and relate icing to cloud types and other factors.

   a. Although ground icing and frost are structural icing, we discuss them separately because of their different effect on an aircraft.

10.2 STRUCTURAL ICING

1. Two conditions are necessary for structural icing in flight:

   a. The aircraft must be flying through visible moisture, such as rain droplets or clouds.

   b. The temperature at the point where the moisture strikes the aircraft must be 0°C or colder.

      1) Note that aerodynamic cooling can lower temperature of an airfoil to 0°C even though the ambient temperature is a few degrees warmer.

2. Supercooled water increases the rate of icing and is essential to rapid accumulation.

   a. Supercooled water is in an unstable liquid state. When an aircraft strikes a supercooled drop, part of the drop freezes instantaneously.

   b. The latent heat of fusion released by the freezing portion raises the temperature of the remaining portion to the melting point.

      1) Aerodynamic effects may cause the remaining portion to freeze.

   c. The way in which the remaining portion freezes determines the type of icing.

      1) The types of structural icing are clear, rime, and a mixture of the two.
      2) Each type has its identifying features.

3. **Clear ice** forms when, after initial impact, the remaining liquid portion of the drop flows out over the aircraft surface, gradually freezing as a smooth sheet of solid ice.

   a. This type forms when drops are large, such as in rain or in cumuliform clouds.

   b. Figure 90 on the next page illustrates ice on the cross-section of an airfoil. Clear ice is shown at the top.

   c. Clear ice is hard, heavy, and unyielding.

      1) Its removal by deicing equipment is especially difficult.

4. **Rime ice** forms when drops are small, such as those in stratified clouds or light drizzle.

   a. The liquid portion remaining after initial impact freezes rapidly before the drop has time to spread over the aircraft surface.

   b. The small frozen droplets trap air between them, giving the ice a white appearance, as shown at the center of Figure 90 on the next page.

   c. Rime ice is lighter in weight than clear ice, but its weight is of little significance.

      1) However, its irregular shape and rough surface make it very effective in decreasing aerodynamic efficiency of airfoils, thus reducing lift and increasing drag.

   d. Rime ice is brittle and more easily removed than clear ice.

CLEAR - HARD AND GLOSSY

RIME - BRITTLE AND FROST-LIKE

MIXED - HARD ROUGH
CONGLOMERATE

Figure 90. Clear, Rime, and Mixed Icing on Airfoils

5. **Mixed ice** forms when drops vary in size or when liquid drops are intermingled with snow or
    ice particles. It can form rapidly.

    a.   Ice particles become imbedded in clear ice, building a very rough accumulation
         sometimes in a mushroom shape on leading edges, as shown at the bottom of
         Figure 90 above.

6. The FAA, National Weather Service, the military aviation weather services, and aircraft
    operating organizations have classified aircraft structural icing into intensity categories.

    a.   Part III, Study Unit 4, "Pilot Weather Reports (PIREP)," on page 245, contains a table
         listing these intensities.

         1)   The table is your guide in estimating how ice of a specific intensity will affect your
              aircraft.

         2)   Use the table also in reporting ice when you encounter it.

10.3 INDUCTION SYSTEM ICING

1. Ice frequently forms in the air intake of an engine, robbing the engine of air to support combustion.

    a. This type of icing occurs with both piston and jet engines.
    b. Carburetor icing is one example.

2. The downward moving piston in a piston engine or the compressor in a jet engine forms a partial vacuum in the intake.

    a. Adiabatic expansion in the partial vacuum cools the air.
    b. Ice forms when the temperature drops below freezing and sufficient moisture is present for sublimation.
    c. In piston engines, fuel evaporation produces additional cooling.

3. Induction icing always lowers engine performance and can even reduce intake flow below that necessary for the engine to operate.

    a. Figure 95 below illustrates carburetor icing.

4. Induction icing potential varies greatly among different aircraft and occurs under a wide range of meteorological conditions.

Figure 95. Carburetor Icing

10.4 INSTRUMENT ICING

1.   Icing of the pitot tube as seen in Figure 96 below reduces ram air pressure to the airspeed
      indicator and renders the instrument unreliable.

Figure 96. Internal Pitot Tube Icing

2.   Icing of the static pressure port reduces reliability of all instruments on the pitot-static
      system -- the airspeed and vertical speed indicators and the altimeter.

3.   Ice forming on the radio antenna distorts its shape, increases drag, and imposes vibrations
      that may result in failure in the communications system of the aircraft.

      a.   The severity of this icing depends upon the shape, location, and orientation of the
            antenna.

10.5 ICING AND CLOUD TYPES

1. All clouds at subfreezing temperatures have icing potential.

   a. However, drop size and distribution and aerodynamic effects of the aircraft influence ice formation.

   b. Ice may not form even though the potential exists.

2. The condition most favorable for very hazardous icing is the presence of many large, supercooled water drops.

   a. Conversely, an equal or lesser number of smaller droplets favors a slower rate of icing.

3. Small water droplets occur most often in fog and low-level clouds.

   a. Drizzle or very light rain is evidence of the presence of small drops in such clouds.

      1) In many cases, there is no precipitation at all.

   b. The most common type of icing found in lower-level stratus clouds is rime.

4. Thick extensive stratified clouds that produce continuous rain, such as altostratus and nimbostratus, usually have an abundance of liquid water because of the relatively larger drop size and number.

   a. Such cloud systems in winter may cover thousands of square miles and present very serious icing conditions for prolonged flights.

   b. Particularly in thick stratified clouds, concentrations of liquid water normally are greater with warmer temperatures.

      1) Thus, heaviest icing usually will be found at or slightly above the freezing level where temperature is never more than a few degrees below freezing.

   c. In layer type clouds, continuous icing conditions are rarely found to be more than 5,000 ft. above the freezing level and usually are 2,000 to 3,000 ft. thick.

5. The upward currents in cumuliform clouds are favorable for the formation and support of many large water drops.

   a. When an aircraft enters the heavy water concentrations found in cumuliform clouds, the large drops break and spread rapidly over the leading edge of the airfoil, forming a film of water.

      1) If temperatures are freezing or colder, the water freezes quickly to form a solid sheet of clear ice.

   b. You should avoid cumuliform clouds when possible.

   c. The updrafts in cumuliform clouds lift large amounts of liquid water far above the freezing level.

      1) On rare occasions, icing has been encountered in thunderstorm clouds at altitudes of 30,000 to 40,000 ft. where the free air temperature was colder than −40°C.

   d. While the vertical extent of critical icing potential cannot be specified in cumuliform clouds, their individual cell-like distribution usually limits the horizontal extent of icing conditions.

      1) An exception, of course, may be found in a prolonged flight through a broad zone of thunderstorms or heavy showers.

10.6 OTHER FACTORS IN ICING

1. **Fronts.** A condition favorable for rapid accumulation of clear icing is freezing rain below a frontal surface.

   a. Rain forms above the frontal surface at temperatures warmer than freezing.

      1) Subsequently, it falls through air at temperatures below freezing and becomes supercooled.

      2) The supercooled drops freeze on impact with an aircraft surface.

   b. Figure 98 below diagrams this type of icing. It may occur with either a warm front (top) or a cold front.

      1) The icing can be critical because of the large amount of supercooled water.

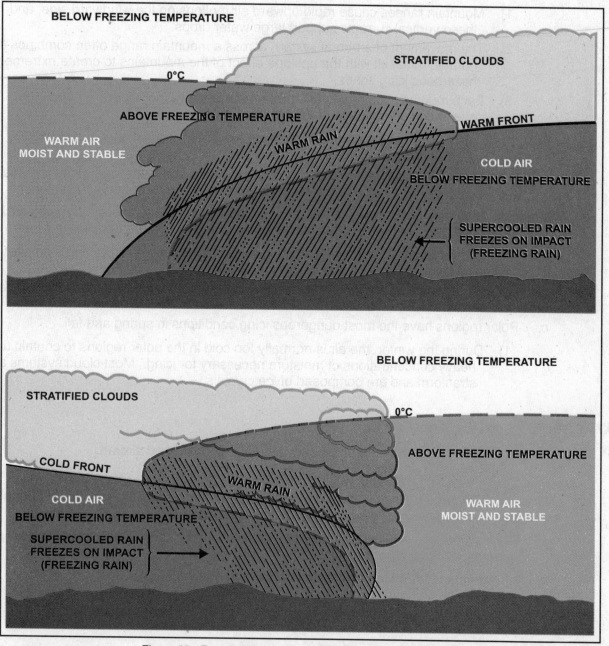

Figure 98. Freezing Rain with a Warm Front and a Cold Front

c. Icing can also become serious in cumulonimbus clouds along a surface cold front, along a squall line, or embedded in the cloud shield of a warm front.

2. **Terrain.** Air blowing upslope is cooled adiabatically. When the air is cooled below the freezing point, any water it contains becomes supercooled.

    a. In stable air blowing up a gradual slope, the cloud drops generally remain comparatively small since larger drops fall out as rain.

        1) Ice accumulation is rather slow and you should have ample time to get out of it before the accumulation becomes extremely dangerous.

    b. When air is unstable, convective clouds develop a more serious hazard.

    c. Icing is more probable and more hazardous in mountainous regions than over other terrain.

        1) Mountain ranges cause rapid upward air motions on the windward side, and these vertical currents support large water drops.

        2) The movement of a frontal system across a mountain range often combines the normal frontal lift with the upslope effect of the mountains to create extremely hazardous icing zones.

        3) Each mountainous region has preferred areas of icing depending upon the orientation of mountain ranges to the wind flow.

            a) The most dangerous icing takes place above the crests and to the windward side of the ridges.

            b) This zone usually extends about 5,000 ft. above the tops of the mountains, but when clouds are cumuliform, the zone may extend much higher.

3. **Seasons.** Icing may occur during any season of the year, but in temperate climates such as those that cover most of the contiguous United States, icing is more frequent in winter.

    a. The freezing level is nearer the ground in winter than in summer, leaving a smaller low-level layer of airspace free of icing conditions.

    b. Cyclonic storms also are more frequent in winter, and the resulting cloud systems are more extensive.

    c. Polar regions have the most dangerous icing conditions in spring and fall.

        1) During the winter, the air is normally too cold in the polar regions to contain the heavy concentrations of moisture necessary for icing. Most cloud systems are stratiform and are composed of ice crystals.

10.7 GROUND ICING

1. Frost, ice pellets, frozen rain, or snow may accumulate on parked aircraft.

    a. You should remove all ice prior to takeoff.

2. Water blown by propellers or splashed by wheels of an airplane as it taxis or runs through pools of water or mud may result in serious aircraft icing.

    a. Ice may form in wheel wells, brake mechanisms, flap hinges, etc., and prevent proper operation of these parts.

3. Ice on runways and taxiways can create traction and braking problems.

10.8 FROST

1. Frost is a hazard to flying.

    a. Pilots must remove all frost from airfoils prior to takeoff.

2. Frost forms near the surface primarily in clear, stable air and with light winds -- conditions which, in all other respects, make weather ideal for flying.

    a. Because of this, the real hazard is often minimized.

3. Thin metal airfoils are especially vulnerable surfaces on which frost will form.

4. Test data have shown that frost, ice, or snow formations having thickness and surface roughness similar to medium or course sandpaper on the leading edge and upper surfaces of a wing can reduce lift by as much as 30% and increase drag by 40%.

    a. Changes in lift and drag can significantly increase stall speed, reduce controllability, and alter the airplane's flight characteristics.

    b. Thicker or rougher frost, ice, or snow formations will have increasingly adverse effects, with the primary influence being surface roughness location on critical portions of an aerodynamic surface, e.g., the leading edge of a wing.

    c. These adverse effects on the aerodynamic properties of an airfoil may result in sudden departure from the desired flight path without any prior indications or aerodynamic warning to the pilot.

        1) Even a small amount of frost on airfoils may prevent an aircraft from becoming airborne at normal takeoff speed.

        2) Also possible is that, once airborne, an aircraft could have insufficient margin of airspeed above stall so that moderate gusts or turning flight could produce incipient or complete stalling.

5. Frost formation in flight offers a more complicated problem. The extent to which it will form is still a matter of conjecture.

    a. At most, it is comparatively rare.

10.9 IN CLOSING

1. Icing reduces aircraft efficiency by increasing weight, reducing lift, decreasing thrust, and increasing drag.

    a. Icing also seriously impairs aircraft engine performance.

2. Structural icing can occur as clear ice, rime ice, or a mixture of the two.

3. Induction system icing, e.g., carburetor icing, lowers engine performance by reducing the intake of air necessary to support combustion.

4. Instrument icing affects the airspeed and vertical speed indicators and the altimeter. Also, ice forming on the radio antenna may result in failure of the communication and/or radio navigation systems.

5. Icing is where you find it. As with turbulence, icing may be local in extent and transient in character.

6. Forecasters can identify regions in which icing is possible.

    a. However, they cannot define the precise small pockets in which it occurs.

7. You should plan your flight to avoid those areas where icing probably will be heavier than your aircraft can handle.

    a. Also, you must be prepared to avoid or to escape the hazard when it is encountered en route.

8.   Here are a few specific points to remember:

   a.   Before takeoff, check weather for possible icing areas along your planned route.

      1)   Check for pilot reports and, if possible, talk to other pilots who have flown along your proposed route.

   b.   If your aircraft is not equipped with deicing or anti-icing equipment, avoid areas of icing.

      1)   Water (clouds or precipitation) must be visible and outside air temperature must be near 0°C or colder for structural ice to form.

   c.   Always remove ice or frost from airfoils before attempting takeoff.

   d.   In cold weather, avoid, when possible, taxiing or taking off through mud, water, or slush.

      1)   If you have taxied through any of these, make a preflight check to ensure freedom of controls.

   e.   When climbing out through an ice layer, climb at an airspeed a little faster than normal to avoid a stall.

   f.   Use deicing or anti-icing equipment before accumulations of ice become too great.

      1)   When such equipment becomes less than totally effective, change course or altitude to get out of the icing as rapidly as possible.

   g.   If your aircraft is not equipped with a pitot-static system deicer, be alert for erroneous readings from your airspeed indicator, vertical speed indicator, and altimeter.

   h.   In stratiform clouds, you can probably alleviate icing by changing to an altitude with above-freezing temperatures or to one colder than −10°C.

      1)   An altitude change also may take you out of clouds.

      2)   Rime icing in stratiform clouds can be very extensive horizontally.

   i.   In frontal freezing rain, you may be able to climb or descend to a layer warmer than freezing.

      1)   Temperature is always warmer than freezing at some higher altitude.

      2)   If you are going to climb, move quickly; procrastination may leave you with too much ice.

         a)   If you are going to descend, you must know the temperature and terrain below.

   j.   Avoid cumuliform clouds if at all possible. Clear ice may be encountered anywhere above the freezing level.

      1)   Most rapid accumulations are usually at temperatures from 0°C to −15°C.

   k.   Avoid abrupt maneuvers when your aircraft is heavily coated with ice because the aircraft has lost some of its aerodynamic efficiency.

   l.   When "iced up," fly your landing approach with power.

9.   Help your fellow pilots and the weather service by sending pilot reports when you encounter icing or when icing is forecast but none is encountered.

END OF STUDY UNIT

STUDY UNIT ELEVEN
THUNDERSTORMS

(18 pages of outline)

Please take a few minutes to study each of the concepts listed above and anticipate/imagine what they are and how they relate to the other listed concepts.

11.1 INTRODUCTION

1. This study unit looks at where and when thunderstorms occur, explains what creates a storm, and looks inside the storm at what goes on and what it can do to an aircraft.

2. In some tropical regions, thunderstorms occur year-round.

   a. In midlatitudes, they develop most frequently in spring, summer, and fall.
   b. Arctic regions occasionally experience thunderstorms during summer.

3. Figures 100 through 104 depict various thunderstorm activity. Note the frequency shown by location (south-central and southeastern states) and by season (summer).

Figure 100. The Average Number of Thunderstorms Each Year

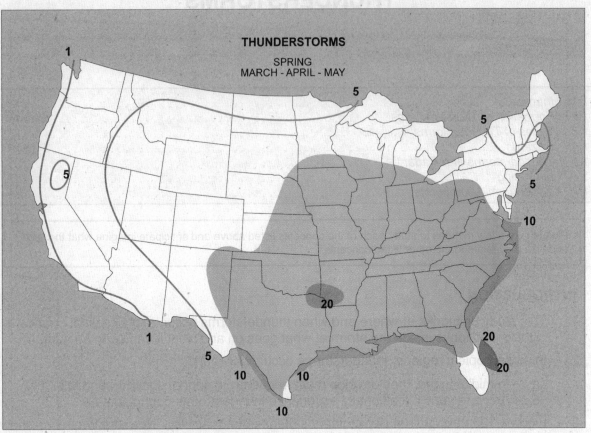

Figure 101. The Average Number of Days with Thunderstorms during Spring

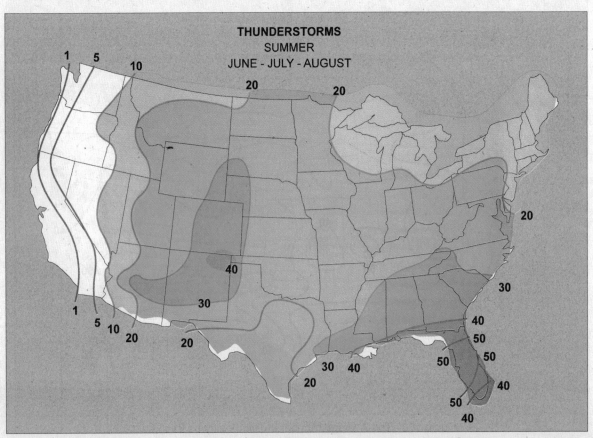

Figure 102. The Average Number of Days with Thunderstorms during Summer

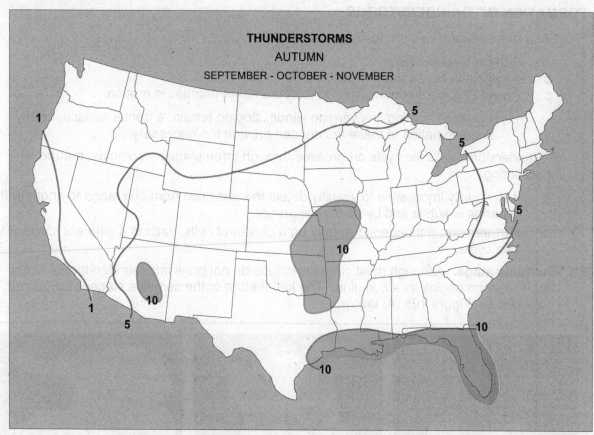

Figure 103. The Average Number of Days with Thunderstorms during Fall

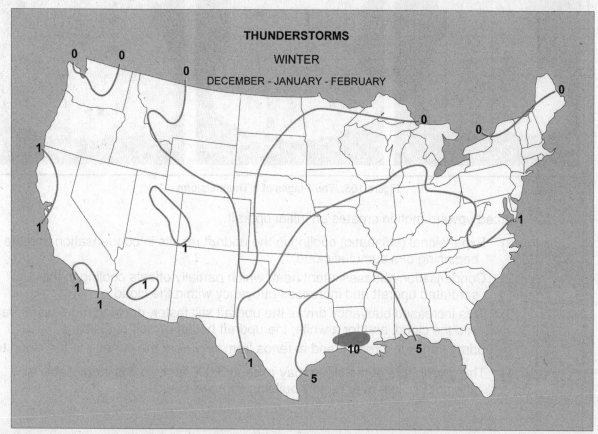

Figure 104. The Average Number of Days with Thunderstorms during Winter

11.2 FORMATION OF THUNDERSTORMS

1. For a thunderstorm to form, the air must have

   a. Sufficient water vapor.
   b. An unstable lapse rate.
   c. An initial upward boost (lifting) to start the storm process in motion.

      1) Surface heating, converging winds, sloping terrain, a frontal surface, or any combination of these factors can provide the necessary lift.

2. A thunderstorm cell's life cycle progresses through three stages – cumulus, mature, and dissipating.

   a. It is virtually impossible to visually detect the transition from one stage to another; the change is subtle and by no means abrupt.

   b. Furthermore, a thunderstorm may be a cluster of cells, each in a different stage of the life cycle.

3. **Cumulus stage.** Although most cumulus clouds do not grow into thunderstorms, every thunderstorm begins as a cumulus. The key feature of the cumulus stage is an updraft, as illustrated in Figure 105 (A) below.

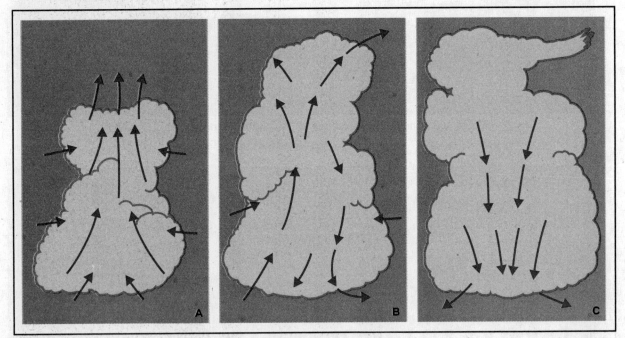

Figure 105. The Stages of a Thunderstorm

   a. Forced upward motion creates an initial updraft.

      1) Expansional (adiabatic) cooling in the updraft results in condensation and the beginning of a cumulus cloud.
      2) Condensation releases latent heat, which partially offsets cooling in the saturated updraft and increases buoyancy within the cloud.
      3) This increased buoyancy drives the updraft still faster, drawing more water vapor into the cloud, and for a while, the updraft becomes self-sustaining.

   b. The updraft varies in strength and extends from very near the surface to the cloud top.

      1) The growth rate of the cloud may exceed 3,000 fpm, so it is inadvisable to attempt to climb over rapidly building cumulus clouds.

    c.   Early during the cumulus stage, water droplets are quite small but grow to raindrop
         size as the cloud grows.

         1) The upwelling air carries the liquid water above the freezing level, creating an
             icing hazard.

         2) As the raindrops grow still heavier, they fall.

    d.   The cold rain drags air with it, creating a cold downdraft coexisting with the updraft; the
         cell has reached the mature stage.

4. **Mature stage.** Precipitation beginning to fall from the cloud base is a sign that a downdraft
    has developed and that the cell has entered the mature stage.

    a.   Cold rain in the downdraft retards compressional (adiabatic) heating, and the
         downdraft remains cooler than surrounding air.

         1) Thus, its downward speed is accelerated and can exceed 2,500 fpm.

         2) The downrushing air spreads outward at the surface, as shown in Figure 105 (B)
             on page 116, producing strong, gusty surface winds, a sharp temperature drop,
             and a rapid rise in pressure.

             a) The surface wind surge is a "plow wind," and its leading edge is the "first
                 gust."

    b.   Meanwhile, updrafts reach a maximum with speeds sometimes exceeding 6,000 fpm.

         1) Updrafts and downdrafts in close proximity create strong vertical shear and a
             very turbulent environment.

    c.   All thunderstorm hazards (discussed later in this study unit) reach their greatest
         intensity during the mature stage.

         1) Duration of the mature stage is closely related to the severity of the
             thunderstorm.

5. **Dissipating stage.** Downdrafts characterize the dissipating stage of the thunderstorm cell,
    as shown in Figure 105 (C) on page 116, and the storm dies rapidly.

    a.   When rain has ended and downdrafts have abated, the dissipating stage is complete.

    b.   When all cells of the thunderstorm have completed this stage, only harmless cloud
         remnants remain.

6. Individual thunderstorms can measure from less than 5 mi. to more than 30 mi. in diameter.

    a.   Cloud bases range from a few hundred feet in very moist climates to 10,000 ft. or
         higher in drier regions.

         1) Tops generally range from 25,000 to 45,000 ft. but occasionally extend above
             65,000 ft.

11.3 TYPES OF THUNDERSTORMS

1. **Air mass thunderstorms** most often result from surface heating.

    a.   When the storm reaches the mature stage, rain falls through or immediately beside the
         updraft.

         1) Falling precipitation induces frictional drag, retards the updraft, and reverses it to
             a downdraft. Thus, the storm is self-destructive.

         2) The downdraft and cool precipitation cool the lower portion of the storm and the
             underlying surface.

             a) This cooling cuts off the inflow of water vapor, causing the storm to run out
                 of energy and die.

         3) A self-destructive cell usually has a life cycle of 20 min. to 1 1/2 hr.

  b.   Since air mass thunderstorms generally result from surface heating, they reach maximum intensity and frequency over land during middle and late afternoon.

   1)   Offshore, they reach a maximum during late hours of darkness when land temperature is coolest and cool air off the land flows over the relatively warm water.

2.   **Steady state thunderstorms** are usually associated with weather systems.

  a.   Fronts, converging winds, and troughs aloft induce upward motion, spawning thunderstorms which often form into squall lines (see page 120).

   1)   Afternoon heating intensifies these storms.

  b.   In a steady state storm, precipitation falls outside the updraft, as shown in Figure 106 below, allowing the updraft to continue unabated.

   1)   Thus, the mature stage updrafts become stronger and last much longer than in air mass storms – hence the name, "steady state."

   2)   A steady state cell may persist for several hours.

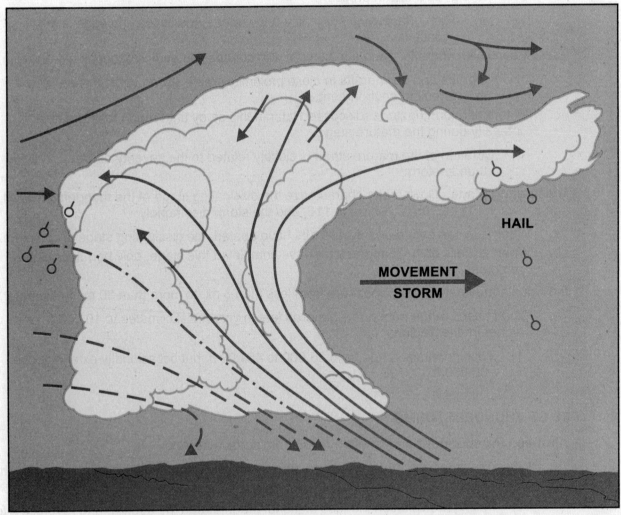

Figure 106. Schematic of the Mature Stage of a Steady State Thunderstorm Cell

11.4 HAZARDS

1. Tornadoes

    a.   The most violent thunderstorms draw air into their cloud bases with great vigor.

        1)   If the incoming air has any initial rotating motion, it often forms an extremely concentrated vortex from the surface well into the cloud.

            a)   Meteorologists have estimated that wind in such a vortex can exceed 200 kt.; pressure inside the vortex is quite low.

        2)   The strong winds gather dust and debris, and the low pressure generates a funnel-shaped cloud extending downward from the cumulonimbus base.

            a)   If the cloud does not reach the surface, it is a **funnel cloud**.
            b)   If it touches a land surface, it is a **tornado**, Figure 107 below.
            c)   If it touches water, it is a **water spout**, Figure 108 below.

Figure 107. A Tornado

Figure 108. A Waterspout

    b.   Tornadoes may occur with isolated thunderstorms, but form more frequently with steady state thunderstorms associated with cold fronts or squall lines.

        1)   Reports or forecasts of tornadoes indicate that atmospheric conditions are favorable for violent turbulence.

    c.   Families of tornadoes have been observed as appendages of the main cloud, extending several miles outward from the area of lightning and precipitation.

        1)   Thus, any cloud connected to a severe thunderstorm carries a threat of violence.

d.   Frequently, cumulonimbus mamma clouds (see Figure 110) occur in connection with violent thunderstorms and tornadoes.

    1)   The cloud displays rounded, irregular pockets or festoons from its base and is a sign of violent turbulence and extreme instability.

Figure 110. Cumulonimbus Mamma Clouds

    2)   Surface aviation reports specifically mention this and other especially hazardous clouds.

e.   Tornadoes occur most frequently in the Great Plains states east of the Rocky Mountains.

    1)   As shown in Figure 111 on the next page, however, they have occurred in every state.

f.   An aircraft entering a tornado vortex is almost certain to suffer structural damage.

    1)   Since the vortex extends well into the cloud, any pilot inadvertently caught on instruments in a severe thunderstorm could encounter a hidden vortex.

2.   **Squall lines.** A squall line is a non-frontal, narrow band of active thunderstorms.

a.   Often it develops ahead of a cold front in moist, unstable air, but it may also develop in unstable air far removed from any front.

b.   The line may be too long to easily detour and too wide and severe to penetrate.

c.   It often contains severe steady-state thunderstorms and presents the single most intense weather hazard to aircraft.

d.   A squall line usually forms rapidly, generally reaching maximum intensity during the late afternoon and the first few hours of darkness.

e.   Figure 112 on the next page is a photograph of an advancing squall line.

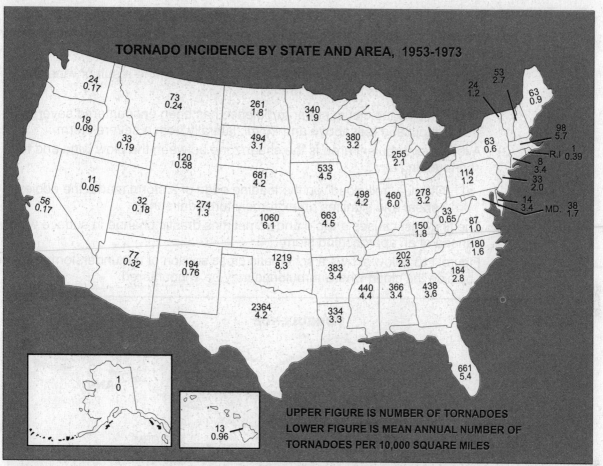

Figure 111. Tornado Incidence by State and Area (1953-1973)

Figure 112. Squall Line Thunderstorms

3. **Turbulence**

    a. Hazardous turbulence is present in **all** thunderstorms and, in a severe thunderstorm, it can seriously damage an airframe.

        1) The strongest turbulence within the cloud occurs as the result of wind shear between updrafts and downdrafts.

            a) Outside the cloud, shear turbulence has been encountered several thousand feet above and 20 mi. laterally from a severe storm.

        2) A low-level turbulent area is the shear zone between the plow wind and the surrounding air.

            a) Often, a "roll cloud" on the leading edge of a storm marks the eddies in this shear and signifies an extremely turbulent zone.

        3) The first gust causes a rapid and sometimes drastic change in surface wind ahead of an approaching storm.

        4) Figure 113 below shows a schematic cross section of a thunderstorm with areas outside the cloud where turbulence may be encountered.

Figure 113. Schematic Cross Section of a Thunderstorm

    b. It is almost impossible to hold a constant altitude in a thunderstorm, and maneuvering in an attempt to do so greatly increases stresses on the aircraft.

        1) Stresses will be least if the aircraft is held in a constant **attitude** and allowed to "ride the waves."

4. **Hail**

    a. Hail competes with turbulence as the greatest thunderstorm hazard to aircraft.

        1) Supercooled drops above the freezing level begin to freeze.

            a) Once a drop has frozen, other drops attach and freeze to it, so the hailstone grows, sometimes into a huge iceball.

        2) Large hail occurs with severe thunderstorms usually built to great heights.

            a) Eventually the hailstones fall, possibly some distance from the storm core.

            b) Hail has been observed in clear air several miles from the parent thunderstorm.

    b. As hailstones fall below the freezing level, they begin to melt, and precipitation may reach the ground as either hail or rain.

        1) Rain at the surface does not mean the absence of hail aloft.

        2) You should anticipate possible hail with **any** thunderstorm, especially beneath the anvil of a large cumulonimbus.

    c. Hailstones larger than 1/2 in. in diameter can significantly damage an aircraft in a few seconds.

        1) Figure 114 below is a photograph of an aircraft flown through hail.

Figure 114. Hail Damage to an Aircraft

5. **Icing**

    a. Updrafts in a thunderstorm support abundant liquid water.

        1) When carried above the freezing level, the water becomes supercooled.
        2) When the temperature in the upward current cools to about −15°C, much of the remaining water vapor sublimates as ice crystals.

            a) Above this level, the amount of supercooled water decreases.

    b. Supercooled water freezes on impact with an aircraft (see Part I, Study Unit 10, "Icing", beginning on page 103).

        1) Clear icing can occur at any altitude above the freezing level; but at high levels, icing may be rime or mixed rime and clear.
        2) The abundance of supercooled water makes clear icing very rapid between 0°C and −15°C, and encounters can be frequent in a cluster of cells.

6. **Low Ceiling and Visibility**

    a. Visibility generally is near zero within a thunderstorm cloud.
    b. Ceiling and visibility also can become restricted in precipitation and dust between the cloud base and the ground.

        1) The restrictions create the same problem as all ceiling and visibility restrictions.

    c. The hazards are increased many times when associated with the other thunderstorm hazards of turbulence, hail, and lightning, which make precision instrument flying virtually impossible.

7. **Effect on Altimeters**

    a. Pressure usually falls rapidly with the approach of a thunderstorm. It then rises sharply with the onset of the first gust and the arrival of the cold downdraft and heavy rain showers, falling back to normal as the storm moves on.

        1) This cycle of pressure change may occur in as little as 15 min.

    b. If the altimeter setting is not corrected, the indicated altitude may be in error by over 100 ft.

8. **Thunderstorm Electricity**

    a. Electricity generated by thunderstorms is rarely a great hazard to aircraft, but it may cause damage and is annoying to flight crews.

        1) Lightning is the most spectacular of the electrical discharges.

    b. **Lightning**

        1) A lightning strike can puncture the skin of an aircraft and can damage communication and electronic navigational equipment.

            a) Lightning has been suspected of igniting fuel vapors causing explosion; however, serious accidents due to lightning strikes are extremely rare.
            b) Nearby lightning can blind the pilot, rendering him momentarily unable to navigate either by instrument or by visual reference.
            c) Nearby lightning can also induce permanent errors in the magnetic compass.
            d) Lightning discharges, even distant ones, can disrupt radio communications on low and medium frequencies.

2) A few pointers on lightning:

 a) The more frequent the lightning, the more severe the thunderstorm.

 b) Increasing frequency of lightning indicates a growing thunderstorm.

 c) Decreasing lightning indicates a storm nearing the dissipating stage.

 d) At night, frequent distant flashes playing along a large sector of the horizon suggest a probable squall line.

c. **Precipitation Static**

1) A steady, high level of noise in radio receivers is called precipitation static and is caused by intense corona discharges from sharp metallic points and edges of flying aircraft.

 a) It is encountered often in the vicinity of thunderstorms.

 b) When an aircraft flies through clouds, precipitation, or a concentration of solid particles (ice, sand, dust, etc.), it accumulates a charge of static electricity.

 c) The electricity discharges onto a nearby surface or into the air, causing a noisy disturbance at lower frequencies.

2) The corona discharge is weakly luminous and may be seen at night. Although it has a rather eerie appearance, it is harmless.

 a) It was named "St. Elmo's Fire" by Mediterranean sailors, who saw the brushy discharge at the top of ships' masts.

11.5 THUNDERSTORMS AND RADAR

1. Weather radar detects water droplets of precipitation size.

 a. The greater the number of drops, the stronger the echo; similarly, the larger the drops, the stronger the echo.

 b. Drop size determines echo intensity to a much greater extent than does drop number.

2. Meteorologists have shown that drop size is almost directly proportional to rainfall rate, and the greatest rainfall rate is in thunderstorms.

 a. Thus, thunderstorms yield the strongest echoes.

 b. Hailstones usually are covered with a film of water and therefore act as huge water droplets, giving the strongest echo of all types of precipitation.

 c. Showers show less intense echoes, and gentle rain and snow return the weakest of all echoes.

3. Since the strongest echoes identify thunderstorms, they also mark the areas of greatest hazards.

 a. Realize, however, that severe turbulence associated with a thunderstorm can also occur outside and below the cell and thus not appear on the radar.

 b. Radar information can be valuable both from ground-based radar for preflight planning and from airborne radar for severe weather avoidance.

4. Thunderstorms build and dissipate rapidly, and they also may move rapidly.

 a. **Do not attempt to preflight plan a course between echoes.**

 b. The best use of ground radar information is to isolate general areas and coverage of echoes.

  1) You must avoid individual storms from in-flight observations either by visual sighting or by airborne radar.

5.   Airborne weather avoidance radar is, as its name implies, for avoiding severe weather, not for penetrating it.

    a.   Whether to fly into an area of radar echoes depends on echo intensity, spacing between the echoes, and your capabilities and those of your aircraft.

    b.   Remember that weather radar detects only precipitation drops; it does not detect minute cloud droplets.

    c.   **The radar scope provides no assurance of avoiding instrument weather due to clouds and fog.**

        1)   Your scope may be clear between intense echoes; this clear area does not necessarily mean you can fly between the storms and maintain visual sighting of them.

6.   The most intense echoes are severe thunderstorms.

    a.   Remember that hail may fall several miles from the cloud, and hazardous turbulence may extend as much as 20 mi. from the cloud.

        1)   Avoid the most intense echoes by at least 20 mi.; that is, echoes should be separated by at least 40 mi. before you fly between them.

        2)   As echoes diminish in intensity, you can reduce the distance by which you avoid them.

    b.   Figure 116 below illustrates use of airborne radar in avoiding thunderstorms.

Figure 116. Use of Airborne Radar to Avoid Heavy Precipitation and Turbulence

7. A **stormscope** senses and displays electrical discharges, as opposed to precipitation.

   a. By definition, a thunderstorm has lightning, which is a discharge of static electricity.

      1) Thus, an indication of discharge on the stormscope implies turbulence.

   b. However, a clear display only indicates a lack of electrical discharge.

      1) Convective activity, hazardous precipitation, and other thunderstorm hazards may still be present.

   c. Experts agree that a combination of stormscope and radar is the best thunderstorm detection system.

11.6 IN CLOSING

1. Thunderstorms progress through three stages: cumulus, mature, and dissipating.

2. Air mass thunderstorms generally result from surface heating, reaching maximum intensity and frequency over land during middle and late afternoon.

3. Steady state thunderstorms, usually associated with weather systems, may persist for several hours.

4. Hazards associated with thunderstorms are tornadoes, squall lines, turbulence, icing, hail, low ceiling and visibility, altimeter inaccuracy due to pressure changes, lightning, and precipitation static.

5. The strongest echoes on weather radar identify thunderstorms, and the most intense echoes are severe thunderstorms.

6. Weather radar detects precipitation, whereas a stormscope senses and displays electrical discharges.

7. Above all, remember this: **Never regard any thunderstorm as "light,"** even when radar observers report the echoes are of light intensity.

   a. **Avoiding thunderstorms is the best policy.**

8. The following are some DOs and DON'Ts of thunderstorm avoidance:

   a. Don't land or take off in the face of an approaching thunderstorm. A sudden wind shift or low level turbulence could cause loss of control.

   b. Don't attempt to fly under a thunderstorm even if you can see through to the other side. Turbulence under the storm could be disastrous.

   c. Do circumnavigate the entire area if the area has 6/10 thunderstorm coverage.

   d. Don't fly without airborne radar into a cloud mass containing scattered embedded thunderstorms. Scattered thunderstorms not embedded usually can be visually circumnavigated.

   e. Don't trust the visual appearance to be a reliable indicator of the turbulence associated with a thunderstorm.

   f. Do avoid by at least 20 NM any thunderstorm identified as severe or giving an intense radar echo. This is especially true under the anvil of a large cumulonimbus.

   g. Do clear the top of a known or suspected severe thunderstorm by at least 1,000 ft. altitude for each 10 kt. of wind speed at the cloud top. This rule would exceed the altitude capability of most aircraft.

   h. Do remember that vivid and frequent lightning indicates the probability of a severe thunderstorm.

   i. Do regard as severe any thunderstorm with tops 35,000 ft. or higher, whether the top is visually sighted or determined by radar.

9.   If you **cannot** avoid penetrating a thunderstorm, following are some DOs **before** entering the storm:

    a.   Tighten your safety belt, put on your shoulder harness if you have one, and secure all loose objects.

    b.   Plan your course to take you through the storm in a minimum time and **hold** it.

    c.   To avoid the most critical icing, establish a penetration altitude below the freezing level or above the level of −15°C.

    d.   Turn on pitot heat and carburetor or jet inlet heat. Icing can be rapid at any altitude and cause almost instantaneous power failure or loss of airspeed indication.

    e.   Establish power settings for reduced turbulence penetration airspeed recommended in your aircraft manual. Reduced airspeed lessens the structural stresses on the aircraft.

    f.   Turn up cockpit lights to highest intensity to lessen danger of temporary blindness from lightning.

    g.   If using automatic pilot, disengage altitude hold mode and speed hold mode. The automatic altitude and speed controls will increase maneuvers of the aircraft, thus increasing structural stresses.

    h.   If using airborne radar, tilt your antenna up and down occasionally.

        1)   Tilting it up may detect a hail shaft that will reach a point on your course by the time you do.

        2)   Tilting it down may detect a growing thunderstorm cell that may reach your altitude.

10.   The following are some DOs and DON'Ts **during** thunderstorm penetration:

    a.   Do keep your eyes on your instruments. Looking outside the cockpit can increase danger of temporary blindness from lightning.

    b.   Don't change power settings; maintain settings for reduced airspeed.

    c.   Do maintain a constant **attitude**; let the aircraft "ride the waves." Maneuvers in trying to maintain constant altitude increase stresses on the aircraft.

    d.   Don't turn back once you are in a thunderstorm. A straight course through the storm most likely will get you out of the hazards most quickly. In addition, turning maneuvers increase stresses on the aircraft.

11.7 ADDENDUM: MICROBURSTS

1.   Microbursts are small-scale, intense downdrafts which, on reaching the surface, spread outward in all directions from the downdraft center. This causes the presence of both vertical and horizontal wind shears that can be extremely hazardous to all types and categories of aircraft, especially at low altitudes.

2.   Parent clouds producing microburst activity can be any of the low or middle layer convective cloud types.

    a.   Microbursts commonly occur within the heavy rain portion of thunderstorms, but also in much weaker, benign-appearing convective cells that have little or no precipitation reaching the ground.

3.   The life cycle of a microburst as it descends in a convective rain shaft is illustrated below.

   a.   T is the time the microburst strikes the ground.

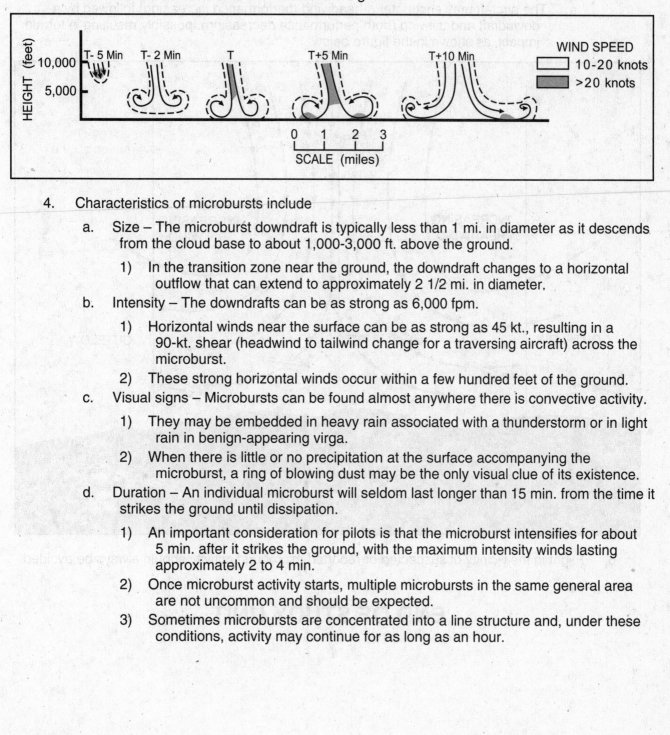

4.   Characteristics of microbursts include

   a.   Size – The microburst downdraft is typically less than 1 mi. in diameter as it descends from the cloud base to about 1,000-3,000 ft. above the ground.

      1)   In the transition zone near the ground, the downdraft changes to a horizontal outflow that can extend to approximately 2 1/2 mi. in diameter.

   b.   Intensity – The downdrafts can be as strong as 6,000 fpm.

      1)   Horizontal winds near the surface can be as strong as 45 kt., resulting in a 90-kt. shear (headwind to tailwind change for a traversing aircraft) across the microburst.

      2)   These strong horizontal winds occur within a few hundred feet of the ground.

   c.   Visual signs – Microbursts can be found almost anywhere there is convective activity.

      1)   They may be embedded in heavy rain associated with a thunderstorm or in light rain in benign-appearing virga.

      2)   When there is little or no precipitation at the surface accompanying the microburst, a ring of blowing dust may be the only visual clue of its existence.

   d.   Duration – An individual microburst will seldom last longer than 15 min. from the time it strikes the ground until dissipation.

      1)   An important consideration for pilots is that the microburst intensifies for about 5 min. after it strikes the ground, with the maximum intensity winds lasting approximately 2 to 4 min.

      2)   Once microburst activity starts, multiple microbursts in the same general area are not uncommon and should be expected.

      3)   Sometimes microbursts are concentrated into a line structure and, under these conditions, activity may continue for as long as an hour.

5. Microburst wind shear may create a severe hazard for aircraft within 1,000 ft. of the ground, particularly during the approach to landing and landing and takeoff phases.

    a. The aircraft may encounter a headwind (performance increasing) followed by a downdraft and tailwind (both performance decreasing), possibly resulting in terrain impact, as shown in the figure below.

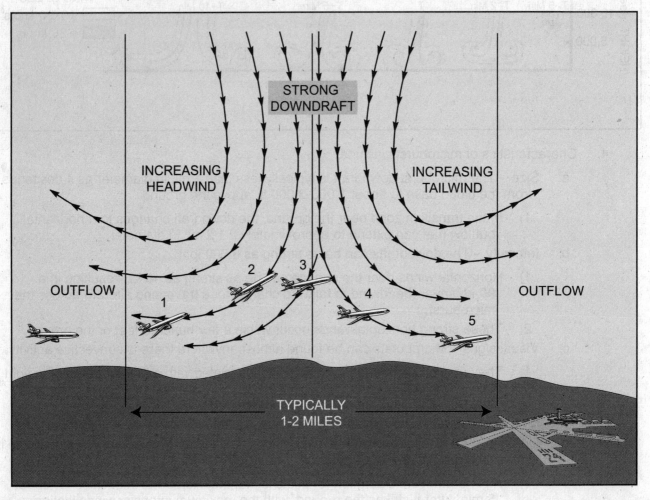

6. Flight in the vicinity of suspected or reported microburst activity should always be avoided.

END OF STUDY UNIT

STUDY UNIT TWELVE
COMMON IFR PRODUCERS

(10 pages of outline)

> Please take a few minutes to study each of the concepts listed above and anticipate/imagine what they are and how they relate to the other listed concepts.

12.1 FOG

1. Fog is a surface-based cloud composed of either water droplets or ice crystals.

   a. Fog is the most frequent cause of reducing surface visibility to below 3 SM and is one of the most common and persistent weather hazards encountered in aviation.

      1) The rapidity with which fog can form makes it especially hazardous.

         a) It is not unusual for visibility to drop from VFR to less than 1 SM in a few minutes.

      2) It is primarily a hazard during takeoff and landing, but it is also important to VFR pilots who must maintain visual reference to the ground.

   b. A small temperature-dew point spread is essential for fog to form.

      1) Therefore, fog is prevalent in coastal areas where moisture is abundant.

         a) However, fog can occur anywhere.

      2) Abundant condensation nuclei enhance the formation of fog.

         a) Thus, fog is prevalent in industrial areas where by-products of combustion provide a high concentration of these nuclei.

      3) Fog occurs most frequently in the colder months, but the season and frequency of occurrence vary from one area to another.

   c. Fog is classified by the way it forms. Formation may involve more than one process. Fog may form

      1) By cooling air to its dew point
      2) By adding moisture to air near the ground

2.   **Radiation fog** is relatively shallow fog. It may be dense enough to hide the entire sky or may conceal only part of the sky.

   a.   "Ground fog" is a form of radiation fog.

   1)   As viewed in flight, dense radiation fog may obliterate the entire surface below you.

   a)   A less dense fog may permit your observation of a small portion of the surface directly below you.

   b)   Tall objects, such as buildings, hills, and towers, may protrude upward through ground fog, giving you fixed references for VFR flight.

   c)   Figure 117 below illustrates ground fog as seen from the air.

Figure 117. Ground Fog as Seen from the Air

   b.   Conditions favorable for radiation fog are clear sky, little or no wind, and a small temperature-dew point spread (high relative humidity).

   1)   The fog forms almost exclusively at night or near daybreak.

   2)   Terrestrial radiation cools the ground; in turn, the cool ground cools the air in contact with it.

   a)   When the air is cooled to its dew point, fog forms.

   3)   When rain soaks the ground followed by clearing skies, radiation fog is not uncommon the following morning.

   c.   Radiation fog is restricted to land because water surfaces cool little from nighttime radiation.

   1)   It is shallow when wind is calm.

   2)   Winds up to about 5 kt. mix the air slightly and tend to deepen the fog by spreading the cooling through a deeper layer.

   a)   Stronger winds disperse the fog or mix the air through a still deeper layer with stratus clouds forming at the tip of the mixing layer.

   d.   Ground fog usually "burns off" rather rapidly after sunrise.

   1)   Other radiation fog generally clears before noon unless clouds move in over the fog.

3.   **Advection fog** forms when moist air moves over colder ground or water.

   a.   It is most common along coastal areas but often develops deep in continental areas.

      1)   At sea, it is called "sea fog."

   b.   Advection fog deepens as wind speed increases up to about 15 kt.

      1)   Wind much stronger than 15 kt. lifts the fog into a layer of low stratus or stratocumulus.

   c.   The west coast of the United States is quite vulnerable to advection fog.

      1)   This fog frequently forms offshore as a result of cold water, as shown in Figure 118 below, and then is carried inland by the wind.

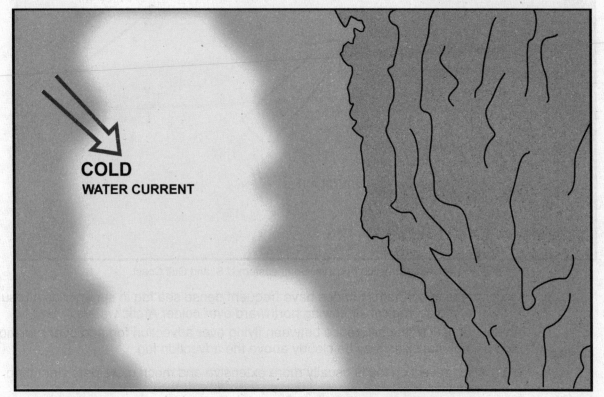

COLD
WATER CURRENT

Figure 118. Advection Fog off the Coast of California

    d.   During the winter, advection fog over the central and eastern United States results when moist air from the Gulf of Mexico spreads northward over cold ground, as shown in Figure 119 below.

        1)   The fog may extend as far north as the Great Lakes.

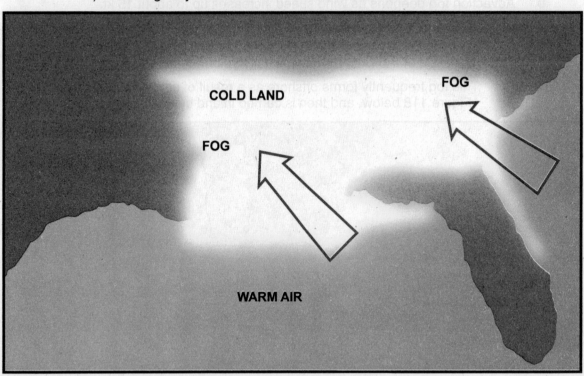

Figure 119. Advection Fog over Southeastern U.S. and Gulf Coast

    e.   Water areas in northern latitudes have frequent dense sea fog in summer as a result of warm, moist, tropical air flowing northward over colder Arctic waters.

    f.   A pilot will notice little difference between flying over advection fog and over radiation fog except that skies may be cloudy above the advection fog.

        1)   Also, advection fog is usually more extensive and much more persistent than radiation fog.

        2)   Advection fog can move in rapidly regardless of the time of day or night.

4.   **Upslope fog** forms as a result of moist, stable air being cooled adiabatically as it moves up sloping terrain.

    a.   Once the upslope wind ceases, the fog dissipates.

    b.   Unlike radiation fog, it can form under cloudy skies.

    c.   Upslope fog is common along the eastern slopes of the Rockies and somewhat less frequent east of the Appalachians.

    d.   Upslope fog often is quite dense and extends to high altitudes.

5. **Precipitation-induced fog** forms when relatively warm rain or drizzle falls through cool air and evaporation from the precipitation saturates the cool air.

    a. Precipitation-induced fog can become quite dense and continue for an extended period of time.

        1) This fog may extend over large areas, completely suspending air operations.

        2) It is most commonly associated with warm fronts but can occur with slow-moving cold fronts and with stationary fronts.

    b. Fog induced by precipitation is in itself hazardous, as is any fog.

        1) It is especially critical, however, because it occurs in the proximity of precipitation and other possible hazards, such as icing, turbulence, and thunderstorms.

6. **Ice fog** occurs in cold weather when the temperature is well below freezing and water vapor sublimates directly as ice crystals.

    a. Conditions favorable for its formation are the same as for radiation fog except for cold temperature, usually –32°C (–25°F) or colder.

        1) It occurs mostly in the Arctic regions but is not unknown in middle latitudes during the cold season.

    b. Ice fog can be blinding to someone flying in the direction of the Sun.

12.2 LOW STRATUS CLOUDS

1. Stratus clouds, like fog, are composed of extremely small water droplets or ice crystals suspended in air.

2. Stratus and fog frequently exist together.

    a. In many cases, there is no real line of distinction between fog and stratus; rather, one gradually merges into the other.

3. Flight visibility may approach zero in stratus clouds.

4. Stratus tends to be lowest during night and early morning, lifting or dissipating due to solar heating during the late morning or afternoon.

    a. Low stratus clouds often occur when moist air mixes with a colder air mass or in any situation where temperature-dew point spread is small.

12.3 HAZE AND SMOKE

1. Haze is a concentration of salt particles or other dry particles not readily classified as dust or other phenomena.

    a. It occurs in stable air, is usually only a few thousand feet thick, but sometimes may extend as high as 15,000 ft.

    b. Haze layers often have definite tops above which horizontal visibility is good.

        1) However, downward visibility from above a haze layer is poor, especially on a slant.

    c. Visibility in haze varies greatly depending upon whether the pilot is facing the Sun.

        1) Landing an aircraft into the Sun is often hazardous when haze is present.

2. Smoke concentrations form primarily in industrial areas when air is stable.

    a. It is most prevalent at night or early morning under a temperature inversion, but it can persist throughout the day.

        1) Figure 120 below illustrates smoke trapped under a temperature inversion.

Figure 120. Smoke Trapped in Stagnant Air under an Inversion

3. When skies are clear above haze or smoke, visibility generally improves during the day; however, the improvement is slower than the clearing of fog.

    a. Fog evaporates, but haze or smoke must be dispersed by movement of air.

        1) Haze or smoke may be blown away; or heating during the day may cause convective mixing that spreads the smoke or haze to a higher altitude, decreasing the concentration near the surface.

    b. At night or in the early morning, radiation fog or stratus clouds often combine with haze or smoke.

        1) The fog and stratus may clear rather rapidly during the day, but the haze and smoke will linger.

        2) A heavy cloud cover above haze or smoke may block sunlight, preventing dissipation; visibility will improve little, if any, during the day.

12.4 BLOWING RESTRICTIONS TO VISIBILITY

1. Strong wind lifts blowing dust in both stable and unstable air.

    a. When air is unstable, dust is lifted to great heights (as much as 15,000 ft.) and may be spread over wide areas by upper winds.

        1) Visibility is restricted both at the surface and aloft.

    b. When air is stable, dust does not extend to as great a height as in unstable air and usually is not as widespread.

    c. Dust, once airborne, may remain suspended and restrict visibility for several hours after the wind subsides.

2. Blowing sand is more local than blowing dust; the sand is seldom lifted above 50 ft. However, visibilities within it may be near zero.

    a. Blowing sand may occur in any dry area where loose sand is exposed to strong wind.

3. Blowing snow can cause visibility at ground level to be near zero, and the sky may become obscured when the particles are raised to great heights.

12.5 PRECIPITATION

1. Rain, drizzle, and snow are the forms of precipitation which most commonly present ceiling and/or visibility problems.

2. Drizzle or snow restricts visibility to a greater degree than rain.

    a. Drizzle falls in stable air and therefore often accompanies fog, haze, or smoke, frequently resulting in extremely poor visibility.

    b. Visibility may be reduced to zero in heavy snow.

3. Rain seldom reduces surface visibility below 1 SM except in brief, heavy showers, but it does limit cockpit visibility.

    a. When rain streams over the aircraft windshield, freezes on it, or fogs over the inside surface, the pilot's visibility to the outside is greatly reduced.

12.6 OBSCURED OR PARTIALLY OBSCURED SKY

1. To be classified as obscuring phenomena, smoke, haze, fog, precipitation, or other visibility restricting phenomena must extend upward from the surface.

    a. When the sky is totally hidden by the surface-based phenomena, the ceiling is the vertical visibility from the ground upward into the obscuration.

    b. If clouds or part of the sky can be seen above the obscuring phenomena, the condition is defined as a partial obscuration.

        1) A partial obscuration does not define a ceiling.
        2) However, a cloud layer above a partial obscuration may constitute a ceiling.

2. An obscured ceiling differs from a cloud ceiling.

    a. With a cloud ceiling, you normally can see the ground and runway once you descend below the cloud base.

    b. With an obscured ceiling, the obscuring phenomena restrict visibility between your altitude and the ground, and you have restricted slant visibility.

        1) Thus, you cannot always clearly see the runway or approach lights even after penetrating the level of the obscuration ceiling, as shown in Figure 122 below.

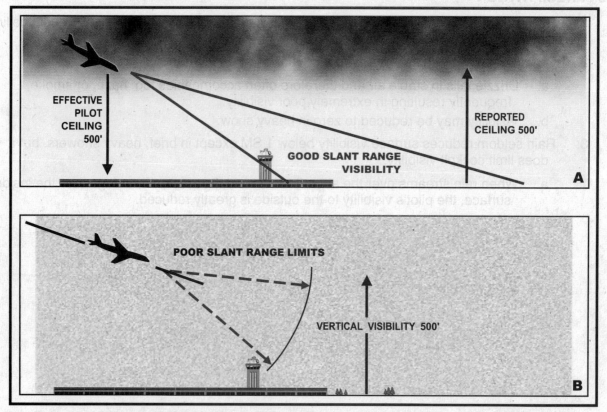

Figure 122. Difference in Visibility When a Ceiling is Caused by a Layer Aloft (A) and by a Surface-based Obscuration (B)

3. Partial obscurations also present a visibility problem for the pilot on approach to land but usually to a lesser degree than the total obscuration.

    a. However, be especially aware of erratic visibility reduction in the partial obscuration.

        1) Visibility along the runway or on the approach can instantaneously become zero.
        2) This abrupt and unexpected reduction in visibility can be extremely hazardous, especially on touchdown.

12.7 HOW TO AVOID IFR WEATHER

1. In your preflight preparation, be aware of phenomena that may produce IFR or marginal VFR flight conditions.

   a. Current charts and special analyses along with forecast and prognostic charts are your best sources of information.

   b. No weather observation is more current or more accurate than the one you make through your cockpit window.

   c. Your understanding of IFR producers will help you make better preflight and in-flight decisions.

2. Do not fly VFR in weather suitable only for IFR.

   a. If you do, you endanger not only your own life but also the lives of others, both in the air and on the ground.

   b. Remember, the single cause of the greatest number of general aviation fatal accidents is "continued VFR into adverse weather."

3. Be especially alert for development of

   a. Fog the following morning when at dusk temperature-dew point spread is 10°C (15°F) or less, skies are clear, and winds are light

   b. Fog when moist air is flowing from a relatively warm surface to a colder surface

   c. Fog when temperature-dew point spread is 3°C (5°F) or less and decreasing

   d. Fog or low stratus when a moderate or stronger moist wind is blowing over an extended upslope

      1) Temperature and dew point converge at about 2°C (4°F) for every 1,000 ft. the air is lifted.

   e. Steam fog when air is blowing from a cold surface (either land or water) over warmer water

   f. Fog when rain or drizzle falls through cool air

      1) This is especially prevalent during winter ahead of a warm front and behind a stationary front or stagnating cold front.

   g. Low stratus clouds whenever there is an influx of low level moisture overriding a shallow cold air mass

   h. Low visibilities from haze and smoke when a high pressure area stagnates over an industrial area

   i. Low visibilities due to blowing dust or sand over semiarid or arid regions when winds are strong and the atmosphere is unstable

      1) This is especially prevalent in spring.

      2) If the dust extends upward to moderate or greater heights, it can be carried many miles beyond its source.

   j. Low visibility due to snow or drizzle

   k. An undercast when you must make a VFR descent

4. Expect little if any improvement in visibility when

   a. Fog exists below heavily overcast skies.
   b. Fog occurs with rain or drizzle and precipitation is forecast to continue.
   c. Dust extends to high levels and no frontal passage or precipitation is forecast.
   d. Smoke or haze exists under heavily overcast skies.
   e. A stationary high persists over industrial areas.

12.8 IN CLOSING

1. Fog is classified by the way it forms.

    a. Radiation fog is relatively shallow, forming at night or near daybreak when the air is cooled to its dew point.

    b. Advection fog forms when moist air moves over colder ground or water.

    c. Upslope fog forms as moist, stable air is cooled adiabatically while moving up sloping terrain.

    d. Precipitation-induced fog forms when evaporation from relatively warm rain or drizzle saturates cooler air.

    e. Ice fog occurs when the temperature is well below freezing, and water vapor sublimates directly as ice crystals.

2. Low stratus clouds frequently exist with fog and may cause flight visibility to approach zero.

3. Haze and smoke must be dispersed by movement of air and will clear more slowly than fog or stratus clouds.

4. Strong wind lifts blowing dust as high as 15,000 ft., restricting visibility at the surface and aloft.

    a. Blowing sand and blowing snow can cause visibility to be near zero.

5. Precipitation presents ceiling and/or visibility problems.

    a. Drizzle or snow restricts visibility to a greater degree than rain.

6. Surface-based phenomena can partially or completely obscure the sky.

    a. The obscuring phenomena restrict visibility between your altitude and the ground, whereas with a cloud ceiling, you can see the ground and runway once you descend below the cloud base.

7. Refer to Subunit 12.7, "How to Avoid IFR Weather," on page 139. Your recognition of phenomena that may produce IFR conditions will help you make better preflight and in-flight decisions.

END OF STUDY UNIT

END OF PART I

PART II:
AVIATION WEATHER -- OVER AND BEYOND

(1 page of outline)

The following four study units are separated into Part II to facilitate study of Part I by pilots without interest in these four special topics. Our Part I outline is 140 pages long, and our Part II outline is 68 pages long.

13. High Altitude Weather
14. Arctic Weather
15. Tropical Weather
16. Soaring Weather

It is less intimidating to group the first 12 study units as Part I and Study Units 13 through 16 as Part II. You can then study only Part II topics that are relevant to you.

As was mentioned in the introduction to Part I, the images in this section were created in 1975. Because of the age of the images, you will notice that they are less rich in color than more recent images. We expect the FAA to revise and refresh this material in the near future. When new and updated images are available from the FAA, we will incorporate them into our text.

STUDY UNIT THIRTEEN
HIGH ALTITUDE WEATHER

(9 pages of outline)

> Please take a few minutes to study each of the concepts listed above and anticipate/imagine what they are and how they relate to the other listed concepts.

13.1 THE TROPOPAUSE

1. The tropopause is a thin layer forming the boundary between the troposphere and stratosphere.

   a. The height of the tropopause varies from about 65,000 ft. over the Equator to 20,000 ft. or lower over the poles.

   b. The tropopause is not continuous but generally descends step-wise from the Equator to the poles.

   1) These steps occur as "breaks."

   2) Figure 123 below is a cross section of the troposphere and lower stratosphere showing the tropopause and associated features.

   a) Note the break between the tropical and the polar tropopauses.

Figure 123. A Cross Section of the Upper Troposphere and Lower Stratosphere

2.   An abrupt change in temperature lapse rate characterizes the tropopause.

   a.   Note in Figure 123 how temperature above the tropical tropopause increases with height and how, over the polar tropopause, temperature remains almost constant with height.

3.   Temperature and wind vary greatly in the vicinity of the tropopause, affecting efficiency, comfort, and safety of flight.

   a.   Maximum winds generally occur at levels near the tropopause.

      1)   These strong winds create narrow zones of wind shear which often generate hazardous turbulence.

   b.   Preflight knowledge of temperature, wind, and wind shear is important to flight planning.

13.2   THE JET STREAM

1.   The jet stream, or jet, is a narrow, shallow, meandering river of maximum winds extending around the globe in a wavelike pattern.

   a.   A second jet stream is not uncommon, and three at one time are not unknown.

      1)   A jet may be as far south as the northern Tropics.
      2)   A jet in midlatitudes generally is stronger than one in or near the Tropics.

   b.   The jet stream typically occurs in a break in the tropopause as shown in Figure 123 on page 143.

      1)   Thus, a jet stream occurs in an area of intensified temperature gradients characteristic of the break.

2.   The concentrated winds, by arbitrary definition, must be 50 kt. or greater to classify as a jet stream.

   a.   The jet maximum (concentration of greatest wind) is not constant; rather, it is broken into segments, shaped somewhat like a boomerang as diagramed in Figure 125 below.

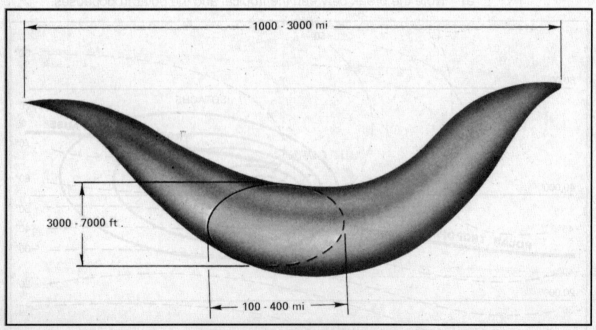

Figure 125.   A Jet Stream Segment

3. Jet stream segments move with pressure ridges and troughs in the upper atmosphere.

    a. In general they travel faster than pressure systems, and maximum wind speed varies as the segments progress through the systems.

    b. In midlatitude, wind speed in the jet stream averages considerably stronger in winter than in summer.

        1) Also, the jet shifts farther south in winter than in summer.

4. In Figure 123 on page 143, the isotachs (lines of equal wind speed) illustrate that the maximum wind speed is at the jet core and that each isotach away from the jet core the wind speed decreases.

    a. The rate of decrease of wind speed is considerably greater on the polar side than on the equatorial side; thus, the magnitude of wind shear is greater on the polar side than on the equatorial side.

5. Figure 126 below shows a map with two jet streams. The paths of the jets approximately conform to the shape of the pressure contours.

50 - 99

100 - 149

150 PLUS

Figure 126. Multiple Jet Streams

a. Note how spacing of the pressure contours is closer and wind speeds higher in the vicinity of the jets than outward on either side.

    1) Thus, horizontal wind shear is evident on both sides of the jet and is greatest near the maximum wind segments.

6.   Strong, long-trajectory jet streams usually are associated with well-developed surface lows and frontal systems beneath deep upper troughs or lows.

   a.   Cyclogenesis (i.e., development of a surface low) is usually south of the jet stream and moves nearer as the low deepens.

   b.   The occluding low moves north of the jet, and the jet crosses the frontal system near the point of occlusion (right-hand side of Figure 127).

   c.   Figure 127 below diagrams mean jet positions relative to surface systems.

Figure 127. Mean Jet Positions Relative to Surface Systems

   d.   These long jets mark high level boundaries between warm and cold air and are favored places for cirriform cloudiness.

13.3 CIRRUS CLOUDS

1.   Air travels in a corkscrew path around the jet core with upward motion on the equatorial side.

   a.   Thus, when high level moisture is available, cirriform clouds form on the equatorial side of the jet.

   b.   Jet stream cloudiness can form independently of well-defined pressure systems.

      1)   Such cloudiness ranges primarily from scattered to broken coverage in shallow layers or streaks.

      2)   The occasional fish hook and streamlined, wind-swept appearance of jet stream cloudiness always indicates very strong upper wind, usually quite far from developing or intense weather systems.

2. The densest cirriform clouds occur with well-defined systems. They appear in broad bands.

   a. Cloudiness is rather dense in an upper trough, thickens downstream, and becomes most dense at the crest of the downwind ridge.

      1) The clouds taper off after passing the ridge crest into the area of descending air.

   b. The poleward boundary of the cirrus band often is quite abrupt and frequently casts a shadow on lower clouds, especially in an occluded frontal system.

3. The upper limit of dense, banded cirrus is near the tropopause; a band may be either a single layer or multiple layers 10,000 ft. to 12,000 ft. thick.

   a. Dense, jet stream cirriform cloudiness is most prevalent along midlatitude and polar jets.

   b. However, a cirrus band usually forms along the subtropical jet in winter when a deep upper trough plunges southward into the Tropics.

4. Cirrus clouds, in themselves, have little effect on aircraft.

   a. However, dense, continuous coverage requires a pilot's constant reference to instruments; most pilots find this more tiring than flying with a visual horizon.

5. A more important aspect of the jet stream cirrus shield is its association with turbulence.

   a. Extensive cirrus cloudiness often occurs with deepening surface and upper lows; and these deepening systems produce the greatest turbulence.

13.4 CLEAR AIR TURBULENCE

1. Clear air turbulence (CAT) implies turbulence devoid of clouds. However, the term is commonly reserved for high-level wind shear turbulence, even when in cirrus clouds.

2. Cold outbreaks colliding with warm air from the south intensify weather systems in the vicinity of the jet stream along the boundary between the cold and warm air.

   a. CAT develops in the turbulent energy exchange between the contrasting air masses.

   b. Cold and warm advection along with strong wind shears develop near the jet stream, especially where curvature of the jet stream sharply increases in deepening upper troughs.

   c. CAT is most pronounced in winter when temperature contrast is greatest between cold and warm air.

3. CAT is found most frequently in an upper trough on the cold (polar) side of the jet stream.

   a. Another frequent CAT location, shown in Figure 129 on page 148, is along the jet stream north and northeast of a rapidly deepening surface low.

4. Even in the absence of a well-defined jet stream, CAT is often experienced in wind shears associated with sharply curved contours of strong lows, troughs, and ridges aloft, and in areas of strong, cold or warm air advection.

   a. Also, mountain waves can create CAT.

      1) Mountain wave CAT may extend from the mountain crests to as high as 5,000 ft. above the tropopause, and can range 100 mi. or more downstream from the mountains.

5.   CAT can be encountered where there seems to be no reason for its occurrence.

    a.   Strong winds may carry a turbulent volume of air away from its source region.

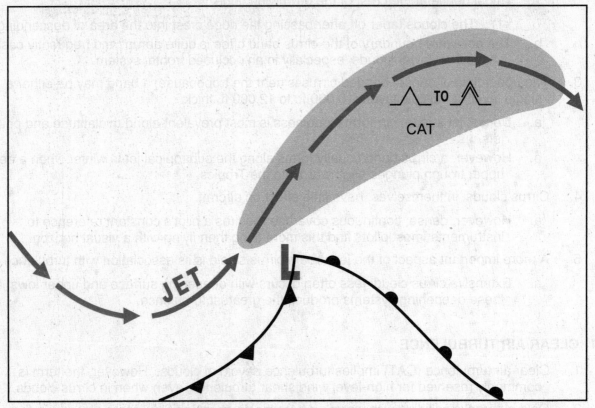

Figure 129. A Frequent CAT Location

    b.   Turbulence intensity diminishes downstream, but some turbulence still may be encountered where it normally would not be expected.

    c.   CAT forecast areas are sometimes elongated to indicate probable turbulence drifting downwind from the main source region.

6.   A forecast of turbulence specifies a volume of airspace which is quite small when compared to the total volume of airspace used by aviation, but is relatively large compared to the localized extent of the hazard.

    a.   Since turbulence in the forecast volume is patchy, you can expect to encounter it only intermittently and possibly not at all.

    b.   A flight through forecast turbulence, on the average, encounters only light and annoying turbulence 10% to 15% of the time.

        1)   About 2% to 3% of the time there is a need to have all objects secured.
        2)   The odds that a pilot will experience control problems are about 1 in 500.

7.   Turbulence is greatest near the jet stream windspeed maxima, usually on the polar sides, where there is a combination of strong wind shear, curvature in the flow, and cold air advection.

    a.   In Figure 126 on page 145, these areas would be to the northwest of Vancouver Island, from north of the Great Lakes to east of James Bay and over the Atlantic east of Newfoundland.

        1)   Also, turbulence in the form of mountain waves is probable in the vicinity of the jet stream from southern California across the Rockies into the Central Plains.

8. In flight planning, use upper air charts and forecasts to locate the jet stream, wind shears, and areas of most probable turbulence.

   a. If impractical to completely avoid an area of forecast turbulence, proceed with caution.

   b. You will do well to avoid areas where vertical shear exceeds 6 kt. per 1,000 ft. or horizontal shear exceeds 40 kt. per 150 mi.

9. If you get into CAT rougher than you care to fly through, and you are near the jet core, you can climb or descend a few thousand feet, or you can simply move farther from the jet core.

   a. If caught in CAT not associated with the jet stream, your best bet is to change altitude since you have no positive way of knowing in which direction the strongest shear lies.

   b. Pilot reports from other flights, when available, are helpful.

10. Flight maneuvers increase stresses on the aircraft, as does turbulence.

    a. The increased stresses are cumulative when the aircraft maneuvers in turbulence.

       1) Therefore, you should always maneuver gently when in turbulence to minimize stress.

    b. The patchy nature of CAT makes current pilot reports extremely helpful to observers, briefers, forecasters, air traffic controllers, and most importantly, to your fellow pilots.

    c. Always, if possible, make in-flight weather reports of CAT or other turbulence encounters.

       1) Negative reports also help when no CAT is experienced where it normally might be expected.

13.5 CONDENSATION TRAILS

1. A condensation trail, popularly contracted to "contrail," is generally defined as a cloud-like streamer which is frequently generated in the wake of aircraft flying in clear, cold, humid air.

   a. Two distinct types are observed -- exhaust trails and aerodynamic trails.

2. **Exhaust contrails.** The exhaust contrail is formed by the addition to the atmosphere of sufficient water vapor from aircraft exhaust gases to cause saturation or supersaturation of the air.

   a. Since heat is also added to the atmosphere in the wake of an aircraft, the addition of water vapor must be of such magnitude that it saturates or supersaturates the atmosphere despite the added heat.

3. **Aerodynamic contrails.** In air that is almost saturated, aerodynamic pressure reduction around airfoils, engine nacelles, and propellers cools the air to saturation leaving condensation trails from these components.

   a. This type of trail usually is neither as dense nor as persistent as exhaust trails.

      1) However, under critical atmospheric conditions, an aerodynamic contrail may trigger the formation and spreading of a deck of cirrus clouds.

      2) The induced layer may make necessary the strict use of instruments by a subsequent flight at that altitude.

4.   **Dissipation trails (distrails).** The term dissipation trail applies to a rift in clouds caused by the heat of exhaust gases from an aircraft flying in a thin cloud layer.

a.   The exhaust gases sometimes warm the air to the extent that it is no longer saturated, and the affected part of the cloud evaporates.

b.   The cloud must be both thin and relatively warm for a distrail to exist; therefore, they are not common.

13.6 HAZE LAYERS

1.   Haze layers not visible from the ground are, at times, of concern at high altitude.

a.   These layers are really cirrus clouds with a very low density of ice crystals.
b.   The tops of these layers generally are very definite and are at the tropopause.
c.   High-level haze occurs in stagnant air; it is rare in fresh outbreaks of cold polar air.

1)   Cirrus haze is common in Arctic winter.
2)   Sometimes ice crystals restrict visibility from the surface to the tropopause.

2.   Visibility in the haze sometimes may be near zero, especially when one is facing the sun.

a.   To avoid the poor visibility, climb into the lower stratosphere or descend below the haze.
b.   This change may need to be several thousand feet.

13.7 CANOPY STATIC

1.   Canopy static, similar to the precipitation static sometimes encountered at lower levels, is produced by particles brushing against plastic-covered aircraft surfaces.

a.   The discharge of static electricity results in a noisy disturbance that interferes with radio reception.
b.   Discharges can occur in such rapid succession that interference seems to be continuous.

2.   Since dust and ice crystals in cirrus clouds are the primary producers of canopy static, usually you may eliminate it by changing altitude.

13.8 ICING

1.   Although icing at high altitudes is not as common or extreme as at low altitudes, it can occur.

a.   It can form quickly on airfoils and exposed parts of jet engines.
b.   Structural icing at high altitudes usually is rime, although clear ice is possible.

2.   High-altitude icing generally forms in tops of tall cumulus buildups, anvils, and even in detached cirrus.

a.   Clouds over mountains are more likely to contain liquid water than those over more gently sloping terrain because of the added lift of the mountains.

1)   Thus, icing is more likely to occur and to be more hazardous over mountainous areas.

3.   Because ice generally accumulates slowly at high altitudes, anti-icing equipment usually eliminates any serious problems.

a.   However, anti-icing systems currently in use are not always adequate.
b.   If such is the case, avoid the icing problem by changing altitude or by varying course to remain clear of the clouds.

13.9 THUNDERSTORMS

1. A well-developed thunderstorm may extend upward through the troposphere and penetrate the lower stratosphere.

    a. Sometimes the main updraft in a thunderstorm may toss hail out the top or the upper portions of the storm.

        1) An aircraft may thus encounter hail in clear air at a considerable distance from the thunderstorm, especially under the anvil cloud.

    b. Turbulence may be encountered in clear air for a considerable distance both above and around a growing thunderstorm.

2. Thunderstorm avoidance rules apply equally at high altitudes.

    a. When flying in the clear, visually avoid all thunderstorm tops.

        1) In a severe thunderstorm situation, avoid tops by at least 20 mi.

    b. When you are on instruments, weather avoidance radar helps you in avoiding thunderstorm hazards.

        1) If in an area of severe thunderstorms, avoid the most intense echoes by at least 20 mi.

13.10 IN CLOSING

1. High-altitude weather phenomena include

    a. The tropopause -- the thin layer forming the boundary between the troposphere and the stratosphere

        1) Characterized by an abrupt change in temperature lapse rate.

    b. The jet stream -- a river of maximum winds (50 kt. or greater) extending around the globe in a wavelike pattern.

    c. Cirrus clouds -- when dense, require you to refer constantly to your instruments.

        1) The jet stream cirrus shield is associated with turbulence.

    d. Clear air turbulence (CAT) -- a term commonly reserved for high-level wind shear turbulence.

    e. Condensation trails -- cloud-like streamers that are frequently generated in the wake of aircraft flying in clear, cold, humid air.

    f. Haze layers -- really cirrus clouds with a low density of ice crystals.

    g. Canopy static -- discharge of static electricity causing interference with radio reception.

    h. Icing -- can occur at high altitudes, although it is not as common or extreme as at low altitudes.

    i. Thunderstorms -- may extend upward through the troposphere and penetrate the lower stratosphere. Thunderstorm avoidance rules apply equally at high altitudes.

2. Use upper air charts and forecasts (see Part III of this book) to locate areas to avoid.

END OF STUDY UNIT

STUDY UNIT FOURTEEN
ARCTIC WEATHER

(8 pages of outline)

> Please take a few minutes to study each of the concepts listed above and anticipate/imagine what they are and how they relate to the other listed concepts.

14.1 DEFINITION

1. The Arctic is the region shown in Figure 131 below which lies north of the Arctic Circle (66 1/2° latitude).

Figure 131. The Arctic

2.   However, this discussion includes Alaskan weather even though much of Alaska lies south of the Arctic Circle.

14.2 CLIMATE, AIR MASSES, AND FRONTS

1.   The climate of any region is largely determined by the amount of energy received from the sun.

    a.   Local characteristics of the area also influence climate.

2.   **Long Days and Nights**

    a.   A profound seasonal change in length of day and night occurs in the Arctic because of the Earth's tilt and its revolution around the sun.

        1)   Figure 132 below shows that any point north of the Arctic Circle has autumn and winter days when the sun stays below the horizon all day and days in spring and summer with 24 hr. of sunshine.

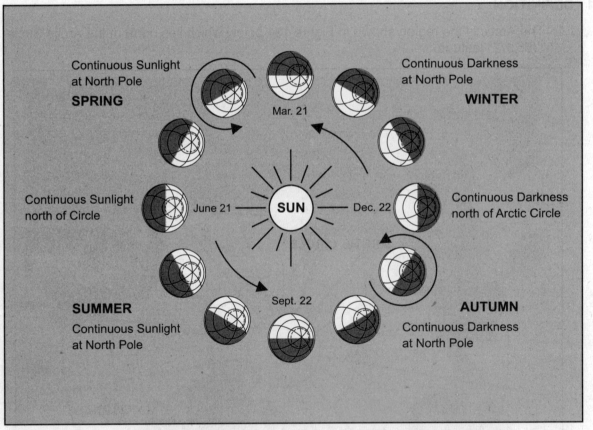

Figure 132. Sunshine in the Northern Hemisphere

        2)   The number of these days increases toward the North Pole; there the sun stays below the horizon for 6 months and shines continuously during the other 6 months.

    b.   Twilight in the Arctic is prolonged because of the shallow angle of the sun below the horizon.

        1)   In more northern latitudes, it persists for days when the sun remains just below the horizon.

        2)   This abundance of twilight often makes visual reference possible at night.

3. **Land and Water**

    a. Figure 133 below shows the water and land distribution in the Arctic.

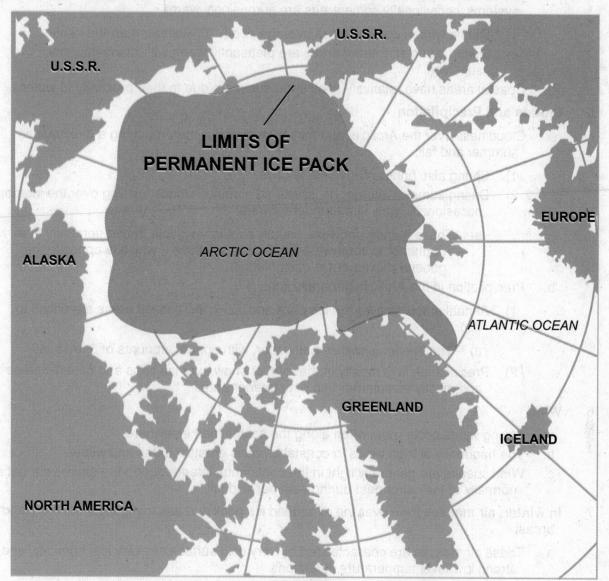

Figure 133. The Permanent Arctic Ice Pack

        1) Arctic mountain ranges are effective barriers to air movement.
        2) Large masses of air stagnate over the inland continental areas.

           a) Thus, the Arctic continental areas are air mass source regions.

    b. A large portion of the Arctic Ocean is covered throughout the year by a deep layer of ice -- the permanent ice pack as shown in Figure 133 above.

        1) Even though the ocean is ice-covered through much of the year, the ice and water below contain more heat than the surrounding cold land, thus moderating the climate to some extent.
        2) Oceanic and coastal areas have a milder climate during winter than would be expected and a cool climate in summer.

           a) As opposed to large water bodies, large land areas show a more significant seasonal temperature variation.

4.   **Temperature**

a.   The Arctic is very cold in winter, but due to local terrain and the movement of pressure systems, occasionally some areas are surprisingly warm.

1)   During winter, coastal areas average about 20° warmer than the interior.

2)   During summer, interior areas are pleasantly warm with many hours of sunshine.

b.   Coastal areas have relatively cool, short summers due to their proximity to water.

5.   **Clouds and Precipitation**

a.   Cloudiness over the Arctic is at a minimum during winter, reaching a maximum in summer and fall.

1)   Spring also brings many cloudy days.

2)   During summer afternoons, scattered cumulus clouds forming over the interior occasionally grow into thundershowers.

a)   These thundershowers, usually circumnavigable, move generally from northeast to southwest in the polar easterlies, which is opposite the general movement in midlatitudes.

b.   Precipitation in the Arctic is generally light.

1)   Annual amounts over the ice pack and along the coastal areas are only 3 to 7 in.

a)   The interior is somewhat wetter, with annual amounts of 5 to 15 in.

2)   Precipitation falls mostly in the form of snow over ice caps and oceanic areas and mostly as summer rain over interior areas.

6.   **Wind**

a.   Strong winds occur more often along the coasts than elsewhere.

b.   The frequency of high winds in coastal areas is greatest in fall and winter.

c.   Wind speeds are generally light in the continental interior during the entire year but are normally at their strongest during summer and fall.

7.   **In winter, air masses** form over the expanded ice pack and adjoining snow-covered land areas.

a.   These air masses are characterized by very cold surface air, very low humidity, and strong low-level temperature inversions.

b.   Occasionally, air from unfrozen ocean areas flows northward over the Arctic.

1)   These intrusions of moist, cold air account for most of the infrequent wintertime cloudiness and precipitation in the Arctic.

8.   **During the summer**, the top layer of the Arctic permafrost melts leaving very moist ground, and the open water areas of the Polar Basin expand markedly.

a.   Thus, the entire area becomes more humid, relatively mild, and semimaritime in character.

b.   The largest amount of cloudiness and precipitation occurs inland during the summer months.

9.   **Fronts.**   Occluded fronts are the rule.

a.   Weather conditions with occluded fronts are much the same in the Arctic as elsewhere -- low clouds, precipitation, poor visibility, and sudden fog formation.

b.   Fronts are much more frequent over coastal areas than over the interior.

14.3 ARCTIC PECULIARITIES

1. **Effects of Temperature Inversion**

    a. The intense low-level inversion over the Arctic during much of the winter causes sound (including people's voices) to carry over extremely long distances.

    b. Light rays are bent as they pass at low angles through the inversion.

        1) This bending creates an effect known as looming -- a form of mirage that causes objects beyond the horizon to appear above the horizon.

        2) Mirages distorting the shape of the sun, moon, and other objects are common with the low-level inversions.

2. **Aurora Borealis**

    a. Certain energy particles from the sun strike the Earth's magnetic field and are carried along the lines of force where they tend to lower and converge near the geomagnetic poles.

        1) The energy particles then pass through rarefied gases of the outer atmosphere, illuminating them in much the same way as an electrical charge illuminates neon gas in neon signs.

    b. The Aurora Borealis takes place at high altitudes above the Earth's surface.

        1) The highest frequency of observations is over the northern United States and northward.

        2) Displays of aurora vary from a faint glow to an illumination of the Earth's surface equal to a full moon.

        3) They frequently change shape and form and are also called dancing lights or northern lights.

3. **Light Reflection by Snow-Covered Surfaces**

    a. Much more light is reflected by snow-covered surfaces than by darker surfaces.

    b. Snow often reflects Arctic sunlight sufficiently to blot out shadows, thus markedly decreasing the contrast between objects.

        1) Dark distant mountains may be easily recognized, but a crevasse normally directly in view may be undetected due to lack of contrasts.

4. **Light from Celestial Bodies**

    a. Illumination from the moon and stars is much more intense in the Arctic than in lower latitudes.

        1) Pilots have found that light from a half-moon over a snow-covered field may be sufficient for landing.

        2) Even illumination from the stars creates visibility far beyond that found elsewhere.

    b. Only under heavy overcast skies does the night darkness in the Arctic begin to approach the degree of darkness in lower latitudes.

14.4 WEATHER HAZARDS

1. **Fog** limits landing and takeoff in the Arctic more than any other visibility restriction.

    a. Water-droplet fog is the main hazard to aircraft operations in coastal areas during the summer.

    b. Ice fog is the major restriction in winter.

2. **Ice fog** is common in the Arctic.

   a. It forms in moist air during extremely cold, calm conditions in winter, occurring often and tending to persist.

   b. Effective visibility is reduced much more in ice fog when one is looking toward the sun.

   c. Ice fog may be produced both naturally and artificially.

   d. Ice fog affecting aviation operations most frequently is produced by the combustion of aircraft fuel in cold air.

      1) When the wind is very light and the temperature is about −30°F or colder, ice fog often forms instantaneously in the exhaust gases of automobiles and aircraft.

      2) It lasts from as little as a few minutes to days.

3. **Steam fog**, often called "sea smoke," forms in winter when cold, dry air passes from land areas over comparatively warm ocean waters.

   a. Moisture evaporates rapidly from the water surface; but since the cold air can hold only a small amount of water vapor, condensation takes place just above the surface of the water and appears as "steam" rising from the ocean.

   b. This fog is composed entirely of water droplets that often freeze quickly and fall back into the water as ice particles.

   c. Low-level turbulence can occur and icing can become hazardous.

4. **Advection fog**, which may be composed either of water droplets or of ice crystals, is most common in winter and is often persistent.

   a. Advection fog forms along coastal areas when comparatively warm, moist, oceanic air moves over cold land.

      1) If the land areas are hilly or mountainous, lifting of the air results in a combination of low stratus and fog.

         a) The stratus and fog quickly diminish inland.

   b. Lee sides of islands and mountains usually are free of advection fog because of drying due to compressional heating as the air descends downslope.

   c. Icing in advection fog is in the form of rime and may become quite severe.

5. **Blowing Snow**

   a. Over the frozen Arctic Ocean and along the coastal areas, blowing snow and strong winds are common hazards during autumn and winter.

   b. Blowing snow is a greater hazard to flying operations in the Arctic than in midlatitudes because the snow is "dry" and fine and can be picked up easily by light winds.

      1) Winds in excess of 8 kt. may raise the snow several feet off the ground, obliterating objects such as runway markers.

      2) A sudden increase in surface wind may cause an unlimited visibility to drop to near zero in a few minutes.

         a) This sudden loss of visibility occurs frequently without warning in the Arctic.

      3) Stronger winds sometimes lift blowing snow to heights above 1,000 ft. and produce drifts over 30 ft. deep.

6. **Icing** is most likely in spring and fall, but is also encountered in winter.

   a. During spring and fall, icing may extend to upper levels along frontal zones.

   b. While icing is mostly a problem over water and coastal areas, it does exist inland.

      1) It occurs typically as rime, but a combination of clear and rime icing is not unusual in coastal mountains.

7. **Frost**

 a. In coastal areas during spring, fall, and winter, heavy frost and rime may form on aircraft parked outside, especially when fog or ice fog is present.

 b. This frost should be removed; it reduces lift and is especially hazardous if surrounding terrain requires a rapid rate of climb.

8. **Whiteout** is a visibility restriction phenomenon that occurs in the Arctic when a layer of cloudiness of uniform thickness overlies a snow- or ice-covered surface.

 a. Parallel rays of the sun are broken up and diffused when passing through the cloud layer so that they strike the snow surface from many angles.

   1) The diffused light then reflects back and forth countless times between the snow and the cloud, eliminating all shadows.

   2) The result is a loss of depth perception.

 b. Buildings, people, and dark-colored objects appear to float in the air, and the horizon disappears.

   1) Low-level flight over icecap terrain or landing on snow surfaces becomes dangerous.

14.5 ARCTIC FLYING WEATHER

1. A great number of pilots who fly Alaska and the Arctic are well-seasoned. They are eager to be of help and are your best sources of information.

 a. Before flying the Arctic, be sure to learn all you can about your proposed route.

2. Generally, flying conditions in the Arctic are good when averaged over the entire year.

 a. However, areas of Greenland compete with the Aleutians for the world's worst weather.

   1) These areas are exceptions.

3. Whiteouts, in conjunction with overcast skies, often present a serious hazard, especially for visual flight.

 a. Many mountain peaks are treeless and rounded rather than ragged, making them unusually difficult to distinguish under poor visibility conditions.

4. **Oceanic and Coastal Areas**

 a. In oceanic and coastal areas, predominant hazards change with the seasons.

   1) In summer, the main hazard is fog in coastal areas.

 b. In winter, ice fog is the major restriction to aircraft operation.

   1) Blowing and drifting snow often restrict visibility as well.

   2) Storms and well-defined frontal passages frequent the coastal areas accompanied by turbulence, especially in the coastal mountains.

 c. Icing is most frequent in spring and fall and may extend to high levels in active, turbulent frontal zones.

   1) Fog is also a source of icing when the temperature is colder than freezing.

5. **Continental Areas**

 a. Over the continental interior, good flying weather prevails much of the year, although during winter, ice fog often restricts aircraft operations.

   1) In terms of ceiling and visibility, the summer months provide the best flying weather.

   2) Thunderstorms develop on occasion during the summer, but they usually can be circumnavigated without much interference with flight plans.

14.6 IN CLOSING

1.   The Arctic climate is influenced by local characteristics:

    a.   Long days and nights
    b.   Land and water distribution
    c.   Temperature
    d.   Clouds and precipitation
    e.   Wind
    f.   Air masses forming over the expanded ice pack in winter
    g.   Melting of the top layer of the Arctic permafrost
    h.   Fronts

2.   Other phenomena peculiar to the Arctic are

    a.   Mirages caused by the effects of low-level temperature inversions.

        1)   Also, sound carries over extremely long distances.

    b.   Aurora Borealis.
    c.   Light reflection by snow-covered surfaces.
    d.   Light from celestial bodies.

3.   Weather hazards include

    a.   Fog,
    b.   Blowing snow,
    c.   Icing,
    d.   Frost, and
    e.   Whiteout.

4.   Interior areas generally have good flying weather, but coastal areas and Arctic slopes often are plagued by low ceiling, poor visibility, and icing.

5.   Whiteout conditions over ice and snow covered areas often cause pilot disorientation.

6.   Flying conditions are usually worse in mountain passes than at reporting stations along the route.

7.   Routes through the mountains are subject to strong turbulence, especially in and near passes.

8.   Beware of a false mountain pass that may lead to a dead end.

9.   Thundershowers sometimes occur in the interior during May through August. They are usually circumnavigable and generally move from northeast to southwest.

10. Always file a flight plan. Stay on regularly traversed routes, and if downed, stay with your plane.

11. If lost during summer, fly down-drainage, that is, downstream. Most airports are located near rivers, and chances are you can reach a landing strip by flying downstream.

    a.   If forced down, you will be close to water on which a rescue plane can land. In summer, the tundra is usually too soggy for landing.

12. Weather stations are few and far between.

    a.   Adverse weather between stations may go undetected unless reported by a pilot in flight.
    b.   A report confirming good weather between stations is also just as important.
    c.   Help yourself and your fellow pilots by reporting weather en route.

END OF STUDY UNIT

STUDY UNIT FIFTEEN
TROPICAL WEATHER

(15 pages of outline)

15.1 DEFINITION

1. Technically, the Tropics lie between latitudes 23 1/2°N and 23 1/2°S.

   a. However, weather typical of this region sometimes extends as much as 45° from the Equator.

2. One generally thinks of the Tropics as uniformly rainy, warm, and humid.

   a. However, the Tropics contain both the wettest and the driest regions of the world.

15.2 CIRCULATION

1. In Part I, Study Unit 4, "Wind," beginning on page 29, we learned that wind blowing out of the subtropical high pressure belts toward the Equator form the northeast and southeast trade winds of the two hemispheres.

   a. These trade winds converge in the vicinity of the Equator where air rises.

      1) This convergence zone is the "intertropical convergence zone" (ITCZ).

   b. In some areas of the world, seasonal temperature differences between land and water areas generate rather large circulation patterns that overpower the trade wind circulation.

      1) These areas are monsoon regions.

2. **Subtropical High Pressure Belts**

   a. If the surface under the subtropical high pressure belts were all water of uniform temperature, the high pressure belts would be continuous highs around the globe.

      1) The belts would be areas of descending or subsiding air and would be characterized by strong temperature inversions and very little precipitation.

      2) However, land surfaces at the latitudes of the high pressure belts are generally warmer throughout the year than are water surfaces.

         a) Thus, the high pressure belts are broken into semipermanent high pressure anticyclones over oceans with troughs or lows over continents.

   b. The subtropical highs shift southward during the Northern Hemisphere winter and northward during summer.

      1) The seasonal shift, the height and strength of the inversion, and terrain features determine weather in the subtropical high pressure belts.

c. **Continental Weather**

1) Along the west coasts of continents under a subtropical high, the air is stable.

   a) The inversion is strongest and lowest where the east side of an anticyclone overlies the west side of a continent.

   b) Moisture is trapped under the inversion; fog and low stratus occur frequently.

      i) However, precipitation is rare since the moist layer is shallow and the air is stable.

   c) Heavily populated areas also add contaminants to the air which, when trapped under the inversion, create an air pollution problem.

2) The situation on eastern continental coasts is just the opposite.

   a) The inversion is weakest and highest where the west side of an anticyclone overlies the eastern coast of a continent.

   b) Convection can penetrate the inversion, and showers and thunderstorms often develop.

3) Low ceiling and fog often prevent landing at a west coast destination, but a suitable alternate generally is available a few miles inland.

   a) An alternate selection may be more critical for an eastern coast destination because of widespread instability and associated hazards.

d. **Weather over Open Sea**

1) Under a subtropical high over the open sea, cloudiness is scant.

2) The few clouds that do develop have tops from 3,000 to 6,000 ft., depending on the height of the inversion.

3) Ceiling and visibility are generally quite ample for VFR flight.

e. **Island Weather**

1) An island under a subtropical high receives very little rainfall because of the persistent temperature inversion.

2) Surface heating over some larger islands causes light convective showers.

3) Cloud tops are only slightly higher than over open water.

4) Temperatures are mild, showing small seasonal and diurnal changes.

3. **Trade Wind Belts**

a. Figures 138 and 139 on page 163 show prevailing winds throughout the Tropics for July and January.

1) Note that trade winds blowing out of the subtropical highs over ocean areas are predominantly northeasterly in the Northern Hemisphere and southeasterly in the Southern Hemisphere.

b. The inversion from the subtropical highs is carried into the trade winds and is known as the "trade wind inversion."

1) As in a subtropical high, the inversion is strongest where the trades blow away from the west coast of a continent and weakest where they blow onto an eastern continental shore.

2) Daily variations from these prevailing directions are small except during tropical storms.

   a) As a result, weather at any specific location in a trade wind belt varies little from day to day.

Figure 138. Prevailing Winds throughout the Tropics in July.

Figure 139. Prevailing Winds in the Tropics in January.

c.   **Weather over open sea.** In the trade wind belt, skies over open water are about one-half covered by clouds on the average.

   1)   Tops range from 3,000 to 8,000 ft., depending on height of the inversion.
   2)   Showers, although more common than under a subtropical high, are still light with comparatively little rainfall.
   3)   Flying weather generally is quite good.

d.   **Continental Weather**

   1)   Where trade winds blow offshore along the west coasts of continents, skies are generally clear and the area is quite arid.
   2)   Where trade winds blow onshore on the east sides of continents, rainfall is generally abundant in showers and occasional thunderstorms.

      a)   Rainfall may be carried a considerable distance inland where the winds are not blocked by a mountain barrier.
      b)   Inland areas blocked by a mountain barrier are deserts.

   3)   Afternoon convective currents are common over arid regions due to strong surface heating.

      a)   Cumulus and cumulonimbus clouds can develop, but cloud bases are high and rainfall is scant because of the low moisture content.

   4)   Flying weather along eastern coasts and mountains is subject to the usual hazards of showers and thunderstorms.

      a)   Flying over arid regions is good most of the time but can be turbulent in afternoon convective currents; be especially aware of dust devils.

         i)   Blowing sand or dust sometimes restricts visibility.

e.   **Island Weather**

   1)   Mountainous islands have the most dramatic effect on trade wind weather.

      a)   Since trade winds are consistently from approximately the same direction, they always strike the same side of the island; this side is the windward side. The opposite side is the leeward side.
      b)   Winds blowing up the windward side produce copious and frequent rainfall, although cloud tops rarely exceed 10,000 ft. Thunderstorms are rare.
      c)   Downslope winds on the leeward slopes dry the air leaving relatively clear skies and much less rainfall.
      d)   Many islands in the trade wind belt have lush vegetation and even rain forests on the windward side while the leeward is semiarid.
      e)   The greatest flying hazard near these islands is obscured mountain tops.

         i)   Ceiling and visibility occasionally restrict VFR flight on the windward side in showers.
         ii)   IFR weather is virtually nonexistent on leeward slopes.

   2)   Islands without mountains have little effect on cloudiness and rainfall.

      a)   Afternoon surface heating increases convective cloudiness slightly, but shower activity is light.

b) Any island in either the subtropical high pressure belt or trade wind belt enhances cumulus development even though tops do not reach great heights.

i) Thus, a cumulus top higher than the average tops of surrounding cumulus usually marks the approximate location of an island.

ii) If it becomes necessary to ditch in the ocean, look for a tall cumulus.

4. **The intertropical convergence zone (ITCZ).** Converging winds in the intertropical convergence zone (ITCZ) force air upward.

a. The inversion typical of the subtropical high and trade wind belts disappears.

1) Figures 138 and 139 on page 163 show the ITCZ and its seasonal shift.

2) The ITCZ is well marked over tropical oceans but is weak and ill-defined over large continental areas.

b. **Weather over islands and open water.** Convection in the ITCZ carries huge quantities of moisture to great heights.

1) Showers and thunderstorms frequent the ITCZ and tops to 30,000 ft. or higher are common, as shown in Figure 137 below.

a) Precipitation is copious.

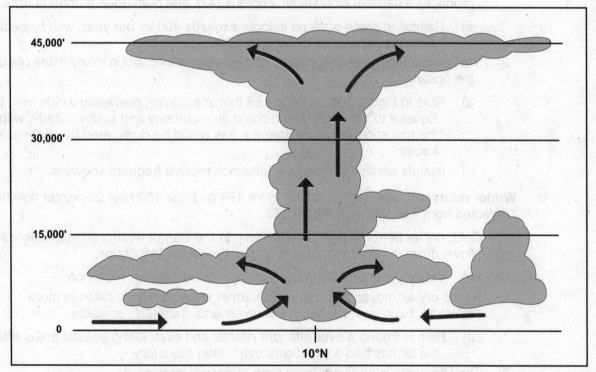

Figure 137. Vertical Cross Section Illustrating Convection in the ITCZ.

2) Since convection dominates the ITCZ, there is little difference in weather over islands and open sea under the ITCZ.

3) Flying through the ITCZ usually presents no great problem if one follows the usual practice of avoiding thunderstorms.

4) Since the ITCZ is ill-defined over continents, we will not attempt to describe ITCZ continental weather as such.

a) Continental weather ranges from arid to rain forests and is more closely related to the monsoon than to the ITCZ.

5. **Monsoon**

    a.   Refer to Figures 23 and 24 in Part I, Study Unit 4, "Wind," on page 35. You can see that over the large land mass of Asia, the subtropical high pressure breaks down completely.

        1)   Asia is covered by an intense high during the winter and a well-developed low during the summer.

        2)   You can also see the same over Australia and central Africa, although the seasons are reversed in the Southern Hemisphere.

    b.   The cold, high pressures in winter cause wind to blow from the deep interior outward and offshore.

        1)   In summer, wind direction reverses, and warm, moist air is carried far inland into the low pressure area.

        2)   This large-scale seasonal wind shift is the monsoon.

            a)   The most notable monsoon is that of southern and southeastern Asia.

    c.   **Summer or wet monsoon weather.** During the summer, the low over central Asia draws warm, moist, unstable maritime air from the southwest over the continent.

        1)   Strong surface heating coupled with rising of air flowing up the higher terrain produces extensive cloudiness, copious rain, and numerous thunderstorms.

            a)   Rainfall at some stations in India exceeds 400 in. per year, with highest amounts between June and October.

        2)   The monsoon is so pronounced that it influences circulation many miles out over the ocean.

            a)   Note in Figure 138 on page 163 that in summer, prevailing winds from the Equator to the south Asian coast are southerly and southeasterly; without the monsoon influence, these areas would be dominated by northeasterly trades.

            b)   Islands within the monsoon influence receive frequent showers.

    d.   **Winter monsoon weather.** Note in Figure 139 on page 163 how the winter flow has reversed from that shown in Figure 138.

        1)   Cold, dry air from the high plateau deep in the interior warms adiabatically as it flows down the southern slopes of the Himalayan Mountains.

            a)   Virtually no rain falls in the interior in the dry winter monsoon.

        2)   As the dry air moves offshore over warmer water, it rapidly takes in more moisture, becomes warmer in low levels and, therefore, unstable.

            a)   Rain is frequent over offshore islands and even along coastal areas after the air has had a significant over-water trajectory.

        3)   The Philippine Islands are in an area of special interest.

            a)   During the summer, they are definitely in southerly monsoon flow and are subjected to abundant rainfall.

            b)   In winter, wind over the Philippines is northeasterly -- in the transition zone between the northeasterly trades and the monsoon flow.

            c)   It is academic whether we call the phenomenon the trade winds or monsoon; in either case, it produces abundant rainfall.

               i)   The Philippines have a year-round humid, tropical climate.

e. **Other monsoon areas.** Australia in July (Southern Hemisphere winter) is an area of high pressure with predominantly offshore winds as shown in Figure 138 on page 163.

    1) Most of the continent is dry during the winter.

    2) In January (Figure 139 on page 163), winds are onshore into the continental low pressure.

       a) However, most of Australia is rimmed by mountains, and coastal regions are wet where the onshore winds blow up the mountain slopes.

       b) The interior is arid where downslope winds are warmed and dried.

    3) Central Africa is known for its humid climate and jungles.

       a) Note in Figures 138 and 139 on page 163 that prevailing wind is onshore much of the year over these regions.

       b) Some regions are wet the year round while others have the seasonal monsoon shift and have a summer wet season and a winter dry season.

    4) In the Amazon Valley of South America during the Southern Hemisphere winter (July), southeast trades, as shown in Figure 138 on page 163, penetrate deep into the valley bringing abundant rainfall which contributes to the jungle climate.

       a) In January, the ITCZ moves south of the valley as shown in Figure 139 on page 163.

       b) The northeast trades are caught up in the monsoon, cross the Equator, and also penetrate the Amazon Valley.

       c) The jungles of the Amazon result largely from monsoon winds.

f. **Flying Weather in Monsoons**

    1) During the winter monsoon, excellent flying weather prevails over dry interior regions.

       a) Over water, you must pick your way around showers and thunderstorms.

    2) In the summer monsoon, VFR flight over land is often restricted by low ceilings and heavy rain.

       a) IFR flight must cope with the hazards of thunderstorms.

    3) Freezing level in the Tropics is quite high -- 14,000 ft. or higher -- so icing is restricted to high levels.

15.3 TRANSITORY SYSTEMS

1. A **wind shear line** found in the Tropics mainly results from midlatitude influences.

    a. In Part I, Study Unit 8, "Air Masses and Fronts," beginning on page 73, we stated that an air mass becomes modified when it flows from its source region.

       1) By the time a cold air mass originating in high latitudes reaches the Tropics, temperature and moisture are virtually the same on both sides of the front.

       2) A shear line, or wind shift, is all that remains.

b. A shear line also results when a semi-permanent high splits into two cells, inducing a trough, as shown in Figure 140 below.

Figure 140. A Shear Line and an Induced Trough Caused by a Polar High Pushing into the Tropics.

c. These shear lines are zones of convergence creating forced upward motion.

1) Consequently, considerable thunderstorm and rain shower activity occurs along a shear line.

2. **Troughs** in the atmosphere, generally at or above 10,000 ft., move through the Tropics, especially along the poleward fringes.

a. As a trough moves to the southeast or east, it spreads middle and high cloudiness over extensive areas to the east of the trough line.

b. Occasionally, a well-developed trough will extend deep into the Tropics, and a closed low forms at the equatorial end of the trough.

1) The low then may separate from the trough and move westward, producing a large amount of cloudiness and precipitation.

2) If this occurs in the vicinity of a strong subtropical jet stream, extensive and sometimes dense cirrus and some convective and clear air turbulence often develop.

c. Troughs and lows aloft produce considerable amounts of rainfall in the Tropics, especially over land areas where mountains and surface heating lift air to saturation.

1) Low pressure systems aloft contribute significantly to the record 460-in. average annual rainfall on Mt. Waialeale on Kauai, Hawaii.

2) Other mountainous areas of the Tropics are also among the wettest spots on Earth.

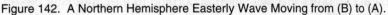

Figure 142. A Northern Hemisphere Easterly Wave Moving from (B) to (A).

Figure 143. Vertical Cross Section along Line A–B in Figure 142.

3.   **Tropical waves** (also called easterly waves) are common tropical weather disturbances, normally occurring in the trade wind belt.

   a.   In the Northern Hemisphere, they usually develop in the southeastern perimeter of the subtropical high pressure systems.

   b.   They travel from east to west around the southern fringes of these highs in the prevailing easterly circulation of the Tropics.

   c.   Surface winds in advance of a wave are somewhat more northerly than the usual trade wind direction.

   d.   As the wave approaches, as shown in Figure 142 on page 169

      1)   The typical wave is preceded by very good weather but followed by extensive cloudiness, as shown in Figure 143 on page 169, and often by rain and thunderstorms.

      2)   The weather activity is roughly in a north-south line.

   e.   Tropical waves occur in all seasons but are more frequent and stronger during summer and early fall.

      1)   Pacific waves frequently affect Hawaii.

      2)   Atlantic waves occasionally move into the Gulf of Mexico, reaching the U.S. coast.

4.   **Tropical cyclone** is a general term for any low that originates over tropical oceans.

   a.   Tropical cyclones are classified according to their intensity based on average 1-min. wind speeds.

      1)   Wind gusts in these storms may be as much as 50% higher than the average 1-min. wind speeds.

   b.   Tropical cyclone international classifications are:

      1)   Tropical Depression -- highest sustained winds up to 34 kt.,
      2)   Tropical Storm -- highest sustained winds of 35 through 64 kt., and
      3)   Hurricane or Typhoon -- highest sustained winds 65 kt. or more.

   c.   Strong tropical cyclones are known by different names in different regions of the world.

      1)   A tropical cyclone in the Atlantic and eastern Pacific is a "hurricane."
      2)   In the western Pacific, "typhoon."
      3)   Near Australia and in the Indian Ocean, simply "cyclone."

   d.   **Development.** Prerequisite to tropical cyclone development are optimal sea surface temperature under weather systems that produce low-level convergence and cyclonic wind shear.

      1)   Favored breeding grounds are tropical (easterly) waves, troughs aloft, and areas of converging northeast and southeast trade winds along the intertropical convergence zone.

      2)   The low-level convergence associated with these systems by itself will not support development of a tropical cyclone.

         a)   The system must also have horizontal outflow -- divergence -- at high tropospheric levels.

         b)   This combination creates a "chimney" in which air is forced upward causing clouds and precipitation.

c)   Condensation releases large quantities of latent heat, which raises the temperature of the system and accelerates the upward motion.

i)   The rise in temperature lowers the surface pressure which increases low-level convergence. This draws more moisture-laden air into the system.

d)   When these chain-reaction events continue, a huge vortex is generated, which may culminate in hurricane force winds.

3)   Figure 144 below shows regions of the world where tropical cyclones frequently develop. Notice that they usually originate between latitudes 5° and 20°.

Figure 144. Principal Regions Where Tropical Cyclones Form and Their Favored Directions of Movement.

a)   Tropical cyclones are unlikely within 5° of the Equator because the Coriolis force is so small near the Equator that it will not turn the winds enough for them to flow around a low-pressure area.

b)   Winds flow directly into an equatorial low and rapidly fill it.

e.   **Movement.** Tropical cyclones in the Northern Hemisphere usually move in a direction between west and northwest while in low latitudes.

1)   As these storms move toward the midlatitudes, they come under the influence of the prevailing westerlies.

a)   At this time, the storms are under the influence of two wind systems, i.e., the trade winds at low levels and prevailing westerlies aloft.

b)   Thus, a storm may move very erratically and may even reverse course, or circle.

2)   Finally, the prevailing westerlies gain control and the storm recurves toward the north, then to the northeast, and finally to the east-northeast.

a)   By this time, the storm is well into midlatitudes.

f.   **Decay.** As the storm curves toward the north or east, it usually begins to lose its tropical characteristics and acquires characteristics of lows in middle latitudes.

   1)   Cooler air flowing into the storm gradually weakens it.

      a)   If the storm tracks along a coastline or over the open sea, it gives up slowly, carrying its fury to areas far removed from the Tropics.

      b)   If the storm moves well inland, it loses its moisture source and weakens from starvation and increased surface friction, usually after leaving a trail of destruction and flooding.

   2)   When a storm takes on middle latitude characteristics, it is said to be "extratropical," meaning "outside the Tropics."

      a)   Tropical cyclones produce weather conditions that differ somewhat from those produced by their higher latitude cousins.

g.   **Weather in a Tropical Depression**

   1)   While in its initial developing stage, the cyclone is characterized by a circular area of broken to overcast clouds in multiple layers.

      a)   Embedded in these clouds are numerous showers and thunderstorms.

      b)   Rain shower and thunderstorm coverage varies from scattered to almost solid.

   2)   The diameter of the cloud pattern varies from less than 100 mi. in small systems to well over 200 mi. in large ones.

h.   **Weather in Tropical Storms and Hurricanes**

   1)   As cyclonic flow increases, the thunderstorms and rain showers form broken or solid lines paralleling the wind flow that is spiraling into the center of the storm.

      a)   These lines are the spiral rain bands frequently seen on radar.

      b)   These rain bands continually change as they rotate around the storm.

      c)   Rainfall in the rain bands is very heavy, reducing ceiling and visibility to near zero.

   2)   Winds are usually very strong and gusty and, consequently, generate violent turbulence.

   3)   Between the rain bands, ceilings and visibilities are somewhat better, and turbulence generally is less intense.

   4)   The "eye" usually forms in the tropical storm stage and continues through the hurricane stage.

      a)   In the eye, skies are free of turbulent cloudiness, and wind is comparatively light.

      b)   The average diameter of the eye is between 15 and 20 mi., but sometimes it is as small as 7 mi. and rarely more than 30 mi. in diameter.

      c)   Surrounding the eye is a wall of cloud that may extend above 50,000 ft.

         i)   This "wall cloud" contains deluging rain and the strongest winds of the storm.

         ii)   Maximum wind speeds of 175 kt. have been recorded in some storms.

5) Figure 145 below is a radar display of a mature hurricane.

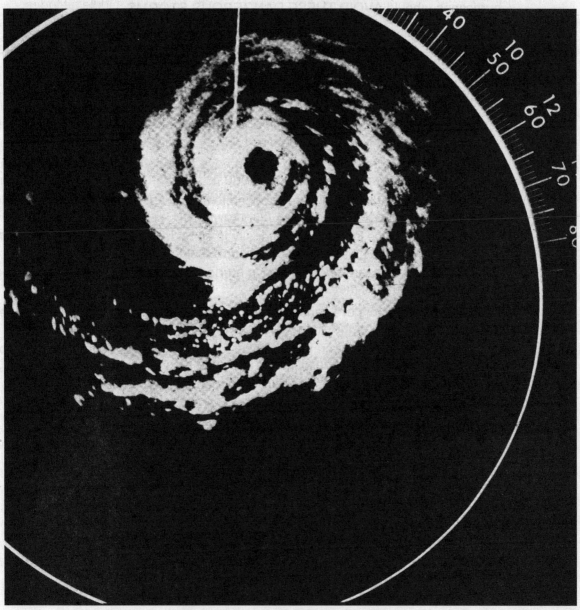

Figure 145. Radar Display of a Hurricane.

i. **Detection and warning.** The National Weather Service has a specialized hurricane forecast and warning service center at Miami, Florida, which maintains a constant watch for the formation and development of tropical cyclones.

1) Weather information from land stations, ships at sea, reconnaissance aircraft, long-range radars, and weather satellites is fed into the center.

a) The center forecasts the development, movement, and intensity of tropical cyclones.

b) Forecasts and warnings are issued to the public and aviation interests by field offices of the National Weather Service.

j.   **Flying.** All pilots, except those especially trained to explore tropical storms and hurricanes, should AVOID THESE DANGEROUS STORMS.

1)   Occasionally, jet aircraft have been able to fly over small and less intense storms, but the experience of weather research aircraft shows hazards at all levels within them.

2)   Tops of thunderstorms associated with tropical cyclones frequently exceed 50,000 ft.

a)   Winds in a typical hurricane are strongest at low levels, decreasing with altitude.

i)   However, research aircraft have frequently encountered winds in excess of 100 kt. at 18,000 ft.

b)   Aircraft at low levels are exposed to sustained, pounding turbulence due to the surface friction of the fast-moving air.

c)   Turbulence increases in intensity in spiral rain bands and becomes the most violent in the wall cloud surrounding the eye.

3)   An additional hazard encountered in hurricanes is erroneous altitude readings from pressure altimeters.

a)   These errors are caused by the large pressure difference between the periphery of the storm and its center.

b)   One research aircraft lost almost 2,000 ft. true altitude traversing a storm while the pressure altimeter indicated a constant altitude of 5,000 ft.

4)   In short, tropical cyclones are very hazardous, so avoid them!

a)   To bypass the storm in a minimum of time, fly to the right of the storm to take advantage of the tailwind.

b)   If you fly to the left of the storm, you will encounter strong headwinds which may exhaust your fuel supply before you reach a safe landing area.

15.4 IN CLOSING

1. The circulation basic to weather in the Tropics includes

   a. Subtropical high-pressure belts which shift southward during the Northern Hemisphere winter and northward during summer.

   b. Trade wind belts. Trade winds blowing out of the subtropical highs over ocean areas are predominantly northeasterly in the Northern Hemisphere.

   c. Intertropical convergence zone (ITCZ). In the ITCZ, converging winds force air upward.

      1) Showers and thunderstorms are common.

   d. Monsoon regions. Cold, high pressures over the land in winter cause wind to blow outward and offshore.

      1) In summer, wind direction reverses, and warm, moist air is carried far inland into the low-pressure area.

2. Transitory (or migrating) tropical weather producers include

   a. Wind shear lines, which are zones of convergence creating forced upward motion.

      1) Considerable thunderstorm and rain shower activity occurs along a shear line.

   b. Troughs aloft, which produce large amounts of rainfall in the Tropics, especially in mountainous areas.

   c. Tropical waves, which normally occur in the trade wind belt.

      1) Typically, they are preceded by very good weather but followed by extensive cloudiness, and often by rain and thunderstorms.

   d. Tropical cyclone -- any low that originates over tropical oceans. International classifications based on average wind speeds are

      1) Tropical depression,
      2) Tropical storm,
      3) Hurricane or typhoon.

         a) Tropical storms and hurricanes are extremely hazardous, and you should avoid them.

END OF STUDY UNIT

STUDY UNIT SIXTEEN
SOARING WEATHER

(32 pages of outline)

> Please take a few minutes to study each of the concepts listed above and anticipate/imagine what they are and how they relate to the other listed concepts.

16.1 INTRODUCTION

1. Soaring bears the relationship to flying that sailing bears to power boating.

   a. Soaring has made notable contributions to meteorology.

      1) For example, soaring pilots have probed thunderstorms and mountain waves with findings that have made flying safer for all pilots.

2. A sailplane must have auxiliary power to become airborne, such as a winch, a ground tow, or a tow by a powered aircraft.

   a. Once the sailcraft is airborne and the tow cable released, performance depends on the weather and the skill of the pilot.

   b. Forward thrust comes from gliding downward relative to the air just as thrust is developed in a power-off glide by a conventional aircraft.

      1) Therefore, to gain or maintain altitude, the soaring pilot must rely on upward motion of the air.

3. To a sailplane pilot, "lift" means the rate of climb (s)he can achieve in an up-current, while "sink" denotes his/her rate of descent in a downdraft or in neutral air.

   a. "Zero sink" means that upward currents are just strong enough to enable the pilot to hold altitude but not to climb.

   b. Sailplanes are highly efficient machines; a sink rate of a mere 2 ft. per second (fps) provides an airspeed of about 40 kt., and a sink rate of 6 fps gives an airspeed of about 70 kt.

4. In lift, a sailplane usually flies 35 to 40 kt. with a sink rate of about 2 fps.

   a. Therefore, to remain airborne, the pilot must have an upward air current of at least 2 fps.

   b. There is no point in trying to soar until weather conditions favor vertical speeds greater than the minimum sink rate of the aircraft.

   c. These vertical currents develop from several sources, which categorize soaring into five classes:

      1) Thermal soaring
      2) Frontal soaring
      3) Sea breeze soaring
      4) Ridge or hill soaring
      5) Mountain wave soaring

16.2 THERMAL SOARING

1. A thermal is simply the updraft in a small-scale convective current.

2. A soaring aircraft is always sinking relative to the air.

    a. To maintain or gain altitude the soaring pilot must therefore spend sufficient time in thermals to overcome the normal sink of the aircraft as well as to regain altitude lost in downdrafts.

        1) The pilot usually circles at a slow airspeed in a thermal and then darts on a beeline to the next thermal, as shown in Figure 147 below.

Figure 147. Thermals Generally Occur over a Small Portion of an Area While Downdrafts Predominate.

3. Low-level heating is prerequisite to thermals; and this heating is mostly from the sun, although it may be augmented by man-made heat sources, such as chimneys, factories, and cities.

    a. Cool air must sink to force warm air upward in thermals.

        1) Therefore, in small-scale convection, thermals and downdrafts coexist side by side.

    b. The net upward displacement of air must equal the net downward displacement.

        1) Fast rising thermals generally cover a small percentage of a convective area, while slower downdrafts predominate over the remaining greater portion, as diagramed in Figure 147 above.

    c. Since thermals depend on solar heating, thermal soaring is virtually restricted to daylight hours with considerable sunshine.

        1) Air tends to become stable at night due to low-level cooling by terrestrial radiation, often resulting in an inversion at or near the surface.

        2) Stable air suppresses convection, and thermals do not form until the inversion "burns off" or lifts sufficiently to allow soaring beneath the inversion.

            a) The earliest that soaring may begin varies from early forenoon to early afternoon, depending on the strength of the inversion and the amount of solar heating.

4. **Locating thermals.** Since convective thermals develop from uneven heating at the surface, the most likely place for a thermal is above a surface that heats readily.

    a. When the sky is cloudless, the soaring pilot must look for those surfaces that heat most rapidly and seek thermals above those areas.

        1) Sandy or rocky surfaces that are barren, plowed fields, stubble fields surrounded by green vegetation, cities, factories, chimneys, etc., are good thermal sources.

    b. The angle of the sun profoundly affects location of thermals over hilly landscapes.

        1) During early forenoon, the sun strikes eastern slopes more directly than others; thus, the most favorable areas for thermals are eastern slopes.

        2) The favorable areas move to southern slopes during midday.

        3) In the afternoon, they move to western slopes before they begin to weaken as the evening sun sinks toward the western horizon.

    c. Surface winds must converge to feed a rising thermal; so when you sight a likely spot for a thermal, look for dust or smoke movement near the surface.

        1) If you can see dust or smoke "streamers" from two or more sources converging on the spot as shown in Figure 148 (A), you have chosen wisely.

            a) If, however, the streamers diverge as shown in Figure 148 (B), a downdraft most likely hovers over the spot and it's time to move on.

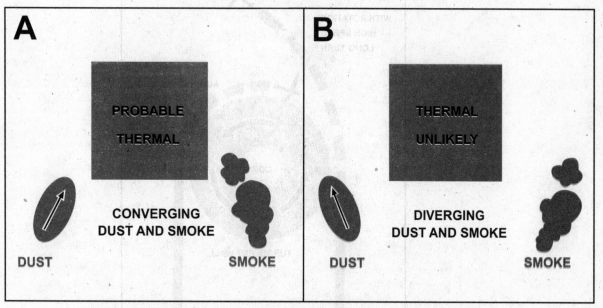

Figure 148. Using Surface Dust and Smoke Movement as Indications of a Thermal.

        2) Rising columns of smoke from chimneys and factories mark thermals augmented by man-made sources.

            a) They are good sources of lift if upward speed is great enough to support the aircraft and if they are broad enough to permit circling.

        3) Towns or cities may provide thermals; but to use a thermal over a populated area, the pilot must have sufficient altitude to glide clear of the area in the event the thermal subsides.

d.   Dust devils occur under sunny skies over sandy or dusty, dry surfaces and are sure signs of strong thermals with lots of lift.

1)   To tackle this excellent source of lift, you must use caution.

a)   The thermals are strong and turbulent and are surrounded by areas of little lift or possibly areas of sink.

2)   If approaching the dust devil at too low an altitude, an aircraft may sink to an altitude too low for recovery.

a)   A recommended procedure is to always approach the whirling vortex at an altitude 500 ft. or more above the ground.

b)   At this altitude, you have enough airspace for maneuvering in the event you get into a downdraft or turbulence too great for comfort.

3)   A dust devil may rotate either clockwise or counterclockwise.

a)   Before approaching the dusty column, determine its direction of rotation by observing dust and debris near the surface.

4)   You should enter against the direction of rotation.

a)   Figure 149 below diagrams a horizontal cross section of a clockwise rotating dust devil and ways of entering it.

Figure 149. Horizontal Cross Section of a Dust Devil Rotating Clockwise.

b)   If you enter with the direction of rotation as on the left, the wind speed is added to your airspeed, giving you a fast circling speed -- probably too great to remain in the thermal.

   i)   Against the rotation as on the right, wind speed is subtracted from airspeed, giving you a slow circling speed.

5)   Stay out of the eye of the vortex.

   a)   Centrifugal force in the center throws air outward, greatly reducing pressure within the hollow center.

   b)   The rarified air in the center provides very little lift, and the wall of the hollow center is very turbulent.

6)   If you are 500 ft. or more above the ground but are having trouble finding lift, the dust devil is well worth a try.

   a)   If the thermal is sufficiently broad to permit circling within it, you have it made.

   b)   The dust column may be quite narrow, but this fact does not necessarily mean the thermal is narrow; the thermal may extend beyond the outer limits of visible dust.

   c)   Approach the dusty column against the direction of rotation at minimum airspeed.

   d)   Enter the column near the outer edge of the dust and stay away from the hollow vortex core.

   e)   Remain alert; you are circling little more than a wing span away from violent turbulence.

e.   Wind causes a thermal to lean with altitude. When seeking the thermal supporting soaring birds or aircraft, you must make allowance for the wind.

1)   The thermal at lower levels usually is upwind from your high-level visual cue.

2)   A thermal may not be continuous from the surface upward to the soaring birds or sailplane; rather it may be in segments or bubbles.

   a)   If you are unsuccessful in finding the thermal where you expect it, seek elsewhere.

f.   When convective clouds develop, thermal soaring is usually at its best and the problem of locating thermals is greatly simplified.

1)   Cumulus clouds are positive signs of thermals, but thermals grow and die.

   a)   A cloud grows with a rising thermal, but when the thermal dies, the cloud slowly evaporates.

   b)   Because the cloud dissipates **after** the thermal ceases, the pilot who can spot the difference between a growing and dying cumulus has enhanced his/her soaring skill.

2)   The warmest and most rapidly rising air is at the center of the thermal.

   a)   Therefore, the cloud base will be highest in the center, giving a concave shape to the cloud base as shown in the left and center of Figure 150 below.

   b)   When the thermal ceases, the base assumes a convex shape as shown on the right.

   c)   Another cue to look for is the outline of the cloud sides and top.

      i)   The outline of the growing cumulus is firm and sharp.

      ii)   The dying cumulus has fragmentary sides and lacks the definite outline as shown on the right of Figure 150.

Figure 150. Cumulus Clouds and Thermals.

   d)   You can expect to find a thermal beneath either of the growing cumuli in Figure 150.

      i)   On the average, the infant cumulus on the left would be the better choice because of its longer life expectancy.

      ii)   This, of course, is a gamble, since all cumuli do not grow to the same size.

3)   As a cumulus cloud grows, it may shade the surface that generated it.

   a)   The surface cools, temporarily arresting the thermal.

   b)   As the cloud dissipates or drifts away with the wind, the surface again warms and regenerates the thermal.

   c)   This intermittent heating is one way in which thermals occur as segments or bubbles.

4) Although abundant convective cloud cover reduces thermal activity, we cannot quote a definite amount that renders thermals too weak for soaring.

    a) About 5/10 cover seems to be a good average approximation.

    b) Restriction of thermals by cumulus cloudiness first becomes noticeable at low levels.

    c) A sailplane may be unable to climb more than a few hundred feet at a low altitude while pilots at higher levels are maintaining height in or just beneath 6/10 to 8/10 convective cloud cover.

g. When air is highly unstable, the cumulus cloud can grow into a more ambitious towering cumulus or cumulonimbus.

    1) The energy released by copious condensation can increase buoyancy until the thermals become violent.

        a) Towering cumulus can produce showers.

    2) The cumulonimbus is the thunderstorm cloud producing heavy rain, hail, and icing.

        a) Well-developed **towering cumulus and cumulonimbus are for the experienced pilot only**.

        b) Some pilots find strong lift in or near convective precipitation, but they avoid hail, which can seriously batter the aircraft.

    3) Violent thermals just beneath and within these highly developed clouds often are so strong that they will continue to carry a sailplane upward even with nose down and airspeed at the redline.

h. Dense, broken, or overcast middle and high cloudiness shade the surface, cutting off surface heating and convective thermals.

    1) On a generally warm, bright day but with thin or patchy middle or high cloudiness, cumulus may develop, but the thermals are few and weak.

    2) The high-level cloudiness may drift by in patches.

        a) Thermals may surge and wane as the cloudiness decreases and increases.

    3) Never anticipate optimal thermal soaring when plagued by these mid- and high-level clouds.

    4) Altocumulus castellanus clouds, which are middle-level convective clouds, develop in updrafts at and just below the cloud levels.

        a) They do not extend upward from the surface.

        b) If a sailplane can reach levels near the cloud bases, the updrafts with altocumulus castellanus can be used in the same fashion as thermals formed by surface convection.

        c) The problem is reaching the convective level.

i. Wet ground favors thermals less than dry ground since wet ground heats more slowly.

    1) Some flat areas with wet soil such as swamps and tidewater areas have reputations for being poor thermal soaring areas.

        a) Convective clouds may be abundant but thermals generally are weak.

    2) Showery precipitation from scattered cumulus or cumulonimbus is a sure sign of unstable air favorable for thermals.

        a) When showers have soaked the ground in localized areas, however, downdrafts are almost certain over these wet surfaces. Avoid shower-soaked areas when looking for lift.

5.   **Thermal structure.** Thermals are as varied as trees in a forest. No two are exactly alike.

    a.   When surface heating is intense and continuous, a thermal, once begun, continues for a prolonged period in a steady column as in Figure 153 below.

        1)   Sometimes called the "chimney thermal," this type seems from experience to be most prevalent.

        2)   In the chimney thermal, lift is available at any altitude below a climbing sailplane or soaring birds.

    b.   When heating is slow or intermittent, a "bubble" may be pinched off and forced upward; after an interval ranging from a few minutes to an hour or more, another bubble forms and rises as in Figure 154 below.

        1)   As explained earlier, intermittent shading by cumulus clouds forming atop a thermal is one reason for the bubble thermal.

        2)   A sailplane or birds may be climbing in a bubble, but an aircraft attempting to enter the thermal at a lower altitude may find no lift.

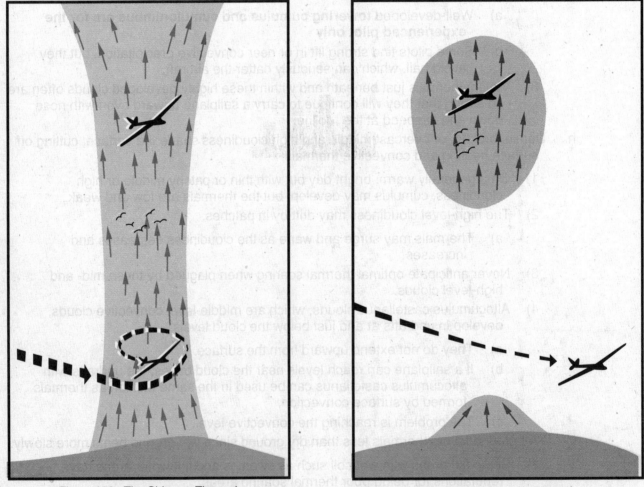

Figure 153. The Chimney Thermal.   Figure 154. Thermal Bubble.

c.   A favored theoretical structure of some bubble thermals is the vortex shell, which is much like a smoke ring blown upward as diagramed in Figure 155 below.

   1)   Lift is strongest in the center of the ring; downdrafts may occur in the edges of the ring or shell; and outside the shell, one would expect weak downdrafts.

Figure 155. Vortex Ring of a Bubble Thermal.

d.   Wind and wind shear. Thermals develop with a calm condition or with light, variable wind. However, it seems that a surface wind of 5 to 10 kt. favors more organized thermals.

1)   A surface wind in excess of 10 kt. usually means stronger winds aloft, resulting in vertical wind shear.

a)   This shear causes thermals to lean noticeably.

b)   When seeking a thermal under a climbing sailplane and you know or suspect that thermals are leaning in shear, look for lift upwind from the higher aircraft as shown in Figure 156 below.

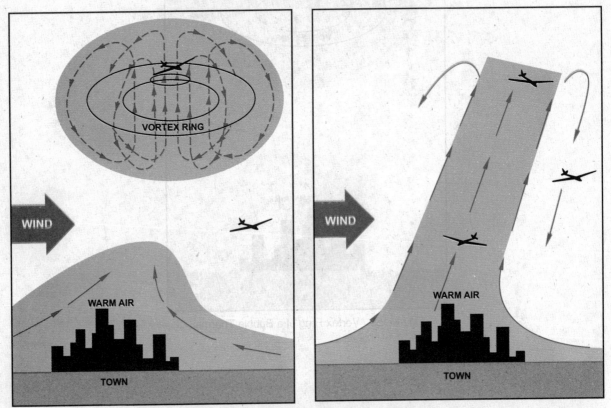

Figure 156. Wind Causes Thermals to Lean.

2)   Effect of shear on thermals depends on the relative strength of the two.

a)   Strong thermals can remain fairly well organized with strong vertical wind shear; surface wind may even be at the maximum that will allow a safe launch.

b)   Weak thermals are disorganized and ripped to shreds by strong vertical wind shear; individual thermal elements become hard to find and often are too small to use for lift.

c)   A shear in excess of 3 kt. per 1,000 ft. distorts thermals to the extent that they are difficult to use.

3)   No critical surface wind speed can tell us when to expect such a shear. However, shearing action often is visible in cumulus clouds.

a)   A cloud sometimes leans but shows a continuous chimney.

b)   At other times, the clouds are completely segmented by the shear.

c)   Remember, however, that this shearing action is at cloud level; thermals below the clouds may be well organized.

4) We must not overlook one other vital effect of the low-level wind shear.

    a) On final approach for landing, the aircraft is descending into decreasing headwind.

    b) Inertia of the aircraft into the decreasing wind causes a drop in airspeed. The decrease in airspeed may result in loss of control and perhaps a stall.

    c) A good rule is to add one knot airspeed to normal approach speed for each knot of surface wind.

e. Thermal streets are bands of thermals which become organized into straight lines parallel to each other, often providing lift over a considerable distance.

1) Generally, these streets are parallel to the wind, but on occasion they have been observed at right angles to the wind.

2) They form when wind direction changes little throughout the convective layer and the layer is capped by very stable air.

3) The formation of a broad system of evenly spaced streets is enhanced when wind speed reaches a maximum within the convective layer; that is, wind increases with height from the surface upward to a maximum and then decreases with height to the top of the convective layer.

4) Figure 158 below diagrams conditions favorable for thermal streeting.

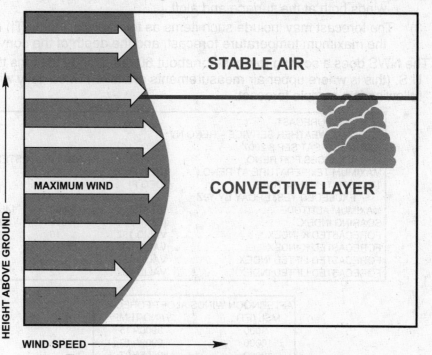

Figure 158. Conditions Favorable for Thermal Streeting.

5) Thermal streets may occur in clear air, or they may be indicated by cumulus clouds, which appear as long, narrow, parallel bands.

    a) If cumulus clouds mark thermal streets, the top of the convective layer is approximately the height of the cloud tops.

6) The distance between streets in such a system is two to three times the general depth of the convective layer.

    a) If convective clouds are present, this distance is two to three times the height of the cloud tops.

7)   Downdrafts between these thermal streets are usually at least moderate and sometimes strong.

8)   Cumulus cloud streets frequently form in the United States behind cold fronts in the cold air of polar outbreaks in which relatively flat cumuli develop.

9)   Cloud streets are advantageous for sailplane pilots because, rather than circling in isolated thermals and losing height between them, the pilot soaring under a thermal street can maintain almost continuous, straight flight.

6.   **Height and Strength of Thermals**

a.   Since thermals are a product of instability, height of thermals depends on the depth of the unstable layer, and their strength depends on the degree of instability.

b.   Most likely you will be soaring from an airport with considerable soaring activity -- possibly the home base of a soaring club -- and you are interested in a soaring forecast.

1)   Your airport may have an established source of a daily soaring weather forecast from the National Weather Service (NWS).

2)   If conditions are at all favorable for soaring, you will be specifically interested in the earliest time soaring can begin, how high the thermals will be, strength of the thermals, extent of cloud coverage -- both convective and higher cloudiness -- visibility at the surface and at soaring altitudes, probability of showers, and winds both at the surface and aloft.

3)   The forecast may include such items as the thermal index (TI) (see page 192), the maximum temperature forecast, and the depth of the convective layer.

c.   The NWS does a soaring forecast for about 60 radiosonde stations throughout the U.S. (this is where upper air measurements are taken twice daily with balloons). The following is a sample forecast:

```
SOARING FORECAST
NATIONAL WEATHER SERVICE – RENO NV
700 AM PDT SAT SEP 8 2007
LOCAL INDICES FOR RENO:                          TODAY   YESTERDAY
MAXIMUM TEMPERATURE AT RENO . . . .  (DEG F) . . . .    91         92
TRIGGER TEMPERATURE . . . . . . . . . . .  (DEG F) . . . .    78         77
       EXCEEDED YESTERDAY BY 19Z
MAXIMUM ALTITUDE. . . . . . . . . . . . . .  (FT MSL) . . .  16600     14600
SOARING INDEX. . . . . . . . . . . . . . . .  (FPM) . . . . .   1038       858
FORECASTED K-INDEX. . . . . . . . . . . . .  VALID 18Z . .     16          7
FORECASTED K-INDEX. . . . . . . . . . . . .  VALID 00Z . .     19          8
FORECASTED LIFTED INDEX. . . . . . . . .  VALID 18Z . .       4          7
FORECASTED LIFTED INDEX. . . . . . . . .  VALID 00Z . .       2          5
```

```
AFTERNOON WINDS ALOFT FORECAST
   MSL (FT)          WIND/TEMP
     9000            9900/+15
    10000            9902/+12
    12000            2505/+07
    14000            2106/+01
    16000            2007/-04
    18000            1911/-09
    24000            2015/-22
    30000            2319/-38
    34000            2429/-46
    39000            2446/-52
```

1)   Each of the Soaring Forecast items is explained as part of the following discussion of the Pseudo-Adiabatic chart. Your author feels that this chart is academic. It is included here because of its inclusion by the FAA in *Aviation Weather*.

7.   **The Pseudo-Adiabatic Chart**

   a.   The pseudo-adiabatic chart is used to graphically compute adiabatic changes in vertically moving air and to determine stability. It can be used to explain how the information in the Soaring Forecast is computed.

      1)   It has five sets of lines shown in Figure 160 below. These lines are:

         a)   Pressure in millibars (horizontal lines),

         b)   Temperature in degrees Celsius (vertical lines),

         c)   Dry adiabats (sloping black lines),

         d)   Lines of constant water vapor or mixing ratio of water vapor to dry air (solid red lines), and

         e)   Moist adiabats (dashed red lines).

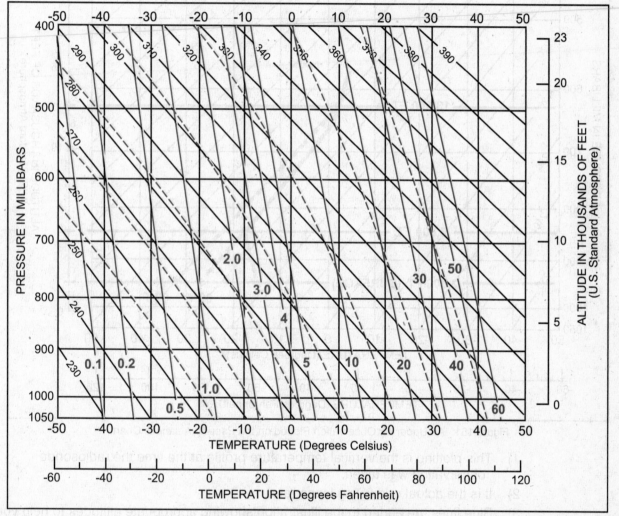

Figure 160. The Pseudo-Adiabatic Chart.

      2)   The chart also has an altitude scale in thousands of feet above sea level (ASL) in a standard atmosphere along the right margin and a Fahrenheit temperature scale across the bottom.

      3)   The chart used in actual practice has a much finer grid than the one shown in Figure 160 above.

4)   The following examples deal with dry thermals and since the red lines in Figure 160 on page 189 concern moist adiabatic changes, they are omitted from the examples.

a)   If you care to delve deeper into use of the chart, you will find moist adiabatic processes even more complicated than dry processes.

b.   An upper air observation, or sounding, is plotted on the pseudo-adiabatic chart as shown by the heavy, solid black line in Figure 161 below.

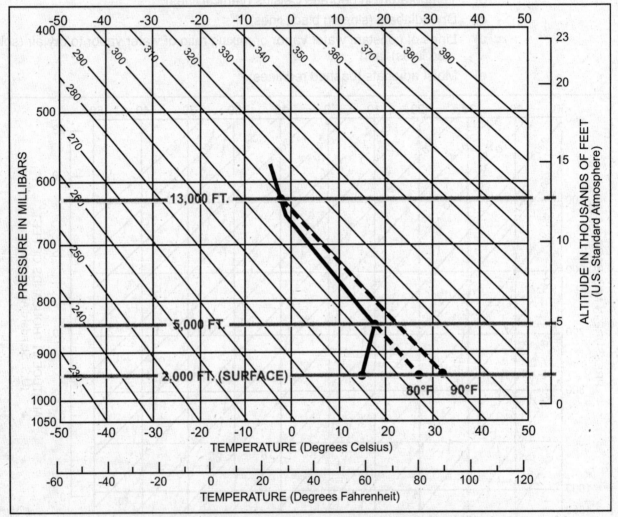

Figure 161. An Upper Air Observation Plotted on the Pseudo-Adiabatic Chart.

1)   This plotting is the vertical temperature profile at the time the radiosonde observation was taken.

2)   It is the actual or existing lapse rate.

3)   Blue lines are added to the illustration showing appropriate altitudes to help you interpret the chart.

c. Depth of Convective Layer (Height of Thermals)

   1) We know that for air to be unstable, the existing lapse rate must be equal to or greater than the dry adiabatic rate of cooling.

      a) In other words, in Figure 161 on page 190, the solid black line representing the plotted existing lapse rate would slope parallel to or slope more than the dry adiabats. Obviously it does not from the surface to 5,000 ft. ASL.

      b) Therefore, at the time the sounding was taken, the air was stable: There was no convective or unstable layer and thermals were nonexistent. Thermal soaring was impossible.

   2) As the surface temperature rises during the day, air is warmed and forced upward (i.e., convection), cooling at the dry adiabatic rate.

      a) This movement continues until the temperature of the air moving upward is the same as the surrounding air.

   3) Assume that the sounding (as shown by the solid black line) in Figure 161 on page 190 was made at sunrise with a surface temperature of 59°F (15°C). The forecast temperature at noon is 80°F and the maximum temperature of the day is forecast at 90°F. By using the chart in Figure 161 on page 190, you can determine the height of the thermals at these times.

      a) Plot 80°F (about 27°C) at the surface elevation and draw a dashed line parallel to the dry adiabats (sloping lines) to the point at which it intersects the sounding (solid line), which is 5,000 ft. ASL.

         i) Convection lifts the warmer air to a level at which it cools adiabatically (represented by the dashed line) to the temperature of the surrounding air.

         ii) The thermal height is 5,000 ft. ASL (3,000 ft. AGL).

      b) Repeat the process using the maximum temperature of 90°F (about 30°C). The thermal height is 13,000 ft. ASL (11,000 ft. AGL).

         i) The Soaring Forecast provides the maximum forecast temperature for a specific station.

   4) Remember that we are talking about dry thermals.

      a) If convective clouds form below the indicated maximum thermal height, they will greatly distort the picture.

      b) However, if cumulus clouds do develop, thermals below the cloud base should be strengthened.

      c) If more higher clouds develop than were forecast, they will curtail surface heating, and the maximum temperature will most likely be cooler than forecast.

         i) Thermals will be weaker and will not reach as high an altitude.

   5) The Soaring Forecast provides you with the thermal height. It is listed as "top of the lift" (see the Soaring Forecast on page 188).

   6) The Soaring Forecast also provides you with the surface temperature that will provide usable lift, and it is listed as "first usable lift."

d.   Thermal Index (TI)

1)   Since thermals depend on sinking cold air forcing warm air upward, strength of thermals depends on the temperature difference between the sinking air and the rising air -- the greater the temperature difference the stronger the thermals.

    a)   To arrive at an approximation of this difference, the forecaster computes a thermal index (TI).

2)   A thermal index may be computed for any level but, for the Soaring Forecast, they are computed for 5,000 ft. ASL (850-mb) and 10,000 ft. ASL (700-mb) as shown on the Soaring Forecast samples on page 188.

    a)   These levels are selected because they are in the altitude domain of routine soaring and because temperature data are routinely available for these two levels (i.e., Constant Pressure Analysis Chart).

3)   Three temperature values are needed -- the observed 850-mb and 700-mb temperatures and the forecast maximum temperature.

4)   Assume a sounding as in Figure 162 on page 193 with an 850-mb temperature of 15°C, a 700-mb temperature of 10°C, and forecast maximum of 86°F (30°C).

    a)   Plot the three temperatures, using care to place the maximum temperature plot at field elevation (2,000 ft. in Figure 162 on page 193).

    b)   Now draw a line (the black dashed line) through the maximum temperature parallel to the dry adiabats.

    c)   Note that the dashed line intersects the 850-mb level at 20°C and the 700-mb level at 4°C.

    d)   Subtract these temperatures from actual sounding temperatures at corresponding levels.

    e)   Note the difference is –5°C at 850 mb (15 – 20 = –5) and +6°C at 700 mb (10 – 4 = +6).

    f)   These values are the TIs at the two levels.

5)   Strength of thermals is proportional to the magnitude of the negative value of the TI.

    a)   A TI of –8 or –10 predicts very good lift and a long soaring day.

    b)   Thermals with this high a negative value will be strong enough to hold together even on a windy day.

    c)   A TI of –3 indicates a very good chance of sailplanes reaching the altitude of this temperature difference.

        i)   The height of the –3 index is given on the Soaring Forecast, as shown on page 188.

    d)   A TI of –2 to zero leaves much doubt; and a positive TI offers even less hope of thermals reaching the altitude.

6) Remember that the TI is a forecast value.

    a) A miss in the forecast maximum or a change in temperature aloft can alter the picture considerably.

    b) The example in Figure 162 below should promise fairly strong thermals to above 5,000 ft. (TI of –5).

        i) The "top of the lift" is indicated at the intersection of the dashed line and solid line. This value is given in the Soaring Forecast.

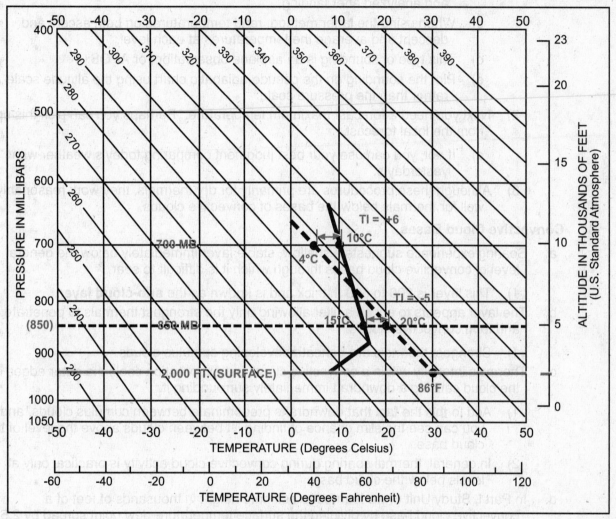

Figure 162. Computing the Thermal Index (TI).

7) The Soaring Forecast also provides the winds from the upper air sounding at the 5,000-ft. and 10,000-ft. levels. See the Soaring Forecast on page 188.

8) Often the National Weather Service will have no upper air sounding taken near a soaring base. Forecasts must be based on a simulated sounding derived from distant observations.

    a) At other times, for some reason a forecast may not be available.

    b) Furthermore, you can often augment the forecast with local observations.

e. Do it yourself. The first step in determining height and strength of thermals is to obtain a local sounding.

1) Send your tow aircraft aloft about sunrise and simply read outside air temperatures from the aircraft thermometer and altitudes from the altimeter.

a) Read temperatures at 500-ft. intervals for about the first 2,000 ft. and at 1,000-ft. intervals at higher altitudes.

b) The information may be radioed back to the ground or recorded in flight and analyzed after landing.

c) When using the latter method, read temperatures on both ascent and descent and average the temperatures at each level.

d) This type of sounding is an airplane observation, or APOB.

e) Plot the sounding on the pseudo-adiabatic chart using the altitude scale rather than the pressure scale.

2) Next you need a forecast maximum temperature. Perhaps you can pick this up from the local forecast.

a) If not, you can use your best judgment comparing today's weather with yesterday's.

3) Although these procedures are primarily for dry thermals, they work reasonably well for thermals below the bases of convective clouds.

8. **Convective Cloud Bases**

a. Soaring experience suggests a shallow, stable layer immediately below the general level of convective cloud bases through which it is difficult to soar.

1) This layer is 200 to 600 ft. thick and is known as the **sub-cloud layer**.

b. The layer appears to act as a filter allowing only the strongest thermals to penetrate it and form convective clouds.

1) Strongest thermals are beneath developing cumulus clouds.

c. Thermals intensify within a convective cloud, but evaporation cools the outer edges of the cloud causing a downdraft immediately surrounding it.

1) Add to this the fact that downdrafts predominate between cumulus clouds, and you can see the slim chance of finding lift between clouds above the level of the cloud base.

2) In general, thermal soaring during convective cloud activity is practical only at levels below the cloud base.

d. In Part I, Study Unit 6, we learned to estimate height in thousands of feet of a convective cloud base by dividing the surface temperature-dew point spread by 2.5 (for Celsius) or 4.4 (for Fahrenheit).

1) If the rising column were self-contained -- that is, if no air were drawn into the sides of the thermal -- the method would give a fairly accurate height of the base. However, this is not the case.

2) Air is entrained or drawn into the sides of the thermal, which lowers the water vapor content of the thermal, allowing it to reach a somewhat higher level before condensation occurs.

a) Bases of the clouds are generally 10% to 15% higher than the computed height.

3) Entrainment is a problem; observers and forecasters can only estimate its effect.

a) Until a positive technique is developed, heights of cumulus bases will tend to be reported and forecast too low.

9.   **Cross-Country Thermal Soaring**

   a.   A pilot can soar cross-country using either isolated thermals or thermal streets.

      1)   When using isolated thermals, (s)he gains altitude circling in thermals and then proceeds toward the next thermal in the general direction of his/her cross-country.

      2)   Under a thermal street, (s)he may be able to proceed with little, if any, circling if his/her chosen course parallels the thermal streets.

      3)   (S)he can obtain the greatest distance by flying in the direction of the wind.

   b.   In the central and eastern United States, the most favorable weather for cross-country soaring occurs behind a cold front.

      1)   Four factors contribute to making this pattern ideal.

         a)   The cold polar air is usually dry, and thermals can build to relatively high altitudes.

         b)   The polar air is colder than the ground, and thus, the warm ground aids solar radiation in heating the air.

            i)   Thermals begin earlier in the morning and last later in the evening.
            ii)   On occasions, soarable lift has been found at night.

         c)   Quite often, colder air at high altitudes moves over the cold, low-level outbreak, intensifying the instability and strengthening the thermals.

         d)   The wind profile frequently favors thermal streeting -- a real boon to speed and distance.

   c.   The same four factors may occur with cold frontal passages over mountainous regions in the western United States.

      1)   However, rugged mountains break up the circulation; and homogeneous conditions extend over smaller areas than over the eastern parts of the country.

      2)   The western mountain regions and particularly the desert southwest have one decided advantage.

         a)   Air is predominantly dry with more abundant daytime thermal activity favoring cross-country soaring, although it may be for shorter distances.

   d.   Among the world's most favorable tracks for long distance soaring is a high plains corridor along the east slope of the Rocky Mountains stretching from southwest Texas to Canada.

      1)   Terrain in the corridor is relatively flat and high with few trees; terrain surface ranges from barren to short grass.

         a)   These surface features favor strong thermal activity.

      2)   Prevailing wind is southerly and moderately strong, giving an added boost to northbound cross-country flights.

16.3 FRONTAL SOARING

1. Warm air forced upward over cold air above a frontal surface can provide lift for soaring.

   a. However, good frontal lift is transitory and accounts for a very small portion of powerless flight.

   b. Seldom will you find a front parallel to your desired cross-country route, and seldom will it stay in position long enough to complete a flight.

      1) A slowly moving front provides only weak lift.

      2) A fast moving front often plagues the soaring pilot with cloudiness and turbulence.

2. A front can occasionally provide excellent lift for a short period.

   a. On a cross-country, you may be riding wave or ridge lift and need to move over a flat area to take advantage of thermals.

      1) A front may offer lift during your transition.

3. Fronts are often marked by a change in cloud type or amount.

   a. However, the very presence of clouds may deter you from flying into the front.

      1) Spotting a dry front is difficult.

   b. Knowing that a front is in the vicinity and studying your aircraft reaction can tell you when you are in the frontal lift.

      1) Staying in the lift is another problem.

      2) Observing ground indicators of surface wind helps.

4. An approaching front may enhance thermal or hill soaring.

   a. An approaching front or a frontal passage most likely will disrupt a sea breeze or mountain wave.

16.4 SEA BREEZE SOARING

1. In many coastal areas during the warm seasons, a pleasant breeze from the sea occurs almost daily.

   a. Caused by the heating of land on warm, sunny days, the sea breeze usually begins during early forenoon, reaches a maximum during the afternoon, and subsides around dusk after the land has cooled.

   b. The leading edge of the cool sea breeze forces warmer air inland to rise as shown in Figure 165 on page 197.

      1) Rising air from the land returns seaward at higher altitude to complete the convective cell.

   c. A sailplane pilot operating in or near coastal areas often can find lift generated by this convective circulation.

      1) The transition zone between the cool, moist air from the sea and the warm, drier air inland is often narrow and is a shallow, ephemeral kind of pseudo-cold front.

2. Sometimes the wedge of cool air is called a **sea breeze front**.

   a. If sufficient moisture is present, a line of cumuliform clouds just inland may mark the front.

Figure 165. Schematic Cross Section through a Sea Breeze Front.

      1) Whether marked by clouds or not, the upward moving air at the sea breeze front occasionally is strong enough to support soaring flight.

  b. Within the sea breeze (i.e., between the sea breeze front and the ocean), the air is usually stable, and normally no lift may be expected at lower levels.

      1) However, once airborne, pilots occasionally have found lift at higher levels in the return flow aloft.

      2) A visual indication of this lift is cumulus extending seaward from the sea breeze front.

  c. A large difference in land and sea water temperature intensifies the convective cell generating a sea breeze.

      1) Where coastal waters are quite cool, such as along the California coast, and land temperatures warm rapidly in the daytime, the sea breeze becomes pronounced, penetrating perhaps 50 to 75 mi. inland at times.

      2) Copious sunshine and cool sea waters favor a well-developed sea breeze front.

  d. The sea breeze is a local effect.

      1) Strong pressure gradients with a well-developed pressure system can overpower the sea breeze effect.

      2) Winds will follow the direction and speed dictated by the strong pressure gradient.

         a) Therefore, a sea breeze front is most likely when pressure gradient is weak and wind is light.

e.   When convection is very deep, the frontal effect of a sea breeze may sometimes trigger cumulonimbus clouds, provided the lifted air over land contains sufficient moisture.

1)   More often, the cumulus are of limited vertical extent.

2)   Over vegetation where air is usually moist, sea breeze cumulus are the rule.

3)   Over arid regions, little or no cumulus development may be anticipated with a sea breeze front.

f.   Irregular or rough terrain in a coastal area may amplify the sea breeze front and cause convergence lines of sea breezes originating from different areas.

1)   Southern California and parts of the Hawaiian Islands are favorable for sea breeze soaring because orographic lift (lift induced by the presence of mountains) is added to the frontal convection.

a)   Sea breezes occasionally may extend to the leeward sides of hills and mountains unless the ranges are high and long without abrupt breaks.

b)   In either case, the sea breeze front converges on the windward slopes, and upslope winds augment the convection.

2)   Where terrain is fairly flat, sea breezes may penetrate inland for surprising distances but with weaker lift along the sea breeze front.

a)   In the Tropics, sea breezes sometimes penetrate as much as 150 mi. inland, whereas an average of closer to 50 mi. inland is more usual in middle latitudes.

3)   Sea breezes reaching speeds of 15 to 25 kt. are not uncommon.

g.   When a sea breeze front develops, visual observations may provide clues to the extent of lift that you may anticipate.

1)   Expect little or no lift on the seaward side of the front when the sea air is markedly devoid of convective clouds or when the sea breeze spreads low stratus inland.

a)   However, some lift may be present along the leading edge of the sea breeze or just ahead of it.

2)   Expect little or no lift on the seaward side of the front when visibility decreases markedly in the sea breeze air.

a)   This is an indicator of stable air within the sea breeze.

3)   A favorable visual indication of lift along the sea breeze front is a line of cumulus clouds marking the front; cumuli between the sea breeze front and the ocean also indicate possible lift within the sea breeze air, especially at higher levels.

a)   Cumulus bases in the moist sea air are often lower than along the front.

4)   When a sea breeze front is devoid of cumulus but converging streamers of dust or smoke are observed, expect convection and lift along the sea breeze front.

5)   Probably the best combination to be sighted is cumuli and converging dust or smoke plumes along the sea breeze front as it moves upslope over hills or mountains.

a)   The upward motion is amplified by the upslope winds.

6)   A difference in visibility between the sea air and the inland air often is a visual clue to the leading edge of the sea breeze.

a)   Visibility in the sea air may be restricted by haze while visibility inland is unrestricted.

b)   On the other hand, the sea air may be quite clear while visibility inland is restricted by dust or smoke.

3. **Local Sea Breeze Explorations**

   a. Unfortunately, a sea breeze front is not always easy to find, and it is likely that many an opportunity for sea breeze soaring goes unnoticed.

      1) As yet, little experience has been accrued in locating a belt of sea breeze lift without visual clues, such as clouds, haze, or converging smoke or dust plumes.

   b. The sea breeze front moving from the Los Angeles coastal plain into the Mojave Desert has been dubbed the "Smoke Front."

      1) It has intense thermal activity and offers excellent lift along the leading edge of the front.

      2) Associated with the sea breeze that moves inland over the Los Angeles coastal plain are two important zones of convergence, shown in Figure 166 below.

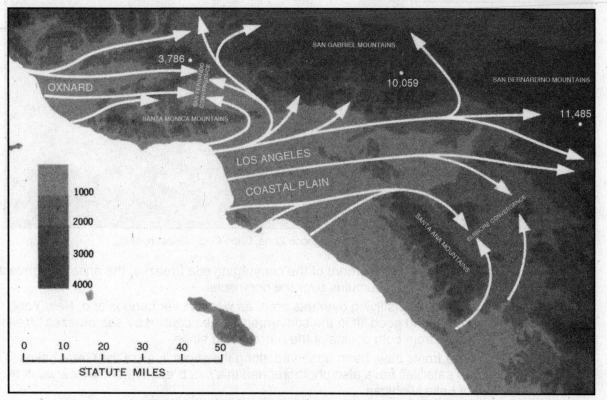

Figure 166. Sea Breeze Flow into the San Fernando Valley.

   a) One convergence line is the "San Fernando Convergence Zone."
   b) A larger scale zone is in the Elsinore area, also shown in Figure 166 above.

      3) This convergence zone apparently generates strong vertical currents because soaring pilots fly back and forth across the valley along the line separating smoky air to the north from relatively clear air to the south.

      4) Altitudes reached depend upon the stability, but usually fall within the 6,000 ft. to 12,000 ft. MSL range for the usual dry thermal type lift.

      a) Seaward, little or no lift is experienced in the sea breeze air marked by poor visibility.

c.   Figure 167 below shows converging air between sea breezes flowing inland from opposite coasts of the Cape Cod Peninsula.

Figure 167. Sea Breeze Convergence Zone, Cape Cod, Massachusetts.

1)   Later in the development of the converging sea breezes, the onset of convection is indicated by cumulus over the peninsula.

2)   Sailplane pilots flying over this area, as well as over Long Island, New York, have found good lift in the convergence lines caused by sea breezes blowing inland from both coasts of the narrow land strips.

d.   Sea breeze fronts have been observed along the shore lines of the Great Lakes. Weather satellites have also photographed this sea breeze effect on the western shore of Lake Michigan.

1)   It is quite likely that conditions favorable for soaring occur in these areas at times.

16.5 RIDGE OR HILL SOARING

1.   Wind blowing toward hills or ridges flows upward, over, and around the abrupt rises in terrain. The upward-moving air creates lift which is sometimes excellent for soaring.

a.   Figure 168 on page 201 is a schematic showing area of best lift.

Figure 168. Schematic Cross Section of Airflow over a Ridge.

2.   **Wind.** To create lift over hills or ridges, wind direction should be within about 30° to 40° of being perpendicular to the ridge line.

   a.   A sustained speed of 15 kt. or more usually generates enough lift to support a sailplane.

   b.   Height of the lift usually is two or three times the height of the rise from the valley floor to the ridge crest.

   c.   Strong winds tend to increase turbulence and low-level eddies without an appreciable increase in the height of the lift.

3.   **Stability** affects the continuity and extent of lift over hills or ridges.

   a.   Stable air allows relatively streamlined upslope flow.

      1)   A pilot experiences little or no turbulence in the steady, uniform area of best lift shown in Figure 168 above.

      2)   Since stable air tends to return to its original level, air spilling over the crest and downslope is churned into a snarl of leeside eddies, also shown in Figure 168 above.

      3)   Thus, stable air favors smooth lift but troublesome leeside low-altitude turbulence.

   b.   When the airstream is moist and unstable, upslope lift may release the instability, generating strong convective currents and cumulus clouds over windward slopes and hill crests.

      1)   The initially laminar flow is broken up into convective cells.

      2)   While the updrafts produce good lift, strong downdrafts may compromise low-altitude flight over rough terrain.

      3)   As with thermals, the lift will be transitory rather than smooth and uniform.

4. **Steepness of slope.** Very gentle slopes provide little or no lift. A smooth, moderate slope is most favorable for soaring.

   a. An ideal slope is about 1 to 4 which, with an upslope wind of 15 kt., creates lift of about 6 fps.

      1) With the same slope, a high-performance sailcraft with a sinking speed of 2 fps presumably could remain airborne with only a 5-kt. wind!

   b. Very steep escarpments or rugged slopes induce turbulent eddies.

      1) Strong winds extend these eddies to a considerable height, usually disrupting any potential lift.

      2) The turbulent eddies also increase the possibility of a low-altitude upset.

5. **Continuity of ridges.** Ridges extending for several miles without abrupt breaks tend to provide uniform lift throughout their length.

   a. In contrast, a single peak diverts wind flow around the peak as well as over it and thus is less favorable for soaring.

   b. Some wind flow patterns over ridges and hills are illustrated in Figure 170 on page 203.

      1) Deviations from these patterns depend on wind direction and speed, on stability, on slope profile, and on general terrain roughness.

6. **Soaring in Upslope Lift**

   a. The soaring pilot, always alert, must remain especially so in seeking or riding hill lift.

   b. When air is unstable, do not venture too near the slope.

      1) You can identify unstable air either by the updrafts and downdrafts in dry thermals or by cumulus building over hills or ridges.

      2) Approaching at too low an altitude may suddenly put you in a downdraft, forcing an inadvertent landing.

   c. When winds are strong, surface friction may create low-level eddies even over relatively smooth slopes.

      1) Also, friction may drastically reduce the effective wind speed near the surface.

      2) When climbing at low altitude toward a slope under these conditions, be prepared to turn quickly toward the valley if you lose lift.

         a) Renew your attempt to climb, farther from the hill.

   d. If winds are weak, you may find lift only very near the sloping surface. Then you must hug the slope to find needed lift.

      1) However, avoid this procedure if there are indications of up- and downdrafts.

      2) In general, for any given slope, keep your distance from the slope proportional to wind speed.

   e. Leeward of hills and ridges is an area where wind is blocked by the obstruction. In soaring circles, this area is called the "wind shadow."

      1) In the wind shadow, downdrafts predominate as shown in Figure 168 on page 201.

      2) If you stray into the wind shadow at an altitude near or below the altitude of the ridge crest, you may be forced into an unscheduled and possibly rough landing.

      3) Try to stay within the area of best lift shown in Figure 168 on page 201.

Figure 170. Wind Flow over Various Types of Terrain.

16.6 MOUNTAIN WAVE SOARING

1. The main attraction of soaring in mountain waves stems from the continuous lift to great heights.

    a. Soaring flights to above 35,000 ft. have frequently been made in mountain waves.

    b. Once a soaring pilot has reached the rising air of a mountain wave, (s)he has every prospect of maintaining flight for several hours.

    c. While mountain wave soaring is related to ridge or hill soaring, the lift in a mountain wave is on a larger scale and is less transitory than lift over smaller rises in terrain.

    d. Figure 171 below is a cross section of a typical mountain wave.

2. **Formation.** When strong winds blow across a mountain range, large standing waves occur downwind from the mountains and upward to the tropopause.

    a. The waves may develop singly but more often they occur as a series of waves downstream from the mountains.

        1) While the waves remain almost stationary, strong winds are blowing through them.

    b. You may compare a mountain wave to a series of waves formed downstream from a submerged rocky ridge in a fast flowing creek or river.

        1) Air dips sharply immediately to the lee of a ridge, then rises and falls in a wave motion downstream.

    c. A strong mountain wave requires:

        1) Marked stability in the airstream disturbed by the mountains.

            a) Rapidly building cumulus over the mountains visually marks the air unstable; convection, evidenced by the cumulus, tends to deter wave formation.

Figure 171. Schematic Cross Section of a Mountain Wave.

2) Wind speed at the level of the summit should exceed a minimum which varies from 15 to 25 kt. depending on the height of the range.

    a) Upper winds should increase or at least remain constant with height up to the tropopause.

3) Wind direction should be within 30° normal to the range. Lift diminishes as winds more nearly parallel the range.

3. **Wave Length and Amplitude**

  a. Wave length is the horizontal distance between crests of successive waves and is usually between 2 and 25 mi.

    1) In general, wave length is controlled by wind component perpendicular to the ridge and by stability of the upstream flow.

      a) Wave length is directly proportional to wind speed and inversely proportional to stability.

    2) Figure 172 below illustrates wave length and also amplitude.

  b. Amplitude of a wave is the vertical dimension and is half the altitude difference between the wave trough and crest.

    1) In a typical wave, amplitude varies with height above the ground.

      a) It is least near the surface and near the tropopause.

    2) Greatest amplitude is roughly 3,000 to 6,000 ft. above the ridge crest.

Figure 172. Wave Length and Amplitude.

    3) Wave amplitude is controlled by the size and shape of the ridge, as well as wind and stability.

      a) A shallow layer of great stability and moderate wind produces a greater wave amplitude than does a deep layer of moderate stability and strong winds.

    4) Also, the greater the amplitude, the shorter the wave length.

  c. Waves offering the strongest and most consistent lift are those with great amplitude and short wave length.

4.   **Visual Indicators**

   a.   If the air has sufficient moisture, lenticular (lens-shaped) clouds mark wave crests.

      1)   Cooling of air ascending toward the wave crest saturates the air, forming clouds.

      2)   Warming of air descending beyond the wave crest evaporates the cloud.

      3)   Thus, by continuous condensation windward of the wave crest and evaporation leeward, the cloud appears stationary although wind may be blowing through the wave at 50 kt. or more.

      4)   Lenticular clouds in successive bands downstream from the mountain mark a series of wave crests.

   b.   Spacing of lenticulars marks the wave length.

      1)   Clearly identifiable lenticulars also suggest larger wave amplitude than clouds that barely exhibit lenticular form.

      2)   These cloud types along with stratiform clouds on the windward slopes and along the mountain crest indicate the stability favorable to mountain wave soaring.

   c.   Thunderstorms or rapidly building cumulus over mountains mark the air as unstable.

      1)   As they reach maturity, the thunderstorms often drift downwind across leeward valleys and plains.

      2)   Strong convective currents in the unstable air deter wave formation.

5.   **Soaring Turbulence**

   a.   A mountain wave, in a manner similar to a thermal, means turbulence to powered aircraft, but to a slowly moving sailcraft, it produces lift and sink above the level of the mountain crest.

   b.   As air spills over the crest like a waterfall, it causes strong downdrafts.

      1)   The violent overturning forms a series of "rotors" in the wind shadow of the mountain, which are hazardous even to a sailplane.

   c.   Clouds resembling long bands of stratocumulus sometimes mark the area of overturning air.

      1)   These "rotor clouds" appear to remain stationary, parallel the range, and stand a few miles leeward of the mountains.

   d.   Turbulence is most frequent and most severe in the standing rotors just beneath the wave crests at or below mountain-top levels.

      1)   This rotor turbulence is especially violent in waves generated by large mountains, such as the Rockies.

      2)   Rotor turbulence with lesser mountains is much less severe but is always present to some extent. The turbulence is greatest in well-developed waves.

6.   **Favored Areas**

   a.   Mountain waves occur most frequently along the central and northern Rockies and the northern Appalachians.

      1)   Occasionally, waves form to the lee of mountains in Arkansas, Oklahoma, and southwestern Texas.

   b.   Weather satellites have observed waves extending great distances downwind from the Rocky Mountains; one series extended for nearly 700 mi.

      1)   The more usual distance is 150 to 300 mi.

   c.   While Appalachian waves are not as strong as those over the Rockies, they occur frequently, and satellites have observed them at an average of 115 mi. downwind.

      1)   Wave length of these waves averages about 10 NM.

7. **Riding the waves.** You often can detect a wave by the uncanny smoothness of your climb.

   a. On first locating a wave, turn into the wind and attempt to climb directly over the spot where you first detected lift, **provided** you can remain at an altitude above the level of the mountain crest.

      1) After cautiously climbing well up into the wave, attempt to determine dimensions of the zone of lift.

         a) If the wave is over rugged terrain, it may be impossible and unnecessary to determine the wave length.

            i) Lift over such terrain is likely to be in patchy bands.

         b) Over more even terrain, the wave length may be easy to determine and use in planning the next stage of flight.

   b. Wave clouds are a visual clue in your search for lift.

      1) The wave-like shape of lenticulars is usually more obvious from above than from below.

      2) Lift should prevail from the crest of the lenticulars upwind about one-third the wave length.

      3) When your course takes you across the waves, climb on the windward side of the wave and fly as quickly as possible to the windward side of the next wave.

      4) Wave lift of 300 to 1,200 fpm is not uncommon.

         a) Soaring pilots have encountered vertical currents exceeding 3,000 fpm, the strongest ever reported being 8,000 fpm.

16.7 IN CLOSING

1. Thermal soaring. The pilot circles in a thermal (updraft) to gain height and heads to the next thermal to regain altitude lost in the downdrafts between them.

   a. Thermals depend on solar heating, so thermal soaring is virtually restricted to daylight hours with considerable sunshine.

      1) The most likely place for a thermal is above a surface that heats rapidly, e.g., sandy or rocky surfaces that are barren, plowed fields, stubble fields surrounded by green vegetation, cities, factories, and chimneys.

      2) Dust devils are excellent sources of lift, but you must use caution because the thermals are strong and turbulent and are surrounded by areas of little lift or possibly of sink.

      3) Thermal soaring is usually at its best when convective clouds develop.

         a) Cumulus clouds are positive signs of thermals.

      4) Wet ground is less favorable for thermals than dry ground because wet ground heats more slowly.

   b. No two thermals are exactly alike.

      1) Some form as chimneys whereas others form bubbles of warm air that rise.

      2) Wind shear can cause the thermal to lean or, at times, can completely break it up.

      3) Thermals may become organized into thermal streets.

         a) A pilot can maintain generally continuous flight under a thermal street and seldom have to circle.

    c.   Daily soaring weather forecasts are available from the National Weather Service.

        1)   You can determine height and strength of thermals by obtaining a local sounding and plotting it on a pseudo-adiabatic chart.

    d.   You can soar cross-country using isolated thermals or thermal streets.

2.   Frontal soaring accounts for a very small portion of powerless flight.

    a.   A front can provide excellent lift for a short period.

    b.   An approaching front may enhance thermal or hill soaring.

3.   Southern California and parts of the Hawaiian Islands are favorable for sea breeze soaring because orographic lift augments convection from the sea breeze front.

    a.   Sea breeze fronts are not always easy to find, and visual clues may not be present.

        1)   A sea breeze front moves from the Los Angeles coastal plain into the Mojave Desert.

        2)   Sailplane pilots have found good lift in the convergence lines caused by sea breezes over Cape Cod, MA and Long Island, NY.

        3)   Sea breeze fronts have also been observed along the shorelines of the Great Lakes.

4.   Ridge or hill soaring. Wind blowing toward hills or ridges flows upward, over, and around the abrupt rises in terrain. Upward-moving air with a wind speed of 15 kt. usually generates enough lift to support a sailplane.

    a.   A smoother, moderate slope is most favorable for soaring.

    b.   When soaring in upslope lift, you must remain alert for unstable air.

5.   Mountain wave soaring is related to ridge or hill soaring, but the lift in a mountain wave is on a larger scale and is less transitory than lift over smaller rises in terrain.

    a.   Mountain waves occur most frequently along the central and northern Rockies and the northern Appalachians.

6.   Records are made to be broken. Altitude and distance records are a prime target of many sailplane enthusiasts.

    a.   Distance records may be possible by flying a combination of lift sources, such as thermal, frontal, ridge, or wave.

    b.   Altitude records are set in mountain waves.

        1)   Altitudes above 46,000 ft. have been attained over the Rocky Mountains.

        2)   Soaring flights to more than 24,000 ft. have been made in Appalachian waves.

        3)   Flights as high as 20,000 ft. have been recorded from New England to North Carolina.

7.   We hope that this chapter has given you an insight into the minute variations in weather that profoundly affect a soaring aircraft.

    a.   When you have remained airborne for hours without power, you have met a unique challenge and experienced a singular thrill of flying.

END OF STUDY UNIT

END OF PART II

PART III:
AVIATION WEATHER SERVICES

(1 page of outline)

Aviation Weather Services is published periodically by the FAA/NWS to keep pilots abreast of weather maps and other services available from their FSSs and from the Internet. AC 00-45F was published in October 2007. We have divided the 9 sections and 10 appendices of AC 00-45F into 36 study units in our book to facilitate study of various weather reports and weather forecasts.

The images contained in this section are the same full-color images found in the FAA text. Some images have greater detail than others. This disparity is merely a reflection of the quality of the images provided in the original FAA texts. Where possible, Gleim has improved the quality of the images to provide the best reference material available.

FAA **Table of Contents** AC 00-45F	Gleim **Table of Contents** This Part III
1. Aviation Weather Service Program 2. Aviation Weather Product Classification and Policy	1. The Aviation Weather Service Program 2. Aviation Weather Product Classification and Policy
3. Observed Text Products	3. Aviation Routine Weather Reports (METAR) 4. Pilot Weather Reports (PIREP) 5. Radar Weather Reports (SD/ROB)
4. Radar and Satellite Imagery	6. Radar Imagery 7. Satellite Imagery
5. Graphical Observations and Derived Products	8. Surface Analysis Charts 9. Constant Pressure Charts 10. Freezing-Level Graphics 11. Lifted Index Analysis Charts 12. Weather Depiction Charts 13. Alaska Weather Depiction Charts 14. Radar Summary Charts 15. Alaska Initial Geopotential Heights and Winds Charts
6. Products for Aviation Hazards	16. Significant Meteorological Information (SIGMET) 17. Airmen's Meteorological Information (AIRMET) 18. Center Weather Advisory (CWA) 19. Additional Products for Convection 20. Tropical Cyclone Products 21. Volcanic Ash Advisory Products
7. Forecast Text Products	22. Area Forecasts (FA) 23. Terminal Aerodrome Forecasts (TAF) 24. International Aviation Route Forecasts (ROFOR) 25. Wind and Temperature Aloft Forecasts (FB)
8. Forecast Charts	26. Short-Range Surface Prognostic (PROG) Charts 27. Low-Level Significant Weather (SIGWX) Charts 28. Mid-Level Significant Weather (SIGWX) Charts 29. High-Level Significant Weather (SIGWX) Charts
9. Supplementary Products	30. Collaborative Convective Forecast Products (CCFP) 31. National Convective Weather Forecasts (NCWF) 32. Current Icing Potential (CIP) 33. Forecast Icing Potential (FIP) 34. Graphical Turbulence Guidance (GTG) 35. Meteorological Impact Statement (MIS)
Appendices A-J	36. Other Weather Related Information

STUDY UNIT ONE
THE AVIATION WEATHER SERVICE PROGRAM

(8 pages of outline)

> Please take a few minutes to study each of the concepts listed above and anticipate/imagine what they are and how they relate to the other listed concepts.

1.1 WEATHER SERVICE: AVIATION EFFORT

1. Providing weather service to aviation is a joint effort of the National Weather Service (NWS), the Federal Aviation Administration (FAA), the Department of Defense (DOD) Weather Service, and other aviation-oriented groups and individuals.

2. Because of international flights and a need for worldwide weather forecasts, foreign weather services also have a vital input into our service.

3. This study unit discusses the civilian agencies of the federal government and their observation and communication services to the aviation community.

1.2 NATIONAL OCEANIC AND ATMOSPHERIC ADMINISTRATION (NOAA)

1. NOAA is an agency of the Department of Commerce and is one of the leading scientific agencies in the U.S. government.

2. Among its six major divisions are the National Environmental Satellite Data and Information Service and the NWS.

1.3 NATIONAL ENVIRONMENTAL SATELLITE DATA AND INFORMATION SERVICE (NESDIS)

1. NESDIS is located in Washington, D.C., and is responsible for directing the weather satellite program.

2. Satellite images are available to NWS meteorologists and a wide range of other users for operational use.

3. The Satellite Analysis Branch (SAB) coordinates the satellite and other known information for the NOAA Volcanic Hazards Alert program under an agreement with the FAA.

    a. The SAB works with the NWS as part of the Volcanic Ash Advisory Center (VAAC), located in Washington, D.C.

1.4 NATIONAL WEATHER SERVICE (NWS)

1. The National Weather Service (NWS) collects and analyzes meteorological and hydrological data and subsequently prepares forecasts on a national, hemispheric, and global scale. The following is a description of the NWS facilities tasked with these duties.

2.   **National Centers for Environmental Prediction (NCEP)**

   a.   Under the NCEP are nine separate national centers, each with its own specific mission. They are the Climate Prediction Center, Space Environment Center, Marine Prediction Center, Hydrometeorological Prediction Center, Environmental Modeling Center, NCEP Central Operations, Storm Prediction Center, Aviation Weather Center, and Tropical Prediction Center.

   b.   We will discuss the centers (items c. through g. below) that provide services to the aviation community.

   c.   The **NCEP Central Operations (NCO),** located in Camp Springs, Maryland, is the focal point of the NWS's weather processing system.

       1)   From worldwide weather reports, the NCO prepares automated weather analysis charts and guidance forecasts for use by NWS offices and other users.

       2)   The winds and temperatures aloft forecast is one example of an NCO product that is specifically prepared for aviation.

       3)   The NCO works with the SAB to fulfill the VAAC responsibilities to the aviation community regarding potential volcanic ash hazards to aviation.

   d.   The **Storm Prediction Center (SPC)** is responsible for monitoring and forecasting severe weather over the 48 contiguous states. The center also develops severe weather forecasting techniques and conducts research.

       1)   The SPC products include convective outlooks and forecasts, as well as severe weather watches.

       2)   The SPC is located in Norman, OK, near the heart of the area most frequently affected by severe thunderstorms.

   e.   The **Aviation Weather Center (AWC),** located in Kansas City, MO, issues warnings, forecasts, and analyses of hazardous weather for aviation interests.

       1)   The AWC identifies existing or imminent weather hazards to aircraft in flight and creates warnings for transmission to the aviation community.

           a)   The AWC also produces operational forecasts of weather conditions expected during the next two days that will affect domestic and international aviation interests.

       2)   As a Meteorological Watch Office (MWO) under the regulations of the International Civil Aviation Organization (ICAO), the AWC meteorologists prepare and issue aviation area forecasts (FA) and inflight aviation weather advisories for the 48 contiguous states.

   f.   The **Tropical Prediction Center (TPC)** is located in Miami, FL. The National Hurricane Center (NHC), a branch of the TPC, issues hurricane advisories for the Atlantic, the Caribbean, the Gulf of Mexico, the eastern Pacific, and adjacent land areas.

       1)   The TPC also develops hurricane forecasting techniques and conducts hurricane research.

       2)   The Central Pacific Hurricane Center, located in Honolulu, HI, issues advisories for the central Pacific Ocean.

       3)   The Tropical Analysis and Forecast Branch (TAFB) of the TPC prepares and distributes tropical weather, aviation and marine forecasts, and warnings.

           a)   As an MWO, the TAFB meteorologists prepare and issue aviation forecasts, SIGMETs (significant meteorological information), and convective SIGMETs for their tropical Flight Information Region (FIR).

   g.   The **Hydrometeorological Prediction Center (HPC),** located in Camp Springs, MD, prepares weather charts which include basic weather elements of temperature, fronts, and pressure patterns.

3.   A **Weather Forecast Office (WFO)** prepares and issues various public, marine, and aviation forecasts and weather warnings for its area of responsibility.

   a.   In support of aviation, WFOs issue terminal aerodrome forecasts (TAF) and transcribed weather broadcasts (TWEB).

   b.   As a MWO, the Honolulu WFO issues aviation area forecasts and inflight advisories.

4.   The **Alaskan Aviation Weather Unit (AAWU)**, located in Anchorage, AK, prepares and disseminates to the FAA and the Internet a suite of graphic products, including a graphic FA and a 24- and 36-hr. forecast of significant weather.

   a.   As an MWO, the AAWU meteorologists prepare and issue International SIGMETs within the Anchorage Continental FIR, Anchorage Oceanic FIR, and the Anchorage Arctic FIR, as well as domestic FAs and AIRMETs (airman's meteorological information) for Alaska and the adjacent coastal waters.

   b.   The AAWU is one of nine VAACs worldwide preparing Volcanic Ash Advisory Statements (VAAS) for the same FIRs listed in item a. above.

5.   **Center Weather Service Units (CWSUs)** are units of NWS meteorologists under contract with the FAA that are stationed at and support the FAA's Air Route Traffic Control Centers (ARTCCs).

   a.   CWSUs provide timely weather consultation, forecasts, and advice to managers within ARTCCs and to other supported FAA facilities.

      1)   This information is based on monitoring, analysis, and interpretation of real-time weather data at the ARTCC through the use of all available data sources including radar, satellite, Pilot Weather Reports (PIREPs), and various NWS products, such as Terminal Aerodrome Forecasts (TAFs), FAs, and inflight advisories.

   b.   Special emphasis is given to those weather conditions hazardous to aviation or which would impede the flow of air traffic within the NAS. Rerouting of aircraft around hazardous weather is based largely on forecasts provided by the CWSU meteorologist.

      1)   They issue the following products in support of their respective ARTCC: Center Weather Advisories (CWA) and Meteorological Impact Statements (MIS).

1.5   FEDERAL AVIATION ADMINISTRATION (FAA)

1.   The Federal Aviation Administration (FAA) is a part of the Department of Transportation and provides a wide range of services to the aviation community. The following is a description of those FAA facilities involved with aviation weather and pilot services.

2.   The **Air Traffic Control System Command Center (ATCSCC)**, also known as "central flow control," is located in Herndon, VA. The ATCSCC has the mission of balancing air traffic demand with system capacity. This balance ensures maximum safety and efficiency for the National Airspace System (NAS) while minimizing delays.

   a.   The ATCSCC utilizes the Traffic Management System, aircraft situation display, monitor alert, follow-on functions, and direct contact with the air route traffic control center (ARTCC) and terminal radar approach control facility (TRACON) traffic management units to manage flow on a national as well as local level.

   b.   Because weather is the most common reason for air traffic delays and reroutings, the ATCSCC is supported full-time by Air Traffic Control System Command Center Weather Unit Specialists (ATCSCCWUS).

      1)   These FAA specialists are responsible for the dissemination of meteorological information as it pertains to national air traffic flow management.

3. An **Air Route Traffic Control Center (ARTCC)** is an en route radar facility established to provide air traffic control service to aircraft operating on IFR flight plans within controlled airspace and principally during the en route phase of flight.

    a. When equipment capabilities and controller workload permit, certain advisory/assistant services may be provided to VFR aircraft.

    b. En route controllers become familiar with pertinent weather information and remain aware of current weather information needed to perform air traffic control duties.

        1) An en route controller will advise pilots of hazardous weather that may impact operations within 150 NM of the controller's assigned sector or area of jurisdiction.

4. **Air Traffic Control Tower (ATCT) and Terminal Radar Approach Control (TRACON).**

    a. An ATCT is a terminal facility that uses air/ground communications, visual signaling, and other devices to provide ATC services to aircraft operating in the vicinity of an airport or on the movement area.

        1) It authorizes aircraft to land or take off at the airport controlled by the tower or to transit the Class D airspace area regardless of flight plan or weather conditions (IFR or VFR).

        2) A tower may also provide approach control services.

    b. TRACONs manage the airspace from 10 to 40 miles outside of selected airports and below 13,000 feet. They also coordinate aircraft spacing as they approach and depart these airports.

        1) Terminal controllers become familiar with pertinent weather information and stay aware of current weather information needed to perform air traffic control duties.

        2) Terminal controllers advise pilots of hazardous weather that may impact operations within 150 NM of the controller's assigned sector or area of jurisdiction.

    c. ATCTs and TRACONs may opt to broadcast hazardous weather information alerts only when any part of the area described is within 50 NM of the airspace under the ATCT's jurisdiction.

        1) The tower controllers are also properly certified and act as official weather observers as required.

5. **Automatic Terminal Information Service (ATIS)** is a continuous broadcast of recorded information in selected terminal areas. Its purpose is to improve controller effectiveness and to relieve frequency congestion by automating the repetitive transmission of current weather information and other noncontrol airport information.

6. **Flight Service Station (FSS)/Automated Flight Service Station (AFSS).**

    a. Flight Service Stations (FSSs) and Automated Flight Service Stations (AFSSs) provide pilot weather briefings, en route weather, receive and process IFR and VFR flight plans, relay ATC clearances, and issue Notices to Airmen (NOTAMs).

    b. They also provide assistance to lost aircraft and aircraft in emergency situations and conduct VFR search and rescue services.

1.6 WEATHER BRIEFINGS

1. The ultimate users of the aviation weather service are pilots and dispatchers.

    a. As a user of the service, you should also contribute to it. Send pilot weather reports (PIREPs) to help briefers, forecasters, and your fellow pilots.

    b. The service can be no better or more complete than the information that goes into it.

2. In the interest of safety and in compliance with Federal Aviation Regulations, you should get a complete briefing before each flight.

    a. You can get a preliminary briefing via recorded information on your telephone or from an Internet weather resource.

    b. Many times the weather situation may be complex, and you may not completely comprehend the information you receive.

    c. You are responsible for ensuring that you have all the information needed to make a go/no-go decision.

3. **How to Get a Good Weather Briefing**

    a. Call a FSS by dialing 800-WX-BRIEF (800-992-7433).

       1) Press "1" or say "briefer" to speak to a briefer when prompted.

       2) You may say the name of the state for which you are seeking a weather briefing, or you may say "any" to get the first available briefer.

          a) Using the "any" service will help you avoid long hold times during peak operation times.

    b. When requesting a briefing, identify yourself as a pilot. Give clear and concise facts about your flight:

       1) Type of flight, VFR or IFR
       2) Aircraft number or your name
       3) Aircraft type
       4) Departure point
       5) Proposed time of departure
       6) Flight altitude(s)
       7) Route of flight
       8) Destination
       9) Estimated time en route (ETE)

    c. With this background, the briefer can proceed directly with the briefing and concentrate on weather relevant to your flight.

    d. The weather briefing you receive depends on the type requested.

       1) A **standard** briefing should include

          a) Adverse conditions -- meteorological or aeronautical conditions reported or forecast that may influence you to alter the proposed flight.

          b) VFR flight not recommended (VNR) -- a statement issued if you indicated that your flight will be conducted under VFR and if the sky conditions or visibilities are present or forecast that, in the judgment of the FSS briefer, would make flight under VFR doubtful.

          c) Synopsis -- a brief statement describing the type, location, and movement of weather systems and/or air masses which may affect your flight.

          d) Current conditions -- a summary of current weather (METAR) reports--departure, en route, and destination.

          e) En route forecast -- a summary of forecast conditions for the flight.

          f) Destination forecast -- forecast data about your destination, including any significant changes expected between 1 hr. before to 1 hr. after your proposed ETA.

          g) Winds aloft -- forecast winds aloft for your route with temperature information available on request.

          h) NOTAMs -- NOTAM information pertinent to your flight.

i)   ATC delays -- information about any known ATC delays and/or flow control advisories that may affect your flight.

j)   Request for PIREPs, if appropriate.

k)   EFAS -- information about the availability of Flight Watch for weather updates.

l)   Any other information you may request, e.g., military training routes, etc.

2)   An **abbreviated** briefing will be provided when the user requests information to

a)   Supplement mass disseminated data from another source

i)   Inform the briefer of the time and source of the previously received information so that necessary information will not be omitted inadvertently.

b)   Update a previous standard briefing

c)   Be limited to specific information

3)   An **outlook** briefing will be provided when the briefing is 6 or more hours in advance of proposed departure.

a)   Briefing will be limited to applicable forecast data for the proposed flight.

e.   The FSSs are here to serve you. You should not hesitate to discuss factors that you do not fully understand.

1)   You have a complete briefing only when you have a clear picture of the weather to expect.

2)   It is to your advantage to make a final weather check immediately before departure if at all possible.

4.   **Have an Alternate Plan of Action**

a.   When weather is questionable, get a picture of expected weather over a broader area.

1)   Preplan a route to take you rapidly away from the weather if it goes sour.

b.   When you fly into weather through which you cannot safely continue, you must act quickly.

1)   Without preplanning, you may not know the best direction in which to turn; a wrong turn could lead to disaster.

c.   A preplanned diversion beats panic. It is better to be safe than sorry.

1.7 DISSEMINATION OF AVIATION WEATHER PRODUCTS

1.   The **Direct User Access Terminal Service (DUATS/DUAT)**, which is funded by the FAA, allows any pilot with a current medical certificate to access weather information and file a flight plan via computer. Two methods of access are available to connect with DUATS.

a.   The first method is via the Internet through Computer Sciences Corporation (CSC) at http://www.duats.com or Data Transformation Corporation at http://www.duat.com.

1)   This method is by far the most commonly utilized by pilots.

b.   The second method requires a modem and a communications program supplied by a DUATS provider.

1)   To access the weather information and file a flight plan by this method, pilots use a toll free telephone number to connect the user's computer directly to the DUATS computer.

2)   The current vendors of DUATS service and the associated phone numbers are listed in Chapter 7 of the *Aeronautical Information Manual (AIM)*.

2. The **Aviation Digital Data Service (ADDS)** provides the aviation community with text, digital and graphical forecasts, analyses, and observations of aviation-related weather variables.

    a. ADDS is a joint effort of NOAA Forecast Systems Laboratory (FSL), NCAR Research Applications Laboratory (RAL), and the AWC.

    b. Access the service online at http://adds.aviationweather.gov.

3. **Telephone Information Briefing Service (TIBS)** is provided by AFSSs and provides continuous telephone recordings of meteorological and/or aeronautical information.

    a. Specifically, TIBS provides area and/or route briefings, airspace procedures, and special announcements (if applicable) concerning aviation interests.

    b. TIBS should also contain, but is not limited to,

        1) Aviation routine weather reports (METARs)
        2) Terminal aerodrome forecasts (TAFs)
        3) Winds/temperatures aloft forecasts

    c. TIBS is available 24 hr. a day. The recorded information will be updated as conditions change or forecasts are updated.

        1) At some AFSSs, TIBS service may be reduced from 2200 to 0600 local time. During this time, an announcement must be recorded and will include a time when full service will resume.

    d. TIBS can be accessed by use of 800-WX-BRIEF (800-992-7433) toll-free.

        1) A touchtone telephone is necessary to access the TIBS program.
        2) Press "3" or say "TIBS" when prompted and then speak the name of the state for which you are requesting information.

    e. Each AFSS will provide at least four route and/or area briefings. An area briefing will encompass a 50-NM radius around a specified airport.

        1) You will have access to Notices to Airmen (NOTAM) information either through TIBS or access to a briefer.

    f. The order and content of the TIBS recording is as follows:

        1) Introduction -- a statement that includes the time the information was recorded and the route and/or area of coverage
        2) Adverse conditions -- a summary of inflight aviation weather advisories, CWAs, AWWs, and any other available information that may adversely affect flight in the route or area
        3) VFR not recommended (VNR) statement -- a statement issued when current or forecast conditions would make flight under VFR doubtful
        4) Synopsis -- a brief statement describing the type, location, and movement of weather systems or air masses that might affect the route or the area
        5) Current conditions -- a summary of current weather conditions over the route or the area
        6) Density altitude -- a "check density altitude" statement for any weather reporting station at an airport with a field elevation at or above 2,000 ft. MSL and meeting certain temperature criteria.
        7) En route forecast -- a summary of appropriate forecast data in logical order (climb out, en route, and descent)
        8) Winds aloft -- a summary of winds aloft forecast for the route or the area for levels through 12,000 ft.
        9) Request for PIREPs, if appropriate

10) NOTAM information that affects the route or the area -- NOTAM information that may be available either from the TIBS recording or by access to a FSS briefer

11) Military training activity, included in the closing statement.

12) Closing announcement -- shall be appropriate for the facility equipment and the mode of operation

4. **Hazardous Inflight Weather Advisory Service (HIWAS)** is a continuous broadcast service (24 hr. a day) over selected VORs of inflight aviation weather advisories, i.e., AIRMETs, SIGMETs, convective SIGMETs, severe weather forecast alerts (AWW), center weather advisories (CWA), and urgent PIREPs.

    a. The HIWAS broadcast will state that there are no hazardous weather advisories if none exist.

    b. The HIWAS broadcast area is defined as the area within 150 NM of a HIWAS outlet.

    c. HIWAS broadcasts will not be interrupted or delayed except in emergency situations.

    d. Once the HIWAS broadcast is updated, an announcement will be made on all communications and navigational aid (NAVAID frequencies (except emergency) and En Route Flight Advisory Service (EFAS).

    e. In the event that a HIWAS outlet is out of service, an announcement will be made on all communications and NAVAID frequencies except emergency and EFAS.

    f. The HIWAS broadcast will include the following:

        1) A statement of introduction, including the appropriate area(s) and a recording time

        2) A summary of inflight aviation advisories, CWAs, AWWs, and any other weather not included in a current hazardous weather advisory

        3) A request for PIREPs, if applicable

        4) A recommendation to contact a FSS or Flight Watch for additional details concerning hazardous weather

5. The **En Route Flight Advisory Service (EFAS),** or Flight Watch, is a weather service from selected FSSs on a common frequency (122.0 MHZ) below flight level (FL) 180 and on assigned discrete frequencies to aircraft at FL 180 and above.

    a. The purpose of EFAS is to provide en route aircraft with timely and meaningful weather information tailored to the type of flight intended, route of flight, and altitude.

        1) Flight Watch is **not** used for routine inflight services, such as flight plan filing and position reporting. For these services, contact the nearest FSS on a published discrete frequency.

    b. Additionally, Flight Watch is a focal point for rapid receipt and dissemination of pilot reports.

    c. To use this service, call FLIGHT WATCH.

        1) EXAMPLE: "(Oakland) Flight Watch, this is . . ."

    d. EFAS is normally available throughout the contiguous U.S. and Puerto Rico from 6 a.m. to 10 p.m., local time.

END OF STUDY UNIT

STUDY UNIT TWO
AVIATION WEATHER PRODUCT CLASSIFICATION AND POLICY

(3 pages of outline)

> Please take a few minutes to study each of the concepts listed above and anticipate/imagine what they are and how they relate to the other listed concepts.

2.1 INTRODUCTION

1. The demand for new and improved aviation weather products continues to grow and, with new products introduced to meet the demand, some confusion has resulted in the aviation community regarding the relationship between regulatory requirements and the new weather products.

2. This section will clarify that relationship by providing

   a. Classification of the weather products and policy guidance in their use,
   b. Descriptions of the types of aviation weather information, and
   c. Categorization of the sources of aviation weather information.

2.2 CLASSIFICATION OF WEATHER PRODUCTS

1. The FAA has developed two classifications of aviation weather products: primary weather products and supplementary weather products.

   a. The classifications are meant to eliminate confusion by differentiating between weather products that may be used to meet regulatory requirements and other weather products that may only be used to improve situational awareness.

   b. A **primary weather product** is an aviation weather product that meets all of the regulatory requirements and safety needs for use in making weather-related flight decisions.

      1) Study Units 3-29 of this text constitute primary weather products.

   c. A **supplementary weather product** is an aviation weather product that may be used for enhanced situational awareness.

      1) A supplementary weather product must only be used in conjunction with one or more primary weather product(s).
      2) Study Units 30-35 of this text constitute supplementary weather products.

2. All flight-related, aviation weather decisions must be based on the primary weather products.

   a. Supplementary weather products augment the primary products by providing additional weather information but may not be used as stand-alone products to meet aviation weather regulatory requirements or without the relevant primary products.

   b. When discrepancies exist between primary and supplementary products pertaining to the same weather phenomena, pilots must base flight-related decisions on the primary weather product.

   c. Furthermore, multiple primary products may be necessary to meet all aviation weather regulatory requirements.

3.   Aviation weather products produced by the federal government (NWS) are primary products unless designated as a supplementary product by the FAA. In addition, the FAA may choose to restrict certain weather products to specific types of usage or classes of users.

a.   Any limitations imposed by the FAA on the use of a product will appear in the product label.

2.3   TYPES OF AVIATION WEATHER INFORMATION

1.   The FAA has identified the following three distinct types of weather information that may be needed to conduct aircraft operations: observations, analyses, and forecasts.

2.   **Observations** are raw weather data collected by some type of sensor(s). The observations can either be made directly (e.g., surface or airborne) or remotely (e.g., weather radar, satellite, profiler, and lightning).

3.   **Analyses** of weather information are an enhanced depiction and/or interpretation of observed weather data.

4.   **Forecasts** are the predictions of the development and/or movement of weather phenomena based on meteorological observations and various mathematical models.

a.   Inflight weather advisories, including Significant Meteorological Information (SIGMET), Convective SIGMETs, Airman's Meteorological Information (AIRMET), Center Weather Advisories (CWA), and Meteorological Impact Statements (MIS), are considered forecast weather information products.

2.4   CATEGORIZING AVIATION WEATHER SOURCES

1.   The regulations pertaining to aviation weather reflect that, historically, the federal government was the only source of aviation weather information. That is, the FAA and NWS, or its predecessor organizations, were solely responsible for the collection and dissemination of weather data, including forecasts. Thus, the term "approved source(s)" referred exclusively to the federal government.

a.   The federal government is no longer the only source of weather information, due to the growing sophistication of aviation operations and scientific and technological advances.

b.   Since all three types of weather information (observations, analyses, and forecasts) are not available from all sources of aviation weather information, the FAA has categorized the sources as follows: federal government, Enhanced Weather Information System (EWINS), and commercial weather information providers.

2.   **Federal Government**

a.   The FAA and NWS collect weather observations.

1)   The NWS analyzes the observations, and produces forecasts, including inflight aviation weather advisories (e.g., SIGMETs).

2)   The FAA and NWS disseminate meteorological observations, analyses, and forecast products through a variety of systems.

b.   The federal government is the only approval authority for sources of weather observations (e.g., contract towers and airport operators).

c.   Commercial weather information providers contracted by the FAA to provide weather observations (e.g., contract towers) are included in the federal government category of approved sources by virtue of maintaining required technical and quality assurance standards under FAA and NWS oversight.

3. **Enhanced Weather Information System (EWINS)**

    a. EWINS is an FAA-approved proprietary system for tracking, evaluating, reporting, and forecasting the presence or absence of adverse weather phenomena.

    b. EWINS is authorized to produce flight movement forecasts (a forecast issued by certain dispatchers for air carrier operations), adverse weather phenomena forecasts, and other meteorological advisories.

    c. To receive FAA approval, an EWINS-approved source must have sufficient procedures, personnel, and communications and data processing equipment to effectively obtain, analyze, and disseminate aeronautical weather data.

    d. An EWINS-approved source may produce weather analyses and forecasts based on meteorological observations provided by the federal government.

    e. Approval to use EWINS weather products is issued on a case by case basis and is currently only applicable to FAR part 121 and 135 certificate holders, who may either act as their own EWINS or contract those services from a separate entity.

        1) For these approved users, the weather analyses and forecasts produced by their approved EWINS are considered primary weather products.

4. **Commercial Weather Information Providers**

    a. Commercial weather providers are a major source of weather products for the aviation community. In general, they produce proprietary weather products based on NWS products with formatting and layout modifications but no material changes to the weather information itself.

        1) This is also referred to as "repackaging."

    b. Commercial providers may also produce forecasts, analyses, and other proprietary weather products and substantially alter the information contained in NWS-produced products.

        1) Operators and pilots contemplating using such services should request and/or review an appropriate description of services and provider disclosure. This should include, but is not limited to,

            a) The type of weather product (e.g., current weather or forecast weather),
            b) The currency of the product (i.e., product issue and valid times), and
            c) The relevance of the product.

    c. Pilots and operators should be cautious when using unfamiliar products, or products not supported by FAA/NWS technical specifications.

    d. Commercially-available proprietary weather products that substantially alter NWS-produced weather products, or information, may only be approved for use by part 121 or part 135 operators or fractional ownership programs if the commercial provider is EWINS-qualified.

    e. Government products that are only repackaged and not altered, or products produced by an EWINS-approved source, are considered primary weather products.

END OF STUDY UNIT

STUDY UNIT THREE
AVIATION ROUTINE WEATHER REPORTS (METAR)

(22 pages of outline)

> Please take a few minutes to study each of the concepts listed above and anticipate/imagine what they are and how they relate to the other listed concepts.

An aviation routine weather report (METAR) is the weather observer's (human or automated) interpretation of the weather conditions at a given site and time. The METAR is used by the aviation community and the NWS to determine the weather conditions (VFR, MVFR, IFR) at an airport, as well as to produce a terminal aerodrome forecast (TAF), if appropriate.

Although the METAR code is being adopted worldwide, each country is allowed to make modifications or exceptions to the code for use in that particular country; e.g., the U.S. will report prevailing visibility in statute miles, runway visual range (RVR) values in feet, wind speed in knots, and altimeter setting in inches of mercury. However, temperature and dew point will be reported in degrees Celsius.

3.1 ELEMENTS

1. A METAR report contains the following sequence of elements in the following order:

   1. Type of report
   2. ICAO station identifier
   3. Date and time of report
   4. Modifier (as required)
   5. Wind
   6. Visibility
   7. Runway visual range (RVR) (as required)
   8. Weather phenomena
   9. Sky condition
   10. Temperature/dew point
   11. Altimeter
   12. Remarks (RMK) (as required)

2. NOTE: The elements in the body of a METAR report are separated by a space, except temperature and dew point, which are separated with a solidus, /. When an element does not occur or cannot be observed, that element is omitted from that particular report.

3.2 EXAMPLE OF A METAR REPORT

METAR KGNV 201953Z 24015KT 3/4SM R28/2400FT +TSRA BKN008 OVC015CB 26/25 A2985
RMK TSB32RAB32

To aid in the discussion, we have divided the report into the 12 elements:

METAR	KGNV	201953Z		24015KT	3/4SM	R28/2400FT	+TSRA
1.	2.	3.	4.	5.	6.	7.	8.

BKN008 OVC015CB	26/25	A2985	RMK TSB32RAB32
9.	10.	11.	12.

1. Aviation routine weather report
2. Gainesville, FL
3. Observation taken on the 20th day at 1953 UTC (or Zulu)
4. Modifier omitted; i.e., not required for this report
5. Wind 240° true at 15 kt.
6. Visibility 3/4 SM
7. Runway 28, runway visual range 2,400 ft.
8. Thunderstorm with heavy rain
9. Ceiling 800 ft. broken, 1,500 ft. overcast, cumulonimbus clouds
10. Temperature 26°C, dew point 25°C
11. Altimeter 29.85
12. Remarks: Thunderstorm began at 32 min. past the hour; rain began at 32 min. past the hour.

3.3 TYPE OF REPORT

The type of report will always appear as the lead element of the report. There are two types of reports:

1. **METAR** -- an aviation routine weather report
2. **SPECI** -- a nonroutine aviation weather report

3.4 ICAO STATION IDENTIFIER

1. The METAR uses the ICAO four-letter station identifier.

2. In the contiguous 48 states, the three-letter domestic location identifier is prefixed with a "K."

    a. EXAMPLE: The domestic identifier for San Francisco, CA is SFO, while the ICAO identifier is KSFO.

3. Elsewhere, the first one or two letters of the ICAO identifier indicate in which region of the world and country (or state) the station is located.

    a. Pacific locations such as Alaska, Hawaii, and the Mariana Islands, start with "P" followed by an "A", "H," or "G" respectively.

        1) The last two letters reflect the specific reporting station identification.

        2) If the station's three-letter identifier begins with an "A," "H," or "G," the "P" is added to the beginning.

            a) If the station's three-letter identifier does NOT begin with an "A," "H," or "G," the last letter is dropped and the "P" is added to the beginning.

        3) EXAMPLES:

            a) ANC (Anchorage, AK) is PANC.
            b) OME (Nome, AK) is PAOM.
            c) HNL (Honolulu, HI) is PHNL.
            d) KOA (Keahole Point, HI) is PHKO.
            e) UAM (Anderson AFB, Guam) is PGUA

b. Canadian station identifiers start with "C," e.g., Toronto, Canada is CYYZ.

c. Mexican and western Caribbean station identifiers start with "M."

d. The identifier for the eastern Caribbean is "T" followed by the individual country's letter; e.g., San Juan, Puerto Rico is TJSJ.

3.5 DATE AND TIME OF REPORT

1. The date and time the observation is taken are transmitted as a six-digit date/time group appended with the letter **Z** to denote Coordinated Universal Time (UTC).

    a. The first two digits are the date followed with two digits for the hour and two digits for minutes.

    b. If the report is a corrected report, the time entered shall be the same time used in the report being corrected.

3.6 MODIFIER

1. There are two modifiers, used as required.

    a. **AUTO** -- identifies the report as an automated weather report with no human intervention

        1) The type of sensor equipment used at the automated station will be encoded in the remarks section of the report (explained in Subunit 14).

        2) The absence of AUTO indicates that the report was made manually or an automated station had human augmentation.

    b. **COR** -- identifies the report as a corrected report to replace an earlier report with an error

3.7 WIND

1. Wind follows the date/time or modifier element.

2. The average 2-minute direction and speed are reported in a five- or six-digit format.

    a. The first three digits are the direction FROM which the wind is blowing. The direction is to the nearest 10-degree increment referenced to TRUE north.

        1) On the other hand, wind direction when verbally broadcast by a control tower or advisory station is referenced to magnetic north. This is done so the pilot can more closely relate the wind direction to the runway in use.

    b. The last two or three digits are the wind speed in knots -- two digits for speeds less than 100 kt., three digits for speeds greater than or equal to 100 kt.

    c. The abbreviation **KT** is appended to denote the use of knots for wind speed.

    d. EXAMPLE: **24015KT** means the wind is from 240° true at 15 kt.

3. If the wind speed is 6 kt. or less and, in the observer's opinion, the wind is varying in direction, the contraction **VRB** is used for wind direction.

    a. EXAMPLE: **VRB04KT** means the wind is variable in direction at 4 kt.

4. A **calm** wind is defined as when no motion of air is detected and is coded as **00000KT**.

5. A **gust** is a variation in wind speed of 10 kt. or more between peaks and lulls.

    a. A gust is reported by the letter **G** after the wind speed, followed by the highest reported gust.

    b. EXAMPLE: **210103G130KT** means the wind is from 210° true at 103 kt. with gusts to 130 kt.

6. If the wind is variable by 60° or more and the wind speed is greater than 6 kt., a variable group consisting of the extremes of the wind directions separated by **V** will follow the wind group.

    a. EXAMPLE: **32012G22KT 280V350** means the wind direction is from 320° true at 12 kt., gusts to 22 kt., wind direction variable between 280° true and 350° true.

7. A SPECI report will be issued if the wind direction changes by 45° or more in less than 15 min. and the sustained winds are 10 kt. or more throughout the wind shift.

3.8 VISIBILITY

1. The visibility reported is called the prevailing visibility.

    a. **Prevailing visibility** is considered representative of the visibility conditions at the observing site.

    b. This representative visibility is the greatest distance at which objects can be seen and identified through at least 180° of the horizon circle, which need not be continuous.

2. Visibility is reported in statute miles with a space and then fractions of statute miles, as needed, with **SM** appended to it.

    a. EXAMPLE: **1 1/2SM** means visibility is one and one-half statute miles.

3. When visibility is less than 7 SM, the restriction to the visibility will be shown in the weather element.

    a. The only exception is that if volcanic ash, low drifting dust, sand, or snow is observed, those restrictions to visibility are reported, even if the visibility is 7 SM or greater.

4. If tower or surface visibility is less than 4 SM, the lesser of the two will be reported in this element; the greater will be reported in the remarks.

5. Automated reporting stations will show visibility less than 1/4 SM as **M1/4SM** and visibility of 10 SM and greater as **10SM**.

    a. For automated reporting stations having more than one visibility sensor, site-specific visibility that is lower than the visibility shown in the body will be shown in remarks.

6. A SPECI report will be issued if the prevailing visibility decreases to less than or, if below, increases to equal or exceed

    a. 3 SM

    b. 2 SM

    c. 1 SM

    d. The lowest standard instrument approach procedure (IAP) as published, or 1/2 SM if no IAP

3.9 RUNWAY VISUAL RANGE (RVR)

1. Runway visual range (RVR) is based on the measurement of a transmissometer (or the New Generation RVR system, which uses forward scatter technology) made near the touchdown point of an instrument runway which represents the horizontal distance a pilot will see down the runway from the approach end.

    a. RVR is based on either the sighting of high-intensity runway lights or the visual contrast of other targets, whichever yields the greater visual range.

2. RVR is reported if the airport has RVR equipment and whenever the prevailing visibility is 1 SM or less and/or the RVR for the designated instrument runway is 6,000 ft. or less.

3. RVR is reported in the following format: **R** identifies the group, followed by the runway heading and parallel designator if needed, a solidus (/), and the visual range in feet (meters in other countries) indicated by **FT**.

    a. EXAMPLE: **R28/1200FT** means Runway 28 visual range is 1,200 ft.

4. When the RVR varies by more than one reportable value, the lowest and highest values are shown with **V** between them.

    a. EXAMPLE: **R19/1000V2000FT** means Runway 19 visual range variable between 1,000 ft. and 2,000 ft.

5. When the observed RVR is above the maximum value that can be determined by the system, it should be reported as **P6000**, where 6,000 ft. is the maximum value for this system.

    a. EXAMPLE: **R04/P6000FT** means Runway 4 visual range is more than 6,000 ft.

6. When the observed RVR is below the minimum value that can be determined by the system, it should be reported as **M0600**, where 600 ft. is the minimum value for this system.

    a. EXAMPLE: **R32/M0600FT** means Runway 32 visual range is less than 600 ft.

7. If RVR should be reported but is missing, **RVRNO** will be in the remarks.

8. A SPECI report will be issued if the highest value from the designated RVR runway decreases to less than or, if below, increases to equal or exceed 2,400 ft. during the preceding 10 min.

3.10 WEATHER PHENOMENA

The weather is reported in the following format:

1. **Intensity.** Intensity may be shown with most precipitation types, including those of a showery nature.

    a. Intensity levels may be shown with obscurations such as blowing dust, sand, or snow.

    b. When more than one type of precipitation is present, the intensity refers to the first precipitation type (most predominant).

    c. The intensity symbols used are shown in Table 3-1 below.

Symbol	Meaning
+	Heavy
(no symbol)	Moderate
−	Light

Table 3-1. – Intensity Qualifiers.

2. **Proximity.** Proximity is applied to and reported only for weather occurring in the vicinity of the airport and is denoted by **VC**.

    a. Vicinity of the airport is defined to be between 5 and 10 SM from the usual point of observation.

    b. VC will replace the intensity symbol; i.e., intensity and VC will never be shown in the same group.

3. **Descriptor.** The following eight descriptors shown in Table 3-2 below further identify weather phenomena and are used with certain types of precipitation and obscurations.

Coded	Meaning	Coded	Meaning
TS	Thunderstorm	DR	Low drifting
SH	Showers	MI	Shallow
FZ	Freezing	BC	Patches
BL	Blowing	PR	Partial

Table 3-2. – Descriptor Qualifiers.

a. MI is used only to further describe fog that has little vertical extent (less than 6 ft.).
b. BC is used only to further describe fog that has little vertical extent and reduces horizontal visibility.
c. DR is used when dust, sand, or snow is raised by the wind to less than 6 ft.
d. BL is used when dust, sand, snow, and/or spray is raised by the wind to a height of 6 ft., or more.
e. Although **TS** and **SH** are used with precipitation and may be preceded with an intensity symbol, the intensity applies to the precipitation and not the descriptor.
    1) EXAMPLE: **+TSRA** means a thunderstorm with heavy rain, not a heavy thunderstorm with rain.

4. **Precipitation.** Precipitation is any form of water particles, whether solid or liquid, that fall from the atmosphere and reach the ground. The nine types of precipitation are shown in Table 3-3 below.

Coded	Meaning	Coded	Meaning
RA	Rain	GR	Hail (¼ in. in diameter or larger)
DZ	Drizzle	GS	Small Hail/Snow Pellets
SN	Snow	PL	Ice Pellets
SG	Snow Grains	IC	Ice Crystals
UP	Unknown Precipitation		

Table 3-3. – Coded Precipitation and Meanings.

a. **UP** is used only by automated weather reporting systems to indicate that the system cannot identify the precipitation with any degree of proficiency. This situation usually occurs when rain and snow are falling at the same time.
b. **GS** is used to indicate hail less than 1/4 in. in diameter.
c. For **IC** to be reported, visibility must be reduced by the ice crystals to 6 SM or less.

5. **Obscurations to visibility.** The eight types of obscuration phenomena are listed in Table 3-3A below. Obscurations are any phenomena in the atmosphere, other than precipitation, that reduce horizontal visibility.

Coded	Meaning	Coded	Meaning
FG	Fog (visibility less than 5/8 SM)	PY	Spray
BR	Mist (visibility 5/8 to 6 SM)	SA	Sand
FU	Smoke	DU	Dust
HZ	Haze	VA	Volcanic Ash

Table 3-3A. – Coded Obstructions to Vision and Meanings.

a.   **FG** is used to indicate fog restricting visibility to less than 5/8 SM.

b.   **BR** is used to indicate mist restricting visibility from 5/8 to 6 SM and is never coded with a descriptor.

c.   **BCFG** and **PRFG** are used to indicate patchy fog or partial fog only if the prevailing visibility is 7 SM or greater.

d.   Precipitation types may be grouped together; obscurations are grouped separately.

    1)   EXAMPLE: **RASN BR HZ**

6.   **Other.** There are six other weather phenomena that are reported when they occur, as shown in Table 3-3B below.

Coded	Meaning	Coded	Meaning
SQ	Squall	SS	Sandstorm
DS	Duststorm	PO	Well-Developed Dust/Sand Whirls
FC	Funnel Cloud	+FC	Tornado or Waterspout

Table 3-3B. – Coded Other Weather Phenomena and Meanings.

a.   A **squall (SQ)** is a sudden increase in wind speed of at least 16 kt., with the speed rising to 22 kt. or more and lasting at least one minute.

b.   **+FC** is used to denote a tornado or waterspout.

    1)   The type is indicated in the remarks.

7.   **Examples of Reported Weather Phenomena**

a.   **TSRA** means thunderstorm with moderate rain.

b.   **+SN** means heavy snow.

c.   **–RA FG** means light rain and fog.

d.   **VCSH** means showers in the vicinity.

8.   If more than one significant weather phenomenon is observed, entries will be listed in the following order: tornadic activity, thunderstorms, and weather phenomena in order of decreasing predominance (i.e., the most dominant type is reported first)

a.   If more than one significant weather phenomenon is observed, except precipitation, separate weather groups will be shown in the report.

    1)   No more than three weather groups are used to report weather phenomenon at, or in the vicinity of, the station.

b.   If more than one type of precipitation is observed, the appropriate codes are combined into a single group with the predominant type being reported first.

    1)   Any intensity refers to the first type of precipitation in the group.

9.   The following weather phenomena require the issuance of a SPECI report:

a.   A tornado, waterspout, or funnel cloud is first observed or disappears from sight.

b.   A thunderstorm begins or ends.

    1)   A SPECI is not required to report the beginning of a new thunderstorm if one is currently reported.

c.   Hail begins or ends.

d.   Freezing precipitation begins, ends, or changes intensity.

e.   Ice pellets begin, end, or change intensity (manual stations).

f.   A volcanic eruption is first noted.

g.   Squalls occur.

3.11 SKY CONDITION

The sky condition is reported in the following format:

1. **Amount.** The amount of sky cover is reported in eighths of sky cover, using contractions in Table 3-4 below.

Contraction	Meaning	Summation Amount
SKC or CLR*	Clear	0 or 0 below 12,000 ft.
FEW	Few	>0 to 2/8
SCT	Scattered	3/8 to 4/8
BKN	Broken	5/8 to 7/8
OVC	Overcast	8/8
VV	Vertical Visibility (indefinite ceiling)	8/8
CB	Cumulonimbus	When present
TCU	Towering Cumulus	When present

* **SKC** will be reported at manual stations. **CLR** will be used at automated stations when no clouds below 12,000 ft. are reported.

Table 3-4. – Reportable Contractions for Sky Cover.

a. A **layer** is defined as clouds or obscuring phenomena aloft when the base is at approximately the same level.

b. A **ceiling** is defined as the height (above ground level or AGL) of the lowest broken or overcast layer aloft or vertical visibility into a surface-based obstruction.

1) There is no provision for reporting thin layers (i.e., a layer through which blue sky or higher sky cover is visible) in the METAR code. A thin layer will be reported the same as if it were opaque.

2. **Height.** Cloud bases are reported with three digits in hundreds of feet AGL.

a. Automated stations cannot report clouds above 12,000 ft.

b. At reporting stations located in the mountains, if the cloud layer is below the station level, the height of the layer will be shown as three solidi, ///.

c. When more than one layer is reported, layers are given in ascending order of height. For each layer above a lower layer(s), the sky cover contraction for that layer will be the **total sky cover**, which includes that layer and all lower layers.

1) EXAMPLE: **FEW010 SCT030 BKN050** reports three layers, as shown in Figure 3-1 on the next page.

a) A few clouds at 1,000 ft. (2/8)
b) A scattered cloud layer at 3,000 ft. (3/8)
c) A broken cloud layer (ceiling) at 5,000 ft. (6/8)

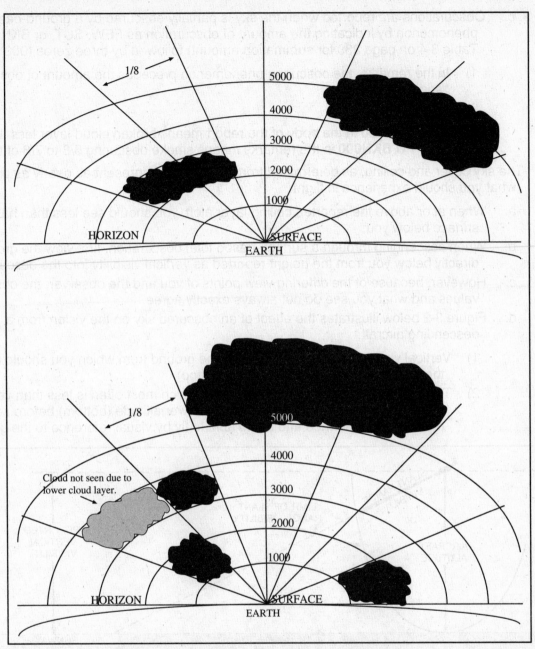

Figure 3-1. – Summation of Cloud Cover in Multiple Layers.

3. **Type or Vertical Visibility**

a. If **towering cumulus clouds (TCU)** or **cumulonimbus clouds (CB)** are present, they are reported after the height which represents their base.

   1) EXAMPLES:

      a) **SCT025TCU BKN080 BKN250** means 2,500 ft. scattered towering cumulus, ceiling 8,000 ft. broken, 25,000 ft. broken.

      b) **SCT008 OVC012CB** means 800 ft. scattered, ceiling 1,200 ft. overcast cumulonimbus clouds.

b. Height into an indefinite ceiling is preceded with **VV** (vertical visibility) followed by three digits indicating the vertical visibility in hundreds of feet AGL.

   1) The layer is spoken of as an "indefinite ceiling" and indicates total obscuration.

   2) EXAMPLE: **1/8SM FG VV006** means visibility 1/8 SM, fog, indefinite ceiling 600 ft.

c.   Obscurations are reported when the sky is partially obscured by a ground-based phenomenon by indicating the amount of obscuration as FEW, SCT, or BKN (see Table 3-4 on page 230 for summation amount) followed by three zeros (000).

1)   In the remarks, the obscuring phenomenon precedes the amount of obscuration and three zeros.

2)   EXAMPLE:

a)   **BKN000** in the body of the report means broken cloud layer less than 50 ft.

b)   **FU BKN000** in the remarks means smoke obscuring 5/8 to 7/8 of the sky.

4.   The sky cover and ceiling, as determined from the ground, represent as nearly as possible what you should experience in flight.

a.   When at or above the reported ceiling layer aloft, you should see less than half of the surface below you.

b.   When descending through a surface-based total obscuration, first view the ground directly below you from the height reported as vertical visibility into the obscuration.

c.   However, because of the differing view points of you and the observer, the observed values and what you see do not always exactly agree.

d.   Figure 3-2 below illustrates the effect of an obscured sky on the vision from a descending aircraft.

1)   Vertical visibility is the altitude above the ground from which you should first see the ground directly below the airplane (top).

2)   The real concern is slant range visibility, which most often is less than vertical visibility. Thus, you must descend to a lower altitude (bottom) before seeing a representative surface and being able to fly by visual reference to the ground.

Figure 3-2. – Effect of Obscured Sky on Aircraft.

5. The following sky conditions require the issuance of a SPECI report:

    a. The ceiling forms or dissipates below, decreases to less than, or, if below, increases to equal or exceed

        1) 3,000 ft.
        2) 1,500 ft.
        3) 500 ft.
        4) The lowest standard IAP minimum as published (if none is published, then 200 ft.)

    b. A layer of clouds or obscurations aloft is present below 1,000 ft., but no layer aloft was reported below 1,000 ft. in the preceding METAR or SPECI report.

3.12 TEMPERATURE/DEW POINT GROUP

1. Dew point is the temperature to which a given parcel of air must be cooled at constant pressure and constant water vapor content for the air to become fully saturated.

2. Temperature and dew point are reported in a two-digit form in whole degrees Celsius (C) separated by a solidus, /.

    a. Temperatures below zero are prefixed with **M**.

3. If the temperature is available but the dew point is missing, the temperature is shown followed by a solidus.

    a. If the temperature is missing, the group is omitted from the report.

4. EXAMPLES:

    a. **15/08** means temperature is 15°C and dew point is 8°C.
    b. **00/M02** means temperature is 0°C and dew point is –2°C.
    c. **M05/** means temperature is –5°C and dew point is missing.

5. An air mass with a 3°C or less temperature/dew point spread is considered saturated.

3.13 ALTIMETER

1. The altimeter setting group provides the current pressure at elevation. This setting is used by the pilot to determine the true altitude above a fixed plane of mean sea level.

2. The altimeter is reported in a four-digit format representing tens, units, tenths, and hundredths of inches of mercury prefixed with **A**. The decimal point is not reported.

    a. EXAMPLE: **A2995** means the altimeter setting is 29.95 inches of mercury.

3. Normal range of altimeter settings is from 28.00 to 31.00 inches of mercury.

3.14 REMARKS

1. Remarks are included in all observations, when appropriate, and are preceded by the contraction **RMK**.

    a. Time entries are shown as minutes past the hour if the time reported occurs during the same hour the observation is taken.

        1) If the hour is different, hours and minutes are shown.

b.   Except for precipitation, phenomena located within 5 SM of the point of observation will be reported as at the station.

   1)   Phenomena between 5 and 10 SM are reported in the vicinity, **VC**.

      a)   Precipitation not occurring at the point of observation but within 10 SM is also reported as VC.

   2)   Phenomena beyond 10 SM are reported as distant, **DSNT**.

c.   Direction of phenomena is indicated with the eight points of the compass (N, NE, E, SE, S, SW, W, NW).

d.   Distance remarks are in statute miles except for automated lightning remarks, which are in nautical miles.

e.   Movement of clouds or weather is indicated by the direction toward which the phenomenon is moving.

f.   There are two categories of remarks, and our discussion will follow the order in which the remarks would be used.

2.   **Automated, manual, and plain language remarks category.** This category of remarks may be generated from either manual or automated weather reporting stations, and they generally elaborate on parameters reported in the body of the report.

a.   **Volcanic eruption.** When first noted, the name of the volcano; latitude/longitude or approximate direction and distance from the reporting station; date/time; size/description/height/movement of ash cloud; and other pertinent information are entered in plain language.

   1)   Pre-eruption volcanic activity is not reported.

   2)   EXAMPLE: MT. ST. HELENS VOLCANO 70 MILES NE ERUPTED 181505 LARGE ASH CLOUD EXTENDING TO APPROX 30000 FEET MOVING SE

b.   **Tornado, funnel cloud, waterspout.** Whenever tornadoes, funnel clouds, or waterspouts begin, are in progress, or end, the phenomena, beginning and/or ending time, location, and movement are shown.

   1)   EXAMPLE: **TORNADO B13 DSNT NE** means that a tornado began 13 min. past the hour to the distant (beyond 10 SM) northeast.

c.   **Automated station type.** This remark is shown only if the **AUTO** modifier was used.

   1)   **AO1** means the automated weather station is without a precipitation (rain/snow) discriminator.

   2)   **AO2** means the automated weather station has a precipitation (rain/snow) discriminator.

d.   **Peak wind.** Whenever the peak wind exceeds 25 kt., **PK WND** will be included in the remarks in the next report with three digits for direction and two or three digits for speed, followed by time in hours and minutes of occurrence (only minutes if the hour can be inferred from the report time).

   1)   EXAMPLES:

      a)   **PK WND 28045/1955** means peak wind, 280° true at 45 kt., occurred at 1955 UTC.

      b)   **PK WND 34050/38** means peak wind, 340° true at 50 kt., occurred at 38 min. past the hour.

e.   **Wind shift.** A wind shift is indicated by a change in wind direction of 45° or more in less than 15 min. with sustained winds of 10 kt. or more throughout the wind shift.

   1)   When a wind shift occurs, **WSHFT** will be included in the remarks, followed by the time the wind shift began.

2) The contraction, **FROPA**, indicates that the wind shift is a result of a frontal passage.

3) EXAMPLES:

   a) **WSHFT 45** means the wind shift began at 45 min. past the hour.

   b) **WSHFT 30 FROPA** means the wind shift began at 30 min. past the hour due to a frontal passage.

f. **Tower or surface visibility.** If either tower (TWR) or surface (SFC) visibility is less than 4 SM, the lesser of the two will be reported in the body of the report; the greater will be reported in the remarks.

1) EXAMPLE: **3/4SM** (in the body) and **TWR VIS 1** (in remarks) mean that the lowest visibility is 3/4 SM, but the tower is reporting visibility of 1 SM.

g. **Variable prevailing visibility.** When the prevailing visibility rapidly increases or decreases by 1/2 SM or more during the observation, and the average prevailing visibility is less than 3 SM, the visibility is variable.

1) Variable visibility is shown in the remarks with the minimum and maximum visibility values.

2) EXAMPLE: **VIS 1V2** means the visibility is variable between 1 and 2 SM.

h. **Sector visibility.** Sector visibility is shown in remarks when it differs from the prevailing visibility and either the prevailing or the sector visibility is less than 3 SM.

1) EXAMPLE: **VIS N 2** means the visibility to the north is 2 SM.

i. **Visibility at second site.** For automated reporting stations having more than one visibility sensor, site-specific visibility that is lower than the visibility shown in the body will be shown in the remarks.

1) EXAMPLE: **VIS 2 RY11** means the visibility is 2 SM at runway 11.

j. **Lightning**

1) When lightning is seen by the weather observer, it will be included in remarks. The frequency of occurrence, type of lightning when observed, and the location will be indicated. The location is determined in reference to point of observation.

   a) The following contractions are used for frequency of lightning:

Contraction	Meaning
OCNL	Occasional (less than 1 flash/min.)
FRQ	Frequent (about 1 to 6 flashes/min.)
CONS	Continuous (more than 6 flashes/min.)

   b) The following contractions are used for type of lightning:

Contraction	Meaning
CG	Cloud-to-ground
IC	In-cloud
CC	Cloud-to-cloud
CA	Cloud-to-air

   c) EXAMPLE: **OCNL LTGICCG 2 NW** means occasional lightning in-cloud and cloud-to-ground 2 SM to the northwest.

2) When lightning is detected by an automated weather system

a) Within 5 NM of the airport location point (ALP), it will be reported as TS in the body of the report with no remarks.

b) Between 5 and 10 NM of the ALP, it will be reported as VCTS in the body of the report with no remarks.

c) Beyond 10 but within 30 NM of the ALP, it will be reported in remarks only as LTG DSNT followed by the direction from the ALP.

k. **Beginning and/or Ending Times for Precipitation and Thunderstorms**

1) When precipitation begins or ends, remarks will show the type of precipitation as well as the beginning and/or ending time(s) of occurrence.

a) Types of precipitation may be combined if beginning or ending at the same time.

b) These remarks are not required in SPECI reports but will be shown in the next METAR report.

c) EXAMPLE: **RAB05E30SNB20E55** means that rain began at 5 min. past the hour and ended at 30 min. past the hour; snow began at 20 min. past the hour and ended at 55 min. past the hour.

2) When thunderstorms begin or end, remarks will show the thunderstorm as well as the beginning and/or ending time(s) of occurrence.

a) These remarks are required in SPECI reports and will also be shown in the next METAR report.

b) EXAMPLE: **TSB05E40** means the thunderstorm began at 5 min. past the hour and ended at 40 min. past the hour.

l. **Thunderstorm location.** Thunderstorm location and movement will be in remarks as TS followed by location and movement.

1) EXAMPLES:

a) **TS OHD MOV N** means thunderstorm overhead, moving north.

b) **TS VC NE MOV NE** means thunderstorm in the vicinity northeast, moving northeast.

m. **Hailstone size.** The size of the largest hailstone, in 1/4-in. increments, is shown in remarks preceded with the contraction for hail, **GR**.

1) EXAMPLE: **GR 3/4** means hailstones 3/4 in. in diameter.

2) If small hail or snow pellets, GS, are encoded in the body of the report, no size remark will be shown.

n. **Virga.** When precipitation is observed but does not reach the ground, **VIRGA** will be shown in remarks. The direction from the station may also be reported.

1) EXAMPLES:

a) **VIRGA** means virga at the station.

b) **VIRGA SW** means virga southwest of the station.

o. **Variable ceiling height.** Whenever the ceiling is below 3,000 ft. and is variable, the remark **CIG** will be shown, followed with the lowest and highest ceiling heights.

1) EXAMPLE: **CIG 005V010** means the ceiling is variable between 500 ft. and 1,000 ft.

p. **Obscurations.** When an obscuration (surface or aloft) is observed, the obscuring phenomenon, followed by the amount of obscuration (FEW, SCT, or BKN) and three zeros, is shown in remarks.

   1) EXAMPLES:

      a) **FG FEW000** means fog is obscuring 1/8 to 2/8 of the sky.

      b) **FU BKN020** means a broken layer of smoke aloft, with bases at 2,000 ft.

q. **Variable sky condition.** When a layer that is 3,000 ft. or less is varying in sky cover, remarks will show the variability range.

   1) If there is more than one cloud layer, the variable layer is identified by including the layer height.

   2) EXAMPLES:

      a) **SCT V BKN** means scattered variable broken.

      b) **BKN025 V OVC** means 2,500 ft. broken variable overcast.

r. **Significant cloud types.** When significant cloud types are observed, they are shown in remarks.

   1) **Cumulonimbus (CB)** or **cumulonimbus mammatus (CBMAM)**, direction from the station, and direction of movement (if known). If the cloud is beyond 10 SM from the airport, DSNT will indicate distance.

      a) EXAMPLES:

         i) **CB W MOV E** means cumulonimbus clouds west of the station moving east.

         ii) **CBMAM DSNT S** means a cumulonimbus mammatus cloud distant south.

   2) **Towering cumulus (TCU)**, location (if known), and direction from station

      a) **TCU OHD** means towering cumulus overhead.

   3) Altocumulus castellanus (ACC), stratocumulus standing lenticular (SCSL), altocumulus standing lenticular (ACSL), cirrocumulus standing lenticular (CCSL), or rotor clouds (ROTOR CLD). Remarks describe the cloud and the direction from the station.

      a) EXAMPLES:

         i) **ACSL SW-S** means altocumulus standing lenticular clouds southwest through south.

         ii) **APRNT ROTOR CLD S** means an apparent rotor cloud to the south.

s. **Ceiling height at second site.** When an automated station uses meteorological discontinuity sensors, remarks will be shown to identify site-specific ceiling heights.

   1) EXAMPLE: **CIG 020 RY11** means ceiling 2,000 ft. at Runway 11.

t. **Pressure rising/falling rapidly.** At designated stations, when the pressure is rising or falling at a rate of at least 0.06 in. per hour and the pressure change totals 0.02 in. or more at time of observation, remarks will show **PRESRR** or **PRESFR**, respectively.

u. **Sea-level pressure.** At designated stations that report sea-level pressure, this remark begins with **SLP** and is coded using tens, units, and tenths of sea-level pressure in hectoPascals (hPa), which are equivalent to millibars.

   1) If no sea-level pressure is available, it will be coded **SLPNO**.

      a) SLPNO is not entered in SPECI reports taken at manual stations.

   2) EXAMPLE: **SLP132** means the sea-level pressure is 1013.2 hPa.

v. **Aircraft mishap.** If a report is taken to document weather conditions when notified of an aircraft mishap, the remark, **(ACFT MSHP)**, including the parentheses, is included in the report.

   1) The remark is not transmitted.

w. **No SPECI available.** At manual weather observing stations that do not take SPECI reports, **NOSPECI** will be shown in remarks of all METAR reports.

x. **Snow increasing rapidly.** The rapid accumulation of snow is reported at designated stations whenever the snow depth increases by one inch or more in the past hour.

   1) The remark **SNINCR** is followed with the depth increase in the past hour, a solidus (/), and the total snow depth on the ground at the time of the report.

      a) EXAMPLE: **SNINCR 2/10** means the snow depth increased 2 in. during the past hour and the current total snow depth on the ground is 10 in.

y. **Other significant information.** Operationally significant information, such as fog dispersal operations, runway conditions, or first and last reports, may be added to remarks here.

3. **Additive and maintenance data remarks category.** Additive data groups are reported only at designated stations, and the maintenance data groups are reported only from automated weather reporting stations.

   a. **Hourly precipitation.** An hourly precipitation group will be reported only at designated weather reporting stations, when precipitation has occurred since the last hour.

      1) This element begins with **P** followed by four digits indicating precipitation amount in hundredths of an inch.

         a) Four zeros indicate that less than one-hundredth of an inch of precipitation fell in the past hour.

   b. **3- and 6-hour precipitation amount.** A precipitation amount group will be reported at designated stations in the 3- and 6-hr. reports when precipitation has occurred since the previous 3- or 6-hr. report.

      1) This element begins with **6** followed by four digits indicating precipitation amount using tens, units, tenths, and hundredths of an inch.

   c. **24-hour precipitation.** A 24-hr. precipitation group will be reported at designated stations in the 1200Z observation (or other designated time) when more than a trace of precipitation has fallen in the past 24-hr. period.

      1) This element begins with a **7** followed by four digits indicating precipitation amount using tens, units, tenths, and hundredths of an inch.

   d. **Snow depth on ground.** A snow depth on the ground report will be reported at designated stations in the 0000Z and 1200Z observation whenever more than a trace of snow is on the ground, and will be included in the 0600Z and 1800Z observation whenever more than a trace of snow is on the ground and more than a trace of precipitation (water equivalent) has occurred in the past 6 hr.

      1) This element begins with **4/** followed by three digits indicating snow depth in inches.

   e. **Water equivalence of snow on the ground.** Water equivalence is reported at designated stations in the 1800Z report if the average snow, snow pellets, ice pellets, ice crystals, or hail depth is 2 in. or more.

      1) This remark is not used if the water equivalent consists entirely of hail.

      2) The remark is preceded with **933** followed by the water equivalent in tens, units, and tenths of an inch.

f. **Cloud types.** Cloud types are reported at designated stations in 3- and 6-hr. reports. The predominant low, middle, and high cloud types are coded.

1) This element begins with **8/** followed with coding used by the World Meteorological Organization for cloud identification.

2) FAA reporting stations will not encode this group.

g. **Duration of sunshine.** This remark is included in the 0800Z report at designated sunshine duration measuring stations.

1) If the station is closed at 0800Z, the remark is included in the first 6-hr. METAR report after the station opens.

2) The remark begins with **98** followed by three digits of the number of minutes of sunshine in hundreds, tens, and units taken from a sunshine sensor.

h. **Hourly temperature/dew point.** An hourly temperature/dew point group will be reported at designated stations to show hourly temperature and dew point to the tenth of a degree Celsius.

1) The element begins with **T** followed with **0**, if the temperature is 0°C or higher, or **1** to denote the temperature is less than 0°C, followed by the temperature in tens, units, and tenths; then 0 or 1 again; and then the dew point in tens, units, and tenths.

i. **6-hr. maximum temperature.** A 6-hr. maximum temperature group will be reported at designated stations to show the maximum temperature for the last 6 hr.

1) This element begins with **1** to identify maximum temperature, followed with **0** or **1** to denote whether the temperature is higher or lower than 0°C, respectively, and then the temperature in tens, units, and tenths.

j. **6-hr. minimum temperature.** A 6-hr. minimum temperature group will be reported at designated stations to show the minimum temperature for the last 6 hr.

1) This element begins with **2** to identify minimum temperature. Then it is coded in the same manner as maximum temperature.

k. **24-hr. maximum/minimum temperature.** A maximum/minimum temperature group will be reported at designated stations to show the maximum and minimum temperatures for the last 24 hr.

1) This element begins with **4** and is coded in the same manner as the maximum temperature element.

l. **3-hr. pressure tendency.** At designated stations, the 3- and 6-hr. reports include a remark regarding pressure tendency.

1) This element begins with **5** followed with 0 through 9 from the pressure characteristic and then the change in pressure over the past 3 hr.

2) The change in pressure is based on either the station pressure or the altimeter and is reported in tens, units, and tenths.

m. **Sensor Status Indicators**

1) If the RVR element in the body should be reported but is missing, **RVRNO** will be shown here.

a) **RVRNO** means that runway visual range information is not available.

2) If an automated weather reporting station is equipped with the following sensors and they are not working, the following remarks will appear:

   a) **PWINO** -- present weather identifier not available
   b) **PNO** -- precipitation amount not available
   c) **FZRANO** -- freezing rain information indicator not available
   d) **TSNO** -- lightning information not available
   e) **VISNO** -- visibility sensor information not available
   f) **CHINO** -- cloud height indicator information not available

n. **Maintenance indicator.** A maintenance indicator (dollar) sign, **$**, is included when an automated weather reporting system detects that maintenance is needed on the system.

3.15 AUTOMATED SURFACE OBSERVING SYSTEM (ASOS)

1. The ASOS is the primary surface weather observing system of the U.S.

   a. An upgraded version of ASOS, called the Automated Weather Sensing System (AWSS), is also available and seeing limited implementation.

      1) The data received from the two systems is identical. You should consider all of the following information to apply equally to ASOS and AWSS.

2. ASOS/AWSS is designed to support aviation operations and weather forecast activities.

   a. The program to install and operate up to 1,700 systems throughout the U.S. is a joint effort of the NWS, the FAA, and the Department of Defense.

   b. The ASOS/AWSS will provide continuous minute-by-minute observations and perform the basic observing functions necessary to generate a METAR report and other aviation weather information.

3. ASOS/AWSS weather information may be transmitted over a discrete VHF radio frequency or the voice portion of a local navigation aid (NAVAID).

   a. ASOS/AWSS transmissions on a discrete VHF frequency are engineered to be receivable to a maximum of 25 NM from the ASOS/AWSS site and a maximum altitude of 10,000 ft. AGL.

      1) Local conditions may limit the maximum reception distance and/or altitude.

4. While the automated system and the human observer may differ in their methods of data collection and interpretation, both produce an observation that is similar in form and content.

   a. For the "objective" elements (i.e., pressure, ambient temperature, dew point temperature, wind, and precipitation accumulation), both the ASOS/AWSS and the observer use a fixed location and time-averaging technique.

   b. For the "subjective" elements, observers use a fixed-time, spatial-averaging technique to describe the visual elements (i.e., sky condition, visibility, and present weather), while the ASOS/AWSS uses a fixed-location, time-averaging technique.

      1) Although this is a fundamental change, the manual and automated techniques yield remarkably similar results within the limits of their respective capabilities.

   c. Among the basic strengths of the ASOS/AWSS observation is the fact that critical weather parameters (e.g., sky condition and visibility) are measured at specific locations where they are needed most.

5. **System Description**

   a. The ASOS/AWSS at each airport location consists of four main components:

      1) Individual weather sensors
      2) Data collection and processing units
      3) Acquisition control unit
      4) Peripherals and displays

   b. The ASOS/AWSS sensors perform the basic function of data acquisition.

      1) They continuously sample and measure the ambient environment, derive raw sensor data, and make them available to the collection and processing units.

6. Every ASOS/AWSS will contain the following basic set of sensors:

   a. Cloud height indicator (one or possibly three)
   b. Visibility sensor (one or possibly three)
   c. Precipitation identification sensor
   d. Freezing rain sensor (at select sites)
   e. Pressure sensors (two sensors at small airports; three sensors at large airports)
   f. Ambient temperature/dew point temperature sensor
   g. Anemometer (wind direction and speed sensor)
   h. Rainfall accumulation sensor

7. The ASOS/AWSS data outlets include

   a. Those necessary for on-site airport users

   b. National communications networks

   c. Computer-generated voice (available through FAA radio broadcast to pilots and/or dial-in telephone line)

8. An ASOS/AWSS report without human intervention will contain only that weather data capable of being reported automatically.

   a. The modifier for this METAR report is **AUTO**.

      1) When an observer backs up an ASOS/AWSS site, the **AUTO** modifier is not used.

9. There are two types of automated stations.

   a. **AO1** for automated stations without a precipitation discriminator
   b. **AO2** for automated stations with a precipitation discriminator

      1) A precipitation discriminator can determine the difference between liquid and frozen/freezing precipitation.

3.16 AUTOMATED WEATHER OBSERVING SYSTEM (AWOS)

1. AWOS is the predecessor to ASOS; i.e., ASOS is "better than" AWOS. AWOS installations are becoming increasingly common, however, due to a smaller price tag.

2. ASOS will always prepare a METAR report, while only some AWOS sites will prepare METAR reports.

   a. Generally, AWOS is operated by the FAA or state government agencies.

3. Some AWOS locations will be augmented by certified observers who will provide weather and obstruction-to-vision information in the remarks of the report when the reported visibility is less than 7 SM.

   a. These sites, along with the hours of augmentation, are to be published in the *Airport/Facility Directory (A/FD)*.

   b. Augmentation is identified in the observation as "Observer Weather."

4. The AWOS wind speed, direction and gusts, temperature, dew point, and altimeter setting are exactly the same as for manual observations.

   a. AWOS will also report density altitude when it exceeds the field elevation by more than 1,000 ft.

   b. The reported visibility is derived from a sensor near the touchdown point of the primary runway.

      1) The visibility is a runway visibility value (RVV), using a 10-min. harmonic average.

      2) The AWOS sensors have been calibrated against the FAA transmissometer standards used for runway visual range values.

      3) Since the AWOS visibility is an extrapolation of a measurement at the touchdown point of the runway, it may differ from the standard prevailing visibility.

5. The reported sky condition/ceiling is derived from a ceilometer located next to the visibility sensor.

   a. The AWOS algorithm integrates the last 30 min. of ceilometer data to derive cloud layers and heights.

   b. This output may also differ from the observed sky condition in that the AWOS is totally dependent upon the cloud advection over the sensor site.

6. AWOS sites are operationally classified into the following four basic levels:

   a. **AWOS-A** -- only reports altimeter setting

   b. **AWOS-1** -- usually reports altimeter setting, wind data, temperature, dew point, and density altitude

   c. **AWOS-2** -- provides the information provided by AWOS-1 plus visibility

   d. **AWOS-3** -- provides the information provided by AWOS-2 plus cloud/ceiling data

7. AWOS information (system level, frequency, telephone number, etc.) concerning specific locations is published, as the systems become operational, in the *A/FD* and, if applicable, in published instrument approach procedures (IAP).

   a. Selected AWOS sites may be incorporated into nationwide data collection and dissemination networks in the future.

8. **AWOS Broadcasts**

   a. A computer-generated voice is used in AWOS to automate the broadcast of the minute-by-minute weather observations via VHF radio and/or telephone.

      1) Some AWOS sites are configured to permit the addition of an operator-generated voice message, e.g., weather remarks following the automated parameters.

   b. AWOS information is transmitted over a discrete VHF radio frequency or the voice portion of a local NAVAID.

      1) AWOS VHF radio transmissions are engineered to be receivable to a maximum of 25 NM from the AWOS site to a maximum altitude of 10,000 ft. AGL.

         a) Local conditions may limit AWOS reception.

      2) The system transmits a 20- to 30-sec. weather message updated each minute.

   c. Most AWOS sites have a dial-up capability so that the weather message can be accessed via telephone.

9. The phraseology used generally follows that used for other weather broadcasts. Following are explanations of the exceptions:

    a. The location/name of the airport and the phrase "Automated Weather Observation," followed by the time, are announced.

        1) The word "Test" is added following "Observation" when the system is not in commissioned (operational) status.

        2) The phrase "Temporarily Inoperative" is added when the system is inoperative.

    b. The lowest reported visibility value in AWOS is "less than 1/4 (SM)."

        1) The phrase "Visibility Missing" is announced only if the AWOS site has a visibility sensor and the information is not available.

    c. In the future, some AWOS sites are to be configured to determine the occurrence of precipitation.

    d. Ceiling and sky cover

        1) With the exception of an indefinite ceiling, all ceiling heights are measured (by a ceilometer).

        2) "No clouds detected" is announced as "No clouds below XXX" or, in newer systems, as "Sky clear below XXX," where XXX is the range limit of the sensor.

        3) "Sky condition missing" is announced only if the system is configured with a ceilometer and the ceiling and sky cover information is not available.

    e. Remarks

        1) Automated remarks include

            a) Density altitude
            b) Variable visibility
            c) Variable wind direction

        2) Manual input remarks are prefaced with the phrase "Observer Weather" and are generally limited to

            a) Type and intensity of precipitation
            b) Thunderstorm and direction
            c) Obstruction to vision when the visibility is less than 3 SM

10. If an AWOS is capable of producing a METAR report, the modifier **AUTO** will be used if it is done without human intervention.

    a. The remarks section will contain either **AO1** or **AO2**, depending on if the site has a precipitation discriminator.

    b. When an observer backs up an AWOS site, the **AUTO** modifier is not used.

11. **Weather Observing Programs Summary Table**

WEATHER OBSERVING PROGRAMS						
Element Reported	**AWOS-A**	**AWOS-1**	**AWOS-2**	**AWOS-3**	**ASOS**	**Manual**
Altimeter	X	X	X	X	X	X
Wind		X	X	X	X	X
Temperature/Dew Point		X	X	X	X	X
Density Altitude		X	X	X	X	
Visibility			X	X	X	X
Clouds/Ceiling				X	X	X
Precipitation					X	X
Remarks					X	X

If you encounter an inoperative or erroneous report from an AWOS or ASOS/AWSS station, please report it immediately to FSS or ATC. Also telephone in the problem.

AWOS: (770) 210-7756
ASOS/AWSS: (800) 242-8194

END OF STUDY UNIT

STUDY UNIT FOUR
PILOT WEATHER REPORTS (PIREP)

(6 pages of outline)

Please take a few minutes to study each of the concepts listed above and anticipate/imagine what they are and how they relate to the other listed concepts.

4.1 PURPOSE

1. No observation is more timely than the one made from the cockpit. In fact, aircraft in flight are the **only** means of directly observing cloud tops, icing, and turbulence.

2. PIREPs are also valuable in that they help fill the gaps between reporting stations.

3. You should report any observation that may be of concern to other pilots.

4. Also, if conditions were forecast but not encountered, you should provide a PIREP.

    a. This will help the NWS verify forecast products and create accurate products for the aviation community.

5. Pilots should help themselves, the aviation public, and the aviation weather forecasters by sending pilot reports.

4.2 FORMAT

1. A PIREP is usually transmitted in a prescribed format (shown in Table 4-1 on page 246).

2. Required elements for all PIREPs are type of report, location, time, flight level, type of aircraft, and at least one weather element encountered.

3. When not required, elements without reported data are omitted.

4. All altitude references are MSL unless otherwise noted.

5. Distances for visibility are in statute miles, and all other distances are in nautical miles.

6. Time is in UTC.

7. To lessen the chance of misinterpretation, icing and turbulence reports state intensities using standard terminology when possible.

    a. If a PIREP stated, "Pretty rough at 6,500...," the description of the strength of the turbulence at 6,500 ft. could have many interpretations.

        1) A report of "light," "moderate," or "severe" turbulence would have been more concise and understandable.

    b. If a pilot's description of an icing or turbulence encounter cannot readily be translated into standard terminology, the pilot's description should be transmitted verbatim.

UUA/UA	Type of report: URGENT (UUA) - Any PIREP that contains any of the following weather phenomena: tornadoes, funnel clouds, or waterspouts; severe or extreme turbulence, including clear air turbulence (CAT); severe icing; hail; volcanic ash; low-level wind shear (LLWS) (pilot reports air speed fluctuations of 10 knots or more within 2,000 feet of the surface); any other weather phenomena reported which are considered by the controller to be hazardous, or potentially hazardous, to flight operations. ROUTINE (UA) - Any PIREP that contains weather phenomena not listed above, including low-level wind shear reports with air speed fluctuations of less than 10 knots.
/OV	Location: Use VHF NAVAID(s) or an airport using the three- or four-letter location identifier. Position can be over a site, at some location relative to a site, or along a route. Ex: /OV KABC; /OV KABC090025; /OV KABC045020-DEF; /OV KABC-KDEF
/TM	Time: Four digits in UTC. Ex: /TM 0915
/FL	Altitude/Flight level: Three digits for hundreds of feet with no space between FL and altitude. If not known, use UNKN. Ex: /FL095; /FL310; /FLUNKN
/TP	Aircraft type: Four digits maximum; if not known, use UNKN. Ex: /TP L329; /TP B737; /TP UNKN
/SK	Sky cover: Describes cloud amount, height of cloud bases, and height of cloud tops. If unknown, use UNKN. Ex: /SK SCT040-TOP080; /SK BKNUNKN-TOP075; /SK BKN-OVC050-TOPUNKN; /SK SCT030-TOP060/OVC12O; /SK FEW030; /SK SKC
/WX	Flight visibility and weather: Flight visibility (FV) reported first and use standard METAR weather symbols. Intensity (– for light, no qualifier for moderate, and + for heavy) shall be coded for all precipitation types except ice crystals and hail. Ex: /WX FV05SM - RA; /WX FV01SM SN BR; /WX RA
/TA	Temperature (Celsius): If below zero, prefix with an "M." Temperature should also be reported if icing is reported. Ex: /TA 15; /TA M06
/WV	Wind: Direction from which the wind is blowing coded in tens of degrees using three digits. Directions of less than 100 degrees shall be preceded by a zero. The wind speed shall be entered as a two- or three-digit group immediately following the direction, coded in whole knots using the hundreds, tens, and units digits. Ex: /WV 27045KT; /WV 280110KT
/TB	Turbulence: Use standard contractions for intensity and type (CAT or CHOP when appropriate). Include altitude only if different from FL. (See Table 4-2 on page 247.) Ex: /TB EXTRM; /TB OCNL LGT-MDT BLW 090; /TB MOD-SEV CHOP 080-110
/IC	Icing: Describe using standard intensity and type contractions. Include altitude only if different from FL. (See Table 4-3 on page 249.) Ex: /IC LGT-MDT RIME; /IC SEV CLR 028-045
/RM	Remarks: Use free form to clarify the report putting hazardous elements first Ex: /RM LLWS -15 KT SFC-030 DURC RWY 22 JFK

Table 4-1. – Encoding PIREPs.

4.3 TURBULENCE

1. Table 4-2 below classifies each turbulence intensity according to its effects on aircraft control, structural integrity, and articles and occupants within the aircraft.

Intensity	Aircraft Reaction	Reaction Inside Aircraft
Light	Turbulence that momentarily causes slight, erratic changes in altitude and/or attitude (pitch, roll, yaw). Report as **light turbulence** or **light clear air turbulence (CAT).** or Turbulence that causes slight, rapid, and somewhat rhythmic bumpiness without appreciable changes in altitude or attitude. Report as **light chop.**	Occupants may feel a slight strain against belts or shoulder straps. Unsecured objects may be displaced slightly. Food service may be conducted and little or no difficulty is encountered in walking.
Moderate	Turbulence that causes changes in altitude and/or attitude occurs but the aircraft remains in positive control at all times. It usually causes variations in indicated airspeed. Report as **moderate turbulence** or **moderate CAT.** or Turbulence that is similar to light chop but of greater intensity. It causes rapid bumps or jolts without appreciable changes in aircraft or attitude. Report as **moderate chop.**	Occupants feel definite strains against seat belts or shoulder straps. Unsecured objects are dislodged. Food service and walking are difficult.
Severe	Turbulence that causes large, abrupt changes in altitude and/or attitude. It usually causes large variations in indicated airspeed. Aircraft may be momentarily out of control. Report as **severe turbulence** or **severe CAT.**	Occupants are forced violently against seat belts or shoulder straps. Unsecured objects are tossed about. Food service and walking are impossible.
Extreme	Turbulence in which the aircraft is violently tossed about and is practically impossible to control. It may cause structural damage. Report as **extreme turbulence** or **extreme CAT.**	

Table 4-2. – Turbulence Reporting Criteria.

2. Pilots should report location(s), time (UTC), altitude, aircraft type, proximity to clouds, intensity, and, when applicable, type (chop or CAT) and duration (occasional, intermittent, or continuous) of turbulence.

    a. Definition of duration terms

        1) Occasional means less than 1/3 of the time.
        2) Intermittent means 1/3 to 2/3 of the time.
        3) Continuous means more than 2/3 of the time.

3. High-level turbulence (normally above 15,000 ft. AGL) that is not associated with cumuliform clouds (including thunderstorms) shall be reported as clear air turbulence (CAT).

4.4 LOCATIONS OF PROBABLE TURBULENCE BY INTENSITIES

1. **Light Turbulence**

   a. In hilly and mountainous areas, even with light winds
   b. In and near small cumulus clouds
   c. In clear-air convective currents over heated surfaces
   d. With weak wind shears in the vicinity of

   1) Troughs aloft
   2) Lows aloft
   3) Jet streams
   4) The tropopause

   e. In the lower 5,000 ft. of the atmosphere

   1) When winds are near 15 kt.
   2) Where the air is colder than the underlying surfaces

2. **Moderate Turbulence**

   a. In mountainous areas with a wind component of 25 to 50 kt. perpendicular to and near the level of the ridge

   1) At all levels from the surface to 5,000 ft. above the tropopause with preference for altitudes

   a) Within 5,000 ft. of the ridge level
   b) At the base of relatively stable layers below the base of the tropopause
   c) Within the tropopause layer

   2) Extending downstream from the lee of the ridge for 150 to 300 NM

   b. In and near thunderstorms in the dissipating stage
   c. In and near other towering cumuliform clouds
   d. In the lower 5,000 ft. of the troposphere

   1) When surface winds are 30 kt. or more
   2) Where heating of the underlying surface is unusually strong
   3) Where there is an invasion of very cold air

   e. In fronts aloft
   f. In areas where the vertical wind shear exceeds 6 kt. per 1,000 ft., and/or horizontal wind shear exceeds 18 kt. per 150 NM

3. **Severe Turbulence**

   a. In mountainous areas with a wind component exceeding 50 kt. perpendicular to and near the level of the ridge

   1) In 5,000-ft. layers

   a) At and below the ridge level in rotor clouds or rotor action
   b) At the tropopause
   c) Sometimes at the base of other stable layers below the tropopause

   2) Extending downstream from the lee of the ridge for 50 to 150 NM

   b. In and near growing and mature thunderstorms
   c. Occasionally in other towering cumuliform clouds
   d. 50 to 100 NM on the cold side of the center of the jet stream, in troughs aloft, and in lows aloft where

   1) Vertical wind shear exceeds 10 kt. per 1,000 ft., and
   2) Horizontal wind shear exceeds 40 kt. per 150 NM.

4. **Extreme Turbulence**

    a. In mountain wave situations, in and below the level of well-developed rotor clouds. Sometimes it extends to the ground.

    b. In severe thunderstorms. A severe thunderstorm is indicated by

        1) Large hailstones (diameter 3/4 in. or greater),
        2) Strong radar echoes, or
        3) Almost continuous lightning.

4.5 ICING

1. Table 4-3 below classifies each intensity according to its operational effects on the aircraft.

Intensity	Airframe Ice Accumulation	Pilot Report
Trace	Ice becomes perceptible. Rate of accumulation slightly greater than rate of sublimation. Deicing/anti-icing equipment is not used unless encountered for an extended period of time (over one hour).	Location, time, altitude/FL, aircraft type, temperature, and icing intensity and type
Light	The rate of accumulation may create a problem if flight is prolonged in this environment (over one hour). Occasional use of deicing/anti-icing equipment removes/prevents accumulation. It does not present a problem if the deicing/anti-icing equipment is used.	Location, time, altitude/FL, aircraft type, temperature, and icing intensity and type
Moderate	The rate of accumulation is such that even short encounters become potentially hazardous and use of deicing/anti-icing equipment or diversion is necessary.	Location, time, altitude/FL, aircraft type, temperature, and icing intensity and type
Severe	The rate of accumulation is such that deicing/anti-icing equipment fails to reduce or control the hazard. Immediate diversion is necessary.	Location, time, altitude/FL, aircraft type, temperature, and icing intensity and type

Table 4-3. – Icing Intensities, Airframe Ice Accumulation, and Pilot Report.

2. **Types of Icing Reported**

    a. **Rime ice** is rough, milky, opaque ice formed by the instantaneous freezing of small supercooled water droplets.

    b. **Clear ice** is a glossy, clear, or translucent ice formed by the relatively slow freezing of large supercooled water drops.

    c. **Mixed ice** is a combination of rime and clear ice.

4.6 WIND SHEAR

1. Because unexpected changes in wind speed and direction can be hazardous to aircraft operations at low altitudes on approach to, and departing from, airports, pilots are urged to promptly volunteer reports of wind shear conditions they encounter to controllers.

2. An advanced warning of this information will assist other pilots in avoiding or coping with a wind shear on approach or departure.

3. When describing conditions, pilots should avoid the use of the terms "negative" or "positive" wind shear.

    a. PIREPs of "negative wind shear on final," intended to describe loss of airspeed and lift, have been interpreted to mean that no wind shear was encountered.

4. The pilot should report the loss or gain of airspeed and the altitudes at which it was encountered.

    a. Pilots who are not able to report wind shear in these specific terms are encouraged to make reports in terms of the effects on their aircraft.

4.7 EXAMPLES

1. KORD UUA/OV ORD/TM 1235/FLUNKN/TP B727/TB MOD/RM LLWS +/–20KT BLW 003 DURD RWY27L.

    a. Urgent PIREP (due to a report of wind shear) over Chicago O'Hare at 1235 UTC, flight level unknown. The pilot of a Boeing 727 reported moderate turbulence and low-level wind shear (LLWS) with airspeed fluctuations of plus to minus 20 kt. below 300 ft. during descent to Runway 27 left.

2. KOKC UA/OV KOKC090064/TM 1522/FL080/TP C172/SK SCT090-TOPUNKN/WX FV05SM HZ/TA M04/WV 24540KT/TB LGT/RM IN CLR.

    a. Routine PIREP, 64 NM east (090 radial) of the Oklahoma City VOR at 1522 UTC, flight level 8,000 ft. MSL. The pilot of a Cessna 172 reported a scattered cloud layer with bases at 9,000 ft. MSL and top height unknown. Flight visibility is 5 SM in haze, outside air temperature is –4°C, wind is 245 at 40 kt., light turbulence, and the airplane is in clear skies.

3. Nonmeteorological PIREPs sometimes help air traffic controllers. A plain language report stated the following:

...3N PNS LARGE FLOCK OF BIRDS HDG GEN N MAY BE SEAGULLS FRMN...

    a. This PIREP alerted pilots and controllers to a bird hazard.

END OF STUDY UNIT

STUDY UNIT FIVE
RADAR WEATHER REPORTS (SD/ROB)

(3 pages of outline)

> Please take a few minutes to study each of the concepts listed above and anticipate/imagine what they are and how they relate to the other listed concepts.

5.1 INTRODUCTION

1. General areas of precipitation, including rain, snow, and thunderstorms, can be observed by radar.

    a. Radar stations report each hour at H+35 (35 min. past the hour).

2. The radar weather report (SD/ROB) is a textual product that includes the type, intensity, and location of the echo top of the precipitation.

    a. The information can be up to 80 minutes old and should only be used if no other radar information is available.

    b. The intensity trend of the precipitation is not coded on the SD/ROB.

3. All heights are reported above mean sea level (MSL).

4. Table 5-1 below explains symbols denoting intensity.

Symbol	Intensity
–	Light
(none)	Moderate
+	Heavy
++	Very Heavy
X	Intense
XX	Extreme

Table 5-1. – Precipitation Intensity.

5. Table 5-2 below lists the symbols used to denote types of precipitation.

    a. Note that these symbols do not reflect the METAR code.

    b. The SD/ROB is automatically generated from WSR-88D weather radar data, and the type of precipitation is determined by computer models and is limited to the ones listed below.

Symbol	Meaning
R	Rain
RW	Rain Shower
S	Snow
SW	Snow Shower
T	Thunderstorm

Table 5-2. – Symbols Used in SD/ROB.

5.2 EXAMPLE OF AN SD/ROB

TLX 1935 LN 8TRW++ 86/40 164/60 20W C2425 MTS 570 AT 159/65

AUTO ^ MO1 NO2 ON3 PM34 QM3 RL2=

To aid in the discussion, we have divided the SD/ROB into the following elements numbered 1 through 10:

TLX 1935	LN	8	TRW++	86/40 164/60
1.	2.	3.	4.	5.

20W	C2425	MTS 570 AT 159/65	AUTO
6.	7.	8.	9.

^ MO1 NO2 ON3 PM34 QM3 RL2=
      10.

1. Location identifier and time of radar observation (Oklahoma City at 1935 UTC)

2. Echo pattern (LN, or line, in the example). The following echo pattern, or configuration, codes may be used.

    a. LN (line) -- a line of convective echoes with precipitation intensities that are heavy or greater, at least 30 NM long, at least four times as long as it is wide, and at least 25% coverage within the line

    b. AREA (area) -- a group of echoes of similar type and not classified as a line

    c. CELL (cell) -- a single isolated convective echo, such as a rain shower

3. Coverage, in tenths, of precipitation in the defined area. In this example, 8 means 8/10 coverage in the line.

4. Type and intensity of weather. In this example, the line of echoes contains thunderstorms (T) with very heavy rain showers (RW++).

    a. The table below defines the reportable intensities.

Symbol	Intensity	dBZ
–	Light	0-29
(no entry)	Moderate	30-40
+	Heavy	41-45
++	Heavy	46-49
X	Extreme	50-56
XX	Extreme	57 or more

Table 5-3. – SD/ROB Reportable Intensities.

5. Azimuth, referenced to true north, and range in NM from the radar site of points defining the echo pattern. In this example, the center points of the line are located at 86° at 40 NM and 164° at 60 NM.

    a. For lines and areas, two azimuth and range sets define the pattern.
    b. For cells, there will be only one azimuth and range set.

6. Dimension of echo pattern. The dimensions of an echo pattern are given when azimuth and range define only the center line of the pattern.

    a. In this example, 20W means the line has a total width of 20 NM – 10 NM on either side of a center line drawn from the points provided in item 5. above.

7. Cell movement. Movement is coded only for cells; it will not be coded for lines or areas.

   a. In this example, C2425 means the cells within the line are moving from 240° at 25 kt.

8. Maximum top and location. Maximum top may be coded with the symbols "MT" or "MTS."

   a. MTS means that satellite data as well as radar information were used to measure the top of the precipitation.

   b. In this example, MTS 570 AT 159/65 means the maximum precipitation top (measured by satellite and radar data) is 57,000 ft. located 159° at 65 NM from the radar site.

9. AUTO means the SD/ROB is automated from WSR-88D weather radar data.

10. Digital section. This information is used for preparing the radar summary chart.

5.3 BLANK REPORTS

1. When a radar weather report is transmitted but does not contain any encoded weather observation, a contraction is sent that indicates the operational status of the radar.

Contraction	Operational Status
PPINE	Radar is operating normally, but no echoes are being detected.
PPINA	Radar observation is not available.
PPIOM	Radar is inoperative or out of service.
AUTO	Automated radar report from WSR-88D.

Table 5-4. – Contractions of Radar Operational Status.

   a. EXAMPLE: TLX 1135 PPINE AUTO means that the Oklahoma City, OK radar at 1135 UTC detects no echoes.

5.4 USING SDs/ROBs

1. When using hourly and special SDs/ROBs in preflight planning, note the location and coverage of echoes, the type of weather reported, the intensity, and especially the direction of movement.

2. A WORD OF CAUTION: Remember that the WSR-88D (or any weather radar) detects particles in the atmosphere that are of precipitation size or larger.

   a. It does **not** display locations of cloud-size particles and, thus, neither ceilings nor restrictions to visibility.

3. An area may be blanketed with fog or low stratus, but the SD/ROB would not include information about it.

4. You should use SDs/ROBs along with METARs, satellite photos, and forecasts when planning a flight.

5. SDs/ROBs will help you to plan ahead to avoid thunderstorm areas. Once airborne, however, you must depend on contact with Flight Watch (which has the capability to view current radar images), airborne radar, or visual sighting to evade individual storms.

END OF STUDY UNIT

STUDY UNIT SIX
RADAR IMAGERY

(14 pages of outline)

Please take a few minutes to study each of the concepts listed above and anticipate/imagine what they are and how they relate to the other listed concepts.

6.1   DESCRIPTION OF WEATHER RADAR

1.   Weather radar is used to locate, track, and classify precipitation as well as forecast a target's future position and intensity.

   a.   WSR-88D Doppler radar displays these targets on a variety of products, which can be found on the National Weather Service (NWS) Doppler Radar Images website at http://radar.weather.gov/ridge/.

   b.   The map below depicts the WSR-88D radar stations operated by the NWS.

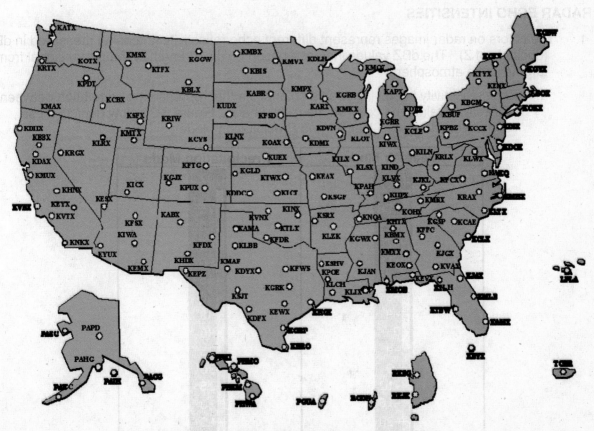

Figure 6-1. WSR 88-D Weather Radar Network Sites

6.2 MODES OF OPERATION

1. The WSR-88D Doppler radar has two operational modes: Clear Air and Precipitation.

    a. In **Clear Air Mode**, the radar is in its most sensitive operation.

        1) This mode has the slowest antenna rotation rate, which permits the radar to sample the atmosphere longer.

        2) This slower sampling increases the radar's sensitivity and ability to detect smaller objects in the atmosphere.

        3) The term "clear air" does not imply "no-precipitation" mode.

            a) Even in Clear Air Mode, the WSR-88D can detect light, stratiform precipitation (e.g., snow) due to the increased sensitivity.

            b) Many of the radar returns in Clear Air Mode are airborne dust and particulate matter.

        4) The WSR-88D images are updated every 10 minutes when operating in this mode.

    b. The WSR-88D is operated in **Precipitation Mode** whenever precipitation is present although some non-precipitation echoes can still be detected in this operating mode.

        1) Precipitation targets typically provide stronger return signals to the radar than non-precipitation targets.

        2) The faster rotation of the WSR-88D in Precipitation Mode allows images to update at a faster rate, approximately every 4 to 6 minutes.

6.3 RADAR ECHO INTENSITIES

1. The colors on radar images represent different echo reflectivity (intensity) measured in dBZ (decibels of Z). The dBZ values increase based on the strength of the return signal from targets in the atmosphere.

    a. Each reflectivity image includes a color scale that represents a correlation between reflectivity value and color on the radar image. Figure 6-2 below depicts these correlations for both Clear Air and Precipitation Mode.

Figure 6-2. WSR-88D Weather Radar Echo Intensity Legend

      1) For Clear Air Mode, the scale ranges from –28 to +28 dBZ.

      2) For Precipitation Mode, the scale ranges from 5 to 75 dBZ.

  b. The color on each scale remains the same in both operational modes; only the dBZ values change. The scales also include **ND** correlated to black, which indicates no data was measured.

2. Reflectivity is correlated to intensity of precipitation.

  a. EXAMPLE: In Precipitation Mode, when the dBZ value reaches 15, light precipitation is present.

  b. The higher the indicated reflectivity value, the higher the rainfall rate.

  c. The interpretation of reflectivity values is the same for both Clear Air and Precipitation Modes.

3. Reflectivity is also correlated with intensity terminology (phraseology) for air traffic control purposes. Table 6-1 below defines this correlation.

Reflectivity (dBZ) Ranges	Weather Radar Echo Intensity Terminology
<30 dBZ	Light
30-40 dBZ	Moderate
>40-50 dBZ	Heavy
50+ dBZ	Extreme

Table 6-1. WSR-88D Weather Radar Precipitation Intensity Terminology

  a. Values below 15 dBZ are typically associated with clouds. However, they may also be caused by atmospheric particulate matter, such as dust, insects, pollen, or other phenomena.

  b. The scale cannot be used to determine the intensity of snowfall. However, snowfall rates generally increase with increasing reflectivity.

6.4 WEATHER RADAR PRODUCTS

1. The NWS produces numerous radar products of interest to the aviation community. This subunit will discuss base reflectivity and composite reflectivity both available through the National Weather Service (NWS) Doppler Radar Images website at http://radar.weather.gov/ridge/.

2. **Base reflectivity** is a display of both the location and intensity of reflectivity data.

  a. Base reflectivity images encompass several different elevation angles (tilts) of the antenna.

      1) The base reflectivity image currently available on the ADDS website begins at the lowest tilt angle (0.5°), more specifically 0.5° above the horizon.

b.   Both a short-range (Figure 6-3) and long-range (Figure 6-4) image is available from the 0.5° base reflectivity product.

Figure 6-3. WSR-88D Weather Radar Short Range (124 NM) Base Reflectivity Product Example

Figure 6-4. WSR-88D Weather Radar Long Range (248 NM) Base Reflectivity Product Example

1)   The maximum range of the short-range base reflectivity product is 124 NM from the radar location.

a)   This view will not display echoes farther than 124 NM from the radar site, although precipitation may be occurring at such distances.

2)   The maximum range of the long-range view increases coverage out to 248 NM.

3)   If you need more radar information than that provided by the short- and long-range products, you should either select adjacent radar stations or view a radar mosaic.

c.   **Uses of Base Reflectivity**

1)   The base reflectivity product can be used to determine the

a)   Location of precipitation and non-precipitation echoes,

b)   Intensity of liquid precipitation, and

c)   General movement of precipitation when animating the image.

2)   If the echo is precipitation, the product can be used to determine if it is convective or stratiform in nature.

3)   Stratiform precipitation (Figure 6-5) has the following characteristics:

a)   Widespread in aerial coverage.

b)   Weak reflectivity gradients.

c)   Precipitation intensities are generally light or moderate (39 dBZ or less).

i)   Occasionally, precipitation intensities can be stronger

d)   Echo patterns change slowly when animating the image.

Figure 6-5. WSR-88D Weather Radar Stratiform Precipitation on the 0.5° Base Reflectivity Product Example

4)   Hazards associated with stratiform precipitation include

a)   Possible widespread icing above the freezing level,

b)   Low ceilings, and

c)   Reduced visibilities.

5)   Convective precipitation (Figure 6-6) can be described using the following characteristics:

a)   Echoes tend to form as lines or cells.

b)   Reflectivity gradients are strong.

c)   Precipitation intensities generally vary from moderate to extreme.

i)   Occasionally, precipitation intensities can be light.

d)   Echo patterns change rapidly when animating the image.

Figure 6-6. WSR-88D Weather Radar Convective Precipitation on the 0.5° Base Reflectivity Product Example

6)   Hazards associated with convective precipitation include

    a)   Turbulence,

    b)   Low-level wind shear (LLWS),

    c)   Strong and gusty surface winds,

    d)   Icing above the freezing level,

    e)   Hail,

    f)   Lightning,

    g)   Tornadoes, and

    h)   Localized IFR conditions with heavy precipitation.

d.   Strengths of Base Reflectivity

1)   Location of precipitation and non-precipitation echoes is depicted.

2)   Intensity and movement of precipitation is relatively easy and straightforward to determine.

e.   Limitations of Base Reflectivity

1)   The radar beam may overshoot targets.

    a)   Radar beam overshooting may occur because the radar beam (typically the 0.5° slice) can be higher than the top of precipitation. This will most likely occur with stratiform precipitation and low-topped convection.

        i)   EXAMPLE: At a distance of 124 NM from the radar, the 0.5° base reflectivity radar beam is at an altitude of approximately 18,000 feet; at 248 NM, the beam height is approximately 54,000 feet.

          •   Any precipitation with tops below these altitudes and distances will not be displayed on the image.

          •   Therefore, it is quite possible that precipitation may be occurring where none appears on the radar image.

2)   The image may be contaminated by one of the following:

    a)   Beam blockage

        i)   Beam blockage (Figure 6-7) occurs when the radar beam is blocked by terrain and is particularly predominant in mountainous terrain.

Figure 6-7. WSR-88D Weather Radar Beam Blockage on Base Reflectivity Product Example

ii) Beam blockage is most easily seen on the 0.5° base reflectivity images where it appears as a pie-shaped area(s) almost or entirely void of echoes.

iii) When animating the imagery, the beam blockage area will remain clear of echoes even as precipitation and other targets pass through.

b) Ground clutter

i) Ground clutter (Figure 6-8) consists of radar echo returns from trees, buildings, or other objects on the ground. It appears as a roughly circular region of high reflectivity at ranges close to the radar.

Figure 6-8. WSR-88D Weather Radar Ground Clutter Example

ii) Ground clutter appears stationary when animating images and can mask precipitation located near the radar.

iii) Most ground clutter is automatically removed from WSR-88D imagery, so typically it does not interfere with image interpretation.

c) Anomalous propagation (AP)

i) Anomalous propagation (Figure 6-9) is an extended pattern of ground echoes caused by super-refraction of the radar beam.

• Super-refraction causes the radar beam to bend downward and strike the ground. It differs from ground clutter because it can occur anywhere within the radar's range, not just at ranges close to the radar.

Figure 6-9. WSR-88D Weather Radar Anomalous Propagation (AP) Example

    ii)   AP typically appears as speckled or blotchy, high-reflectivity echoes. When animating images, AP tends to "bloom up" and dissipate and has no continuity of motion.

    iii)   AP can sometimes be misinterpreted as thunderstorms; differentiating between the two is determined by animating images.

       •   Thunderstorms move with a smooth, continuous motion while AP appears to "bloom up" and dissipate randomly.

  d)   Ghosts

    i)   A ghost (Figure 6-10) is a diffused echo in apparently clear air caused by a "cloud" of point targets, such as insects, or by refraction returns of the radar beam in truly clear air.

       •   The latter case commonly develops at sunset due to super-refraction during the warm season.

Figure 6-10. WSR-88D Weather Radar Ghost Example

ii) The ghost develops as an area of low reflectivity echoes (typically less than 15 dBZ) near the radar site and quickly expands.

iii) When animating the imagery, the ghost echo shows little movement.

e) Angels

i) Angels are echoes caused by a physical phenomenon not discernible by the eye at the radar site.

- They are usually caused by bats, birds, or insects.

ii) Angels typically appear as a donut-shaped echo with low reflectivity values (Figure 6-11).

Figure 6-11. WSR-88D Weather Radar Angel Example

iii) When animated, the echo expands and becomes more diffuse with time.

iv) Angels typically appear only when the radar is in Clear Air Mode because of their weak reflectivity.

- Echoes caused by birds are typically detected in the morning, when they take flight for the day.

- Echoes caused by bats are typically detected in the evening, when they are departing from caves.

3. **Composite reflectivity** is the maximum echo intensity (reflectivity) detected within a column of the atmosphere above a location.

a. The radar scans through all of the elevation slices to determine the highest dBZ value in the vertical column (Figure 6-12) then displays that value on the product.

b. When compared with base reflectivity, the composite reflectivity can reveal important storm structure features as well as intensity trends of storms.

Figure 6-12. Creation of a Composite Reflectivity Product

c.   The maximum range of the long-range composite reflectivity product (Figure 6-13) is 248 NM from the radar.

   1)   The "blocky" appearance of this product is due to its lower spatial resolution as it has one-fourth the resolution of the base reflectivity product.

Figure 6-13. WSR-88D Weather Radar Long Range (248 NM) Composite Reflectivity Product Example

2)   For a higher-resolution (1.1 × 1.1 NM grid) composite reflectivity image, users must select the short-range view (Figure 6-14). The image is less "blocky" as compared to the long-range image.

   a)   Maximum range is reduced to 124 NM from the radar location.

Figure 6-14. WSR-88D Weather Radar Short Range (124 NM) Composite Reflectivity Product Example

d.   **Uses of Composite Reflectivity**

1)   The primary use of the composite reflectivity product, which offers the highest reflectivity value in a vertical column, is to determine the vertical structure of the precipitation.

   a)   The image must be compared with the base reflectivity image to determine the vertical structure of the precipitation.

b)   Figure 6-15 includes the 0.5° base reflectivity and composite reflectivity images for the same location and period of time.

    i)   In Figure 6-15, within location A, the intensity of the echoes is higher on the composite reflectivity image. Within area B, many more echoes are present on the composite reflectivity image.

    ii)   Since the composite reflectivity product displays the highest reflectivity of all elevation scans, it is detecting these higher reflectivities at some higher altitude/elevation than the base reflectivity product, which is sampling closer to the ground.

    iii)   This often occurs when precipitation and especially thunderstorms are developing.

Figure 6-15. WSR-88D Weather Radar 0.5° Base Reflectivity Versus Composite Reflectivity Comparison

e.   **Strengths of Composite Reflectivity**

1)   The primary strength of the composite reflectivity product is its three-dimensional view of reflectivity.

    a)   The method used to determine this three-dimensional view is described in item 3.a. on page 263.

f.   **Limitations of Composite Reflectivity**

1)   The limitations for composite reflectivity and base reflectivity are the same.

2)   See item 2.e. on page 260 to review the radar limitations for base reflectivity.

6.5 RADAR MOSAICS

1. A radar mosaic consists of multiple single site radar images combined to produce a radar image on a regional or national scale. Regional and national mosaics can be found at the National Weather Service (NWS) Doppler Radar Images website: http://radar.weather.gov/ridge/.

    a. The mosaics are located toward the bottom of the page.

2. **0.5° Mosaics – Contiguous U.S. and Hawaii**

    a. The NWS produces a set of regional and national mosaics (Table 6-2) in the contiguous U.S. using the 124 NM 0.5° base reflectivity product (Figure 6-16).

Pacific Northwest	Pacific Southwest
Upper Mississippi Valley	Southern Mississippi Valley
Northeast	Southeast
Southern Rockies	Northern Rockies
Southern Plains	Great Lakes
Low Resolution National	High Resolution National

Table 6-2. NWS Radar Mosaic Products

Figure 6-16. Great Lakes Regional Radar Mosaic Example

b.   The most recent image from single site radars is used to create the product. Single site data older than 15 minutes from the current time of the product are excluded from the image. Therefore, data on the mosaics will be no greater than 15 minutes old.

1)   Where radar coverage overlaps, the highest dBZ value will be plotted on the image.

3.   **0.5° Mosaics – Alaska**

a.   The Alaskan mosaic (Figure 6-17) differs from the contiguous product in only one way: it is created using the 248 NM 0.5° base reflectivity single site product.

b.   The long-range base reflectivity product is used because the radar sites are located at greater distances from each other. Even with the use of the long-range product, many areas of Alaska do not have radar coverage. These areas are shaded gray on Figure 6-17.

Figure 6-17. Alaskan Regional Radar Mosaic Example

END OF STUDY UNIT

STUDY UNIT SEVEN
SATELLITE IMAGERY

(5 pages of outline)

Please take a few minutes to study each of the concepts listed above and anticipate/imagine what they are and how they relate to the other listed concepts.

7.1 TYPES OF SATELLITES

1. Two types of weather satellites are in use today by the U.S.

    a. Geostationary operational environmental satellites (GOES) are used for short-range warning and "now-casting."

    b. Polar-orbiting environmental satellites (POES) are used for longer-term forecasting.

2. Two GOES are used for imaging.

    a. One GOES is stationed over the equator at 75°W longitude and is referred to as GOES EAST since it covers the eastern U.S.

    b. The other GOES is stationed over the equator at 135°W longitude and is referred to as GOES WEST since it covers the western U.S.

    c. Together, these satellites cover North and South America and the surrounding waters.

    d. Each satellite transmits an image of the earth, pole to pole, every 15 min.

    e. When disastrous weather threatens the U.S., the satellites can scan small areas rapidly so that an image can be received as often as every 1 min.

        1) Data from these rapid scans are used at NWS offices.

3. Complementing the GOES are two POES.

    a. Each satellite is a polar orbiter and orbits the Earth on a track that nearly crosses the north and south poles.

    b. These satellites are able to monitor the entire Earth, tracking atmospheric variables and providing atmospheric data and cloud images. They track weather conditions that eventually affect the weather and climate of the U.S.

    c. Operating as a pair, these satellites ensure that data from any region of the Earth are no more than 6 hr. old.

7.2 TYPES OF SATELLITE IMAGERY

1. Three types of imagery are available, and when combined, they give a great deal of information about clouds.

2. Through interpretation, the analyst can determine the type of cloud, the temperature of cloud tops (from this the approximate height of the cloud can be determined), and the thickness of cloud layers.

    a. From this information, the analyst gets a good idea of the associated weather.

3.   One type of imagery is visible imagery. With a visible image, we are looking at clouds and the Earth reflecting sunlight to the satellite sensor.

    a.   The greater the reflected sunlight reaching the sensor, the whiter the object is on the image.

        1)   The amount of reflectivity reaching the sensor depends upon the height, thickness, and ability of the object to reflect sunlight.

           a)   The data legend on a visible image displays albedo, or reflectance, expressed as a percentage.

              i)   EXAMPLE: An albedo of 72 means that 72 percent of the sunlight that struck a feature was reflected back to space.

        2)   Since clouds are much more reflective than the Earth, clouds will usually show up white on the image, especially thick clouds.

        3)   Thus, the visible image is primarily used to determine the presence of clouds and the type of cloud from shape and texture.

    b.   Because visible images rely on reflected sunlight, these products are only available during daylight hours.

    c.   The image below is an example of a visible satellite image.

Figure 7-1. Visible Satellite Image – U.S. Example

4. The second type of satellite imagery is infrared (IR) imagery. Infrared images display temperatures of the Earth's surface, clouds, and particulate matter.

    a. Generally speaking, the warmer an object, the more infrared energy it emits. The satellite sensor measures this energy and calibrates it to temperature units using a very simple physical relationship.

    b. Clouds that are very high in the atmosphere are generally quite cold (perhaps −50°C) whereas clouds very near the Earth's surface are generally quite warm (perhaps +5°C).

        1) Likewise, land may be even warmer than the lower clouds (perhaps +20°C).

        2) Those colder clouds emit much less infrared energy than the warmer clouds, and the land emits more than those warm clouds.

        3) Because this product depends on temperature measurement, IR images are available both day and night.

    c. The data measured by satellite is calibrated and colorized according to the temperature.

        1) If the temperature of the atmosphere decreases with height (which is typical), cloud-top temperature can be used to roughly determine which clouds are high-level and which are low-level.

    d. When clouds are present, the temperature displayed on the infrared images is that of the tops of clouds.

        1) When clouds are not present, the temperature is that of the ground or the ocean.

    e. The data legend on an infrared image is calibrated to temperature expressed in degrees Celsius.

        1) The legend may vary based on the satellite image provider.

    f. The following figure is an example of an IR satellite image.

        1) Unenhanced versions are in black and white, but computers can be used to add coloration and further sharpen the contrast between different temperature zones.

Figure 7-2. Infrared (Color) Satellite Image – U.S. Example

5.   The third type of satellite imagery is water vapor imagery. A water vapor image displays the quantity of water vapor generally located in the middle and upper troposphere within the layer between 700 millibars (FL100) to 200 millibars (FL390).

    a.   The actual numbers displayed on the water vapor images correspond to temperature in degrees Celsius.

        1)   No direct relationship exists between these values and the temperatures of clouds, unlike IR imagery.

        2)   Because this product does not rely on a visible measurement, water vapor images are available both day and night.

    b.   Water vapor imagery does not really "see" clouds but "sees" high-level water vapor instead.

    c.   The most useful information to be gained from the water vapor images is the locations and movements of weather systems, jet streams, and thunderstorms.

    d.   Another useful tidbit is aided by the color scale used on the images.

        1)   In general, regions displayed in shades of red are VERY dry in the upper atmosphere and MAY correlate to crisp blue skies from a ground perspective.

        2)   On the contrary, regions displayed in shades of blue or green are indicative of lots of high-level moisture and may also indicate cloudiness.

           a)   This cloudiness could simply be high-level cirrus types or thunderstorms.

           b)   That determination cannot be gained from this image by itself but could easily be determined when used in conjunction with corresponding visible and infrared satellite images.

    e.   The data legend on a water vapor image is calibrated to temperature expressed in degrees Celsius.

        1)   The actual data values on the water vapor images are not particularly useful. Interpretation of the patterns and how they change over time is more important.

        2)   The legend may vary depending on the satellite image provider.

    f.   The following image is an example of a water vapor satellite image:

Figure 7-3. Water Vapor Satellite Image – U.S. Example

7.3 USING SATELLITE IMAGES

1. Satellite images are processed by the NWS as well as by private companies. Thus, satellite images can be viewed through the use of many different sources.

2. Depending on the source of the satellite images, they may be updated anywhere from every 15 min. to every hour.

    a. Thus, it is important to note the time on the images when interpreting them.

3. By viewing satellite images, the development and dissipation of weather can be seen and followed over the entire country and coastal regions.

END OF STUDY UNIT

STUDY UNIT EIGHT
SURFACE ANALYSIS CHARTS

(6 pages of outline)

Please take a few minutes to study each of the concepts listed above and anticipate/imagine what they are and how they relate to the other listed concepts.

8.1 PRODUCT DESCRIPTION

1. Surface analysis charts are analyzed charts of surface weather observations.

   a. The chart depicts the distribution of several items including

      1) Sea level pressure;

      2) The positions of highs, lows, ridges, and troughs;

      3) The location and character of fronts; and

      4) The various boundaries, such as drylines, outflow boundaries, sea-breeze fronts, and convergence lines.

   b. Other symbols are often added, depending upon the intended use of the chart.

   c. Pressure is referred to in mean sea level (MSL) on the surface analysis chart while all other elements are presented as they occur at the surface point of observation.

   d. A chart in this general form is commonly referred to as the "weather map."

   e. Surface analysis charts are commonly used to give pilots a "big picture" view of the weather over a large area.

      1) These charts can help pilots plan flights around inclement weather as well as to plan ahead for the weather on an upcoming flight days in advance.

2. Five National Weather Service (NWS) offices issue surface analysis charts.

   a. The Hydrometeorological Prediction Center (HPC) in Camp Springs, Maryland, is responsible for the land areas of North America.

      1) The North America charts are available at http://www.hpc.ncep.noaa.gov/html/sfc2.shtml.

      2) The United States chart is available at http://www.hpc.ncep.noaa.gov/html/avnsfc.shtml.

   b. The Ocean Prediction Center (OPC) in Camp Springs, Maryland, is responsible for the Atlantic and Pacific Oceans north of 30°N latitude.

      1) The charts are available at http://www.opc.ncep.noaa.gov/.

   c. The Tropical Prediction Center (TPC) in Miami, Florida, is responsible for the tropical regions of the western hemisphere south of 30°N latitude and east of 160°E longitude.

      1) The charts are available at http://www.nhc.noaa.gov/marine_forecasts.shtml.

   d. The Alaskan Aviation Weather Unit (AAWU) in Anchorage, Alaska, is responsible for the state of Alaska.

      1) The chart is available at http://aawu.arh.noaa.gov/surface.php.

e.   The Weather Forecast Office in Honolulu, Hawaii (WFO HNL), is responsible for the tropical Pacific Ocean south of 30°N latitude and west of 160°E longitude.

1)   The charts are available at http://www.prh.noaa.gov/hnl/pages/analyses.php.

3.   There are slight differences in the symbols and station plot models of the various surface analysis charts.

a.   This study unit will address the common elements of all charts.

4.   An HPC Surface Analysis Chart is reproduced below.

a.   The information contained in the remainder of the study unit will help you to understand this chart.

Figure 8-1. HPC Surface Analysis Chart Example

8.2 PRODUCT ISSUANCE AND VALID TIME

1.   Surface analysis charts are issued from the HPC every 3 hours and from every other NWS office every 6 hours beginning at midnight Universal Coordinated Time (UTC).

2.   Each chart's valid time corresponds to the time of the plotted observations. A date-time group in UTC tells the user when conditions portrayed on the chart occurred.

8.3 PLOTTED DATA

1. Analysis symbols are used to graphically illustrate various weather observations.

    a. A table of common symbols appears below.

Figure 8-2. HPC Surface Analysis Chart Symbols

2. The observations from a number of stations are plotted on the chart to aid in analyzing and interpreting the surface weather features.

    a. These plotted observations are referred to as **station models**.

3. Various types of station models are plotted on the chart.

    a. A round station symbol represents a location where the observations are taken by observers.

    b. A square station symbol represents a location where the sky cover was determined by an automated system.

    c. Other plotted station models that appear over water on the chart are data from ships, buoys, and offshore oil platforms.

4. Figure 8-3 below is an example of a station model that shows the standard layout of information on the chart.

Figure 8-3. HPC Surface Analysis Chart Station Plot Model

a. The figures itemized below will help explain the decoding of the station model.

1) Figure 8-4 on page 279 – Sky cover value
2) Figure 8-5 on page 280 – Pressure tendency
3) Figure 8-6 on page 280 – Weather symbols

8.4   ANALYSIS OF THE CHART

1. Isobars, pressure systems, and fronts are the most common analyses depicted on surface analysis charts.

2. **Isobars** are solid lines depicting the sea-level pressure pattern and are usually spaced at 4-mb (millibar) or 4-hPa (hectoPascal) intervals. HectoPascal (hPa) is a metric unit of pressure (1 mb = 1 hPa).

a. When the pressure gradient is weak, dashed isobars are sometimes inserted at 2-mb/hPa intervals to define the pressure pattern more clearly.

b. Each isobar is labeled.

1) EXAMPLES: 1032 signifies 1032.0 mb/hPa, 1000 signifies 1000.0 mb/hPa, and 992 signifies 992.0 mb/hP.

3. **Pressure systems** are denoted with the letter "L" for a low-pressure center and the letter "H" for a high-pressure center.

a. The pressure at each center is indicated by a three- or four-digit number, which is the central pressure in millibars or hectoPascals.

b. A trough, or an elongated area of low atmospheric pressure, will be depicted as a thick, dashed line running through the center of the trough and identified with the word "TROF."

c. The symbol for a ridge, or an elongated area of low atmospheric pressure, is very rarely, if at all, depicted. When shown, it is depicted with saw-toothed symbols.

d. Tropical storms, hurricanes, and typhoons are low-pressure systems with their names and central pressures denoted.

4. Fronts are displayed on the chart to denote the type of front and the direction in which the front is moving.

    a. The "pips" on the front indicate the type of front and point in the direction toward which the front is moving.

        1) Pips on both sides of a front indicate a stationary front (little or no movement).

    b. Briefing offices sometimes color the symbols to facilitate use of the map.

    c. Two short lines across a front indicate a change in classification.

    d. If the front has arrowhead-shaped symbols, it is a cold front.

    e. If the front has half-moon symbols, it is a warm front.

8.5 USING THE CHART

1. The surface analysis chart provides a ready means of locating pressure systems and fronts.

    a. It also gives an overview of winds, temperatures, and dew point temperatures at chart time.

2. When using the chart, keep in mind that weather moves and conditions change.

    a. The surface analysis chart must be used in conjunction with other information to give a more complete weather picture.

Figure 8-4. HPC Surface Analysis Chart Sky Cover Symbols

Figure 8-5. HPC Surface Analysis Chart Pressure Trends

Figure 8-6. HPC Surface Analysis Chart Common Weather Symbols

END OF STUDY UNIT

STUDY UNIT NINE
CONSTANT PRESSURE CHARTS

(10 pages of outline)

Please take a few minutes to study each of the concepts listed above and anticipate/imagine what they are and how they relate to the other listed concepts.

9.1 PRODUCT DESCRIPTION

1. A constant pressure chart, also known as an isobaric chart, is a graphical weather map representing conditions on a surface of equal atmospheric pressure.

    a. For example, a 500 millibar (mb) chart will display conditions at the level of the atmosphere at which the atmospheric pressure is 500 mb.

    1) The height above sea level at which the pressure is that particular value may vary from one location to another at any given time and also varies with time at any one location. Therefore, it does not represent a surface of constant altitude/height

    2) The 500 mb level may be at a different height above sea level over Dallas than over New York at a given time and may also be at a different height over Dallas from one day to the next.

    3) Under standard conditions, the 500 mb chart should correspond with FL180.

    a) Because the atmosphere is rarely at standard conditions, this correlation should be considered loosely.

2. Weather information for computer-generated constant pressure charts is observed primarily by balloon-ascending radiosonde packages.

    a. Each package consists of weather instruments and a radio transmitter.

    b. During ascent, instrument data are continuously transmitted to the observation station. The data are used to prepare constant pressure charts twice a day.

    c. Radiosondes are released at selected observation sites across the U.S. at 0000Z and 1200Z.

3. Additional supporting data may be taken from

    a. Weather reconnaissance aircraft observations,

    b. Aircraft observations on-time and on-level,

    c. Aircraft observations off-time or off-level, and/or

    d. Satellite wind estimates.

4. Other data observed for the construction of this product but not plotted comes from

    a. Ships,

    b. Buoys,

    c. Tide gauges,

    d. Wind profilers,

    e. WSR-88D weather radar VAD wind profiles, and/or

    f. Satellite sounder.

9.2 TYPE AND TIME OF REPORT

1. Any surface of equal pressure in the atmosphere is a constant pressure surface. A constant pressure analysis chart is an upper-air weather map on which all the information depicted is at the specified pressure of the chart.

2. Constant pressure charts are prepared for the following selected pressure levels: 850 mb/hPa, 700 mb/hPa, 500 mb/hPa, 300 mb/hPa, and 200 mb/hPa.

    a. Charts with higher pressure present information at lower altitudes, and charts with lower pressure present information at higher altitudes.

    b. These charts are valid at the time of observations (0000Z and 1200Z).

    c. Access all of the charts on the NWS Fax Chart website at http://weather.noaa.gov/fax/barotrop.shtml.

3. Pressure altitude (height in the standard atmosphere) for each of the five pressure surfaces is shown in Table 9-1 below.

    a. For example, 700 mb/hPa of pressure has a pressure altitude of 10,000 ft. in the standard atmosphere.

        1) In the real atmosphere, 700 mb/hPa of pressure only approximates 10,000 ft. because the real atmosphere is seldom standard.

    b. For direct use of a constant pressure chart, assume a flight is planned at 10,000 ft. MSL.

        1) The 700-mb/hPa chart is approximately 10,000 ft. MSL and is the best source for observed temperature, temperature-dew point spread, moisture, and wind for that flight level.

4. Figures 9-1 through 9-5 on pages 288 through 290 are the five standard charts that make up the constant pressure analysis charts.

Constant Pressure Chart	Pressure Altitude (MSL)		Isotachs	Contour Interval (meters)	Height Plot Decoding		Examples of Height Plotting	
					Prefix	Suffix	Plotted	Height (meters, MSL)
850MB	5,000 ft	1,500 m	No	30 m	1	-	530	1,530 m
700MB	10,000 ft	3,000 m	No	30 m	2 or 3*	-	180	3,180 m
500MB	18,000 ft	5,500 m	No	60 m	-	0	582	5,820 m
300MB	30,000 ft	9,000 m	Yes	120 m	-	0	948	9,480 m
200MB	39,000 ft	12,000 m	Yes	120 m	1	0	164	11,640 m

Note: Pressure altitudes are rounded to the nearest 1,000 for feet and 500 for meters.
* Prefix a "2" or "3," whichever brings the height closer to 3,000 meters.

Table 9-1. Features of Constant Pressure Charts

9.3 PLOTTED DATA

1. Table 9-2 on the next page illustrates and decodes the different data plots found on a constant pressure chart. Tables 9-3 through 9-6 beginning on page 284 give a station data plot example for each chart level and observation method.

2. Data from each observation station are plotted around a station circle on each constant pressure chart. The station circle identifies the station location, and the following data are plotted on each chart:

    a.   Temperature (°C)
    b.   Temperature-dew point spread (°C)
    c.   Wind (direction referenced to true north, wind speed in kt.)
    d.   Height of the pressure surface above sea level in meters (m)
    e.   Height change of the pressure surface over the previous 12-hr. period (meters)

3.   The station circle is blackened when the temperature-dew point spread is 5° or less (moist atmosphere).

    a.   The station circle is clear when the temperature-dew point spread is more than 5° (dry atmosphere).

4.   Aircraft and satellite observations are also used as information sources for constant pressure charts. These observations are particularly useful over sparse radiosonde data areas. Data from aircraft and satellites are plotted on the constant pressure charts closest to their reporting altitudes.

    a.   A square is used to identify an aircraft reporting position. Data plotted include

        1)   The flight level of the aircraft in hundreds of feet MSL
        2)   Temperature
        3)   Wind
        4)   Time (to the nearest hour UTC)

    b.   A star is used to identify a satellite reporting position. Satellite information is determined by identifying cloud drift and height of cloud tops. Data plotted include

        1)   Flight level in hundreds of feet MSL
        2)   Wind
        3)   Time (to the nearest hour UTC)

Radiosonde	Reconnaissance Aircraft (RECCO)	Aircraft Report (AIREP)	Satellite Wind Estimate
TT ● hhh DD $h_c h_c$	TT □ hhh DD R	TT □ $P_a P_a P_a$	★ $P_a P_a P_a$

SYMBOL	MEANING
(wind flag symbol)	Wind plotted in standard notation. The stem points in the direction from which the wind is blowing plotted to 36 compass points, relative to true north. Wind speed is denoted by a combination of flags (50 knots), barbs (10 knots), and half barbs (5 knots).
TT	Temperature rounded to the nearest whole degree Celsius, with minus sign prefixed if negative.
hhh	Height of the constant pressure surface in meters MSL. See the Table 5-8 to see how each chart abbreviates height.
$P_a P_a P_a$	Pressure altitude in hundreds of feet MSL.
DD	Temperature-dew point spread (depression of the dew point temperature) rounded to the nearest whole degree Celsius. When DD is less than or equal to 5 degrees Celsius, the station circle is darkened so a region of high moisture content will stand out. If DD is greater than 5 degrees Celsius, the station circle is not shaded. If the DD is too large to measure, an **X** is plotted. For RECCO reports, DD will be missing when the temperature is colder than -41°C.
R	Reconnaissance aircraft type.

Table 9-2. Constant Pressure Chart Plotting Models

TT ⟋hhh DD hₒhₒ	20 504 5 -01	08 156 6 -02	-11 582 X +01	-36 956 21 -05	-56 214 7 -02
Plotting Model	**850MB**	**700MB**	**500MB**	**300MB**	**200MB**
⟋ **Wind***	190°/20 kt	190°/25 kt	270°/15 kt	240°/70 kt	250°/115 kt
TT **Temperature**	20°C	8°C	-11°C	-36°C	-56°C
hhh **Height**	1,504 m	3,156 m	5,820 m	9,560 m	12,140 m
DD **Temperature -Dew Point Spread**	5°C	6°C	Too dry to measure	21°C	7°C
hₒhₒ **Height Change**	-10 m	-20 m	+10 m	-50 m	-20 m

* Wind direction assumes that north is at the top of the page. Latitude and longitude lines, as well as other geographical references, must be used to determine actual compass direction.

Table 9-3. Examples of Radiosonde Plotted Data

TT ⟋hhh DD R	19 366 1 AA329A	09 146 1 AA921A	-05 580 2 AA923A	-28 966 3 AA924A	-53 242 AA916A
Plotting Model	**850MB**	**700MB**	**500MB**	**300MB**	**200MB**
⟋ **Wind***	150°/90 kt	130°/35 kt	180° /60 kt	240°/30 kt	110°/30 kt
TT **Temperature**	19°C	9°C	-5°C	-28°C	-53°C
hhh **Height**	1,366 m	3,146 m	5,800 m	9,660 m	12,420 m
DD **Temperature -Dew Point Spread**	1°C	1°C	2°C	3°C	Missing
R **RECCO Type**	AA329A	AA921A	AA923A	AA924A	AA916A

* Wind direction assumes that north is at the top of the page. Latitude and longitude lines, as well as other geographical references, must be used to determine actual compass direction.

Table 9-4. Reconnaissance Aircraft (RECCO) Plotting Model Examples

TT PₐPₐPₐ	-05 060	12 100 LV	-10 180	-38 330	-54 360
Plotting Model	**850MB**	**700MB**	**500MB**	**300MB**	**200MB**
⟋ **Wind***	20 °/10 kt	Light and Variable	300 °/30 kt	190 °/5 kt	290°/50 kt
TT **Temperature**	-5°C	12°C	-10°C	-38°C	-54°C
PₐPₐPₐ **Pressure Altitude (MSL)**	6,000 ft	10,000 ft	18,000 ft	33,000 ft	36,000 ft

* Wind direction assumes that north is at the top of the page. Latitude and longitude lines, as well as other geographical references, must be used to determine actual compass direction.

Table 9-5. Aircraft Report (AIREP) Plotting Model Examples

Plotting Model	850MB	700MB	500MB	300MB	200MB
Wind*	290°/30 kt	360°/20 kt	240°/10 kt	140°/165 kt	310°/60 kt
$P_aP_aP_a$ Pressure Altitude (MSL)	7,000 ft	11,000 ft	17,000 ft	33,000 ft	36,000 ft

* Wind direction assumes that north is at the top of the page. Latitude and longitude lines, as well as other geographical references, must be used to determine actual compass direction.

Table 9-6. Satellite Wind Estimate Plotting Model Examples

9.4 ANALYSIS

1. All constant pressure charts contain analyses of height and temperature variations. Also, selected charts have analyses of wind speed variations.

   a. Contours are lines of equal heights, isotherms are lines of equal temperature, and isotachs are lines of equal wind speed.

2. **Contours**

   a. Contours are lines of constant height, in meters, above MSL.

      1) Contours are used to map the height variations of the pressure surface, which fluctuates in altitude, and to identify and characterize pressure systems on the constant pressure charts.

   b. Contours are drawn as solid lines and are identified by a three-digit code located on each contour.

      1) See Table 9-1 on page 282 for information on how to decode the height plot.

   c. The **contour interval** is the height difference between each contour. A standard contour interval is used for each chart.

      1) The contour intervals are 30 meters (m) for the 850 and 700 mb/hPa charts; 60 m for the 500 mb/hPa chart; and 120 m for the 300, 250, and 200 mb/hPa charts.

      2) The location of a High or Low is marked with a ⊗ symbol together with a larger **H** or **L**, and the central value in decameters printed under the center location.

   d. The **contour gradient** is the distance between the contours. Contour gradients identify slopes of the pressure surfaces.

      1) Strong gradients are closely spaced contours and identify steep slopes.
      2) Weak gradients are widely spaced contours and identify shallow slopes.
      3) Wind speeds are directly proportional to contour gradients.

         a) Faster wind speeds are associated with strong contour gradients and slower wind speeds are associated with weak contour gradients.

         b) In mountainous areas, winds are often variable on constant pressure charts with altitudes near terrain elevation due to friction.

   e. The contours display height patterns, with the common types being lows, highs, troughs, and ridges. These contour patterns on constant pressure charts can be interpreted the same way as isobar patterns on the surface chart. For example, an area of low height is the same as an area of low pressure.

f.   The contour patterns on the constant pressure charts can be further characterized by size and intensity.

1)   Sizes can range from large (more than 1,000 mi. across) to small (less than 1,000 mi. across).

2)   Intensities can range from strong (closely spaced contours) to weak (widely spaced contours).

g.   Since constant pressure charts are depicted levels above the surface friction layer, the winds are considered to flow parallel to the contours.

1)   In the Northern Hemisphere, winds flow counterclockwise around lows and clockwise around highs.

2)   Contours have the effect of "channeling" the wind.

3.   **Isotherms**

a.   Isotherms are lines of equal temperature and are used to map temperature variations over a pressure surface.

b.   Isotherms are drawn as bold, dashed lines on the constant pressure charts.

1)   Isotherm values are identified by a two-digit block on each line.

a)   The two digits are prefaced by "+" for above-freezing values as well as the zero isotherm and "−" for below-freezing values.

2)   Isotherms are drawn at 5° intervals on each chart.

c.   Isotherm gradients identify the magnitude of temperature variations.

1)   Strong gradients are closely spaced isotherms and identify large temperature variations.

2)   Weak gradients are widely spaced isotherms and identify small temperature variations.

d.   By inspecting the isotherm pattern, one can determine if a flight would be toward colder or warmer air.

1)   Subfreezing temperatures and a temperature-dew point spread of 5°C or less would indicate the possibility of icing.

4.   **Isotachs**

a.   Isotachs are lines of constant wind speed and are used to map wind speed variations over a pressure surface.

1)   Isotachs are drawn on only the 300, 250, and 200 mb/hPa charts.

b.   Isotachs are drawn as short, fine dashed lines.

1)   Isotach values are identified by a two- or three-digit number followed by a "K" located on each line.

a)   EXAMPLES:

i)   "10K" means a wind speed of 10 kt.
ii)   "130K" means a wind speed of 130 kt.

2)   Isotachs are drawn at 20-kt. intervals beginning at 10 kt.

c.   Isotach gradients identify the magnitude of wind speed variations.

1)   Strong gradients are closely spaced isotachs and identify large wind speed variations.

2)   Weak gradients are widely spaced isotachs and identify small wind speed variations.

    d.   Hatched and unhatched areas are alternated at 40-kt. intervals beginning at 70 kt. Areas between the 70-kt. and 110-kt. isotachs are hatched, and areas between the 110-kt. and 150-kt. isotachs are unhatched.

        1)   This alternating pattern is continued until the strongest winds on the chart are highlighted.

        2)   Highlighted isotachs assist in the identification of jet streams.

9.5 THREE-DIMENSIONAL ASPECTS

1.   It is important to assess weather in both the horizontal and the vertical dimensions. This advice applies not only to clouds, precipitation, and other significant conditions but also to pressure systems and winds.

    a.   The characteristics of pressure systems vary horizontally and vertically in the atmosphere.

2.   The horizontal distribution of pressure systems is depicted by the constant pressure charts and the surface analysis chart. Pressure systems appear on each pressure chart as pressure patterns.

    a.   Pressure charts identify and characterize pressure systems by their location, type, size, and intensity.

    b.   For example, "a large, strong surface low over Illinois" could describe a pressure system as it is identified and characterized on a pressure chart.

3.   The vertical distribution of pressure systems must be determined by comparing pressure patterns on vertically adjacent pressure charts.

    a.   For example, compare the surface analysis chart with the 850-mb/hPa chart, the 850-mb/hPa chart with the 700-mb/hPa chart, and so forth.

    b.   Changes of pressure patterns with height can be in the form of position, type, size, or intensity.

        1)   For example, a surface low over Illinois may change type and position with height and be a trough over Nebraska at the 500-mb/hPa level.

4.   The three-dimensional assessment of pressure systems implies the assessment of the three-dimensional variations of wind.

9.6 USING THE CHARTS

1.   Constant pressure charts are used to provide an overview of selected observed en route flying conditions. Use all pressure charts for a general overview of conditions.

2.   Select the chart closest to the desired flight altitude for assessment of en route conditions.

    a.   Review the winds along the route considering their direction and speed.

        1)   For high altitude flights, identify jet stream positions.

        2)   Note whether pressure patterns cause significant wind shifts or speed changes.

        3)   Determine if these winds will be favorable or unfavorable (tailwind, headwind, crosswind).

        4)   Consider vertically adjacent charts and determine if a higher or lower altitude would have a more desirable en route wind.

        5)   Interpolate winds between charts for flights between chart levels.

    b.   Review other conditions along the route.

        1)   Evaluate temperatures by identifying isotherm values and patterns.

        2)   Evaluate areas with moist air and cloud potential by identifying station circles shaded black.

3.   Consider the potential for hazardous flight conditions.

   a.   Evaluate the potential for icing. Freezing temperatures and visible moisture produce icing.

   b.   Evaluate the potential for turbulence. In addition to convective conditions and strong surface winds, turbulence is also associated with wind shear and mountain waves.

   c.   Wind shear occurs with strong curved flow and speed shear. Strong lows and troughs and strong isotach gradients are indicators of strong shear.

      1)   Vertical wind shear can be identified by comparing winds on vertically adjacent charts.

   d.   Mountain waves are caused by strong perpendicular flow across mountain crests. Use winds on the pressure charts near mountain crest level to evaluate mountain wave potential.

4.   Pressure patterns cause and characterize much of the weather.

   a.   As a general rule, lows and troughs are associated with clouds and precipitation, while highs and ridges are associated with good weather.

      1)   However, this rule is more complicated when pressure patterns change with height.

   b.   Compare pressure pattern features on the various pressure charts with other weather charts, such as the weather depiction and radar summary charts.

      1)   Note the association of pressure patterns on each chart with the weather.

5.   Pressure systems, winds, temperatures, and moisture change with time. For example, pressure systems move, change size, and change intensity. Forecast products predict these changes.

   a.   Compare observed conditions with forecast conditions and be aware of any changes.

Figure 9-1. 850MB Analysis Chart Example

Figure 9-2. 700MB Analysis Chart Example

Figure 9-3. 500MB Analysis Chart Example

Figure 9-4. 300MB Analysis Chart Example

Figure 9-5. 200MB Analysis Chart Example

END OF STUDY UNIT

STUDY UNIT TEN
FREEZING-LEVEL GRAPHICS

(4 pages of outline)

Please take a few minutes to study each of the concepts listed above and anticipate/imagine what they are and how they relate to the other listed concepts.

10.1 PRODUCT DESCRIPTION

1. The **freezing level** is the lowest altitude in the atmosphere over a given location at which the air temperature reaches 0°C.

   a. This altitude is also known as the height of the 0°C constant-temperature surface.

   b. A freezing level chart shows the height of the 0°C constant-temperature surface.

2. The concept of freezing level becomes slightly more complicated when more than one altitude is determined to be at a temperature of 0°C.

   a. These "multiple freezing layers" occur when a temperature inversion at altitudes above the defined freezing level are present.

   b. For example, if the first freezing level is at 3000 ft. MSL and the second is at 7000 ft. MSL, a temperature inversion exists between these two altitudes.

      1) This would indicate temperatures rising above freezing above 3000 ft. MSL and then back below freezing at 7000 ft. MSL.

3. **Source**

   a. The Aviation Weather Center (AWC) provides freezing level graphics on the Aviation Digital Data Service (ADDS) website at http://adds.aviationweather.noaa.gov/icing/frzg_nav.php.

      1) The graphics are produced in color.

         a) See Figure 10-1 on the next page for an example of a freezing level graphic.

Lowest freezing level (100s of feet MSL)

Analysis valid 1900 UTC Tue 19 Oct 2004

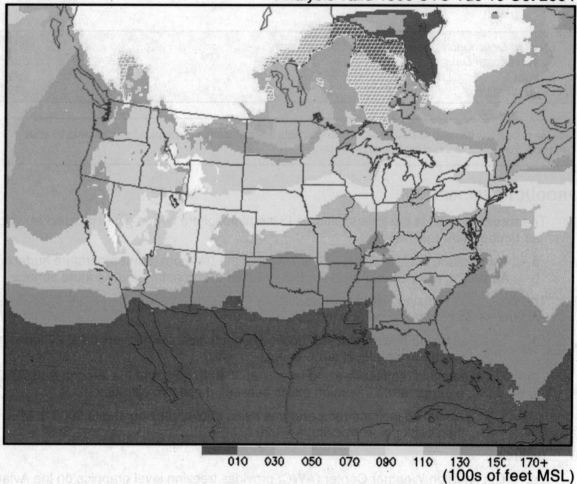

| 010 | 030 | 050 | 070 | 090 | 110 | 130 | 150 | 170+ |

(100s of feet MSL)

Figure 10-1. RUC 00-hour Freezing Level Graphic Example

4. **Issuance**

a.   The ADDS Freezing Level graphics provide an initial analysis and forecasts at 3-, 6-, 9-, and 12-hours into the future.

1)   The forecasts are based on output from the National Weather Service's (NWS) Rapid Update Cycle (RUC) numerical forecast model.

b.   The initial analysis and 3-hour forecast graphics are updated hourly. The 6-, 9-, and 12-hour forecast graphics are updated every three hours.

10.2 OBSERVATIONAL DATA

1.   The RUC forecast model incorporates all of the latest weather observations in order to produce the best available analysis and forecast. These observations include

a.   Commercial aircraft

b.   Profilers – A **profiler** is an instrument designed to measure horizontal winds directly above its location, and thus measures the vertical wind profile. Profilers operate on the same principles as Doppler radar.

      1)   Wind profilers (404 and boundary layer 915 MHz)
      2)   VAD (Velocity Azimuth Display) winds from WSR-88D radars
      3)   RASS (Radio Acoustic Sounding System)
      4)   Rawinsondes and special dropwinsondes

  c.   Surface

      1)   GPS total precipitable water estimates
      2)   GOES cloud-top data (pressure and temperature)
      3)   GOES total precipitable water estimates
      4)   SSM/I total precipitable water estimates
      5)   GOES high-density visible and infrared (IR) cloud drift winds

  d.   Experimental

      1)   Radar reflectivity (3-D)
      2)   Lightning
      3)   Regional aircraft data with moisture (TAMDAR)

10.3 FORMAT

1.   Freezing-level graphics are produced in color and are color-coded to various altitudes in increments of 2,000 feet.

2.   The colors represent the height in hundreds of feet above mean sea level (MSL) of the lowest freezing level.

  a.   Regions with white indicate the surface and the entire depth of the atmosphere are below freezing.

  b.   Hatched regions represent areas where the surface temperature is below freezing with multiple freezing levels aloft.

  c.   Areas where the surface temperature is above freezing with multiple freezing levels aloft are in regions where adjacent pixels change by more than one color when compared against the color scale (e.g., orange to dark blue).

10.4 USING THE CHART

1.   Freezing level graphics are used to assess the lowest freezing level heights and their values relative to flight paths.

  a.   Clear, rime, and mixed icing are found in layers with below-freezing (negative) temperatures and super-cooled water droplets.

2.   Users should be aware that official forecast freezing level information is specified within the AIRMET Zulu Bulletins (Contiguous U.S. and Hawaii) and the AIRMET "ICE AND FZLVL" information embedded within the Area Forecasts (Alaska only).

  a.   The low-level significant weather prognostic chart shows anticipated changes in the freezing level as well.

  b.   Remember, freezing levels tend to be lower behind cold fronts and rise ahead of warm fronts.

3.   The following examples illustrate the interpretation and use of the graphic. Use Figure 10-2 on the next page to see what happens to the temperature in each example.

Figure 10-2. RUC 00-hour Freezing Level Graphic Example

a. CASE 1 represents the condition where temperature is below freezing at the surface and all levels above the surface (represented in the graphic above by white-colored pixels).

b. CASE 2 represents the condition where the temperature goes above and below freezing two or more times vertically through the atmosphere while the surface temperature is less than 0°C. These regions are hatched with white. The underlying color represents the lowest height where the temperature crosses the 0°C line as shown by the blue arrow on the vertical temperature graphic.

c. CASE 3 represents the condition where the temperature goes above and below freezing three or more times vertically through the atmosphere while the surface temperature is higher than 0°C. These regions are located in areas where adjacent pixels change by more than one color when compared against the color scale.

d. CASE 4 is relatively simple and represents the condition where the temperature at the surface is above freezing and the air generally cools with height crossing the 0°C line once.

END OF STUDY UNIT

STUDY UNIT ELEVEN
LIFTED INDEX ANALYSIS CHARTS

(4 pages of outline)

> Please take a few minutes to study each of the concepts listed above and anticipate/imagine what they are and how they relate to the other listed concepts.

11.1 PRODUCT DESCRIPTION

1. The Lifted Index Analysis Chart (Figure 11-1 below) provides a data plot of observed lifted index (LI) and K index values for radiosonde (balloon observation) sites and an analysis of the LI for the contiguous U.S., southern Canada, and northern Mexico.

Figure 11-1. Lifted Index Analysis Chart Example

2. Each data plot consists of two values separated by a horizontal line. The top number is the lifted index, and the lower number is the K index.

   a. An **"M"** in either position indicates the data is missing.

3.   This product is issued at 00Z and 12Z.

    a.   All data is taken from weather balloon observations.

    b.   The most current chart is available at the NWS Fax Chart website at http://weather.noaa.gov/pub/fax/QXUA00.TIF.

11.2   READING THE LIFTED INDEX

1.   The **lifted index (LI)** is a common measure of atmospheric stability. LI is obtained by lifting a parcel of air near the surface to 500 mb/hPa (approximately 18,000 ft. MSL). As the air is lifted, it cools due to expansion. This cooling rate is either 3°C/1,000 ft., if the air is unsaturated, or 2°C/1,000 ft., if the air is saturated. The temperature the parcel of air would have at 500 mb/hPa is then subtracted from the actual (environmental) 500 mb/hPa temperature. This difference is the lifted index, which can be positive, negative, or zero and indicates the stability of the parcel of air.

    a.   A **positive LI** means that a parcel of air, if lifted, would be colder than the surrounding air at 500 mb/hPa.

        1)   The air is stable and would resist vertical motion.
        2)   The more positive the LI, the more stable the air.
        3)   Large positive values (+8 or greater) would indicate very stable air.

    b.   A **negative LI** means that a parcel of air, if lifted to 500 mb/hPa, would be warmer than the surrounding air.

        1)   The air is unstable and suggests the potential for thunderstorms.
        2)   The more negative the LI, the more unstable the air, and the stronger the updrafts are likely to be with any developing thunderstorms.
        3)   Large negative values (–6 or less) would indicate very unstable air.

    c.   A **zero LI** means that a parcel of air, if lifted to 500 mb/hPa, would have the same temperature as the actual air at 500 mb/hPa.

        1)   The air is said to be neutrally stable (neither stable nor unstable).

    d.   Lifted index values are decreased (made less stable) by increasing surface dew point (moisture), increasing surface temperature, and decreasing the 500 mb/hPa temperature.

        1)   Lifted index values are increased (made more stable) by decreasing surface dew point, decreasing surface temperature, and increasing the 500 mb/hPa temperature.
        2)   Note that the LI can change considerably just by daytime heating (decreasing the LI) and nighttime cooling (increasing the LI).

    e.   When using this chart, remember that the lifted index assumes the air near the surface will be lifted to 500 mb/hPa. Whether the air near the surface will be lifted to 500 mb/hPa depends on what is happening below.

        1)   It is possible to have a negative LI with no thunderstorm development because either the air below 500 mb/hPa is not being lifted high enough or the air does not contain enough moisture.
        2)   Also, it is possible to have a positive LI and still have thunderstorm development. This can happen if a layer of air above the surface is unstable and gets sufficiently lifted.

f. For use, the lifted index is indicative of the severity of the thunderstorms, if they occur, rather than the probability of general thunderstorm occurrence (see Table 11-1 below).

Lifted Index (LI)	Severe Potential
0 to –2	Weak
–3 to –5	Moderate
≤ –6	Strong

Table 11-1. Thunderstorm Severity Potential

1) It is essential to note that a negative (unstable) LI value does not necessarily mean thunderstorms will occur.

11.3 READING THE K INDEX

1. The **K index** is primarily for the meteorologist. It examines the temperature and moisture profile of the environment. The K index is not really a stability index because the parcel of air is not lifted and compared to the environment. The K index is computed using three terms:

$$K = (850 \text{ mb/hPa temp} - 500 \text{ mb/hPa temp}) + (850 \text{ mb/hPa dew point}) -$$
$$(700 \text{ mb/hPa temp/dew point spread}).$$

a. The first term (850 mb/hPa temp – 500 mb/hPa temp) compares the temperature at 850 mb/hPa (approximately 5,000 ft. MSL) to the temperature at 500 mb/hPa (approximately 18,000 ft. MSL)

1) The larger the temperature difference, the more unstable the air and the higher the K index.

b. The second term (850 mb/hPa dew point) is a measure of low-level moisture.

1) Note that, since the dew point variable is added, high moisture content at 850 mb/hPa increases the K index.

c. The third term (700 mb/hPa temp/dew point spread) is a measure of saturation at 700 mb/hPa (approximately 10,000 ft. MSL).

1) The greater the temperature/dew point spread, the drier the air; and since the term is subtracted, it lowers the K index.

2) The greater the degree of saturation at 700 mb/hPa, the larger the K index.

d. During the warm season, a large K index indicates conditions favorable for thunderstorms.

1) However, K index values and meanings can decrease significantly for thunderstorm development associated with steady-state thunderstorms.

a) Remember that steady-state thunderstorms are usually associated with weather systems, and these systems will affect the variables used in computing the K index.

e. In winter, because of cold temperatures and low moisture values, the temperature terms completely dominate the K index value computation.

1) Because of the lack of moisture, even fairly large values do not mean conditions are favorable for thunderstorms.

2) Be aware that the K index can change significantly over a short time period due to temperature and moisture advection.

f.   Reference Table 11-2 below for information on the coverage of thunderstorms predicted by the K index.

K INDEX West of the Rockies	K INDEX East of the Rockies	Coverage of General Thunderstorms
less than 15	less than 20	None
15 to 20	20 to 25	Isolated thunderstorms
21 to 25	26 to 30	Widely scattered thunderstorms
26 to 30	31 to 35	Scattered thunderstorms
Above 30	Above 35	Numerous thunderstorms
Note: K value may not be representative of airmass if 850 mb level is near the surface.		

Table 11-2. K Index and General Coverage of Thunderstorms

The chart only uses <u>radiosonde</u> data in its K index analysis. This means only large synoptic-scale stability patterns can be determined. Smaller, mesoscale K index variations will be missed.

11.4   USING THE CHART

1.   Stability is based on the lifted index only.

2.   Station circles are blackened for LI values of zero or below.

3.   Contour lines are drawn for values of +4 and below at intervals of 4 (+4, 0, –4, –8, etc.).

4.   When clouds and precipitation are forecast or are occurring, the LI is used to determine the type of clouds and precipitation. That is, stratiform clouds and continuous precipitation occur with stable air, while convective clouds and showery precipitation occur with unstable air.

5.   Stability is also very important when considering the type, extent, and intensity of aviation weather hazards. For example, a quick estimate of areas of probable convective turbulence can be made by associating the areas with unstable air.

a.   An area of extensive icing would be associated with stratiform clouds and steady precipitation, which are characterized by stable air.

END OF STUDY UNIT

STUDY UNIT TWELVE
WEATHER DEPICTION CHARTS

(4 pages of outline)

Please take a few minutes to study each of the concepts listed above and anticipate/imagine what they are and how they relate to the other listed concepts.

12.1 INTRODUCTION

1. The weather depiction chart, Figure 12-2 on page 301, is computer-prepared (with the frontal analysis from a forecaster) from aviation routine weather reports (METARs).

   a. The weather depiction chart gives a broad overview of the observed flying category conditions at the valid time of the chart (e.g., VFR, MVFR, or IFR).

   b. This chart begins at 01Z (0100Z) each day, is transmitted at 3-hr. intervals, and is valid at the time of the plotted data.

2. It is primarily used as a briefing tool to alert aviation interests to the location of critical or near-critical operational minimums at terminals in the conterminous U.S. and surrounding areas.

12.2 PLOTTED DATA

1. Data for the chart come from the observations reported by both manual and automated observation stations.

   a. The automated stations are denoted by a bracket (]) plotted to the right of the station circle.

   b. If the stations on the chart are crowded together, the weather, visibility, and cloud height may be moved up to 90° around the station circle for better legibility.

   c. Most stations are not plotted due to space limitations.

      1) All reporting stations are used in the weather flying category analysis.

2. When reports are frequently updated, as at some automated stations (every 20 min.) or when weather changes significantly, the observation used is the latest METAR received instead of using one closest to the stated analysis time.

3. Reference Figure 12-1 on the next page to understand how to interpret station model plotted data. The plotted data for each station includes the following:

   a. **Visibility**

      1) When visibility is 5 miles or less, it is entered to the left of the station.
      2) Visibility is entered in statute miles and fractions of a mile.

   b. **Present Weather**

      1) Present weather symbols are entered to the left of the station.
      2) When several types of weather and/or obstructions to visibility are reported, the most significant weather element is plotted.

c. **Sky Cover**

1) Sky cover represents the summation total of the sky condition element from the METAR report.

2) EXAMPLE: If the METAR sky condition element was **SCT030 BKN060 OVC090**, the sky cover would be overcast.

d. **Ceiling**

1) Ceiling is the height from the base of the lowest layer aloft covering more than one-half the sky to the ground.

   a) Additionally, vertical visibility into a total surface-based obscuration is defined as a ceiling.

   b) For a METAR report, the first broken (BKN) or overcast (OVC) layer is the ceiling.

   c) EXAMPLE: If the METAR sky condition element is **SCT030 BKN060 OVC090**, the ceiling is 6,000 feet.

2) For stations with broken to overcast layers, the ceiling height is plotted below the station.

   a) Ceilings are reported as hundreds of feet above ground level (AGL).

3) For a total surface-based obscuration, no ceiling is plotted and the METAR must be consulted.

4) Partial obscurations are not identified.

   a) For a partial obscuration with no layer above, the sky cover symbol will be plotted as missing (Figure 12-1 below).

   b) For partial obscuration with a layer above, the sky cover and ceiling height will be plotted for the cloud layer only.

   c) The METAR report should be consulted to identify the partial obscuration.

5) If the sky cover is clear, few, or scattered, no ceiling is plotted.

Figure 12-1. Weather Depiction Chart Station Plot Model

Figure 12-2. Weather Depiction Chart Example

12.3 ANALYSIS

1. The chart (Figure 12-2 above) shows observed ceiling and visibility by categories as follows:

    a. IFR – ceiling less than 1,000 ft. and/or visibility less than 3 SM shaded area outlined by a solid line

    b. MVFR (marginal VFR) – ceiling 1,000 to 3,000 ft. inclusive and/or visibility 3 to 5 SM inclusive; non-shaded area outlined by a solid line

    c. VFR – no ceiling or ceiling greater than 3,000 ft. and visibility greater than 5 SM; not outlined

        1) VFR does not necessarily imply that the sky is clear.

2. The three categories are also explained in the lower right portion of the chart for quick reference.

3. The chart also shows fronts and troughs from the surface analysis chart for the preceding hour. These features are depicted the same as on the surface analysis chart.

    a. One exception is that fronts and troughs are omitted on the 1000Z and 2300Z charts.

12.4 USING THE CHART

1. The weather depiction chart is an ideal place to begin preparing for a weather briefing and flight planning.

    a. From this chart, you can get a bird's-eye view of areas of favorable and adverse weather conditions for chart time.

2. This chart may not completely represent the en route conditions because of variations in terrain and possible weather occurring between reporting stations.

    a. Due to the delay between data and transmission time, changes in the weather could occur.

    b. You should update the chart with current METAR reports.

    c. After initially sizing up the general weather picture, final flight planning must consider forecasts; progs; and the latest pilot, radar, and surface weather reports.

END OF STUDY UNIT

STUDY UNIT THIRTEEN
ALASKA WEATHER DEPICTION CHARTS

(6 pages of outline)

NOTE: This product is similar to the standard weather depiction chart discussed in Study Unit 12. The differences between the two charts are explained in Subunit 2.

13.1 PRODUCT DESCRIPTION

1. The Alaska Weather Depiction Charts display color-coded station plots, which show

   a. Temperature,
   b. Dew point,
   c. Ceiling,
   d. Visibility, and
   e. Wind direction/speed.

2. A key to the station plots is found on each map.

3. Thirteen charts cover Alaska (except for the Aleutians) and adjacent areas of Canada.

4. The charts are issued hourly and can be found on the Alaska Aviation Weather Unit (AAWU) website at http://aawu.arh.noaa.gov/Sigwx.php.

   a. The charts will first appear at about 10 minutes past the hour with a second update at about 25 minutes past the hour.

5. The Alaska Weather Depiction Charts depict numerous parameters, including the flying category (e.g., IFR, MVFR, and VFR), sky cover, and wind.

   a. Subunit 3, "Plotted Data," explains each type of information found on Alaska Weather Depiction Charts.

6.   The image below is a sample Alaska Weather Depiction Chart.

Figure 13-1. Alaska Weather Depiction Chart

13.2 DIFFERENCES WHEN COMPARED WITH STANDARD WEATHER DEPICTION CHART

1.   Numerous differences exist between the Alaska Weather Depiction Chart and the standard Weather Depiction Chart.

2.   The Alaska Weather Depiction Chart displays the same information found on the Weather Depiction Chart plus the following additional information.

   a.   The Alaska Weather Depiction Chart is color-coded to show areas of IFR, MVFR, and VFR.

   b.   Temperature and dew point are displayed.

   c.   Wind direction and speed are displayed.

   d.   The station identifier is displayed.

3.   Several items are coded differently from what is found on the standard Weather Depiction Chart.

   a.   On the Alaska Weather Depiction Chart, if no ceiling is present, it will be coded as "999," whereas on the standard Weather Depiction Chart, if the sky cover is clear, few, or scattered, no ceiling is plotted.

   b.   The Alaska Weather Depiction Chart uses the older Surface Aviation Observation codes/symbols to show the present weather.

4.   The Alaska Weather Depiction Chart is issued hourly, whereas the Weather Depiction Chart is issued eight times daily at the set schedule.

13.3 PLOTTED DATA

1. The Alaska Weather Depiction Charts depict 10 important items. All are explained below.

2. **Flying Category**

   a. Each station plot is color-coded according to the weather flying category reported.

      1) Red indicates instrument flight rules (IFR).
      2) Blue indicates marginal visual flight rules (MVFR).
      3) Black is plotted for stations reporting visual flight rules (VFR).

   b. The table below outlines the flying category and the ceiling and visibility parameters of each.

      1) Remember, VFR flying conditions are not synonymous with clear skies.

Flying Category	Ceiling (feet)	Visibility (miles)
VFR (black)	Greater than 3,000 feet	Greater than 5 miles
MVFR (blue)	1,000 to 3,000 feet	3 to 5 miles
IFR (red)	Less than 1,000 feet	Less than 3 miles

Table 13-1. AAWU Alaska Weather Flying Categories and Criteria

3. **Station Plot**

   a. METAR elements are plotted for each station on the chart.

      1) Some stations are not plotted due to space limitations, particularly on the chart which covers the entire state of Alaska.

   b. The image below explains the types and positions of information contained in the station plots.

      1) Remember that the station plots on this chart are in color and correspond to the flying conditions present at each particular station.

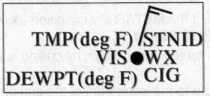

Figure 13-2. AAWU Alaska Weather Depiction Chart Station Plot Legend

4. **Sky Cover**

   a. The sky cover symbol is plotted at the station location and is filled according to the summation total of the sky condition element from the METAR report.

   b. For example, if the METAR sky condition element was **SCT030 BKN060 OVC090**, the sky cover would be overcast. Sky cover symbols are listed in Figure 13-3 below.

Figure 13-3. Sky Cover Symbols

5. **Station Identifier (STNID)**

    a. The four-letter ICAO station identifier is entered to the upper right of the station.
    b. All Alaskan stations begin with the letter "P."

6. **Wind**

    a. Wind is plotted in increments of 5 knots (kt.).
    b. The wind direction is referenced to "true" north and is depicted by a stem (line) pointed in the direction from which the wind is blowing.
    c. Wind speed is determined by adding the values of the flags (50 kt.), barbs (10 kt.), and half barbs (5 kt.) found on the stem.
    d. A single circle over the station with no wind symbol indicates a calm wind.

7. **Temperature (TMP °F)**

    a. Temperature in degrees Fahrenheit is plotted to the upper left of the sky cover symbol.

8. **Visibility (VIS)**

    a. Visibility in statute miles is plotted to the left of the sky cover symbol.
    b. Decimals are used to represent tenths of miles when necessary.

9. **Dew Point Temperature (DEWPT °F)**

    a. Dew point temperature in degrees Fahrenheit is plotted to the lower left of the sky cover symbol.

10. **Ceiling (CIG)**

    a. Ceiling is the height from the base of the lowest layer aloft covering more than one-half of the sky.

        1) Additionally, vertical visibility into a total surface-based obscuration is defined as a ceiling.

    b. For a METAR report, the first broken (BKN) or overcast (OVC) layer is the ceiling.

        1) For example, if the METAR sky condition element is **SCT030 BKN060 OVC090**, the ceiling is 6,000 feet.

    c. For a total surface-based obscuration, no ceiling is plotted, and the METAR must be consulted.
    d. The ceiling is plotted to the lower right of the station circle.

        1) Ceilings are reported as hundreds of feet above ground level (AGL). If no ceiling is present, the code **999** will be plotted.

11. **Present Weather (WX)**

    a. Present weather symbols are entered to the left of the station.

        1) Note that the older Surface Aviation Observation (SAO) code is used instead of Surface Analysis Chart symbols or the modern METAR code.

    b. The following tables explain the weather symbols used on the Alaska Weather Depiction Chart:

Symbol	Meaning
T	Thunderstorm
R	Rain
RW	Rain Shower
L	Drizzle
ZR	Freezing Rain
ZL	Freezing Drizzle
A	Hail
IP	Ice Pellets
IPW	Ice Pellet Showers
S	Snow
SW	Snow Showers
SP	Snow Pellets
SG	Snow Grains
IC	Ice Crystals

Table 13-2. Alaska Weather Depiction Charts
Precipitation Symbols

Symbol	Meaning
BD	Blowing Dust
BN	Blowing Sand
BS	Blowing Snow
BY	Blowing Spray
D	Dust
F	Fog
GF	Ground Fog
H	Haze
IF	Ice Fog
K	Smoke

Table 13-3. Alaska Weather Depiction Charts
Obstruction to Visibility Symbols

Symbol	Meaning
-	Light
(No symbol)	Moderate
+	Heavy

Table 13-4. Alaska Weather Depiction Charts
Precipitation Intensity Symbols

13.4 USING THE CHART

1.   The Alaska Weather Depiction Charts provide an overview of weather flying categories and other adverse weather conditions for the chart's valid time.

     a.   The chart often does not completely represent the en route conditions because of terrain variations and the possibility of weather occurring between reporting stations.

2.   These charts should be used in addition to the latest METAR/SPECIs, pilot weather reports, and radar and satellite imagery for a complete look at the latest flying conditions.

END OF STUDY UNIT

STUDY UNIT FOURTEEN
RADAR SUMMARY CHARTS

(8 pages of outline)

Please take a few minutes to study each of the concepts listed above and anticipate/imagine what they are and how they relate to the other listed concepts.

14.1 INTRODUCTION

1. The Radar Summary Chart is a computer-generated mosaic of radar echo intensity contours based on Radar Weather Reports over the contiguous U.S.

    a. Possible precipitation types, intensity, coverage, cell movements, maximum tops, locations of line echoes, and remarks are plotted on the Radar Summary Chart.

        1) Much of this information is often truncated due to space limitations.

    b. Severe thunderstorm and tornado watches are plotted if they are in effect when the chart is valid.

2. The Radar Summary Chart is available on the National Weather Service (NWS) Fax Charts website at http://weather.noaa.gov/pub/fax/QAUA00.TIF.

3. Radar Summary Charts are issued hourly and are valid upon issuance.

4. Figure 14-1 on the next page depicts the WSR-88D radar network from which the Radar Summary Chart is developed.

5. Figure 14-2 on the next page depicts a sample Radar Summary Chart.

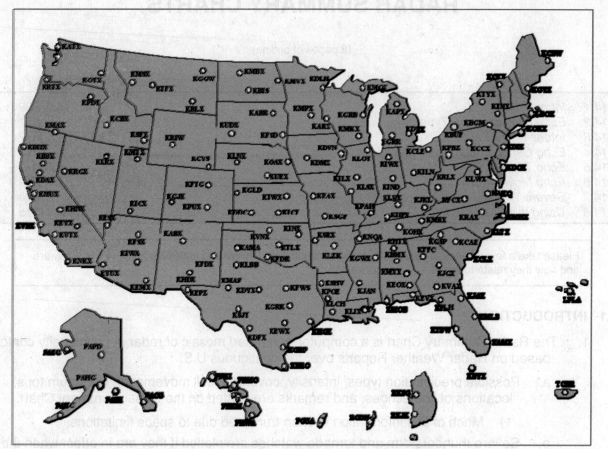

Figure 14-1. WSR 88-D Weather Radar Network Sites

Figure 14-2. Radar Summary Chart

14.2 ECHO (PRECIPITATION) TYPE

1. The types of precipitation are indicated by symbols adjacent to the depicted precipitation areas on the Radar Summary Chart.

   a. Freezing precipitation is not reported in Radar Weather Reports and is not plotted on the Radar Summary Chart.

2. The left column of Table 14-1 below lists the symbols used to denote types of precipitation. Note that these symbols (code) do not reflect the METAR code.

   a. Since the input data for the Radar Summary Chart are the automated SDs/ROBs, the type of precipitation is determined by computer models and is limited to the ones listed in Table 14-1.

Symbols Used on Chart

Symbol	Meaning	Symbol	Meaning
R	Rain	↗ 35	Cell movement to the northeast at 35 knots
RW	Rain shower	LM	Little movement
S	Snow		
SW	Snow shower	WS999	Severe thunderstorm watch number 999
T	Thunderstorm	WT210	Tornado watch number 210
NA	Not available	SLD	8/10 or greater coverage in a line
NE	No echoes		
OM	Out for maintenance		Line of echoes

Table 14-1. Key to Radar Summary Chart

14.3 INTENSITY

1.   The intensity is obtained from the amount of energy returned to the radar from targets (DBZs) and is indicated on the Radar Summary Chart by contours.

   a.   Six precipitation intensity levels (or digits) are reduced into three contour intervals as indicated in Table 14-2 on page 314.

      1)   Precipitation intensity is correlated only for liquid precipitation, not solid precipitation (e.g., snow).

   b.   These digits were once commonly referred to as VIP levels because precipitation intensity (digits) was derived by using a video integrator processor (VIP).

      1)   Since the WSR-88D, and not the VIP, is now used to determine precipitation intensity, the NWS suggests that the term "VIP level" should no longer be used.

ATC Weather Radar Echo Terminology	Precipitation Description	Reflectivity (dBZ)
Light	Trace to light rain	<30 dBZ
Moderate	Light to moderate rain	30-40 dBZ
Heavy	Heavy rain; possible small granules	>40-50 dBZ
Extreme	Very heavy rain; hail; pea/marble or greater size hail	50+ dBZ

450   **Highest echo top in area in hundreds of feet MSL (45,000 feet MSL).**

Figure 14-3. Radar Summary Chart Precipitation Intensity

2.   When determining intensity levels from the radar summary chart, it is recommended that the maximum possible intensity for that contour be used.

3.   Finally, it is very important to remember that the intensity trend (increasing or weakening) is no longer coded on either the Radar Summary Chart or the Radar Weather Report (SD/ROB).

14.4 ECHO CONFIGURATION AND COVERAGE

1. The configuration is the arrangement of echoes. There are three designated arrangements: a **line** of echoes, an **area** of echoes, and an isolated **cell**.

2. Coverage is simply the area covered by echoes. All of the hatched area inside of the contours on the chart is considered to be covered by echoes.

    a. However, actual precipitation coverage is less. This is because only a fraction of a grid box needs to be covered with echoes for the entire grid box to be plotted as precipitation on the chart.

3. When the echoes are reported as a line, a line will be drawn through them on the chart.

    a. If there is 8/10 coverage or more, the line is labeled as solid (SLD) at both ends.

        1) In the absence of this label, it can be assumed that there is less than 8/10 coverage.

    b. EXAMPLE: In Figure 14-2 on page 310, there is a solid line of thunderstorms with intense to extreme rain showers over north-central Texas.

14.5 ECHO TOPS

1. Echo tops are obtained from both radar and, on occasion, satellite data and displayed for **precipitation** tops. Individual Radar Weather Reports should be used to determine if satellite data was used for precipitation echo tops.

2. Echo tops are the maximum heights of the precipitation in hundreds of feet MSL, as coded on a Weather Radar Report. These heights should be considered only as approximations because of radar wave propagation limitations.

    a. Tops are plotted in 3-digit groups representing height in hundreds of feet MSL and are underlined, with the top height displayed being the highest in the indicated area.

    b. Where it is necessary to offset a top for reasons of insufficient space, a line is drawn from one end of the underline to a small black square which represents the location of the top.

    c. Maximum echo top does not equal maximum cloud top. The maximum echo top is the altitude of the highest light precipitation echo, not highest cloud top.

3. It is assumed that all precipitation is reaching the surface.

14.6 ECHO MOVEMENT

1.   Cell movement is the average motion of all cells within a configuration.

2.   Individual cell direction of movement is indicated by an arrow with the speed in knots entered as a number near the arrowhead.

    a.   Little movement is identified by "LM."

3.   EXAMPLES (See Table 14-2 below):

Radar Summary Chart Cell Movement Examples

SYMBOL	MEANING
35 (arrow pointing northeast)	Cell movement to the northeast at 35 knots
24 (arrow pointing east)	Cell movement to the east at 24 knots
18 (arrow pointing south)	Cell movement to the south at 18 knots
12 (arrow pointing southwest)	Cell movement to the southwest at 12 knots
LM	Little cell movement

Table 14-2. Radar Summary Chart Cell Movement Examples

4.   Movement of areas and lines can be significantly different from the motion of the individual cells that comprise these configurations.

    a.   Line or area movement is not indicated on the Radar Summary Chart.

14.7 SEVERE WEATHER WATCH AREAS

1.   Severe weather watch areas are outlined by heavy dashed lines, usually in the form of a large rectangular box.

    a.   There are two types: tornado watches **(WT)** and severe thunderstorm watches **(WS)**.

b. Reference Table 14-3 below for examples of each.

Radar Summary Chart Weather Watch Area Examples

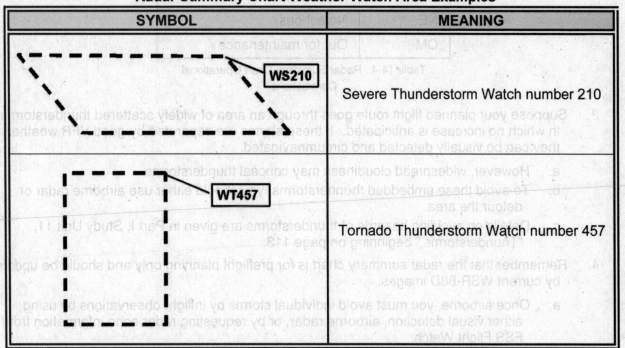

SYMBOL	MEANING
WS210	Severe Thunderstorm Watch number 210
WT457	Tornado Thunderstorm Watch number 457

Table 14-3. Radar Summary Chart Weather Watch Area Examples

2. The type of watch and the watch number are enclosed in a small rectangle (see Table 14-1 on page 311) and positioned as closely as possible to the northeast corner of the watch box.

a. Weather watch areas also are listed by type and number at the bottom of the chart (over Mexico) together with the issuance time and "valid until" time.

1) The absence of weather watch areas will be indicated by the word "NONE."

14.8 USING THE CHART

1. The Radar Summary Chart helps preflight planning by identifying general areas and movement of precipitation and/or thunderstorms.

a. Radar detects **only** drops or ice particles of precipitation size; it **does not** detect clouds and fog.

b. Therefore, the Radar Summary Chart only displays precipitation; it does not display clouds.

c. Thus, the absence of echoes does not guarantee clear weather, and cloud tops will most likely be higher than the precipitation tops detected by radar.

d. The chart must be used in conjunction with other charts, reports, and forecasts.

2. Examine chart notations carefully. Always determine location and movement of echoes.

a. If echoes are anticipated near your planned route, take special note of echo intensity.

b. Be sure to examine the chart for missing radar reports (e.g., NA, OM) before assuming that no echoes are present.

c. Table 14-4 on the next page explains the three station operational contractions that may appear on a radar summary chart.

Symbol	Meaning
NA	Not available
NE	No echoes
OM	Out for maintenance

Table 14-4. Radar Summary Chart Operational
Contractions

3. Suppose your planned flight route goes through an area of widely scattered thunderstorms in which no increase is anticipated. If these storms are separated by good VFR weather, they can be visually detected and circumnavigated.

    a. However, widespread cloudiness may conceal thunderstorms.

    b. To avoid these embedded thunderstorms, you should either use airborne radar or detour the area.

    c. Details on avoiding hazards of thunderstorms are given in Part I, Study Unit 11, "Thunderstorms," beginning on page 113.

4. Remember that the radar summary chart is for preflight planning only and should be updated by current WSR-88D images.

    a. Once airborne, you must avoid individual storms by inflight observations by using either visual detection, airborne radar, or by requesting radar echo information from FSS Flight Watch.

    b. FSS Flight Watch has access to current WSR-88D imagery.

5. There can be an interpretation problem concerning an area of precipitation that is reported by more than one radar site.

    a. EXAMPLE: Station A may report RW with cell movement toward the northeast at 10 kt. For the same area, station B may be reporting TRW with cell movement toward the northeast at 30 kt.

    b. This difference in reports may be due to a different perspective and distance of the radar site from the area of echoes. The area may be moving away from station A and approaching station B.

        1) The general rule is to use the plotted data associated with the area that presents the greatest hazard to aviation. In this case, the station B report would be used.

END OF STUDY UNIT

STUDY UNIT FIFTEEN
ALASKA INITIAL GEOPOTENTIAL
HEIGHTS AND WINDS CHARTS

(7 pages of outline)

NOTE: This product is essentially the same as the constant pressure chart discussed in Study Unit 9. The differences between the two charts are explained in Subunit 2.

15.1 PRODUCT DESCRIPTION

1.   The Alaska Initial Geopotential Heights and Winds Charts consist of 5 separate charts that display an analysis of the observed height contours and winds at selected constant pressure surfaces (flight levels).

2.   Charts are issued at 00Z and 12Z and are valid at their issuance times.

   a.   Forecast charts are also issued for 6 hours and 12 hours after each official release.

      1)   These charts do not contain pressure contours, only forecast wind velocity.

3.   The following table explains the relationship between the 5 charts and their corresponding pressure altitudes.

   a.   Remember, as atmospheric pressure varies from standard conditions, the altitudes that correspond with each analysis level will change as well.

   b.   Think of the altitudes shown below as reference points to help you plan flights near these flight levels.

CHART	PRESSURE ALTITUDE (Feet, MSL)	PRESSURE ALTITUDE (Meters, MSL)
200 MB	39,000	12,000
300 MB	30,000	9,000
500 MB	18,000	5,500
700 MB	10,000	3,000
850 MB	5,000	1,500

Table 15-1. Pressure Altitudes of Alaska Initial Geopotential Heights and Winds Charts

4.   The analysis of both height contours and winds are based on output from the North American Mesoscale (NAM) computer forecast model.

5.   The charts can be found on the Alaska Aviation Weather Unit (AAWU) website at http://aawu.arh.noaa.gov/upperwinds.php.

15.2 DIFFERENCES WHEN COMPARED TO CONSTANT PRESSURE CHARTS

1. Contours are drawn as solid lines and labeled in meters. The intervals at which the contours are drawn are 60 meters on all of the charts.

   a. The contour intervals change on constant pressure charts based on what chart level you reference.

2. The scale of the Alaskan chart is much smaller, meaning that more information can be displayed.

   a. The decreased scale makes it easier to read the chart because the station models are not packed into a small space.

3. Pressure systems (e.g., highs and lows) are not depicted on the Alaskan chart.

4. Station model data is not included on the Alaskan chart.

   a. Only wind direction and speed indicators are shown.

      1) Station model data is not used to construct this chart.

      2) All information on the Alaskan chart is based on output from the North American Mesoscale (NAM) computer forecast model.

15.3 PLOTTED DATA

1. **Height Contours**

   a. Height contours are lines of constant height referenced to MSL and are used to map the height variations of constant pressure surfaces.

   b. They identify and characterize pressure systems on constant pressure charts.

   c. Contours are drawn as solid lines and labeled in meters.

      1) The intervals at which the contours are drawn are 60 meters on all of the charts.

2. **Winds**

   a. Wind is plotted in increments of 5 knots (kt.).

   b. The wind direction is referenced to "true" north and is depicted by a stem (line) pointed in the direction from which the wind is blowing.

   c. Wind speed is determined by adding the values of the flags (50 kt.), barbs (10 kt.), and half barbs (5 kt.) found on the stem.

   d. A single circle over the station with no wind symbol indicates a calm wind.

   e. Figure 15-1 on the next page contains some examples of wind symbols found on this chart.

Figure 15-1. Alaskan Initial Geopotential Heights and Winds Chart Wind Plotting Model

15.4 USING THE CHART

1. The Alaska Initial Geopotential Heights and Winds Charts are used to provide an overview of heights, pressure patterns, and winds at specified pressure altitudes.

2. Pressure patterns cause and characterize much of the weather.

    a.   Typically, lows and troughs are associated with bad weather, clouds, and precipitation, while highs and ridges are associated with good weather.

3. The first five of the following seven images are examples of the five different charts available. The sixth and seventh images are examples of a 6- and 12-hour forecast chart, respectively.

Figure 15-2. Alaskan Initial Geopotential Heights and Winds Chart - 200MB Winds and Contours Chart Example

Figure 15-3. Alaskan Initial Geopotential Heights and Winds Chart - 300MB Winds and Contours Chart Example

Figure 15-4. Alaskan Initial Geopotential Heights and Winds Chart - 500MB Winds and Contours Chart Example

Figure 15-5. Alaskan Initial Geopotential Heights and Winds Chart - 700MB Winds and Contours Chart Example

Figure 15-6. Alaskan Initial Geopotential Heights and Winds Chart - 850MB Winds and Contours Chart Example

Figure 15-7. Alaskan Initial Geopotential Heights and Winds Chart - 6-Hour Forecast Chart Example

Figure 15-8. Alaskan Initial Geopotential Heights and Winds Chart - 12-Hour Forecast Chart Example

END OF STUDY UNIT

STUDY UNIT SIXTEEN
SIGNIFICANT METEOROLOGICAL INFORMATION (SIGMET)

(13 pages of outline)

> Please take a few minutes to study each of the concepts listed above and anticipate/imagine what they are and how they relate to the other listed concepts.

16.1   PRODUCT DESCRIPTION

1.   Significant Meteorological Information (SIGMET) provides aircraft operators and aircrews notice of potentially hazardous en route phenomena, such as thunderstorms and hail, turbulence, icing, sand and dust storms, tropical cyclones, and volcanic ash.

   a.   Domestic SIGMETs for the conterminous U.S. (CONUS) are available on the Aviation Digital Data Service (ADDS) website at http://adds.aviationweather.noaa.gov/airmets/.

   b.   International SIGMETs (including Alaska and Hawaii) are available on the Aviation Weather Center (AWC) website at http://aviationweather.gov/products/sigmets/intl/.

      1)   Alaska SIGMETs are also available on the Alaska Aviation Weather Unit (AAWU) website at http://aawu.arh.noaa.gov/.

      2)   Hawaii SIGMETs are also available on the NWS WFO Honolulu website at http://www.prh.noaa.gov/hnl/pages/aviation.php.

2.   **SIGMETs** may be issued when any of the following conditions occur or are expected to occur in an area affecting at least 3,000 square miles or an area deemed to have a significant effect on the safety of aircraft operations:

   a.   Severe or greater Turbulence (SEV TURB)
   b.   Severe Icing (SEV ICE)
   c.   Widespread Duststorm (WDSPR DS)
   d.   Widespread Sandstorm (WDSPR SS)
   e.   Volcanic Ash (VA)
   f.   Tropical Cyclone (TC)

3.   **Convective SIGMETs** (also known as SIGMETs for Convection) are issued for the contiguous U.S. instead of SIGMETs when convective activity occurs and/or is forecast to occur.

   a.   Each bulletin includes one or more Convective SIGMETs for a specific region of the CONUS.

   b.   Convective SIGMETs are issued for thunderstorms and related phenomena and do not include references to all weather associated with thunderstorms, such as turbulence, icing, low-level wind shear, and IFR conditions.

      1)   **Convection** is used to describe vertical movement of heat and moisture in the atmosphere, especially by updrafts and downdrafts in an unstable atmosphere.

2)   The terms "convection" and "thunderstorms" are often used interchangeably, although thunderstorms are only one form of convection.

   a)   CBs (Cumulonimbus), towering cumulus clouds, and ACCAS clouds (**A**lto**C**umulus **CAS**tellanus) are all visible forms of convection. However, convection is not always made visible by clouds.

3)   Convection that occurs without cloud formation is called dry convection, while the visible convection processes referred to above are forms of moist convection.

c.   Convective SIGMETs may be issued when any of the following occurs and/or is forecast to occur:

1)   Severe thunderstorms and embedded thunderstorms occurring for more than 30 minutes of the valid period regardless of the size of the area.

   a)   A thunderstorm is classified as severe when it is accompanied by tornadoes, hail 3/4-inch or greater, or wind gusts of 50 knots or greater.

   b)   A thunderstorm is classified as embedded when it is obscured by haze, non-convective clouds, or precipitation.

2)   A line of thunderstorms must be at least 50 miles long with thunderstorms affecting at least 40% of its length.

3)   An area of active thunderstorms affecting at least 3,000 square miles.

   a)   Thunderstorms are classified as active when they are heavy (>40 dBZ) or greater and affect at least 40% of the area. In the absence of radar, AWC meteorologists may identify active thunderstorms using satellite or lightning information.

   b)   Obscured, embedded, or squall line thunderstorms do not have to reach 3000 square miles to be included in Convective SIGMETs.

4.   A **Special Convective SIGMET** may be issued when either of the following criteria is occurring or expected to occur for more than 30 minutes of the valid period of the current Convective SIGMET:

a.   Tornado, hail greater than or equal to 3/4 inch, or wind gusts greater than or equal to 50 knots is reported or indicated when the previous Convective SIGMET did not mention severe thunderstorms.

b.   Indications of rapidly changing conditions, if, in the forecaster's judgment, they are not sufficiently described in existing Convective SIGMETs.

16.2 ISSUANCE

1.   SIGMETs are issued from Meteorological Watch Offices (MWO). The three U.S. MWOs and their areas of responsibility are identified below.

a.   The Aviation Weather Center (AWC)

1)   The conterminous U.S. (CONUS) out to the domestic Flight Information Region (FIR) boundary

2)   The New York, Houston, Miami, and San Juan Oceanic FIRs

3)   The Oakland Oceanic FIR north of 30° north latitude and the portion east of 140° west longitude which is between the equator and 30° north latitude

b.   The Alaska Aviation Weather Unit (AAWU)

1)   Anchorage FIR

c.   The Weather Forecast Office (WFO) in Honolulu

1)   Oakland Oceanic FIR south of 30° north latitude to the equator and between 140° west and 160° east longitude

d. The following figures graphically depict the areas of responsibility for these MWOs.

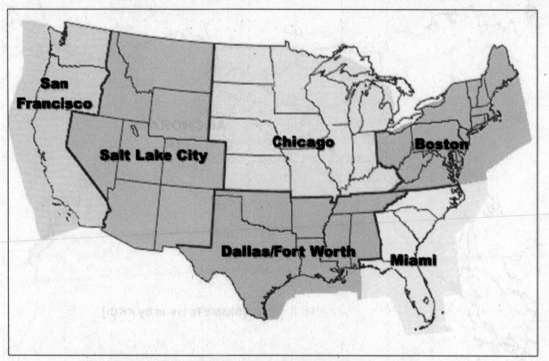

Figure 16-1. AWC SIGMET Areas of Responsibility – Conterminous U.S.

Figure 16-2. AWC SIGMET Areas of Responsibility - Atlantic Basin

Figure 16-3. AWC SIGMET Areas of Responsibility – Pacific Basin

2. When a SIGMET is issued, it is assigned a unique series identifier.

   a. AWC for CONUS will be assigned **NOVEMBER** through **YANKEE**, excluding **SIERRA** and **TANGO**.

   b. AWC for Oakland Oceanic FIR will be assigned **ALFA** through **HOTEL**.

   c. Honolulu MWO for Oakland Oceanic FIR will be assigned **NOVEMBER** through **ZULU**.

   d. AAWU for Anchorage FIR will be assigned **INDIA** through **MIKE**.

3. A number is assigned sequentially with each issuance until the phenomenon ends.

   a. At 0000 UTC each day, all continuing SIGMETs are renumbered to one (1) regardless of a continuation of the phenomena.

   b. EXAMPLES: **YANKEE 1, YANKEE 2, YANKEE 3**, etc.

4. **SIGMET Valid Period and Cancelation**

   a. SIGMETs for volcanic ash or tropical cyclones are valid up to 6 hours with an outlook of up to 12 hours beyond the valid period.

      1) They are reissued at least every 6 hours while the volcanic ash or tropical cyclone exists or is forecast to exist.

2)   SIGMET messages for volcanic ash or tropical cyclones expected to affect a FIR are issued up to 12 hours before the start of the valid period or as soon as practicable if such advance warning of the existence of these phenomena is not available.

   b.   SIGMETs for all other phenomena (other than Convective SIGMETs) have a valid period not to exceed 4 hours.

1)   These SIGMETs are issued up to 4 hours before the initial valid time.

2)   SIGMETs for continuing phenomena are reissued at least every 4 hours as long as SIGMET criteria are met.

   c.   SIGMETs are canceled when the phenomena is no longer occurring or expected to occur in the area.

5.   **SIGMET Amendments and Corrections**

   a.   Amendments (AMD) and corrections (COR) to SIGMETs are issued as necessary. This is done by issuing a new SIGMET in the current series, which advances the SIGMET number and replaces the previous SIGMET.

1)   The valid time of the new SIGMET is updated to reflect a new 4-hour period.

   b.   The start time of the new SIGMET is updated, but the end valid time remains the same as the original SIGMET.

   c.   If a correction is being made, a tag is added at the end of the SIGMET that reads "CORRECTS SIGMET {SERIES} {#}", where {SERIES} is the SIGMET designator and {#} is the series number.

6.   SIGMETs are issued as the need for them arises, but Convective SIGMETs are issued hourly.

   a.   Three Convective SIGMET bulletins describing conditions in the eastern, central, and western regions of the CONUS are issued hourly at 55 minutes past the hour.

1)   The figure below shows the division of the CONUS into the eastern, central, and western regions.

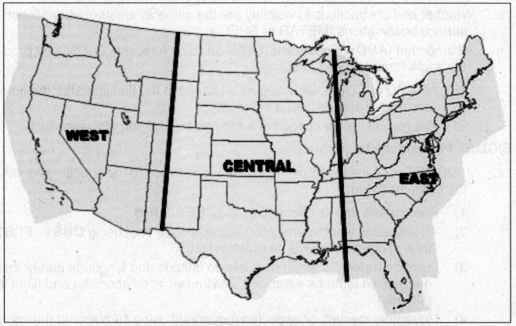

Figure 16-4. AWC Convective SIGMET Areas of Responsibility

   b.   Special Convective SIGMETs are issued as required.

c.   Each Convective SIGMET bulletin is made up of one or more individually numbered Convective SIGMETs for conditions within the region and is valid for up to 2 hours or until superseded by the next hourly issuance.

    1)   An outlook message is included, which describes areas where Convective SIGMET issuances are expected between 2 and 6 hours after issuance time.

d.   Since the Convective SIGMET bulletin is a scheduled product, a message must be transmitted each hour.

    1)   If no Convective SIGMETs are expected within a region, a bulletin with **CONVECTIVE SIGMET...NONE** is transmitted.

e.   Convective SIGMETs are not canceled but expire as soon as the next bulletin is issued.

16.3 FORMAT AND CONTENT

1.   SIGMET Standardization

a.   All heights or altitudes are referenced to Mean Sea Level (MSL) and consist of three digits depicting height in hundreds of feet.

    1)   Flight Level (FL) is used for heights at or above 18,000 feet.

    2)   EXAMPLES: 100 = 10,000 ft. MSL, FL190 = Equals approximately 19,000 feet MSL.

b.   References to latitude and longitude are in whole degrees and minutes with a space between latitude and longitude and a hyphen between successive points.

    1)   Products issued by AWC have the N, S, W, or E behind the latitude/longitude numbers.

    2)   EXAMPLE: N3106 W07118 = 31 degrees, 6 minutes North by 7 degrees, 118 minutes West.

c.   Messages are prepared using approved ICAO contractions, abbreviations, and numerical values of a self-explanatory nature.

d.   Weather and obstructions to visibility are the same as weather abbreviations used for surface observations (METAR or SPECI).

e.   All amended (AMD) or corrected (COR) en route forecasts or advisory products follow the same format procedures.

    1)   An AMD or COR is identified as a change in the first line after the time and date, and where appropriate, a comment.

    2)   The reason for the change is added as the last line of the product.

2.   SIGMET Phenomena Information

a.   A SIGMET contains the following information related to the specific phenomena and in the order indicated:

    1)   Phenomena and its description, e.g., **SEV TURB**.

    2)   An indication whether the information is observed, using **OBS** or **FCST** with the time of observation will be given in UTC.

    3)   Location (referring, when possible, to latitude and longitude and/or locations or geographic features which are well known internationally) and flight level (altitude).

    4)   Movement towards or expected movement using 16 points of the compass, with speed in knots or stationary, if appropriate.

    5)   Thunderstorm maximum height as FL.

6) Changes in intensity, using as appropriate, the abbreviations Intensifying **(INTSF)**, Weakening **(WKN)**, or No Change **(NC)**.

7) On the last line, an outlook beyond the valid period for forecast trajectory of a volcanic ash cloud or tropical cyclone.

3. **SIGMET Format**

a. The WMO (World Meteorological Organization) SIGMET header for non-convective SIGMETs is **WS**.

b. The table below shows an example of a domestic SIGMET.

```
LINE
1 – SFOR UWS 100130
2 – SIGMET ROMEO 1 VALID UNTIL 100530
3 – OR WA
4 – FROM SEA TO PDT TO EUG TO SEA
5 – OCNL MOGR CAT BTN FL280 AND FL350 EXP DUE TO
     JTSTR.  CONDS BGNG AFT 0200Z CONTG BYD 0530Z AND
     SPRDG OVR CNTRL ID BY 0400Z.
```

Table 16-1. SIGMET for the Conterminous U.S. Decoding Example

c. The table below shows how to decode the example domestic SIGMET shown previously.

LINE	CONTENT	DESCRIPTION
1	SFO R WS 100130	SIGMET area identifier SIGMET series letter Product type Issuance UTC date/time
2	SIGMET ROMEO 1 VALID UNTIL 100530	Product type SIGMET series name Issuance number Ending valid UTC date/time
3	OR WA	Phenomenon location (states)
4	FROM SEA TO PDT TO EUG TO SEA	Phenomenon location (VOR coordinates)
5	OCNL MOGR CAT BTN FL280 AND FL350 EXP DUE TO JTSTR. CONDS BGNG AFT 0200Z CONTG BYD 0530Z AND SPRDG OVR CNTRL ID BY 0400Z	Phenomenon description

Table 16-2. Decoding a Domestic SIGMET for the Conterminous U.S.

d. The table below explains the example domestic SIGMET shown previously.

Line 1	SIGMET ROMEO series issued for the San Francisco Area at 0130 UTC on the 10th day of the month.
Line 2	This is the first issuance of the SIGMET ROMEO series and is valid until the 10th day of the month at 0530 UTC.
Line 3	The affected states within the SFO area are Oregon and Washington.
Line 4	From Seattle, WA; to Pendleton, OR; to Eugene, OR; to Seattle, WA.
Line 5	Occasional moderate or greater clear air turbulence between Flight Level 280 and Flight Level 350, expected due to jet stream. Conditions beginning after 0200Z continuing beyond 0530Z and spreading over central Idaho by 0400Z

Table 16-3. Domestic SIGMET Explained

e.   The table below shows an example of SIGMET issued for an area outside of the CONUS.

```
LINE
1 –  WSPA07 PHFO 010410
2 –  SIGPAT
3 –  KZOA SIGMET TANGO 2 VALID 010410/010800 PHFO-
4 –  OAKLAND OCEANIC FIR FRQ TS OBS AND FCST WI 200NM
     N3006 W14012 - N2012 W15016 CB TOP FL400 MOV W
     10KT WKN.
```

Table 16-4. SIGMET Outside the Conterminous U.S. Decoding Example

f.   The table below shows how to decode the example SIGMET issued for an area outside of the CONUS.

LINE	CONTENT	DESCRIPTION
1	WSPA07 PHFO 010410	ICAO communication header Issuance MWO Issuance UTC date/time
2	SIGPAT	NWS AWIPS communication header
3	KZOA SIGMET TANGO 2 VALID 010410/010800 PHFO	Area Control Center Product type SIGMET series Issuance number Valid period UTC date/time Issuance office
4	OAKLAND OCEANIC FIR FRQ TS OBS AND FCST WI 200NM N3006 W14012 - N2012 W15016 CB TOP FL400 MOV W 10KT WKN.	Flight Information Region (FIR) Phenomenon description

Table 16-5. Decoding a SIGMET Outside of the Conterminous U.S.

g.   The table below explains the example SIGMET issued for an area outside of the CONUS.

Line 1	The WMO product header is WSPA07. Issued by the PHFO on the 1st day of the month at 0410 UTC.
Line 2	The NWS AWIPS communication header is SIGPAT.
Line 3	For the Oakland (KZOA) Area Control Center. This is the 2nd issuance of SIGMET Tango series, valid from the 1st day of the month at 0410 UTC until the 1st day of the month at 0800 UTC, issued by the Honolulu Meteorological Watch Office.
Line 4	Concerning the Oakland Oceanic Flight Information Region (FIR), frequent thunderstorms observed and forecast within 200 nautical miles of 30 degrees and 6 minutes north; 140 degrees and 12 minutes west; to 20 degrees and 12 minutes north, 150 degrees and 16 minutes west, cumulonimbus tops to flight level 400 moving west at 10 knots, weakening.

Table 16-6. Outside of Conterminous U.S. SIGMET Explained

h. The table below shows an example of a Convective SIGMET.

```
LINE
1 -   MKCC WST 221855
2 -   CONVECTIVE SIGMET 20C
3 -   VALID UNTIL 2055Z
4 -   ND SD
5 -   FROM 90W MOT-GFK-ABR-90W MOT
6 -   INTSFYG AREA SEV TS MOVG FROM 24045KT.  TOPS
      ABV FL450.  WIND GUSTS TO 60KTS RPRTD.
      TORNADOES...HAIL TO 2 IN...WIND GUSTS TO 65KTS
      POSS ND PTN.
```

Table 16-7. Convective SIGMET Decoding Example

i. The table below shows how to decode the example Convective SIGMET shown previously.

LINE	CONTENT	DESCRIPTION
1	MKC C WST 221855	Issuing Office W, C, or E Contraction WST Six-digit date/time group (DDHHMM)
2	CONVECTIVE SIGMET 20 C	Product type Issuance number Location (West, Central or East)
3	VALID UNTIL 2055Z	Ending valid UTC date/time
4	ND SD	Phenomenon location (states)
5	FROM 90W MOT-GFK-ABR-90W MOT	Phenomenon location (VOR coordinates)
6	INTSFYG AREA SEV TS MOVG FROM 24045KT. TOPS ABV FL450. WIND GUSTS TO 60KTS RPRTD. TORNADOES... HAIL TO 2 IN... WIND GUSTS TO 65KTS POSS ND PTN	Phenomenon description

Table 16-8. Decoding a Convective SIGMET

j. The table below explains the example Convective SIGMET shown previously.

Line 1	Convective SIGMET issued for the central portion of the United States on the 22nd at 1855Z.
Line 2	This is the 20th Convective SIGMET issued on the 22nd for the central United States as indicated by "20C."
Line 3	Valid until 2055Z.
Line 4	The affected states are North and South Dakota.
Line 5	From 90 nautical miles west of Minot, ND; to Grand Forks, ND; to Aberdeen, SD; to 90 nautical miles west of Minot, ND.
Line 6	An intensifying area of severe thunderstorms moving from 240 degrees at 45 knots (to the northeast). Thunderstorm tops above Flight Level 450. Wind gusts to 60 knots reported. Tornadoes, hail to 2 inches in diameter, and wind gusts to 65 knots possible in the North Dakota portion.

Table 16-9. Convective SIGMET Explained

16.4 USING THE PRODUCT

1. SIGMETs are important weather reports that can alert pilots to potentially hazardous conditions.

    a. These conditions are usually very severe in nature.

2. Most general aviation pilots do not consider the importance of SIGMETs when planning a flight, but this practice can be an extremely hazardous mistake.

    a. Review SIGMETs, especially Convective SIGMETs, before each and every flight to ensure that you are aware of the conditions in which you intend to operate.

3. The following examples are actual SIGMET reports followed by plain-English interpretations. Read through these examples to ensure that you understand SIGMET terminology and interpretation.

```
BOSR WS 050600
SIGMET ROMEO 2 VALID UNTIL 051000
ME NH VT
FROM MLT TO YSJ TO CON TO MPV TO MLT
OCNL SEV TURB BLW 080 EXP DUE TO STG NWLY FLOW.   CONDS CONTG BYD 1000Z.
```

SIGMET issued for the Boston Area Forecast region on the 5th day of the month at 0600 UTC. This is the second (2nd) issuance of SIGMET series Romeo and is valid until the 5th day of the month at 1000 UTC. The affected states are Maine (ME), New Hampshire (NH) and Vermont (VT). Within an area bounded from Millinocket, Maine; to St. Johns, New Brunswick; to Concord, New Hampshire; to Montpelier, Vermont; to Millinocket, Maine. Occasional severe turbulence below 8,000 feet due to strong northwesterly flow. Conditions are expected to continue beyond 1000 UTC.

```
KZOA SIGMET TANGO 1 VALID 010400/010800 PHFO-
OAKLAND OCEANIC FIR ACT TS OBS BY SATELLITE WITHIN 100 NM EITHER SIDE
OF LINE N3006 W14012 - N2012 W15016.  CB TO TOPS FL400.  MOV W 10 KT.
WKN.
```

SIGMET issued for the Honolulu area of the Oakland Oceanic FIR. This first (1) issuance of SIGMET Series Tango valid from the 1st day of the month at 0400 UTC to the 1st day of the month at 0800 UTC. Issued by the Honolulu Weather Forecast Office. Within the Oakland Oceanic FIR, active thunderstorms observed by satellite within 100 nautical miles either side of a line from 30 degrees, 6 minutes north to 140 degrees, 12 minutes west to 20 degrees 12 minutes north, 150 degrees, 16 minutes west. Cumulonimbus tops to 40,000 feet. The thunderstorms are moving west at 10 knots and weakening.

```
KZOA SIGMET DELTA 2 VALID 081530/081930 KKCI-
OAKLAND OCEANIC FIR FRQ TS WITHIN AREA BOUNDED BY N3935 W16920 - N3414
W17050 - N3010 2 17325 TOPS FL470 MOV NNE 10KT NC.
```

SIGMET issued for the Aviation Weather Center's area of the Oakland FIR. This is the second (2) issuance of SIGMET series Delta valid from the 8th day of the month at 1530 UTC to the 8th day of the month at 1930 UTC. Within the Oakland Oceanic FIR, frequent thunderstorms within an area bounded by 39 degrees 35 minutes north, 169 degrees 20 minutes west to 34 degrees 14 minutes north, 170 degrees, 50 minutes west to 30 degrees 10 minutes north, 173 degrees 25 minutes west. Thunderstorm tops to 47,000 feet, thunderstorms are moving to the north-northeast at 10 knots with no change observed.

```
DFWY WS 121450 COR
SIGMET YANKEE 4 VALID UNTIL 121700
MO AR LA MS
FROM STL TO 30 N MEI TO BTR TO MLU TO STL
OCNL SVR MXD ICING 90 TO 130 EXPCD.
FRZLVL 80 E TO 120 W.   CONDS CONTG BYD 1700Z
CORRECTS YANKEE 3
```

Corrected SIGMET issued for the Dallas/Fort Worth Area Forecast region on the 12th day of the month at 1450 UTC. This is the fourth (4) issuance of SIGMET series Yankee and is valid until the 12th day of the month at 1700 UTC. The affected states are Missouri (MO), Arkansas (AR), Louisiana (LA) and Mississippi (MS). Bounded within an area from Saint Louis, Missouri; to 30 nautical miles north of Meridian, Mississippi; to Baton Rouge, Louisiana; to Monroe, Louisiana; to Saint Louis, Missouri. Occasional severe mixed icing between 9,000 and 13,000 feet is expected. The freezing level is 8,000 feet over the eastern portion of the Area Forecast region to 12,000 feet over the western portion of the Area Forecast region. Conditions are expected to continue beyond 1700 UTC. This SIGMET corrects SIGMET YANKEE 3.

4. **SIGMETs for Volcanic Ash**

   a. A SIGMET for volcanic ash (VA) may be issued for all volcanic eruptions, regardless of the eruption's magnitude.

      1) Volcanic ash SIGMETs are issued until the ash cloud is no longer a threat to aviation.

   b. The forecast position information for the volcanic ash cloud is based on advisories provided by a Volcanic Ash Advisory Center (VAAC).

   c. Initial VA SIGMETs may be issued based on credible pilot or aircraft reports in the absence of a Volcanic Ash Advisory (VAA) but are updated once a VAA is issued.

   d. The following are two examples of a SIGMET for Volcanic Ash. They are produced in a readable format, thus no additional interpretation is necessary.

```
ANCI UWS 190530
PAZA SIGMET INDIA 1 VALID 190530/190930 PANC-
SATELLITE IMAGERY SHOWS DEVELOPING VA FROM ANOTHER POSSIBLE
ERUPTION OF CHIKURACHKI VOLCANO AT 0500 UTC IN THE NORTHERN KURIL
ISLANDS.  HEIGHT IS ESTIMATED AT FL300 MOVEMENT IS E AT 75KTS.  FURTHER
UPDATES TO FOLLOW ASAP.
FCSTR APRIL 2003 AAWU

ANCI UWS 190930
PAZA SIGMET INDIA 2 VALID 190930-191330Z PANC-
AT 0830 UTC SATELLITE IMAGERY SHOWED THE PLUME FROM THE 0500 UTC
ERUPTION OF CHIKURACHKI VOLCANO IN THE NORTHERN KURIL ISLANDS BECOMING
VERY DIFFUSE IN AN APPROXIMATELY 60 NM WIDE BAND FROM N48/E167 AND
EXTENDING SE FOR 250 NM.  HEIGHT IS ESTIMATED AT FL300.  MOVEMENT IS E
AT 90 KTS.  THE PLUME IS MOVING SE OF ALASKA AIRSPACE INTO THE
WASHINGTON VAAC AREA OF RESPONSIBILITY.  SEE WASHINGTON VAAC VOLCANIC
ASH SIGMETS AND ADVISORIES FOR FURTHER FORECASTS.
RB APRIL 2003
```

5.   SIGMETs for Tropical Cyclones

a.   A SIGMET for a tropical cyclone may be issued for non-frontal synoptic-scale cyclones over oceanic FIRs meeting the following criteria:

   1)   Originate over tropical or sub-tropical waters with organized convection and definite cyclonic surface wind circulation; and

   2)   Wind speeds reach 34 knots or more, independent of the wind averaging time used by the Tropical Cyclone Advisory Center (TCAC).

b.   SIGMETs for tropical cyclones do not include references to associated turbulence and icing.

c.   The following is an example of a SIGMET for Tropical Cyclone and its plain-English interpretation.

```
KZNY SIGMET CHARLIE 4 VALID 081500/082100 KKCI-
NEW YORK OCEANIC FIR TO KYLE OBS N3106 W07118 AT 1500Z CB TOPS FL500
WI 80NM OF CENTER MOV SSW 5KT NC FCST 2100Z TC CENTER N2930 W07130
OTLK TC CENTER 090000 N3018 W07142 091200 UTC N2918 W07224
```

SIGMET issued by the Aviation Weather Center (AWC) for the New York Area Control Center. This is the fourth (4th) issuance of SIGMET series Charlie valid from the 8th day of the month at 1500 UTC to the 8th day of the month at 2100 UTC. Within the New York Oceanic FIR. Tropical Cyclone Kyle was observed at 31 degrees 6 minutes north, 71 degrees 18 minutes west at 1500 UTC. Cumulonimbus tops at 50,000 feet within 80 nautical miles of the center, moving south-southwest at 5 knots, with no change observed. At 2100 UTC, the tropical cyclone's center is forecast to be located at 29 degrees, 30 minutes north and 71 degrees, 30 minutes west. The outlook on the 9th day of the month at 0000 UTC is for the tropical cyclone center to be located at 30 degrees, 18 minutes north and 71 degrees, 42 minutes west. On the 9th day of the month at 1200 UTC, the center is forecast to be at 29 degrees, 18 minutes north and 72 degrees, 24 minutes west.

6. **Convective SIGMETs**

   a. The following is an example of a Convective SIGMET and its plain-English interpretation.

   ```
   CONVECTIVE SIGMET 54C
   VALID UNTIL 18555Z
   WI IL
   FROM 30E MSN-40ESE DBQ
   DMSHG LINE TS 15 NM WIDE MOV FROM 30025KT.   TOPS TO FL450.   WIND GUSTS
   TO 50 KT POSS.

   CONVECTIVE SIGMET 55C
   VALID UNTIL 1855Z
   TX OK NM
   FROM 70SE TBE-60NW AMA-40NW TCC-30ESE CIM-70SE TBE
   AREA SEV TS MOV FROM 33025KT.   TOPS TO FL400.
   HAIL TO 2 IN...WIND GUSTS TO 70KT POSS.

   OUTLOOK VALID 251855-252255
   FROM 60NW ISN-INL-TVC-GIJ-UIN-FSD-BIL-60NW ISN
   WST ISSUANCES EXPD.   REFER TO MOST RECENT ACUS01 KWNS FROM STORM
   PREDICTION CENTER FOR SYNOPSIS AND METEOROLOGICAL DETAILS.
   ```

   Convective SIGMET 54C is the 54th Convective SIGMET issued for the central region of the US on the 25th day of the month. Valid until 1855Z. States affected include Wisconsin and Illinois. Bounded within an area from 30 east of Madison, WI; to 40 miles east-southeast of Dubuque, Iowa. A diminishing line of thunderstorms 15 nautical miles wide moving from 300 degrees (to the southeast) at 25 knots. Thunderstorms tops to FL450 (approximately 45,000 ft MSL). Wind gusts to 50 knots are possible.

   Convective SIGMET 55C is the 55th Convective SIGMET issued for the central region of the US on the 25th day of the month. Valid until 1855Z. States affected include Texas, Oklahoma and New Mexico. Bounded within an area from 70 miles southeast of Tuba City, Arizona; to 60 miles northwest of Amarillo, Texas; to 40 northwest of Tucumcari, New Mexico; to 30 miles east-southeast of Cimarron, New Mexico; to 70 miles southeast of Tuba City, Arizona. An area of severe thunderstorms is moving from 330 degrees (to the southeast) at 25 knots. Thunderstorms tops to Flight Level 400 (approximately 40,000 feet MSL). Hail up to 2 inches in diameter and wind gusts to 70 knots are possible.

   The outlook portion of the Convective SIGMET bulletin is valid from the 25th day of the month at 1855 UTC to the 25th day of the month at 2255 UTC. Within an area bounded by 60 miles northwest of Williston, North Dakota; to International Falls, Minnesota; to Traverse City, Michigan; to Niles, Michigan; to Quincy, Illinois; to Sioux Falls, South Dakota; to Billings, Montana; to 60 miles northwest of Williston, North Dakota. Convective SIGMET issuances are expected for this area. Refer to the most recent Day 1 Convective Outlook (ACUS01 KWNS) from the Storm Prediction Center for a synopsis and meteorological details.

END OF STUDY UNIT

STUDY UNIT SEVENTEEN
AIRMEN'S METEOROLOGICAL INFORMATION (AIRMET)

(7 pages of outline)

> Please take a few minutes to study each of the concepts listed above and anticipate/imagine what they are and how they relate to the other listed concepts.

17.1 PRODUCT DESCRIPTION

1. An AIRMET is one of the three types of inflight aviation weather advisories: the Significant Meteorological Information (SIGMET), the Convective SIGMET, and the Airmen's Meteorological Information (AIRMET). All of these advisories use the same location identifiers (either VORs, airports, or well-known geographic areas) to describe the hazardous weather areas.

2. An AIRMET is a concise description of the occurrence or expected occurrence in time and space of specified en route weather phenomena. The intensities are lower than those of a SIGMET although the phenomena can still affect the safety of aircraft operations. AIRMETs are intended for dissemination to all pilots in flight to enhance safety and are of particular concern to operators and pilots of aircraft sensitive to the phenomena described and to pilots without instrument ratings. Freezing level information is also included.

3. An AIRMET provides notice of significant weather phenomena, issued as scheduled products, for icing, turbulence, strong surface winds and low-level wind shear, and Instrument Flight Rules (IFR) and mountain obscuration, all at intensities that **do not** meet SIGMET criteria.

    a. AIRMETs are available for the conterminous U.S. (CONUS) on the Aviation Digital Data Service (ADDS) website at http://adds.aviationweather.noaa.gov/airmets/.

    b. AIRMETs are available for Alaska on the Alaska Aviation Weather Unit (AAWU) website at http://aawu.arh.noaa.gov/.

    c. AIRMETs are available for Hawaii on the NWS WFO Honolulu website at http://www.prh.noaa.gov/hnl/pages/aviation.php.

4. **AIRMET Series**

    a. There are three AIRMETs: Sierra, Tango, and Zulu.

    b. After the first issuance each day, scheduled or unscheduled bulletins are numbered sequentially for easier identification.

        1) **AIRMET Sierra** describes IFR conditions and/or extensive mountain obscurations.

        2) **AIRMET Tango** describes moderate turbulence; sustained surface winds of 30 knots or greater; and non-convective, low-level wind shear.

        3) **AIRMET Zulu** describes moderate icing and provides freezing-level heights.

5.   **AIRMET Criteria**

    a.   An AIRMET may be issued when certain weather phenomena are occurring or expected to occur over an area of at least 3,000 square miles.

        1)   If the total area to be affected during the forecast period is very large, it could be that in actuality only a small portion of this total area would be affected at any one time.

        2)   An example would be a 3,000-square-mi. phenomenon forecast to move across an area totaling 25,000 square mi. during a forecast period.

    b.   Any of the following weather phenomena would result in the issuance of an AIRMET:

        1)   Sustained surface wind greater than 30 knots -- **STG SFC WND**

           a)   Cause and direction will not be given.

        2)   Ceiling less than 1,000 feet **(IFR, CIG BLW 010)** or visibility less than 3 statute miles **(IFR, VIS BLW 3 SM BR)**

           a)   The cause of the visibility restriction is included but limited to precipitation (PCPN), smoke (FU), haze (HZ), mist (BR), fog (FG), and blowing snow (BLSN).

        3)   Widespread mountain obscuration -- **MTN OBSCN**

           a)   The cause of the mountain obscuration is included but limited to clouds (CLDS) precipitation (PCPN), smoke (FU), haze (HZ), mist (BR), and fog (FG).

        4)   Moderate turbulence -- **MOD TURB**

        5)   Moderate icing -- **MOD ICE**

           a)   Will not reference the location of the icing with respect to either in clouds or in precipitation.

           b)   The freezing level is defined as the lowest freezing level above ground level or the surface (SFC).

           c)   Freezing levels above the surface are delineated using high altitude VOR locations at intervals of 4,000 feet above MSL or the surface (SFC).

           d)   The range of freezing levels over the AIRMET area is included.

        6)   Non-convective LLWS (low level windshear) potential below 2,000 ft. -- **LLWS POTENTIAL**

           a)   Will include a list of affected states and be bounded by high altitude VOR locations.

17.2 ISSUANCE

    1.   AIRMETs are issued from Meteorological Watch Offices (MWO). The three U.S. MWOs and their areas of responsibility are identified below.

        a.   The Aviation Weather Center (AWC)

           1)   The conterminous U.S. and adjacent coastal waters (CONUS)

        b.   The Alaska Aviation Weather Unit (AAWU)

           1)   Alaska and adjacent coastal waters

        c.   The Weather Forecast Office (WFO) in Honolulu

           1)   Hawaii and adjacent waters

2. AIRMETs are issued in AIRMET bulletins, each containing one or more AIRMET messages.

    a. The bulletins are issued on a scheduled basis every 6 hours and unscheduled updates and corrections are issued as necessary.

        1) AIRMETs from the AWC and the Honolulu WFO are issued at 0300, 0900, 1500, and 2100 UTC.

        2) In Alaska, AIRMET bulletins are issued every 6 hours as well, but they are issued with the Area Forecast.

    b. An AIRMET bulletin may be issued for each forecast area.

    c. Each AIRMET bulletin contains any current AIRMETs in effect and an outlook for conditions expected after the AIRMET valid period.

    d. A reference to the appropriate SIGMET series is included in AIRMET bulletins which cover the affected area and for similar phenomena; for example, **SEE SIGMET BRAVO SERIES**.

3. **AIRMET Valid Period**

    a. AIRMETs are issued for conditions occurring or expected to develop within the 6-hour valid time of the AIRMET bulletin.

    b. An AIRMET's valid period is the same as the AIRMET bulletin's valid time unless otherwise noted.

4. **AIRMET Updates, Amendments, and Corrections**

    a. Unscheduled updates to AIRMET bulletins are issued as necessary.

        1) If an AIRMET is amended, **AMD** is added after the date/time group on the FAA product line.

        2) **UPDT** is added to the end of the line containing the list of affected states. The issue time of the AIRMET bulletin is updated to reflect the new beginning valid time with the ending valid time remaining unchanged.

        3) AIRMETs containing errors are corrected by adding **COR** after the date/time group on the FAA product line.

17.3 FORMAT AND CONTENT

1. **AIRMET Standardization**

    a. All heights or altitudes are referenced to Mean Sea Level (MSL) and consist of three digits depicting height in hundreds of feet.

        1) Flight Level (FL) is used for heights at or above 18,000 feet.

        2) EXAMPLES: 100 = 10,000 ft. MSL, FL190 = Equals approximately 19,000 feet MSL.

    b. References to latitude and longitude are in whole degrees and minutes with a space between latitude and longitude and a hyphen between successive points.

        1) Products issued by AWC have the N, S, W, or E behind the latitude/longitude numbers.

        2) EXAMPLE: N3106 W07118 = 31 degrees, 6 minutes North by 7 degrees, 118 minutes West.

    c. Messages are prepared using approved ICAO contractions, abbreviations, and numerical values of self-explanatory nature.

> d.   Weather and obstructions to visibility will be limited to clouds, (CLDS), precipitation (PCPN), smoke (FU), haze (HZ), mist (BR), fog, (FG), and blowing snow (BLSN).
>
> e.   All amended (AMD) or corrected (COR) en route forecasts or advisory products follow the same format procedures.
>
>> 1)   An AMD or COR is identified as a change in the first line after the time and date.

2.   **AIRMET Phenomena Information**

> a.   An AIRMET message contains the following information as necessary and in the order indicated relating to the phenomena that caused the AIRMET to be issued:
>
>> 1)   Location (using locations or geographic features well known nationally if possible)
>>
>> 2)   Phenomena and its description, e.g., **MOD TURB**
>>
>> 3)   If appropriate, level (altitude), or vertical extent
>>
>> 4)   Expected beginning and ending time of phenomena, if different from the AIRMET bulletin's valid time
>>
>> 5)   Remarks
>>
>>> a)   A remark is included at the end of each AIRMET regarding whether the condition is expected to continue after the valid time of the AIRMET.

3.   **AIRMET Format**

> a.   The WMO (World Meteorological Organization) AIRMET header is **WA**.
>
> b.   The table below shows an example of an AIRMET.

```
LINE
1 -  BOSS WA 211945
2 -  AIRMET SIERRA UPDT 3 FOR IFR AND MTN OBSCN VALID
     UNTIL 220200
     .
3 -  AIRMET IFR.ME NH VT MA CT RI NY NJ AND CSTL WTRS
4 -  FROM CAR TO YSJ TO 150E ACK TO EWR TO YOW TO CAR
5 -  CIG BLW 010/VIS BLW 3SM PCPN/BR.  CONDS CONT BYD
     02Z THRU 08Z.
     .
3 -  AIRMET MTN OBSCN..ME NH VT MA NY PA
4 -  FROM CAR TO MLT TO CON TO AVP TO SYR TO CAR
5 -  MTNS OBSCD BY CLDS/PCPN/BR.  CONDS CONT BYD 02Z
     THRU 08Z.
```

Table 17-1. AIRMET Bulletin Decoding Example

c.   The table below shows how to decode the example AIRMET shown previously.

LINE	CONTENT	DESCRIPTION
1	BOS S WA 211945	AIRMET area identifier <u>AIRMET</u> series Product type Issuance UTC date/time
2	AIRMET SIERRA UPDT 3 FOR IFR AND MTN OBSCN VALID UNTIL 220200	Product type <u>AIRMET</u> series Update number Product description Ending UTC date/time
3	AIRMET IFR..ME NH VT MA CT RI NY NJ AND CSTL WTRS AIRMET MTN OBSCN..ME NH VT MA NY PA	Product type/series... Phenomenon location (states)
4	FROM CAR TO YSJ TO 150E ACK TO EWR TO YOW TO CAR FROM CAR TO MLT TO CON TO AVP TO SYR TO CAR	Phenomenon location (VOR locations)
5	CIG BLW 010/VIS BLW 3SM PCPN/BR. CONDS CONT BYD 02Z THRU 08Z. MTNS OBSCD BY CLDS/PCPN/BR. CONDS CONT BYD 02Z THRU 08Z.	Phenomenon description

Table 17-2. Decoding an AIRMET Bulletin

d.   The table below explains the example AIRMET shown previously.

Line 1	AIRMET SIERRA issued for the Boston area at 1945Z on the 21st day of the month. "SIERRA" contains information on Instrument Flight Rules (IFR) and/or mountain obscuration.
Line 2	This is the third updated issuance of this Boston AIRMET series as indicated by "SIERRA UPDT 3" and is valid until 0200Z on the 22nd.
Line 3	The affected states within the BOS area are Maine, New Hampshire, Vermont, Massachusetts, Connecticut, Rhode Island, New York, New Jersey, and coastal waters.
Line 4	From Caribou, ME; to Saint Johns, New Brunswick; to 150 nautical miles east of Nantucket, MA; to Newark, NJ; to Ottawa, Ontario; to Caribou, ME.
Line 5	Ceiling below 1,000 feet/visibility below 3 statute miles, precipitation/mist. Conditions continuing beyond 0200Z through 0800Z.

Table 17-3. AIRMET Explained

17.4 USING THE PRODUCT

1. AIRMETs are commonly used by pilots during personal weather briefings and are also relayed as part of a weather briefing from a Flight Service Station (FSS).

2. Pilots should reference all three AIRMET products to get a well-rounded picture of the potential weather hazards along a specified route of flight.

3. Because AIRMETs are issued every 6 hours, the weather could change after you review an AIRMET. Be sure to check for updates regularly and especially immediately before the flight.

4. The following examples are actual AIRMET reports followed by plain-English interpretations. Read through these examples to ensure that you understand AIRMET terminology and interpretation.

```
CHIS WA 171345
AIRMET SIERRA UPDT 3 FOR IFR AND MTN OBSCN VALID UNTIL 172000
.

AIRMET IFR...NE KS
FROM 60NE BFF TO ANW TO 40NE OBH TO OSW TO 40N GAG TO 40N GLD TO 60NE BFF
CIG BLW 010/VIS BLW 3SM PCPN BR.   CONDS ENDG 18Z.
.

AIRMET IFR...MO IL IN KY
FROM CVG TO HNN TO HMV TO BWG TO RZC TO SGF TO 60S DEC TO CVG
CIG BLW 010/VIS BLW 3SM BR.   CONTG BYD 20Z ENDG 23Z.
```

AIRMET Sierra bulletin for the Chicago Area Forecast region issued on the 17th day of the month at 1345 UTC and contains two AIRMETs. This is the 3rd AIRMET Sierra bulletin update issued for IFR and Mountain Obscurations and is valid until the 17th day of the month at 2000 UTC.

The first AIRMET is for IFR conditions affecting Nebraska and Kansas. Bounded within an area from 60 nautical miles (NM) northeast of Scottsbluff, Nebraska; to Ainsworth, Nebraska; to 40 NM northeast of Wolbach, Nebraska; to Oswego, Kansas; to 40 NM miles north of Gage, Oklahoma; to 60 NM miles northeast of Scottsbluff, Nebraska. s below 1,000 feet and visibilities less than 3 statute miles (SM) with precipitation and mist. Conditions are forecast to end by 1800 UTC.

The second AIRMET is for IFR conditions affecting Missouri, Illinois, Indiana and Kentucky. Bounded within an area from Covington, Kentucky; to Henderson, West Virginia; to Holston Mountain, Tennessee; to Bowling Green, Kentucky; to Razorback, Arkansas; to Springfield, Missouri; to 60 NM miles south of Decatur, Illinois; to Covington, Kentucky. Ceilings below 1,000 feet and visibilities less than 3 SM due to mist. Conditions are forecast to continue beyond 2000 UTC and end by 2300 UTC.

```
HNLS WA 080945
AIRMET SIERRA UPDATE 1 FOR IFR VALID UNTIL 081600.
.
NO SGFNT IFR EXP.
```

AIRMET Sierra bulletin for the Hawaii forecast region issued on the 8th day of the month at 0945 UTC. This is the 1st AIRMET Sierra bulletin update issued for IFR and Mountain Obscurations and is valid until the 8th day of the month at 1600 UTC.

No conditions meeting IFR criteria are expected.

```
HNLT WA 080945
AIRMET TANGO UPDT 1 FOR TURB VALID UNTIL 081600
.
AIRMET TURB...HI
OVR AND IMT S THRU W OF MT OF ALL ISLANDS.
MOD TURB BLW 060.   COND CONT BYD 1600Z THRU 22Z.
```

AIRMET Tango bulletin for the Hawaii Area Forecast region issued on the 8th day of the month at 0945 UTC. This is the 1st AIRMET Tango bulletin update issued for turbulence and is valid until the 8th day of the month at 1600 UTC.

AIRMET for turbulence for Hawaii. Over and immediately south through west of the mountains for all islands. Moderate turbulence is expected below 6,000 feet above MSL. Conditions are expected to continue beyond 1600 UTC through 2200 UTC.

```
SFOZ WA 171345
AIRMET ZULU UPDT 2 FOR ICE AND FRZLVL VALID UNTIL 172000
.
AIRMET ICE...WA OR ID MT
FROM 60SSW YXH TO 70ESE MLP TO PDT TO PDX TO SWA TO BLI TO 60SSW YXH
MOD ICE BTN 120 AND FL200.   CONDS CONTG BYD 20Z THRU 02Z.
.
FRZLVL...RANGING FROM 090-160
   120...ONP-LKV-REO
   160...SNS-40SW BTY
```

AIRMET Zulu bulletin for the San Francisco Area Forecast area issued on the 17th day of the month at 1345 UTC. This is the 2nd AIRMET Zulu bulletin update issued for icing and freezing levels and is valid until the 17th day of the month at 2000 UTC.

AIRMET for icing for Washington, Oregon, Idaho, and Montana. Bounded within an area from 60 miles south-southwest of Medicine Hat, Alberta; to 70 NM miles east-southeast of Mullan Pass, Idaho; to Pendleton, Oregon; to Portland, Oregon; to Seattle, Washington; to Billings, Montana; to 60 NM miles south-southwest of Medicine Hat, Alberta. Moderate icing between 12,000 and 20,000 feet above MSL. Conditions continuing beyond 2000 UTC through 0200 UTC.

Freezing levels over the area ranging between 9,000 and 16,000 feet above MSL, Freezing level at 12,000 feet above MSL along a line from the Newport, Oregon VOR to the Lake County, Oregon VOR to the Rome, Oregon VOR. Freezing level at 16,000 feet above MSL along a line from the Salinas, California VOR to 40 NM southwest of the Beatty, Nevada VOR.

END OF STUDY UNIT

STUDY UNIT EIGHTEEN
CENTER WEATHER ADVISORY (CWA)

(4 pages of outline)

> Please take a few minutes to study each of the concepts listed above and anticipate/imagine what they are and how they relate to the other listed concepts.

18.1 PRODUCT DESCRIPTION

1. A Center Weather Advisory (CWA) is an aviation weather warning for conditions meeting or approaching national inflight advisory (AIRMET, SIGMET, or SIGMET for convection) criteria. The CWA is primarily used by aircrews to anticipate and avoid adverse weather conditions in the en route and terminal environments.

2. CWAs can be issued for any of the following four reasons:

   a. To precede an advisory

      1) When the Aviation Weather Center (AWC) has not yet issued an advisory, but conditions meet or will soon meet advisory criteria based on current pilot reports and this information must be disseminated sooner than the AWC can issue the inflight aviation weather advisory.

      2) In the case of an impending advisory (or SIGMET), the CWA can be issued as an Urgent CWA (UCWA) to allow the fastest possible dissemination.

   b. To revise an existing advisory

      1) To supplement an existing AWC advisory for the purpose of refining or updating the location, movement, extent, or intensity of the weather event relevant to the ARTCC's area of responsibility.

      2) This is important because a SIGMET for severe turbulence is issued by the AWC, and the outline covers the entire ARTCC area for the total 4 hours valid time period.

         a) The forecaster may issue a CWA covering only a relatively small portion of the ARTCC area at any one time during the 4-hour period.

   c. To highlight significant conditions not meeting advisory criteria

      1) When conditions do not meet advisory criteria, but conditions, in the judgment of the CWSU meteorologist, will adversely impact air traffic within the ARTCC area of responsibility.

   d. To cancel a CWA when the phenomenon described in the CWA is no longer expected.

18.2 ISSUANCE AND VALIDITY

1. CWAs are issued by the NWS Center Weather Service Units (CWSUs).

2. A CWA is not a flight planning forecast but a nowcast for conditions beginning within the next 2 hours.

3. CWAs are valid for up to 2 hours and may include forecasts of conditions expected to begin within 2 hours of issuance. If conditions are expected to persist after the advisory's valid period, a statement to that effect is included in the last line of the text. Additional CWAs will subsequently be issued as appropriate. Notice of significant changes in the phenomenon described in a CWA is provided by a new CWA issuance for that phenomenon. If the forecaster deems it necessary, CWAs may be issued hourly for convective activity.

4. CWAs are available on the Aviation Weather Center (AWC) website at http://aviationweather.gov/products/cwsu/.

18.3 CONTENT AND FORMAT

1. **CWA Communications Headers (UCWA/CWA)**

    a. The Urgent CWA (UCWA) communications header is intended for those situations where weather conditions have an immediate effect on the safe flow of air traffic within the ARTCC area of responsibility. It is only used when the CWSU meteorologist believes any delay in dissemination to FAA facilities would impact aviation safety.

    b. The routine CWA header is used for subsequent issuances of the same phenomenon.

2. A sample CWA is reproduced here. Below it is a table explaining all of the coded elements.

```
LINE
1 — ZDV2 CWA 032140
2 — ZDV CWA 202 VALID UNTIL 032340
3 — FROM FMN TO 10N FMN TO 20NE FMN TO 10E FMN TO FMN
4 — ISOLD SEV TS NR FMN MOVG NEWD 10KTS.  TOP FL410.  WND GSTS TO
    55KTS.  HAIL TO 1 INCH RPRTD AT FMN.  SEV TS CONTG BYD 2340Z.
```

Table 18-1. Center Weather Advisory (CWA) Decoding Example

LINE	CONTENT	DESCRIPTION
1	ZDV 2 CWA 032140	ARTCC Identification Phenomenon Number (single digit, 1-6) Product type (UCWA/CWA) Beginning and/or issuance UTC date/time
2	ZDV CWA 2 02 VALID UNTIL 032340Z	ARTCC Identification Product type Phenomenon Number (single digit, 1-6) Issuance Number (issued sequentially for each Phenomenon Number) Ending valid UTC date/time
3	FROM FMN TO 10N FMN TO 20NE FMN TO 10E FMN TO FMN	Phenomenon Location
4	ISOLD SEV TS NR FMN MOVG NEWD 10KTS. TOP FL 410. WND GSTS TO 55KTS. HAIL TO 1 INCH RPRTD AT FMN. SEV TS CONTG BYD 2340Z	Phenomenon Description

Table 18-2. Decoding a Center Weather Advisory (CWA)

3.   The following explanation deciphers the previous CWA.

Line 1	Center Weather Advisory issued for the Denver ARTCC (ZDV) CWSU. The "2" after ZDV in the first line denotes this is the second meteorological event of the local calendar day. This CWA was issued/begins on the 3rd day of the month at 2140 UTC.
Line 2	The Denver ARTCC (ZDV) is identified again. The "202" in the second line denotes the phenomena number again (2) and the issuance number (02) for this phenomenon. This CWA is the valid until the 3rd day of the at 2340 UTC.
Line 3	From Farmington, New Mexico to 10 nautical miles north of Farmington, New Mexico to 20 nautical miles northeast of Farmington, NM to 10 nautical mile east of Farmington, New Mexico to Farmington, New Mexico.
Line 4	Isolated severe thunderstorms near Farmington moving northeastward at 10 knots. Tops to Flight Level 410. Wind gusts to 55 knots. Hail to one inch reported at Farmington. Severe thunderstorms continuing beyond 2340 UTC.

Table 18-3. Center Weather Advisory (CWA) Explained

4.   Time permitting, any CWA overlapping into another center's airspace is coordinated and a statement is included in the text, e.g., **SEE ZOB CWA 201 FOR TS CONDS IN ZOB CTA** (CTA is control area).

   a.   If issuance prior to coordination is necessary, a statement regarding the area(s) affected is included in the text, e.g., **LINE TS EXTDS NW INTO ZOB CTA**.

5.   AIRMETs/SIGMETs being augmented by the CWA will be referenced in a text remark, e.g., **SEE CONVECTIVE SIGMET 8W**.

18.4 USING THE PRODUCT

1.   CWAs are used by controllers to facilitate the safe and orderly flow of air traffic.

   a.   These reports allow controllers to alert pilots and each other about weather hazards that could potentially negatively affect air traffic flow.

   b.   Pilots should use CWAs as part of their personal weather briefings in order to plan for delays in and around airport terminal areas as well as during the en route phase of flight to anticipate diversions and reroutes before they occur.

2.   Several examples of CWAs are provided here along with explanations of the report elements.

```
ZME1 CWA 081300
ZME CWA 101 VALID TIL 081500
FROM MEM TO JAN TO LIT TO MEM
OCNL TS MOV FM 26025KT.  TOPS TO FL450.
```

Center Weather Advisory issued for the Memphis, Tennessee ARTCC on the 8th day of the month at 1300 UTC. The "1" after the ZME in the first line denotes this CWA has been issued for the first weather phenomenon to occur for the local calendar day. The "101" in the second line denotes the phenomenon number again (1) and the issuance number (01) for this phenomenon. The CWA is valid until the 8th day of the month at 1500 UTC. From Memphis, Tennessee to Jackson, Mississippi to Little Rock, Arkansas to Memphis, Tennessee. Occasional thunderstorms moving from 260 degrees at 25 knots. Tops to Flight Level 450.

```
ZLC3 CWA 271645
ZLC CWA 303 VALID TIL 271745
CNL CWA 302.
SEE CONVECTIVE SIGMET 8W.
```

Center Weather Advisory issued for the Salt Lake City, Utah ARTCC on the 27th day of the month at 1645 UTC. The "3" after the ZLC in the first line denotes this CWA has been issued for the third weather phenomenon to occur for the local calendar day. The "303" in the second line denotes the phenomenon number again (3) and the issuance number (03) for this phenomenon. The CWA is valid until the 27th day of the month at 1745 UTC. CWA number 302 has been canceled. See Convective SIGMET 8W.

```
ZME1 CWA 040100
ZME CWA 101 VALID TIL 040300
VCY MEM
SEV CLR ICE BLW 020 DUE TO FZRA.  NUMEROUS ACFT REP RAPID
ACCUMULATION OF ICE DRG DES TO MEM.  NO ICE REPS ABV 020.  CONDS CONTG
AFT 03Z.  NO UPDATES AFT 040200Z.
```

Center Weather Advisory issued for the Memphis, Tennessee ARTCC on the 4th day of the month at 0100 UTC. The "1" after the ZLC in the first line denotes this CWA has been issued for the first weather phenomenon to occur for the local calendar day. The "101" in the second line denotes the phenomenon number again (1) and the issuance number (01) for this phenomenon. The CWA is valid until the 4th day of the month at 0300 UTC. For the Memphis, Tennessee vicinity. Severe clear icing below 2,000 feet MSL due to freezing rain. Numerous aircraft report rapid accumulation of icing during descent to Memphis. No icing reports above 2,000 feet MSL. Conditions continuing after 0300 UTC. No updates after 4th day of the month at 0200 UTC.

```
ZNY5 UCWA 021400
ZNY CWA 502 VALID TIL 021600
FROM BGM TO 18WNW JFK TO HAR TO SLT TO BGM
NUMEROUS ACFT REP SEV TURB AND WS BLW 020.
CONDS EXTD NE INTO ZBW CTA.  CONDS EXP TO CONT AFT 16Z.
```

Urgent Center Weather Advisory issued for the New York ARTCC on the 2nd day of the month at 1400 UTC. The "5" after the ZNY in the first line denotes this CWA has been issued for the fifth weather phenomenon to occur for the local calendar day. The "502" in the second line denotes the phenomenon number again (5) and the issuance number (02) for this phenomenon. The CWA is valid until the 2nd day of the month at 1600 UTC. From Binghamton, New York; to 18 nautical miles west-northwest of New York (JFK Airport), New York; to Harrisburg, Pennsylvania; to Slate Run, Pennsylvania; to Binghamton, New York. Numerous aircraft report severe turbulence and wind shear below 2,000 feet MSL. Conditions extending northeast into Nashua, New Hampshire control area. Conditions expected to continue after 1600 UTC.

```
ZNY4 UCWA 041500
ZNY CWA 401 VALID TIL 041700
40N SLT TO 18WNW JFK
DEVELOPING LINE TS 25 NM WIDE MOV 24020KT.  TOPS ABV FL350.
LINE TS EXTDS NW INTO ZOB CTA.
```

Urgent Center Weather Advisory issued for the New York ARTCC on the 4th day of the month at 1500 UTC. The "4" after the ZNY in the first line denotes this CWA has been issued for the fourth weather phenomenon to occur for the local calendar day. The "401" in the second line denotes the phenomenon number again (4) and the issuance number (01) for this phenomenon. The CWA is valid until the 4th day of the month at 1700 UTC. From 40 nautical miles north of Slate Run, Pennsylvania; to 18 nautical miles west-northwest of New York (JFK Airport), New York. Developing line of thunderstorms 25 nautical miles wide moving from 240 degrees at 20 knots. Tops above flight level 350. The line of thunderstorms extends northwest into the Oberlin, Ohio control area.

STUDY UNIT NINETEEN
ADDITIONAL PRODUCTS FOR CONVECTION

(10 pages of outline)

Please take a few minutes to study each of the concepts listed above and anticipate/imagine what they are and how they relate to the other listed concepts.

19.1 INTRODUCTION

1. In addition to the SIGMETs (Study Unit 16), Convective SIGMETs (Study Unit 16), and Center Weather Advisories (CWAs) (Study Unit 18) already discussed, the National Weather Service (NWS) offers a few more products informing the aviation community about the potential for convective weather.

2. **Convection** by definition is, generally, the transport of heat and moisture by the movement of a fluid.

   a. In meteorology, the term is used specifically to describe the vertical transport of heat and moisture in the atmosphere, especially by updrafts and downdrafts in an unstable atmosphere.

   b. The terms "convection" and "thunderstorms" often are used interchangeably, although thunderstorms are only one form of convection.

   c. Cumulonimbus clouds, towering cumulus clouds, and altocumulus castellanus (ACCAS) clouds are all visible forms of convection. However, convection is not always made visible by clouds.

   d. Convection that occurs without cloud formation is called dry convection, while the visible convection processes referred to above are forms of moist convection.

   e. **Terms of Convection**

      1) **Elevated convection** – Occurs within an elevated layer, i.e., a layer in which the lowest portion is based above the Earth's surface.

         a) Elevated convection often occurs when air near the ground is relatively cool and stable (e.g., during periods of lifting where air is traveling along an upward-sloping surface) when an unstable layer of air is present aloft.

         b) In cases of elevated convection, stability indices based on near-surface measurements (such as the lifted index) typically will underestimate the amount of instability present.

         c) Severe weather is possible from elevated convection but is less likely than it is with surface-based convection.

      2) **Level of free convection (LFC)** – The level at which a parcel of saturated air becomes warmer than the surrounding air and begins to rise freely.

         a) This occurs most readily in a conditionally unstable atmosphere.

      3) **Popcorn convection** – Slang for showers and thunderstorms that form on a scattered basis with little or no apparent organization, usually during the afternoon in response to diurnal heating.

         a) Individual thunderstorms typically are of the type sometimes referred to as air-mass thunderstorms; they are small, short-lived, very rarely severe, and almost always dissipate near or just after sunset.

4)   **Surface-based convection** – Occurs within a surface-based layer, i.e., a layer in which the lowest portion is based at or very near the Earth's surface.

a)   Contrary to elevated convection.

3.   Convection is measurable in real-time, but due to the importance of predicting the occurrence of convective weather before if appears, the convection products in this study unit are all forecasts.

a.   Some products forecast farther in the future than others, but remember when you analyze convection products that you are looking at forecast information based on computer modeling, not observed conditions.

b.   Carefully examine the issuance date and time of all weather reports, especially convection products, to be sure you are looking at valid, pertinent information.

c.   Convection conditions can change wildly and unexpectedly. Remember that convection products are an aid to pilot planning, not a guaranteed model of the exact weather conditions that will exist at your time of departure.

19.2 CONVECTIVE OUTLOOKS (AC)

1.   A Convective Outlook (AC) is a forecast containing the area(s) of expected thunderstorm occurrence and expected severity over the contiguous United States, issued several times daily by the Storm Prediction Center (SPC). The terms listed in the report (slight risk, moderate risk, and high risk) are used to describe severe thunderstorm potential.

a.   The AC is a textual translation of the images provided in the Convective Outlook Chart.

1)   The Convective Outlook and the Convective Outlook Chart are usually presented as a single unit, with the chart available to be used as a reference to the text and vice-versa.

b.   The AC is a tool for planning flights later in the day to avoid thunderstorms.

2.   The SPC issues narrative and graphical convective outlooks to provide the contiguous U.S. NWS Weather Forecast Offices (WFOs), the public, the media, and emergency managers with the potential for severe and non-severe convection and specific severe weather threats during the following eight days.

a.   **Severe** is defined as the expected occurrence of

1)   A tornado,
2)   Wind gusts 50 knots or greater, or
3)   Hail of 3/4 inch diameter size or greater.

b.   The Day 1, Day 2, and Day 3 outlooks are considered to be the most accurate, given that the predictability of severe weather decreases the further into the future a forecaster looks.

1)   A severe weather area depicted in the Day 4-8 period indicates a 30% or higher probability that severe thunderstorms will occur within 25 miles of any point.

2)   If the predictability of thunderstorms is too uncertain during the Day 4-8 period, the narrative and the chart will indicate this to the user and not provide any forecast information.

3.   The Convective Outlook defines areas of slight risk **(SLGT)**, moderate risk **(MDT)**, or high risk **(HIGH)** of severe thunderstorms for a 24-hour period beginning at 1200 UTC.

a.   The Day 1 and Day 2 Convective Outlooks depict areas of general thunderstorms **(GEN TSTMS)**.

b.   The Day 1, Day 2, and Day 3 Convective Outlooks may use **SEE TEXT** for areas where convection may approach or slightly exceed severe criteria.

c.   Additional forecast graphics are available for the Day 1 outlook on the SPC website shown below. These graphics are self-explanatory and thus not detailed in this study unit. For your reference, they are itemized here.

1)   Probabilistic Tornado Graphic
2)   Probabilistic Damaging Wind Graphic
3)   Probabilistic Large Hail Graphic

4.   **Issuance**

a.   The table below explains when each outlook is issued as well as its valid times.

Convective Outlook	Issuance Time (UTC)	Valid Period (UTC)
Day 1	0600	1200 – 1200
	1300	1300 – 1200
	1630	1630 – 1200
	2000	2000 – 1200
	0100	0100 – 1200
Day 2	0730 (Daylight Savings Time) 0830 (Standard Time)	Day 2/1200 – 1200
	1730	Day 2/1200 – 1200
Day 3	1100	Day 3/1200 – 1200
Day 4-8	1100	Day 4-8/1200 – 1200

Table 19-1. Convective Outlook Issuance Schedule

b.   The outlooks are available on the SPC website at:
http://www.spc.noaa.gov/products/outlook/.

5.   **Using the Product**

a.   The format of the Convective Outlook narrative is reproduced here.

```
SPC AC ddhhmm [SPC - issuing office, AC – product type, ddhhmm – date and time the product was issued

DAY (ONE, TWO OR THREE) CONVECTIVE OUTLOOK
NWS STORM PREDICTION CENTER NORMAN OK
time am/pm time_zone day mon dd yyyy

VALID DDHHMM - DDHHMMZ

THERE IS A (SLIGHT, MODERATE, HIGH) RISK OF SEVERE THUNDERSTORMS TO
THE RIGHT OF LINE (LIST OF ANCHOR POINTS AND DIRECTION AND DISTANCE IN
STATUTE MILES FROM THE LINE).  THE LINE WILL ENCLOSE THE AREA OF RISK.
THERE MAY BE ONE OR MORE AREAS OF RISK AT THE APPROPRIATE LEVEL OF
RISK.  WHEN A MODERATE OR HIGH RISK IS FORECAST, THE INDIVIDUAL STATES
ARE ALSO LISTED WITH THE TWO LETTER POSTAL STATE IDENTIFIERS.

GEN TSTMS ARE FCST TO THE RIGHT OF A LINE FROM (LIST OF ANCHOR POINTS
AND DIRECTION AND DISTANCE IN STATUTE MILES FROM THE LINE).  THERE MAY
BE ONE OR MORE AREAS OF GEN TSTMS LISTED.

...AREA OF CONCERN #1...

AREAS OF HIGHEST RISK ARE DISCUSSED FIRST (HIGH SEVERE RISK,
MODERATE SEVERE RISK, SLIGHT SEVERE RISK, APPROACHING SEVERE
LIMITS).  THE FORECAST PROVIDES A NARRATIVE TECHNICAL DISCUSSION.

...AREA OF CONCERN #2...
NARRATIVE TECHNICAL DISCUSSION

$$

...FORECASTER NAME... MM/DD/YY
```

b.   A sample Convective Outlook narrative is reproduced here.

```
SPC AC 081633

   DAY 1 CONVECTIVE OUTLOOK
   NWS STORM PREDICTION CENTER NORMAN OK
   1133 AM CDT WED AUG 08 2007

   VALID 081630Z - 091200Z

   ...THERE IS A SLGT RISK OF SVR TSTMS OVER THE NRN/CENTRAL PLAINS EWD
   ACROSS THE MIDDLE MS VALLEY INTO THE UPPER OH VALLEY...

   ...MID MS VALLEY INTO UPPER OH VALLEY...
   VISIBLE SATELLITE IMAGERY INDICATES MCV OVER ERN IA/NRN IL BORDER
   MOVING EWD TOWARD NRN IL/NRN INDIANA.  DOWNSTREAM ENVIRONMENT IS
   CHARACTERIZED BY VERY WARM/MOIST LOW LEVELS WITH SURFACE DEW POINTS
   IN THE LOW/MID 70S...AND LIMITED CLOUDS FROM CENTRAL IL ACROSS
   INDIANA INTO OH SHOULD PROMOTE STRONG DIABATIC HEATING THIS
   AFTERNOON.  ALTHOUGH MID LEVEL TEMPERATURES ARE RATHER WARM /AROUND
   -4C AT 500 MB/ RESULTING IN MODEST LAPSE RATES OF 6 C/KM...AIR MASS
   IS LIKELY TO BECOME MODERATELY UNSTABLE WITH MLCAPE OF 2500-3000
   J/KG THIS AFTERNOON.  WEAK CONVERGENCE ASSOCIATED WITH
   QUASI-STATIONARY FRONT FROM NRN IL INTO THE LOWER GREAT LAKES AND
   OLD OUTFLOW BOUNDARIES SOUTH OF THE FRONT COUPLED WITH A WEAKENING
   CAP WILL BE SUFFICIENT FOR SCATTERED THUNDERSTORMS TO DEVELOP BY
   MID-LATE AFTERNOON.  30-35 KT WLY WINDS AT 500 MB ARE CONTRIBUTING
   TO 35-40 KT OF DEEP LAYER SHEAR WHICH WILL BE SUPPORTIVE OF
   ORGANIZED DEEP CONVECTION INCLUDING THE POSSIBILITY OF ISOLATED
   SUPERCELLS.  ALTHOUGH WARM MID LEVEL TEMPERATURES AND HIGH FREEZING
   LEVELS SHOULD LIMIT THREAT FOR SEVERE HAIL AT THE GROUND...LARGE
   CAPE AND DRY AIR ALOFT INDICATE POTENTIAL FOR DAMAGING WIND GUSTS
   WITH STRONGER CELLS THIS AFTERNOON AND EVENING.
```

[ADDITIONAL CONTENT EXCLUDED BY GLEIM]

```
   ..WEISS/JEWELL..  08/08/2007
```

c.   A sample Convective Outlook chart is reproduced on the next page.

1)   The arrows define the areas where the indicated risk of severe weather exists.

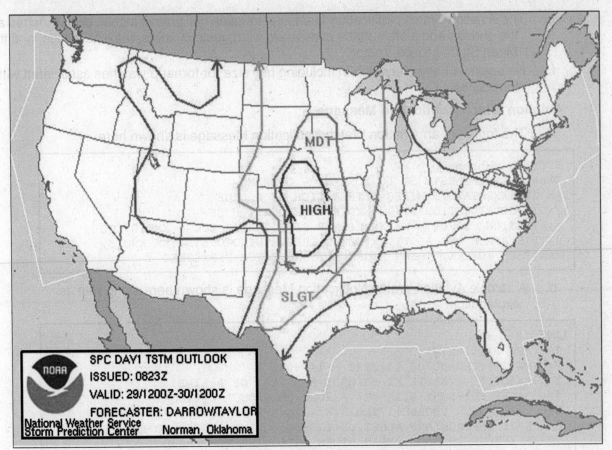

Figure 19-1. Day 1 Categorical Convective Outlook Graphic Example

19.3 WATCH NOTIFICATION MESSAGES

1. The NWS Storm Prediction Center issues Watch Notification Messages to alert the aviation community, NWS offices (WFOs), the public, the media, and emergency managers to organized thunderstorms forecast to produce tornadic and/or severe weather in the conterminous U.S.

2. SPC issues three types of Watch Notification Messages:
    a. Aviation Watch Notification Message
    b. Public Severe Thunderstorm Watch Notification Message
    c. Public Tornado Watch Notification Message
    d. They are available on the SPC website at: http://www.spc.noaa.gov/products/watch/

3. Watch Notification Messages are non-scheduled, event-driven products valid from the time of issuance to expiration or cancelation time.
    a. Valid times are in UTC.
    b. The SPC will correct watches for format and grammatical errors.
    c. When tornadoes or severe thunderstorms have developed, the local NWS Weather Forecast Offices (WFOs) will issue the warnings for the storms.
    d. SPC forecasters may define the watch area as a rectangle (some number of miles either side of a line from point A to point B) or as a parallelogram (some number of miles north and south or east and west of a line from point A to point B).
        1) The axis coordinates are measured in statute miles.
        2) The aviation coordinates are measured in nautical miles and referenced to VHF Omni-Directional Range (VOR) navigational aid locations.

e.   The Aviation Watch Notification Message contains hail size in inches or half inches at the surface and aloft, surface convective wind gusts in knots, maximum tops, and the Mean Storm Motion Vector.

f.   Forecasters have discretion in including hail size for tornado watches associated with hurricanes.

4.   **Aviation Watch Notification Message**

a.   The format of an Aviation Watch Notification Message is shown here.

```
SPC AWW ddhhmm
WWnnnn SEVERE TSTM ST LO DDHHMMZ - DDHHMMZ
AXIS...XX STATUTE MILES EITHER SIDE OF A LINE
XXDIR CCC/LOCATION ST/ - XXDIR CCC/LOCATION ST
..AVIATION COORD..  XX NM EITHER SIDE /XXDIR CCC - XXDIR CCC
HAIL SURFACE AND ALOFT..X X/X INCHES.   WIND GUSTS..XX KNOTS.
MAX TOPS TO XXX.   MEAN STORM MOTION VECTOR DIR/SPEED
```

b.   A sample Aviation Watch Notification Message is shown here along with its explanation.

```
LINE
1 -  SPC AWW 132101
2 -  WW568 TORNADO OK 132130Z - 140300Z
3 -  AXIS..80 STATUTE MILES EAST AND WEST OF A LINE..
4 -  50SSE FSI/FORT SILL OK/ - 20NW PNC-PONCA CITY OK/
5 -  ..AVIATION COORDS..70NM E/W/ 21E SPS - 43S ICT/
6 -  HAIL SURFACE AND ALOFT..3 INCHES.  WIND GUSTS..70 KNOTS.
     MAX TOPS TO 550.  MEAN STORM MOTION VECTOR 26030.
```

Line 1	Alert Severe Weather Watch Bulletin (AWW), issued by the Storm Prediction Center on the 13th at 2101Z,
Line 2	for Tornado Watch number 568 (WW568) for Oklahoma, valid from the 13th at 2130Z until the 14th at 0300Z.
Line 3	The Tornado Watch area is along and 80 statute miles east and west of a line from...
Line 4	50 statute miles south southeast of Fort Sill (Lawton), OK to 20 statute miles northwest of Ponca City, OK.
Line 5	Aviation coordinates for this Tornado Watch are 70 nautical miles east and west of a line from 21 nautical miles east of Sheppard AFB (Wichita Falls), TX to 43 nautical miles south of Wichita, KS.
Line 6	Hail surface and aloft to 3 inches in diameter, wind gusts to 70 knots, max tops to Flight Level 550, mean storm motion from 260 degrees at 30 knots

5.   **Public Severe Thunderstorm Watch Notification Message**

a.   The SPC issues a Public Severe Thunderstorm Watch Notification Message when forecasting six or more hail events of 3/4 inch (penny) diameter or greater or damaging winds of 50 knots (58 mph) or greater.

b.   The forecast event minimum threshold is at least 2 hours over an area of at least 8,000 square miles.

1)   Below these thresholds, SPC, in collaboration with affected NWS offices, may issue convective watches along coastlines, near the Canadian and Mexican borders, and for any ongoing, organized severe convection.

c. A Public Severe Thunderstorm Watch Notification Message contains the

1) Area description and axis,
2) Watch expiration time,
3) Description of hail size and thunderstorm wind gusts expected,
4) Definition of the watch,
5) Call to action statement,
6) List of other valid watches,
7) Brief discussion of meteorological reasoning, and
8) Technical information for the aviation community.

d. The SPC includes the term **adjacent coastal waters** when the watch affects coastal waters adjacent to the Pacific/Atlantic coast, Gulf of Mexico, or Great Lakes.

1) Adjacent coastal waters refers to a WFO's near-shore responsibility (out to 20 miles for oceans), except for convective watches which include portions of the Great Lakes.

e. SPC issues a watch cancelation message when no counties, parishes, independent cities and/or marine zones remaining are in the watch area prior to the expiration time.

1) The text of the message will specify the number and area of the canceled watch.

f. The format of a Public Severe Thunderstorm Watch Notification Message is shown here.

```
WWUS20 KWNS ddhhmm (ICAO communication header)

URGENT - IMMEDIATE BROADCAST REQUESTED
SEVERE THUNDERSTORM WATCH NUMBER nnnn
NWS STORM PREDICTION CENTER NORMAN OK
time am/pm time zone day mon dd yyyy

THE STORM PREDICTION CENTER HAS ISSUED A
SEVERE THUNDERSTORM WATCH FOR PORTIONS OF

        PORTION OF STATE
        PORTION OF STATE
        AND ADJACENT COASTAL WATERS (IF REQUIRED)
EFFECTIVE (TIME PERIOD) UNTIL hhmm am/pm time zone.

...THIS IS A PARTICULARLY DANGEROUS SITUATION (IF FORECAST)...

HAIL TO X INCHES IN DIAMETER...THUNDERSTORM WIND GUSTS TO XX MPH...AND
DANGEROUS LIGHTNING ARE POSSIBLE IN THESE AREAS.

NARRATIVE DESCRIPTION OF WATCH AREA USING A LINE AND ANCHOR
POINTS.  DISTANCES TO EITHER SIDE OF THE LINE WILL BE IN STATUTE MILES.

CALL TO ACTION STATEMENTS

OTHER WATCH INFORMATION...OTHER WATCHES IN EFFECT AND IF THIS
WATCH REPLACES A PREVIOUS WATCH.

NARRATIVE DISCUSSION OF REASON FOR THE WATCH.

AVIATION...BRIEF DESCRIPTION OF SEVERE WEATHER THREAT TO AVIATORS.
HAIL SIZE WILL BE GIVEN IN INCHES AND WIND GUSTS IN KNOTS.  MAXIMUM
STORM TOPS AND A MEAN STORM VECTOR WILL ALSO BE GIVEN.

$$

..FORECASTER NAME..  MM/DD/YY
```

g.   A sample Public Severe Thunderstorm Watch Notification Message is shown here.

```
WWUS20 KWNS 161711 (ICAO communication header)
SPC WW 161710

URGENT - IMMEDIATE BROADCAST REQUESTED
SEVERE THUNDERSTORM WATCH NUMBER 647
NWS STORM PREDICTION CENTER NORMAN OK
1210 PM CDT FRI JUL 16 2004

THE NWS STORM PREDICTION CENTER HAS ISSUED A
SEVERE THUNDERSTORM WATCH FOR PORTIONS OF

        EASTERN IOWA
        NORTHERN ILLINOIS
        NORTHWEST INDIANA
        LAKE MICHIGAN

EFFECTIVE THIS FRIDAY AFTERNOON FROM 1210 PM UNTIL 500 PM CDT.

HAIL TO 2 INCHES IN DIAMETER...THUNDERSTORM WIND GUSTS TO 70
MPH...AND DANGEROUS LIGHTNING ARE POSSIBLE IN THESE AREAS.

THE SEVERE THUNDERSTORM WATCH AREA IS ALONG AND 75 STATUTE MILES
EITHER SIDE OF A LINE FROM 40 MILES SOUTHEAST OF SOUTH BEND
INDIANA TO 35 MILES SOUTHWEST OF CEDAR RAPIDS IOWA.

REMEMBER...A SEVERE THUNDERSTORM WATCH MEANS CONDITIONS ARE
FAVORABLE FOR SEVERE THUNDERSTORMS IN AND CLOSE TO THE WATCH AREA.
PERSONS IN THESE AREAS SHOULD BE ON THE LOOKOUT FOR THREATENING
WEATHER CONDITIONS AND LISTEN FOR LATER STATEMENTS AND POSSIBLE
WARNINGS.  SEVERE THUNDERSTORMS CAN AND OCCASIONALLY DO PRODUCE
TORNADOES.

OTHER WATCH INFORMATION...CONTINUE...WW 646...

DISCUSSION...THUNDERSTORMS WILL CONTINUE TO INCREASE ACROSS WATCH
AREA WHERE AIR MASS HAS BECOME STRONGLY UNSTABLE AND UNCAPPED.
VEERING SHEAR PROFILE SUPPORT STORMS EVOLVING INTO SHORT LINE
SEGMENTS ENHANCING WIND DAMAGE POTENTIAL

AVIATION...A FEW SEVERE THUNDERSTORMS WITH HAIL SURFACE AND ALOFT
TO 2 INCHES.  EXTREME TURBULENCE AND SURFACE WIND GUSTS TO 60
KNOTS.  A FEW CUMULONIMBI WITH MAXIMUM TOPS TO 500.  MEAN STORM
MOTION VECTOR 33025

....HALES
```

6.   Public Tornado Watch Notification Message

a.   SPC issues a Public Tornado Watch Notification Message when forecasting three or more tornadoes or any tornado which could produce F2 or greater damage.

b.   The forecast event minimum thresholds are at least 2 hours over an area of at least 8,000 square miles.

1)   Below these thresholds, SPC, in collaboration with affected NWS offices, may issue convective watches along coastlines, near the Canadian and Mexican borders, and for any ongoing, organized severe convection.

c. A Public Tornado Watch Notification Message contains the

1) Area description and axis,
2) Watch expiration time,
3) Term "damaging tornadoes,"
4) Description of the largest hail size and strongest thunderstorm wind gusts expected,
5) Definition of the watch,
6) Call to action statement,
7) List of other valid watches,
8) Brief discussion of meteorological reasoning, and
9) Technical information for the aviation community.

d. SPC issues a watch cancelation message whenever it cancels a watch prior to the expiration time.

1) The text of the message will specify the number and area of the canceled watch.

e. The format of a Public Tornado Watch Notification Message is shown here.

```
WWUS20 KWNS ddhhmm (ICAO communication header)

URGENT - IMMEDIATE BROADCAST REQUESTED
TORNADO WATCH NUMBER nnnn
NWS STORM PREDICTION CENTER NORMAN OK
time am/pm time zone day mon dd yyyy

THE STORM PREDICTION CENTER HAS ISSUED A
TORNADO WATCH FOR PORTIONS OF

        PORTION OF STATE
        PORTION OF STATE
        AND ADJACENT COASTAL WATERS (IF REQUIRED)

EFFECTIVE (TIME PERIOD) UNTIL hhmm am/pm time zone.

...THIS IS A PARTICULARLY DANGEROUS SITUATION (IF FORECAST)...

DESTRUCTIVE TORNADOES...HAIL TO X INCHES IN DIAMETER...THUNDERSTORM
WIND GUSTS TO XX MPH...AND DANGEROUS LIGHTNING ARE POSSIBLE IN THESE
AREAS.

NARRATIVE DESCRIPTION OF WATCH AREA USING A LINE AND ANCHOR POINTS.
DISTANCES TO EITHER SIDE OF THE LINE WILL BE IN STATUTE MILES.

CALL TO ACTION STATEMENTS

OTHER WATCH INFORMATION...OTHER WATCHES IN EFFECT AND IF THIS WATCH
REPLACES A PREVIOUS WATCH.

NARRATIVE DISCUSSION OF REASON FOR THE WATCH.

AVIATION...BRIEF DESCRIPTION OF SEVERE WEATHER THREAT TO AVIATORS.
HAIL SIZE WILL BE GIVEN IN INCHES AND WIND GUSTS IN KNOTS.  MAXIMUM
STORM TOPS AND A MEAN STORM VECTOR WILL ALSO BE GIVEN.

$$

..FORECASTER NAME..  MM/DD/YY
```

f.   A sample Public Tornado Watch Notification Message is shown here.

```
WWUS20 KWNS 050550 (ICAO communication header)

URGENT - IMMEDIATE BROADCAST REQUESTED
TORNADO WATCH NUMBER 243
NWS STORM PREDICTION CENTER NORMAN OK
1250 AM CDT MON MAY 5 2003

THE NWS STORM PREDICTION CENTER HAS ISSUED A
TORNADO WATCH FOR PORTIONS OF

      WESTERN AND CENTRAL ARKANSAS
      SOUTHERN MISSOURI
      FAR EASTERN OKLAHOMA

EFFECTIVE THIS MONDAY MORNING FROM 1250 AM UNTIL 600 AM CDT.

...THIS IS A PARTICULARLY DANGEROUS SITUATION...

DESTRUCTIVE TORNADOES...LARGE HAIL TO 2 INCHES IN DIAMETER...
THUNDERSTORM WIND GUSTS TO 70 MPH...AND DANGEROUS LIGHTNING ARE
POSSIBLE IN THESE AREAS.

THE TORNADO WATCH AREA IS ALONG AND 100 STATUTE MILES EAST AND
WEST OF A LINE FROM 15 MILES WEST NORTHWEST OF FORT LEONARD WOOD
MISSOURI TO 45 MILES SOUTHWEST OF HOT SPRINGS ARKANSAS.

REMEMBER...A TORNADO WATCH MEANS CONDITIONS ARE FAVORABLE FOR
TORNADOES AND SEVERE THUNDERSTORMS IN AND CLOSE TO THE WATCH AREA.
PERSONS IN THESE AREAS SHOULD BE ON THE LOOKOUT FOR THREATENING
WEATHER CONDITIONS AND LISTEN FOR LATER STATEMENTS AND POSSIBLE
WARNINGS.

OTHER WATCH INFORMATION...THIS TORNADO WATCH REPLACES TORNADO
WATCH NUMBER 237.  WATCH NUMBER 237 WILL NOT BE IN EFFECT AFTER
1250 AM CDT.  CONTINUE...WW 239...WW 240...WW 241...WW 242...

DISCUSSION...SRN MO SQUALL LINE EXPECTED TO CONTINUE EWD...WHERE
LONG/HOOKED HODOGRAPHS SUGGEST THREAT FOR EMBEDDED
SUPERCELLS/POSSIBLE TORNADOES.  FARTHER S...MORE WIDELY SCATTERED
SUPERCELLS WITH A THREAT FOR TORNADOES WILL PERSIST IN VERY STRONGLY
DEEP SHEARED/LCL ENVIRONMENT IN AR.

AVIATION...TORNADOES AND A FEW SEVERE THUNDERSTORMS WITH HAIL
SURFACE AND ALOFT TO 2 INCHES.  EXTREME TURBULENCE AND SURFACE WIND
GUSTS TO 60 KNOTS.  A FEW CUMULONIMBI WITH MAXIMUM TOPS TO 500.  MEAN
STORM MOTION VECTOR 26045

.
...CORFIDI
```

END OF STUDY UNIT

STUDY UNIT TWENTY
TROPICAL CYCLONE PRODUCTS

(10 pages of outline)

> Please take a few minutes to study each of the concepts listed above and anticipate/imagine what they are and how they relate to the other listed concepts.

20.1 INTRODUCTION

1. The NWS issues SIGMETs (Study Unit 16), Convective SIGMETs (Study Unit 16), and Center Weather Advisories (CWAs) (Study Unit 18) to inform the aviation community about the potential or existence of tropical cyclones and the adverse conditions associated with them.

    a. These products are the **primary** source of information.

2. The NWS also issues other products pertaining to tropical convective activity.

    a. These additional products are **supplementary** and are defined in this study unit.

    b. To learn more about the role and use of primary and supplementary weather products, reference Study Unit 2, "Aviation Weather Product Classification and Policy."

20.2 AVIATION TROPICAL CYCLONE ADVISORY (TCA)

1. The Aviation Tropical Cyclone Advisory (TCA) is intended to provide short-term tropical cyclone forecast guidance for international aviation safety and routing purposes.

2. It is prepared by the National Hurricane Center (NHC) in Miami, Florida and the Central Pacific Hurricane Center (CPHC) in Honolulu, Hawaii, for all ongoing tropical cyclone activity in their respective areas of responsibility.

    a. Any valid TCA in the Atlantic or eastern Pacific is available on the NHC website at http://www.nhc.noaa.gov.

    b. Any valid TCA for the central Pacific is available on the CPHC website at http://www.prh.noaa.gov/hnl/cphc/

3. TCAs are issued at 0300, 0900, 1500, and 2100 UTC and are valid from the time of issuance until the next scheduled issuance or update.

4. TCAs list the current tropical cyclone position, motion, and intensity as well as 12-, 18-, and 24-hour forecast positions and intensities.

    a. It is an alphanumeric text product produced by hurricane forecasters and consists of information extracted from the official forecasts.

    b. This forecast is produced from subjective evaluation of current meteorological and oceanographic data as well as output from numerical weather prediction models and is coordinated with affected NWS offices, the NWS National Centers, and the Department of Defense.

5.   The format of the Aviation Tropical Cyclone Advisory is shown here.

```
FKaa2i CCCC DDHHMM (ICAO communication header)

(TROPICAL CYCLONE TYPE) ICAO ADVISORY NUMBER ##
ISSUING OFFICE CITY STATE
time am/pm time.zone day mon DD YYYY

TEXT

$$
```

6.   An example Aviation Tropical Cyclone Advisory is shown here.

```
FKPZ21 KNHC 260215 (ICAO communication header)

TROPICAL DEPRESSION PATRICIA ICAO ADVISORY NUMBER 23
NWS TPC/NATIONAL HURRICANE CENTER MIAMI FL
0300Z SUN OCT 26 2003

TC ADVISORY
DTG:                            20031026/0300Z
TCAC:                           KNHC
TC:                             PATRICIA
NR:                             023
PSN:                            N1612 W11454
MOV:                            NW 05KT
C:                              1008HPA
MAX WIND:                       025KT
FCST PSN + 12 HR:               261200 N1636 W11500
FCST MAX WIND + 12 HR:          020KT
FCST PSN + 18 HR:               261800 N1654 W11506
FCST MAX WIND + 18 HR:          020KT
FCST PSN + 24 HR:               270000 N1712 W11512
FCST MAX WIND + 24 HR:          020KT
NXT MSG:                        NO MSG EXP
```

20.3 TROPICAL CYCLONE PUBLIC ADVISORY (TCP)

1.   A Tropical Cyclone Public Advisory (TCP) is the primary tropical cyclone information product issued to the public.

   a.   The TCP provides critical tropical cyclone watch, warning, and forecast information for the protection of life and property.

2.   The National Hurricane Center (NHC), as a part of the Tropical Prediction Center (TPC); the Central Pacific Hurricane Center (CPHC); and Weather Forecast Office (WFO) Tiyan, Guam, issue TCPs.

   a.   In the Atlantic and central Pacific, NHC and CPHC issue TCPs for all tropical cyclones, respectively.

      1)   Valid TCPs in the Atlantic or eastern Pacific are available on the NHC website at http://www.nhc.noaa.gov.

      2)   Valid TCPs for the central Pacific are available on the CPHC website at http://www.prh.noaa.gov/hnl/cphc/.

   b.   In the eastern Pacific, NHC will issue public advisories when watches or warnings are required, or the tropical cyclone is otherwise expected to impact nearby land areas.

      1)   Valid TCPs in the Atlantic or eastern Pacific is available on the NHC website at http://www.nhc.noaa.gov.

c.   In the western Pacific, WFO Guam will issue public advisories for all tropical cyclones expected to affect land within 48 hours.

1)   TCPs issued by WFO Guam for the western Pacific are available at http://www.prh.noaa.gov/pr/guam/cyclone.php.

3.   **Standard Issuance**

a.   The initial TCP may be issued when data confirm a tropical cyclone has developed. The title of the advisory will depend upon the intensity of the tropical cyclone as listed below.

1)   A tropical depression advisory refers to a tropical cyclone with 1-minute sustained winds up to 33 knots (38 mph).

2)   A tropical storm advisory will refer to tropical cyclones with 1-minute sustained surface winds 34 to 63 knots (39 to 73 mph).

3)   A hurricane/typhoon advisory will refer to tropical cyclones with winds 64 knots (74 mph) or greater.

b.   Public advisories are discontinued when the tropical cyclone

1)   Becomes extra-tropical, which is indicated by the center of the storm becoming colder than the surrounding air, fronts appearing, and the strongest winds moving to the upper atmosphere;

2)   Drops below tropical depression advisory criteria by dissipating or becoming a remnant low; or

3)   Moves inland, and watches and warnings are no longer required.

c.   Tropical Cyclone Public Advisories are issued according to the schedule below and are valid from the time of issuance until the next scheduled issuance or update. Valid position times correspond to the advisory time.

TPC/CPHC ISSUANCE TIME (UTC)	WFO GUAM ISSUANCE TIME (UTC)
0300	0400
0900	1000
1500	1600
2100	2200

Table 20-1. Tropical Cyclone Public Advisory Issuance Schedule

d.   Times in advisories are local time of the affected area; however, local time and UTC are used when noting the storm's location.

e.   All advisories use statute miles and statute miles per hour.

1)   The Tropical Cyclone Center (TPC and CPHC) and WFO Guam, at their discretion, may use nautical miles/knots in parentheses immediately following statute miles/mph.

2)   Advisories include the metric units of kilometers and kilometers per hour following the equivalent English units except when the United States is the only country threatened.

f.   NHC, CPHC, and WFO Guam issue tropical storm/hurricane/typhoon watches if tropical storm/hurricane/typhoon conditions are possible over land areas within 36 hours (48 hours in the western north Pacific).

1)   Tropical storm watches are not issued if the tropical cyclone is forecast to reach hurricane/typhoon intensity within the watch period.

g.   Tropical storm/hurricane/typhoon warnings are issued when tropical storm/hurricane/typhoon conditions along the coast are expected within 24 hours.

1)   Tropical storm warnings are issued at the discretion of the hurricane specialist when gale warnings, not related to the pending tropical storm, are already in place.

2)   Tropical storm warnings may be issued on either side of a hurricane/typhoon warning area.

4.   **Intermediate Issuance**

a.   Intermediate Public Advisories are issued on 2- to 3-hourly intervals between scheduled advisories (see times of issuance below).

	TPC/CPHC ISSUANCE TIME (UTC)	WFO GUAM ISSUANCE TIME (UTC)
3-Hourly Issuances	0000	0100
	0600	0700
	1200	1300
	1800	1900
2-Hourly Issuances	2300	0000
	0100	0200
	0500	0600
	0700	0800
	1100	1200
	1300	1400
	1700	1800
	1900	2000

Table 20-2. Intermediate Tropical Cyclone Public Advisory Issuance Schedule

1)   3-hourly intermediate advisories are issued whenever a tropical storm or hurricane watch/warning is in effect.

2)   2-hourly intermediates are issued whenever tropical storm or hurricane warnings are in effect and coastal radars are able to provide responsible Tropical Cyclone Centers with a reliable hourly center position.

b.   For clarity, when intermediate public advisories are issued, a statement is included at the end of the scheduled public advisory informing users when an intermediate advisory may be issued.

1)   EXAMPLE: "AN INTERMEDIATE ADVISORY WILL BE ISSUED BY THE CENTRAL PACIFIC HURRICANE CENTER AT 2 PM HST FOLLOWED BY THE NEXT COMPLETE ADVISORY ISSUANCE AT 5 PM HST."

c.   Intermediate advisories are not used to issue tropical cyclone watches or warnings.

1)   They can be used to clear all, or parts of, a watch or warning area.
2)   Content is similar to the scheduled advisory.

5. **Advisory Content**

   a. Advisories list all tropical cyclone watches and warnings in effect.

   b. The first advisory in which watches or warnings are mentioned will give the effective time of the watch or warning, except when it is being issued by other countries and the time is not known.

   c. Except for tropical storms and hurricanes/typhoons forming close to land, a watch will precede a warning.

      1) Once a watch is in effect, it will either be replaced by a warning or remain in effect until the threat of the tropical cyclone conditions has passed.

      2) A hurricane/typhoon watch and a tropical storm warning can be in effect for the same section of coast at the same time.

   d. All advisories include the location of the center of the tropical cyclone by its latitude and longitude, and distance and direction from a well-known point, preferably downstream from the tropical cyclone.

      1) If the forecaster is unsure of the exact location of a depression, the position may be given as within 50, 75, etc., miles of a map coordinate.

      2) When the center of the tropical cyclone is over land, its position is given referencing the state or country in which it is located and in respect to some well-known city, if appropriate.

   e. Movement forecasts apply to the tropical cyclone's center.

      1) The present movement is given to 16 points of the compass when possible.

      2) A 24-hour forecast of movement in terms of a continuance or departure from the present movement and speed is also included.

         a) This can be reduced to a 12-hour forecast.

      3) Uncertainties in either the tropical cyclone's location or movement will be explained in the advisory.

      4) An outlook beyond 24 hours (up to 72 hours when appropriate) may be included in the text of the advisory.

   f. Maximum observed 1-minute sustained surface wind speed rounded to the nearest 5 mph is given.

      1) During landfall threats, specific gust values and phrases like "briefly higher in squalls" may be used.

      2) The area (or radius) of both tropical and hurricane/typhoon force winds is given.

      3) The storm may also be compared to some memorable hurricane or referred to by relative intensity.

      4) Where appropriate, the Saffir/Simpson Hurricane Scale (SSHS) is used in public releases (e.g., Category 1-5).

   g. Central pressure values in millibars and inches are provided as determined by available data.

   h. The inland impacts of tropical cyclones will be highlighted in advisories.

      1) This includes the threat of strong winds, heavy rainfall, flooding, and tornadoes.

      2) The extent and magnitude of the inland winds is included as well as anticipated rainfall amounts and the potential for flooding and tornadoes.

      3) Tornado and flood watches will be mentioned as appropriate.

6.   The format of a Tropical Cyclone Public Advisory is shown here.

```
(TROPICAL CYCLONE TYPE) (NAME) ADVISORY NUMBER XX.
(ISSUING OFFICE CITY STATE)
time am/pm time zone day month DD YYYY

...HEADLINE...

TEXT

$$

FORECASTER NAME
```

7.   An example of a Tropical Storm Public Advisory is shown here.

```
BULLETIN
TROPICAL STORM FLOYD ADVISORY NUMBER 4
NWS TPC/NATIONAL HURRICANE CENTER MIAMI FL
11 AM AST WED SEP 08 1999

...FLOYD MOVING WEST-NORTHWESTWARD IN THE TROPICAL ATLANTIC...

AT 11 AM AST...1500Z...THE CENTER OF TROPICAL STORM FLOYD WAS
LOCATED NEAR LATITUDE 15.8 NORTH...LONGITUDE 50.0 WEST OR ABOUT
755 MILES...1210 KM...EAST OF THE LEEWARD ISLANDS.

FLOYD IS MOVING TOWARD THE WEST NORTHWEST NEAR 15 MPH...24
KM/HR...AND THIS MOTION IS EXPECTED TO CONTINUE THROUGH TONIGHT.

MAXIMUM SUSTAINED WINDS ARE NEAR 45 MPH...75 KM/HR...WITH HIGHER
GUSTS...AND SOME SLOW STRENGTHENING IS EXPECTED DURING THE NEXT
24 HOURS.

TROPICAL STORM FORCE WINDS EXTEND OUTWARD UP TO 85 MILES...140
KM FROM THE CENTER.

ESTIMATED MINIMUM CENTRAL PRESSURE IS 1003 MB...29.62 INCHES.

REPEATING THE 11 AM AST POSITION...15.8 N...  50.0 W. MOVEMENT
TOWARD...WEST NORTHWEST NEAR 15 MPH.  MAXIMUM SUSTAINED
WINDS...45 MPH. MINIMUM CENTRAL PRESSURE...1003 MB.

THE NEXT ADVISORY WILL BE ISSUED BY THE NATIONAL HURRICANE
CENTER AT 5 PM AST.

FORECASTER FRANKLIN
```

8.   An example of a Hurricane/Typhoon Public Advisory is shown here.

```
BULLETIN
HURRICANE FLOYD ADVISORY NUMBER 32
NWS TPC/NATIONAL HURRICANE CENTER MIAMI FL
11 AM EDT WED SEP 15 1999

...FRINGES OF HURRICANE CONTINUE TO IMPACT COAST OF NORTH FLORIDA
AND GEORGIA...BUT FLOYD IS HEADING FOR THE CAROLINAS...

AT 11 AM EDT...A TROPICAL STORM WATCH IS EXTENDED NORTHWARD AND
IS NOW IN EFFECT FROM NORTH OF CHINCOTEAGUE VIRGINIA TO
SANDYHOOK NEW JERSEY...INCLUDING DELAWARE BAY.

A HURRICANE WARNING REMAINS IN EFFECT FROM TITUSVILLE FLORIDA
TO THE NORTH CAROLINA/VIRGINIA BORDER...INCLUDING PAMLICO AND
ALBEMARLE SOUNDS.  AT 11 AM EDT...HURRICANE WARNINGS ARE
DISCONTINUED SOUTH OF TITUSVILLE.

A HURRICANE WATCH CONTINUES IN EFFECT FROM THE NORTH
CAROLINA/VIRGINIA BORDER TO CHINCOTEAGUE VIRGINIA...INCLUDING
CHESAPEAKE BAY SOUTH OF SMITH POINT.

INTERESTS ALONG THE FLORIDA EAST COAST SOUTH OF TITUSVILLE
SHOULD EXERCISE CAUTION UNTIL WINDS AND SEAS SUBSIDE.

AT 11 AM EDT...1500Z...THE CENTER OF HURRICANE FLOYD WAS LOCATED
NEAR LATITUDE 29.9 NORTH...LONGITUDE 79.0 WEST OR ABOUT 165 MILES
EAST-SOUTHEAST OF JACKSONVILLE FLORIDA.  THIS POSITION IS ALSO
ABOUT 260 MILES SOUTH OF MYRTLE BEACH SOUTH CAROLINA.

FLOYD IS MOVING TOWARD THE NORTH NORTHWEST NEAR 14 MPH AND A
GRADUAL TURN TOWARD THE NORTH IS EXPECTED TODAY.

MAXIMUM SUSTAINED WINDS ARE NEAR 125 MPH...205 KM/HR...WITH HIGHER
GUSTS.  LITTLE CHANGE IN STRENGTH IS FORECAST BEFORE LANDFALL...
WHICH IS EXPECTED TONIGHT NEAR THE BORDER OF SOUTH AND NORTH
CAROLINA.  ALL PREPARATIONS SHOULD BE RUSHED TO COMPLETION.

HURRICANE FORCE WINDS EXTEND OUTWARD UP TO 140 MILES...220
KM....FROM THE CENTER...AND TROPICAL STORM FORCE WINDS EXTEND
OUTWARD UP TO 230 MILES...370 KM.

THE LATEST MINIMUM CENTRAL PRESSURE REPORTING BY U.S. AIR FORCE
HURRICANE HUNTER AIRCRAFT IS 945 MB...27.85 INCHES.

STORM SURGE FLOODING OF 10 TO 13 FEET ABOVE NORMAL TIDE LEVELS...
ALONG WITH LARGE AND DANGEROUS BATTERING WAVES...ARE EXPECTED
NEAR AND TO THE EAST OF WHERE THE CENTER CROSSES THE COAST.  HEAVY
SURF ADVISORIES ARE IN EFFECT FOR THE U.S. EAST COAST NORTHWARD
TO CHATHAM MASSACHUSETTS.  REFER TO STATEMENTS ISSUED BY LOCAL
NATIONAL WEATHER SERVICE OFFICES FOR ADDITIONAL INFORMATION.

RAINFALL TOTALS OF 5 TO 10 INCHES ARE EXPECTED ALONG THE PATH OF
THE HURRICANE.

ISOLATED TORNADOES ARE POSSIBLE OVER THE COASTAL COUNTIES OF
SOUTH AND NORTH CAROLINA.

REPEATING THE 11 AM EDT POSITION...29.9 N...79.0 W. MOVEMENT
TOWARD...NORTH NORTHWEST NEAR 14 MPH.  MAXIMUM SUSTAINED
WINDS...125 MPH.  MINIMUM CENTRAL PRESSURE...943 MB.

FOR STORM INFORMATION SPECIFIC TO YOUR AREA...PLEASE MONITOR
PRODUCTS ISSUED BY YOUR LOCAL WEATHER OFFICE.

INTERMEDIATE ADVISORIES WILL BE ISSUED BY THE NATIONAL HURRICANE
CENTER AT 1 PM EDT AND 3 PM EDT FOLLOWED BY THE NEXT COMPLETE
ADVISORY AT 5 PM EDT.

FORECASTER LAWRENCE
```

9.   An example of an Intermediate Public Advisory is shown here.

```
BULLETIN
HURRICANE FLOYD INTERMEDIATE ADVISORY NUMBER 32B
NWS TPC/NATIONAL HURRICANE CENTER MIAMI FL
3 PM EDT WED SEP 15 1999
...FRINGES OF HURRICANE CONTINUE TO IMPACT COAST OF NORTH FLORIDA
AND GEORGIA...BUT FLOYD IS HEADING FOR THE CAROLINAS...

A HURRICANE WARNING REMAINS IN EFFECT FROM NORTH OF FERNANDINA
BEACH FLORIDA TO THE NORTH CAROLINA/VIRGINIA BORDER...INCLUDING
PAMLICO AND ALBEMARLE SOUNDS.  AT 3 PM EDT...WARNINGS ARE
DISCONTINUED FROM FERNANDINA BEACH SOUTHWARD.  WARNINGS WILL
LIKELY BE DISCONTINUED FOR PORTIONS OF GEORGIA LATER TODAY.

A HURRICANE WATCH REMAINS IN EFFECT FROM THE NORTH
CAROLINA/VIRGINIA BORDER TO CHINCOTEAGUE VIRGINIA...INCLUDING
CHESAPEAKE BAY SOUTH OF SMITH POINT.

A TROPICAL STORM WATCH REMAINS IN EFFECT FROM NORTH OF
CHINCOTEAGUE VIRGINIA TO MONTAUK POINT LONG ISLAND...INCLUDING
DELAWARE BAY AND LONG ISLAND SOUND.

INTERESTS ALONG THE FLORIDA EAST COAST SHOULD EXERCISE CAUTION
UNTIL WINDS AND SEAS SUBSIDE.

AT 3 PM EDT...1900Z...THE CENTER OF HURRICANE FLOYD WAS LOCATED
NEAR LATITUDE 30.8 NORTH...LONGITUDE 79.1 WEST OR ABOUT 200 MILES
SOUTH OF MYRTLE BEACH SOUTH CAROLINA.

FLOYD IS MOVING ALMOST DUE NORTHWARD AT 15 MPH AND THIS MOTION
IS EXPECTED TO CONTINUE TODAY WITH A GRADUAL TURN TOWARD THE
NORTH-NORTHEAST ON THURSDAY.

MAXIMUM SUSTAINED WINDS HAVE DECREASED TO NEAR 120 MPH...WITH
HIGHER GUSTS.  ALTHOUGH THE HURRICANE HAS BEEN SLOWLY WEAKENING...
IT IS OVER THE WARM WATERS OF THE GULF STREAM COULD MAINTAIN ITS
PRESENT STRENGTH UNTIL LANDFALL TONIGHT.  ALL PREPARATIONS
IN THE WARNING AREA SHOULD BE RUSHED TO COMPLETION.

HURRICANE FORCE WINDS EXTEND OUTWARD UP TO 140 MILES...220 KM...
FROM THE CENTER...AND TROPICAL STORM FORCE WINDS EXTEND
OUTWARD UP TO 230 MILES...370 KM.

THE LATEST MINIMUM CENTRAL PRESSURE REPORTED BY U.S.  AIR FORCE
HURRICANE HUNTER AIRCRAFT IS 947 MB...27.96 INCHES.

STORM SURGE FLOODING OF 10 TO 13 FEET ABOVE NORMAL TIDE LEVELS...
ALONG WITH LARGE AND DANGEROUS BATTERING WAVES...ARE EXPECTED
NEAR AND TO THE EAST OF WHERE THE CENTER CROSSES THE COAST.

HEAVY SURF ADVISORIES ARE IN EFFECT FOR THE U.S.  EAST COAST
NORTHWARD TO CHATHAM MASSACHUSETTS.  REFER TO STATEMENTS ISSUED BY
LOCAL NATIONAL WEATHER SERVICE OFFICES FOR ADDITIONAL INFORMATION.

RAINFALL TOTALS OF 5 TO 10 INCHES ARE EXPECTED ALONG THE PATH OF
THE HURRICANE.

ISOLATED TORNADOES ARE POSSIBLE OVER THE COASTAL COUNTIES OF
SOUTH AND NORTH CAROLINA.

FOR STORM INFORMATION SPECIFIC TO YOUR AREA...PLEASE MONITOR
PRODUCTS ISSUED BY YOUR LOCAL WEATHER OFFICE.

REPEATING THE 3 PM EDT POSITION...30.8 N...79.1 W.  MOVEMENT
TOWARD...NORTH NEAR 15 MPH.  MAXIMUM SUSTAINED WINDS...120 MPH.
MINIMUM CENTRAL PRESSURE...947 MB.

THE NEXT ADVISORY WILL BE ISSUED BY THE NATIONAL HURRICANE
CENTER AT 5 PM EDT.

FORECASTER LAWRENCE
```

10. An example of a Special Public Advisory is shown here.

```
BULLETIN
HURRICANE ANDREW SPECIAL ADVISORY NUMBER 25
NWS TPC/NATIONAL HURRICANE CENTER MIAMI FL
900 AM EDT MON AUG 24 1992

...HURRICANE ANDREW MOVING INTO THE GULF OF MEXICO...

HURRICANE WARNINGS REMAIN POSTED FOR THE FLORIDA WEST COAST
SOUTH OF VENICE TO FLAMINGO AND FOR LAKE OKEECHOBEE.  AT 9 AM
EDT A HURRICANE WATCH WILL GO INTO EFFECT FOR THE NORTHERN GULF
COAST FROM MOBILE ALABAMA TO SABINE PASS TEXAS.  ALL OTHER
POSTED WATCHES AND WARNINGS ARE DISCONTINUED.

WIND GUSTS TO HURRICANE FORCE CONTINUE TO OCCUR ALONG THE
SOUTHEAST FLORIDA COAST BUT WILL GRADUALLY DIMINISH DURING THE
DAY.  SMALL CRAFT ADVISORIES REMAIN IN EFFECT.  RESIDENTS IN THESE
AREAS SHOULD MONITOR LOCAL NWS OFFICES FOR THE LATEST
FORECASTS AND CONDITIONS IN THEIR AREA.

AT 9 AM EDT THE CENTER OF HURRICANE ANDREW WAS LOCATED NEAR
LATITUDE 25.6 NORTH AND LONGITUDE 81.8 WEST OR APPROXIMATELY 45
MILES SOUTH OF NAPLES FLORIDA.

HURRICANE ANDREW IS MOVING TOWARD THE WEST AT 18 MPH.  THIS
MOTION IS EXPECTED TO CONTINUE THIS MORNING WITH A GRADUAL TURN
TO THE WEST NORTHWEST LATER TODAY.

MAXIMUM SUSTAINED WINDS ARE NEAR 140 MPH.  LITTLE CHANGE IN
STRENGTH IS LIKELY DURING THE NEXT 24 HOURS.

HURRICANE FORCE WINDS EXTEND OUTWARD TO 30 MILES...50 KM FROM
THE CENTER WITH TROPICAL STORM FORCE WINDS EXTENDING OUTWARD
TO 140 MILES.  ESTIMATED MINIMUM CENTRAL PRESSURE IS 945 MB...27.91
INCHES

STORM SURGES OF 5 TO 8 FEET ARE POSSIBLE ON THE FLORIDA WEST
COAST NEAR AND TO THE SOUTH OF THE CENTER FOLLOWING PASSAGE OF
THE HURRICANE.  ALONG THE SOUTHEAST COAST OF FLORIDA STORM
SURGE TIDES AND DECREASING.  PRELIMINARY REPORTS FROM THE SOUTH
FLORIDA WATER MANAGEMENT DISTRICT INDICATE A STORM SURGE OF 8
FEET ABOVE NORMAL HAS RECORDED IN BISCAYNE BAY NEAR
HOMESTEAD FLORIDA

RAINFALL AMOUNTS OF 5 TO 8 INCHES AND ISOLATED TORNADOES ARE
POSSIBLE ACROSS SOUTHERN AND CENTERAL FLORIDA TODAY.

FOR STORM INFORMATION SPECIFIC TO YOUR AREA....PLEASE MONITOR
PRODUCTS ISSUED BY YOUR LOCAL WEATHER OFFICE.

REPEATING THE 9 AM EDT POSITION...LATITUDE 25.6 NORTH AND
LONGITUDE 81.8 WEST AND MOVING TOWARD THE WEST AT 18 MPH.
MAXIMUM SUSTAINED WINDS NEAR 140 MPH.  MINIMUM CENTRAL
PRESSURE OF 945 MB...27.91 INCHES.

THE NEXT SCHEDULED ADVISORY WILL BE ISSUED BY THE NATIONAL
HURRICANE CENTER AT 11 AM EDT MON.
```

11. An example of a Public Advisory Correction is shown here.

```
HURRICANE ANDREW ADVISORY NUMBER 25...CORRECTED
NWS TPC/NATIONAL HURRICANE CENTER MIAMI FL
500 AM EDT MON AUG 24 1992

CORRECTED FOR CENTRAL PRESSURE...

BODY OF TEXT
```

END OF STUDY UNIT

STUDY UNIT TWENTY-ONE
VOLCANIC ASH ADVISORY PRODUCTS

(5 pages of outline)

> Please take a few minutes to study each of the concepts listed above and anticipate/imagine what they are and how they relate to the other listed concepts.

In addition to SIGMETs (Study Unit 16), the NWS issues Volcanic Ash Advisory Statements (VAAS) and Volcanic Ash Advisories (VAA) to notify the aviation community of volcanic ash hazards. Both of these products are detailed in this study unit.

21.1 VOLCANIC ASH ADVISORY STATEMENT (VAAS)

1. A Volcanic Ash Advisory Statement (VAAS) provides information on hazards to aircraft flight operations caused by a volcanic eruption.

2. Volcanic Ash Advisory Centers (VAACs) are responsible for providing ash movement and dispersion guidance to Meteorological Watch Offices (MWOs) and neighboring VAACs.

   a. There are nine VAACs worldwide, two of which are located in the U.S.

      1) The two U.S. VAACs are the Anchorage VAAC in Anchorage, Alaska and the Washington VAAC in Camp Springs, Maryland.

   b. Each VAAC issues Volcanic Ash Advisory Statements and provide guidance to Meteorological Watch Offices (MWOs) for SIGMETs involving volcanic ash.

   c. The map below shows the center name and jurisdiction of each VAAC.

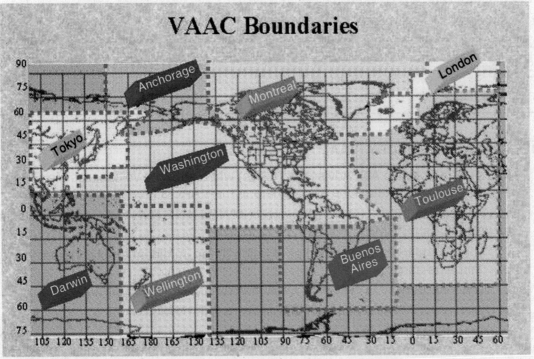

Figure 21-1. Volcanic Ash Advisory Centers (VAACs) Area of Responsibility

3. **Issuance and Format**

    a.   A VAAS may be issued within 6 hours of an eruption and every 6 hours thereafter.

        1)   It can be issued more frequently if new information about the eruption is received.

    b.   A VAAS summarizes the known information about an eruption.

        1)   It may include the

           a)   Location of the volcano,
           b)   Height of the volcano summit,
           c)   Height of the ash plume,
           d)   Latitude/longitude box of the ash dispersion cloud, and
           e)   Forecast of ash dispersion.

    c.   The height of the ash cloud is estimated by meteorologists analyzing satellite imagery and satellite cloud drift winds combined with any pilot reports, volcano observatory reports, and upper-air wind reports.

    d.   The following is an example VAAS report.

```
VOLCANIC ASH ADVISORY
ISSUED:  2003JUL10/1300Z         VAAC:  WASHINGTON

VOLCANO:  ANATAHAN 0804-20
LOCATION:  N1621E14540          AREA:  MARIANA ISLANDS

SUMMIT ELEVATION:  2585 FT (788 M)

ADVISORY NUMBER:  2003/251

INFORMATION SOURCE:  GOES 9 IMAGERY.  GFS MODEL WINDS FORECAST

ERUPTION DETAILS:  ASH AND GAS EMISSIONS SINCE MAY 10.

OBS ASH DATE/TIME:  09/1202Z.

OBS ASH CLOUD:  ASH NOT IDENTIFIABLE FROM SATELLITE DATA.

WINDS SFC/FL080 MOVING SW 10-15 KNOTS.

FCST ASH CLOUD +6H:  SEE SIGMETS.

REMARKS:  THE ASH PLUME OBSERVED IN VISIBLE IMAGERY IS TOO THIN AND
DIFFUSE TO BE SEEN IN INFRARED AND MULTISPECTRAL IMAGERY.  ANY ASH UP
TO FL080 SHOULD MOVE TOWARDS THE SW AT 10-15 KNOTS.

NEXT ADVISORY:  WILL BE ISSUED BY 2003JUL10/1900Z.
```

21.2 VOLCANIC ASH ADVISORY (VAA)

1.   VAACs issue Volcanic Ash Advisories (VAAs) when airborne volcanic ash is observed or reported which may affect the atmosphere in the VAAC's area of responsibility.

2.   The VAA is intended as guidance to support MWOs in meeting their responsibility to issue the volcanic ash SIGMET.

    a.   The VAA also may be issued as a watch for an imminent eruption expected to produce airborne ash.

    b.   The VAA may be accessed in either a textual or graphical format.

3.   The U.S. has two VAACs with responsibilities to issue VAAs.

    a.   The Washington VAAC is jointly managed by the National Environmental Satellite Data and Information Service (NESDIS) Satellite Analysis Branch (SAB) and the NWS National Centers for Environmental Prediction (NCEP) Central Operations (NCO).

    1)   The areas of responsibility for the Washington VAAC are

        a)   The Flight Information Regions (FIRs) in the continental United States (CONUS) and adjacent coastal waters.

            i)   A FIR describes airspace with specific dimensions in which a Flight Information Service and an alerting service are provided. It is the largest regular division of airspace in use in the world today.

        b)   The Oakland Oceanic FIR over the Pacific Ocean.

        c)   The New York FIR over the western Atlantic Ocean.

        d)   FIRs over and adjacent to the Caribbean, and Central and South America north of 10 degrees south latitude.

  b.   The Anchorage VAAC is managed by the AAWU.

    1)   The areas of responsibility for the Alaska VAAC are

        a)   The Anchorage FIR

        b)   Russian FIRs north of 60 degrees north latitude and east of 150 degrees east longitude

4. **Issuance and Updates**

  a.   The VAA may be issued as soon as possible after credible information is received on the presence of airborne volcanic ash in the VAAC's area of responsibility or when responsibility for an existing VAA is transferred between VAACs.

  b.   The VAA contains information on an ash cloud for up to 18 hours.

    1)   It may be issued any time to account for changing or new information.

    2)   Any necessary updates are issued at a minimum of every 6 hours.

5. **Content and Cancelation**

  a.   The VAA follows international recommendations as specified by the ICAO. It contains the

    1)   Name of the erupting volcano and number, if known;

    2)   Location (latitude and longitude) and summit height (in meters or feet);

    3)   Information source;

    4)   Volcano aviation color code, if applicable;

    5)   Eruption details;

    6)   Date and time of the observed ash;

    7)   Information about the observed ash cloud;

    8)   Forecast area and height of the ash cloud at 6, 12, and 18 hours after the issuance of the VAA;

    9)   Pertinent remarks on the eruption/ash event, if any; and

    10) Next VAA issuance time.

    b.   A **VAA watch** is not an official WMO/ICAO product.

        1)   If it is issued, it contains all information except for the eruption details and observed and forecast ash clouds.

        2)   Information on the direction the ash likely will spread in the event of an eruption will be included in remarks.

        3)   In Alaska, a VAA watch may be issued for a non-erupting, seismically-monitored volcano in color code orange or red.

            a)   A one-time VAA Watch may be issued when a monitored Alaska volcano goes from color code green to yellow.

    c.   The VAA will be canceled when it is determined that airborne volcanic ash is no longer a threat to aircraft or has moved out of the VAAC's area of responsibility.

6.   **Interchange of VAAs among Volcanic Ash Advisory Centers (VAAC)**

    a.   When an ash cloud is forecast to move from one VAAC's area of responsibility into another VAAC's area of responsibility, the two VAACs will coordinate by telephone or telephone fax on handoff procedures.

    b.   The VAAC passing off responsibility will include in the remarks of its last VAA the name of the VAAC assuming responsibility for issuing subsequent VAAs for the event, the new WMO header, and the date/time of the next expected issuance.

    c.   The accepting VAAC will include in the remarks the name of the VAAC from which it is accepting responsibility and the WMO header of the current VAA it will be updating.

    d.   Generally, only one VAAC will issue VAAs for a particular ash event.

        1)   If the ash area affects more than one VAAC area of responsibility, the VAAC issuing the VAA will include the entire ash area in the advisory.

        2)   In the rare situation of large or persistent ash emissions, adjacent responsible VAACs, upon coordination, may agree to divide operational responsibilities.

7.   The following is an example VAA report:

```
VOLCANIC ASH ADVISORY - ALERT

ISSUED 2003 APR 19/0615Z

VAAC:  ANCHORAGE

VOLCANO:  CHIKURACHKI, 900-36

LOCATION:  N5019 E15527

AREA:  KAMCHATKA NORTHERN KURIL ISLANDS

SUMMIT ELEVATION:  7674 FT (2339 M)

ADVISORY NUMBER:  2003-02

INFORMATION SOURCE:  SATELLITE

AVIATION COLOR CODE:  NOT GIVEN

ERUPTION DETAILS:  A NEW ERUPTION OCCURRED AT APPROXIMATELY 190500
UTC.  HEIGHT IS ESTIMATED AT FL300.  ESTIMATE IS BASED ON OBSERVED
AND MODEL WINDS.  MOVEMENT APPEARS TO BE E AT 75 KTS.

OBS ASH DATA/TIME:  19/0500Z

OBS ASH CLOUD:  VA EXTENDS FM NEAR VOLCANO EWD TO N50 E160.
FCST ASH CLOUD +6HR:  30NM EITHER SIDE OF LN FM NIPPI N49 E159 -
N50 E175.

FCST ASH CLOUD +12HR:  30 NM EITHER SIDE OF LN FM N50 E168 -
N50 E185.

FCST ASH CLOUD +18HR:  30 NM EITHER SIDE OF LN FM N51 E175 -
N50 E185.

NEXT ADVISORY:  20030419/1500Z

REMARKS:  UPDATES AS SOON AS INFO BECOMES AVAILABLE.
```

21.3 USING VAAC PRODUCTS

1.   The products discussed in this study unit are strictly for advance flight planning purposes.

   a.   They are not intended to take the place of SIGMETs issued regarding volcanic eruptions and ash.

2.   The actual presentation of the VAAC products may change as international requirements are reviewed.

END OF STUDY UNIT

STUDY UNIT TWENTY-TWO
AREA FORECASTS (FA)

(13 pages of outline)

> Please take a few minutes to study each of the concepts listed above and anticipate/imagine what they are and how they relate to the other listed concepts.

22.1 PRODUCT DESCRIPTION

1. The NWS issues Area Forecasts (FA) to provide an overview of regional weather conditions that could impact aviation operations in the U.S. and adjacent coastal waters. Area forecasts are issued by the following offices for the following areas:

   a. The Aviation Weather Center (AWC)

      1) Conterminous U.S. and adjacent coastal waters (CONUS)
      2) Gulf of Mexico
      3) Caribbean Sea and North Atlantic Ocean

   b. The Alaskan Aviation Weather Unit (AAWU)

      1) Alaska and adjacent coastal waters

   c. WFO Honolulu, Hawaii

      1) Hawaii and adjacent coastal waters

2. They are all available on the Aviation Weather Center (AWC) website at http://aviationweather.gov/products/fa/.

3. **CONUS (FAUS) and Hawaii (FAHW) Area Forecast**

   a. CONUS (FAUS) and Hawaii (FAHW) Area Forecast describe, in abbreviated language, specified en route weather phenomena below FL450.

   b. To understand the complete weather picture, the FA must be used in conjunction with the current AIRMETs and SIGMETs.

      1) Together, they are used to determine forecast en route weather and to interpolate conditions at airports for which no Terminal Aerodrome Forecasts (TAFs) are issued.

   c. The FA contains forecast information for VFR/MVFR clouds and weather for a 12-hour period with a 12- to 18-hour categorical outlook forecast for IFR, MVFR, and/or VFR.

      1) The following weather elements are included in the 12-hour forecast:

         a) Thunderstorms and precipitation;

         b) Sky condition (cloud height, amount, and tops) if bases are at or below (AOB) FL180 MSL;

            i) Tops will only be forecast for broken (BKN) or overcast (OVC) clouds.

         c) Obstructions to visibility (fog, mist, haze, blowing dust, etc.) if surface visibilities are three (3) to six (6) miles; and

         d) Sustained surface wind speed of 20 knots or greater.

d.   Hazardous weather (e.g., IFR, icing, turbulence, etc.) meeting AIRMET or SIGMET criteria is not forecast in the CONUS or Hawaii FA.

1)   Valid AIRMETs and SIGMETs must be used in conjunction with the FA to determine hazardous weather information for the flight.

e.   The AWC issues CONUS FAs for six geographical areas shown below.

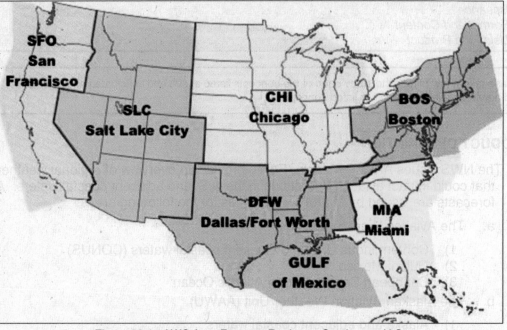

Figure 22-1. AWC Area Forecast Regions - Contiguous U.S.

f.   WFO Honolulu issues FAs for the main Hawaiian Islands and coastal waters extending out to 40 NM of the coastlines, as shown below.

Figure 22-2. WFO Honolulu Area Forecast Region and WMO Header - Hawaii

4. **Gulf of Mexico Area Forecast (FAGX)**

    a.   The Gulf of Mexico FA (FAGX) is an overview of weather conditions that could impact aviation operations over the northern Gulf of Mexico, as shown below.

Figure 22-3. AWC Area Forecast Region and WMO Header - Gulf of Mexico

    b.   It serves as a flight-planning and weather briefing aid and describes weather of significance to general aviation (GA), military, and helicopter operations.

    c.   The FAGX is a 24-hour forecast product with the synopsis valid the entire 24-hour period; the forecast section is valid the first 12 hours, and the outlook section is valid the last 12 hours.

    d.   Each FA contains a statement before the synopsis indicating that heights not reported in MSL are denoted, and a reminder of what thunderstorm activity implies.

5. **Caribbean Area Forecast (FACA)**

a. The Caribbean FA (FACA) is an overview of weather conditions that could impact aviation operations over the Caribbean Sea and adjacent landmasses and islands as well as the southwestern portions of the New York Oceanic FIR, as shown in the figure below.

Figure 22-4. AWC Area Forecast Region and WMO Header - Caribbean

b. Specifically, it covers the Atlantic, south of 32°N and west of 57°W, and the Caribbean from the surface to FL240 (approximately 400 millibars).

c. The clouds/weather forecast section includes the following areas:

1) Atlantic (Southwestern New York and Miami Oceanic FIRs)

2) Caribbean Sea (San Juan FIR; Western Piarco FIR; Santo Domingo, Port au Prince and Havana FIRs; Northern Maiquetia, Curacao, and Northern Barranquilla FIRs; Kingston and Northern Central America FIRs; Northern Merida FIR; and Eastern Monterrey FIR)

6. **Alaska Area Forecast**

    a. The Alaskan FAs contain an overview of weather conditions that could impact aviation operations over Alaska and its coastlines.

    b. The Alaskan FAs contain a short synopsis for the entire area and a forecast for each of a specified number of aviation zones, as shown in the figure below.

Figure 22-5. AAWU Flight Advisory and Area Forecast Zones - Alaska

    c. The valid period of the synopsis and flight precautions section is 12 hours. The outlook section is for 18 hours beyond the forecast valid period.

    d. Each FA contains AIRMETs and references to SIGMETs. In addition, a statement about conditions implied by a forecast of thunderstorms and a reference to how heights not reported in MSL are denoted is included.

22.2 ISSUANCE

1. **Area Forecast Issuance**

   a. CONUS FAUSs are issued three times daily for each of the six covered areas (see the following table).

Area Forecast (FAUS)	Boston and Miami (UTC)	Chicago and Fort Worth (UTC)	San Francisco and Salt Lake City (UTC)
1st Issuance	0845 DT 0945 ST	0945 DT 1045 ST	1045 DT 1145 ST
2nd Issuance	1745 DT 1845 ST	1845 DT 1945 ST	1945 DT 2045 ST
3rd Issuance	0045 DT 0145 ST	0145 DT 0245 ST	0245 DT 0345 ST

   Table 22-1. Area Forecast (FASU) Issuance Schedule - CONUS

   b. The Hawaii Area Forecast is issued four times daily at 0340, 0940, 1540, and 2140 UTC.

   c. The Gulf of Mexico (FAGX) Area Forecasts is issued twice daily at 1030 and 1830 UTC.

   d. The Caribbean Area Forecast is issued four times daily at 0330, 0930, 1530, and 2130 UTC.

   e. The Alaska FAs are produced four times daily (see the following table).

Alaska Area Forecast	Standard Time (UTC)	Daylight Time (UTC)
1st Issuance	0245	0145
2nd Issuance	0845	0745
3rd Issuance	1445	1345
4th Issuance	2045	1945

   Table 22-2. Area Forecast Issuance Schedule - Alaska

2. **FA Amendments**

   a. An amended FA may be issued to notify pilots and briefers that a weather phenomena and/or condition that was not forecast is now expected or a forecast phenomena or condition has improved or did not develop as expected.

   b. The new condition is expected to exceed half of the time of a regular issuance and is expected to no longer affect low-level flights.

   c. An amended FA is denoted by an **AMD** after the date/time group on the FAA product line and will contain an **UPDT** contraction following the affected geographical area in the CLDS/WX section.

   d. Gulf of Mexico FAs are amended at the forecaster's discretion.

      1) The product will not be amended between 0200 and 1100 UTC.

   e. Alaskan FAs are under continuous review and amended at the discretion of the forecaster.

      1) An amended FA contains **AAA** after the date/time group on the WMO heading line for the first amendment, **AAB** for the second, and continuing for all subsequent amendments.

      2) **AMD** is also included after the date/time group on the FAA product line.

3. **FA Corrections**

    a. FAs containing errors are corrected as soon as the error is noticed.

        1) This is identified by **COR** after the date/time group on the FAA product line.

    b. The first time indicated is the issuance time with the ending valid time unchanged.

    c. A corrected FA contains **UPDT** following the affected geographical area in the CLDS/WX section.

4. **Routine Delayed (RTD) FAs**

    a. For FAs delayed in transmission, **RTD** is added after the date/time group on the FAA product line.

    b. The first time indicated is the issuance time with the ending valid time unchanged.

22.3 FORMAT AND CONTENT

1. **Area Forecast Standardization**

    a. All referenced heights or altitudes are referenced above mean sea level (MSL), unless otherwise noted, and are annotated using the height in hundreds of feet, consisting of three digits (e.g., 040).

        1) For heights at or above 18,000 feet, the level will be preceded by FL (e.g., FL180).

    b. For all Area Forecasts, all heights are referenced to MSL except when prefaced by **AGL, CIG,** or **CEILING**. Tops are always referenced to MSL.

    c. EXAMPLES:

        SCT030 BKN100
        Scattered at 3,000 feet MSL, broken at 10,000 feet MSL.

        AGL SCT030 CIG BKN050
        Scattered at 3,000 feet AGL, broken at 5,000 feet AGL.

        AGL SCT-BKN015-025. TOPS 070-090
        Scattered to broken at 1,500 to 2,500 feet AGL. Tops 7,000 to 9,000 feet MSL.

    d. Messages are prepared in abbreviated plain language using contractions from the Federal Aviation Administration (FAA) Order 7340.1Y for domestic products and International Civil Aviation Organization (ICAO) document 8400 for international products issued for Oceanic FIRs.

        1) A limited number of non-abbreviated words, geographic names and numerical values of a self-explanatory nature may also be used.

        2) For Gulf of Mexico Area Forecasts, Caribbean Area Forecasts, and Alaska Area Forecasts, messages are prepared using approved ICAO contractions, abbreviations, and numerical values of self-explanatory nature.

    e. All Area Forecasts weather and obstructions to visibility are described using the standard weather abbreviations for surface observations (METAR or SPECI).

2.   **CONUS and Hawaii Area Forecast Format and Content**

    a.   The FA is an 18-hour forecast composed of the following 4 sections:

        1)   **Communication and Product Header**

            a)   The Communication and Product Header section (Table 22-3) contains descriptive information about the product.

            b)   Study Table 22-3 that provides an example of this section of the Area Forecast. Then, reference Table 22-4 to learn how to decipher the section.

LINE	
1	DFWC FA 120945
2	SYNOPSIS AND VFR CLDS/WX
3	SYNOPSIS VALID UNTIL 130400
4	CLDS/WX VALID UNTIL 122200...OTLK VALID 122200-130400
5	OK TX AR TN MS AL AND CSTL WTRS

Table 22-3. Area Forecast - Communication and Product Header Example

Line	Content	Description
1	DFW C FA 120945	Area Forecast region identifier Indicates VFR clouds and weather forecast Product type Issuance and beginning of valid date/time (UTC)
2	SYNOPSIS AND VFR CLDS/WX	Statement of weather information contained in this forecast message
3	SYNOPSIS VALID UNTIL 130400	Synopsis valid date and time
4	CLDS/WX VALID UNTIL 122200...OTLK VALID 122200-130400	The main forecast for VFR clouds and weather valid time. The valid date and time of the outlook.
5	OK TX AR TN MS AL AND CSTL WTRS	Description of the area for which the FA is valid.

Table 22-4. Decoding the Communications and Product Header

        2)   **Precautionary Statements**

            a)   The Precautionary Statements section consists of three lines.

            b)   Study the table below and then reference the text immediately following it to learn the purpose of each line.

LINE	
1	SEE AIRMET SIERRA FOR IFR CONDS AND MTN OBSCN.
2	TS IMPLY SEV OR GTR TURB SEV ICE LLWS AND IFR CONDS.
3	NON MSL HGTS DENOTED BY AGL OR CIG.

Table 22-5. Area Forecast - Precautionary Statements Example

            i)   Line 1 is included to alert users that IFR conditions and/or mountain obscurations may be occurring or are forecast to occur and are not included in the product.

            ii)   Line 2 is included as a reminder of all hazards associated with thunderstorms. These hazards are not spelled out in the body of the FA.

iii) Line 3 indicates height references are MSL unless they are preceded by **AGL** or **CIG**.

3) **Synopsis**

a) The Synopsis section contains a brief summary of the location and movement of fronts, pressure systems, and other circulation features for the entire 18 hour valid period.

b) Study the synopsis example below and then read the explanation of it.

```
SYNOPSIS...LOW PRES TROF 10Z OK/TX PNHDL AREA
FCST MOV EWD INTO CNTRL-SWRN OK BY 04Z.
WRMFNT 10Z CNTRL OK-SRN AR-NRN MS FCST LIFT
NWD INTO NERN OK-NRN AR XTRM NRN MS BY 04Z.
```

Table 22-6. Area Forecast - Synopsis Example

c) The Synopsis is decoded as follows:

Synopsis...low pressure through at 1000 UTC over the Oklahoma and Texas Panhandle area forecast to move eastward into central/ southwestern Oklahoma by 0400 UTC. A warm front at 1000 UTC from central Oklahoma to southern Arkansas to northern Mississippi is forecast to lift northward into northeastern Oklahoma to northern Arkansas to extreme northern Mississippi by 0400 UTC.

4) **Visual Flight Rules (VFR) Clouds and Weather Forecast (CLD/WX)**

a) The VFR CLDS/WX section describes conditions consisting of

i) MVFR cloud ceilings (1,000 to 3,000 feet AGL),

ii) MVFR obstructions to visibility (3-5 statute miles), and

iii) Any other significant VFR clouds (bases at or below FL180) or VFR precipitation.

b) The CLDS/WX section also includes widespread, sustained surface winds of 20 knots or greater.

c) Occasionally, IFR conditions may be forecast in the Hawaii FA as IFR conditions may not reach AIRMET geographical coverage criteria.

d) This section contains a 12-hour forecast, followed by a 6-hour categorical outlook of IFR, MVFR and/or VFR, giving a total forecast period of 18 hours.

e) In the CONUS, the CLDS/WX section is divided into regions with generally uniform weather conditions. These divisions may be by geographical regions (e.g., LM – Lake Michigan) or states using their 2-letter designators (e.g., ND – North Dakota).

f)   Study the example below of a CLD/WX section and then read the explanation of it.

```
S CNTL AND SERN TX
AGL SCT-BKN010.   TOPS 030.   VIS 3-5SM BR.   14-16Z
BCMG AGL SCT 030.   19Z AGL SCT050.   OTLK...VFR.
.
OK
PNHDL AND NW...AGL SCT030 SCT-BKN100.   TOPS FL200.   15Z
AGL SCT040 SCT100.   AFT 20Z SCT TSRA DVLPG..FEW POSS
SEV.   CB TOPS FL450.   OTLK...VFR.
REMAINDER OF STATE...CIG BKN020.   TOPS 050.   VIS 3-5SM
BR.   14Z AGL SCT-BKN040.   TOPS 100.   18Z CIG BKN060.
TOPS FL180.   22Z SCT TSRA DVLPG..FEW POSS SEV.   CB
TOPS ABV FL450.   OTLK...VFR.
.
```

Table 22-7. Area Forecast - VFR Clouds and Weather Example

g)   The VFR CLDS/WX section is decoded as follows:

South central and southeast Texas.
Scattered to broken at 1,000 feet above ground level (AGL). Tops at 3,000 feet above mean sea level (MSL). Visibility 3 to 5 statute miles in mist. Between 1400 and 1600 UTC...clouds becoming scattered at 3,000 feet AGL. 1900 UTC...scattered at 5,000 feet AGL. Outlook...VFR.

Oklahoma
Panhandle and northwest...scattered at 3,000 feet AGL, scattered to broken at 10,000 feet AGL. Tops at flight level 20,000 feet MSL. 1500 UTC...scattered at 4,000 feet AGL, scattered at 10,000 feet AGL. After 2000 UTC...scattered thunderstorms with rain showers developing.. a few possible severe. Cumulonimbus tops to flight level 45,000 feet MSL. Outlook...VFR.

Remainder of the state...Ceilings broken at 2,000 feet AGL. Tops at 5,000 feet MSL. Visibilities 3 to 5 statute miles in mist. 1400 UTC... scattered to broken at 4,000 feet AGL. Tops at 10,000 feet MSL. 1800 UTC...ceilings broken 6,000 feet AGL. Tops to flight level 18,000 feet MSL. 2200 UTC...scattered thunderstorm with rain showers developing...a few possibly severe. Cumulonimbus tops above flight level 45,000 feet MSL. Outlook...VFR.

3. **Gulf of Mexico Area Forecast Content**

   a. The FAGX is a single product combining information contained in FAs prepared for the conterminous U.S. and the inflight advisories -- AIRMET/SIGMET.

      1) Each section describes the phenomena impacting the respective areas and will always have an entry even if it is negative.

   b. The FAGX contains a synopsis and a weather forecast section. The weather section includes:

      1) Flight precautions at or below 12,000 feet MSL for thunderstorms which are at least scattered or meet Convective SIGMET criteria.
      2) Moderate or greater turbulence.
      3) Moderate or greater icing.
      4) Wind speeds greater than or equal to 25 knots below 1,000 feet MSL.
      5) Ceilings and/or visibilities less than 1,000 feet and/or three (3) miles.
      6) Significant clouds and weather.
      7) Icing and freezing level.
      8) Turbulence.

4. **Caribbean Area Forecast Content**

   a. FACA is very similar to the Gulf of Mexico FA.
   b. This product has only four sections.

      1) Synopsis

         a) A brief description of the location and movement of fronts, pressure systems, and other circulations, as well as the weather associated with them.

      2) Significant CLD/WX

         a) A 12-hour forecast of clouds and weather (including IFR conditions) plus a 12-hour categorical outlook (IFR/MVFR/VFR/WND). The cause of IFR/MVFR conditions is specified. Wind is noted when 25 knots or greater.

      3) Ice and FZ LVL

         a) The location and altitudes of moderate or greater icing and the associated freezing levels.

      4) TURB

         a) The location and altitudes of moderate or greater turbulence.

5. **Alaska Area Forecast Content**

    a. The Alaskan FA zones contain sections on Clouds and Weather, Turbulence, and Icing and Freezing Levels.

        1) The Clouds and Weather section includes

            a) SIGMETs for Thunderstorms and Volcanic Ash;

            b) AIRMETs for IFR ceiling and visibility, mountain obscuration, and strong surface winds;

            c) Bases and tops of significant cloud layers;

            d) Visibilities of six (6) miles or less and restricting phenomena;

            e) Precipitation and thunderstorms;

            f) Surface winds of 20 kt. or greater;

            g) Outlook using categorical terms (i.e., VFR CIG, MVFR BR, IFR SN WND); and

            h) Mountain-pass conditions using categorical terms (for selected zones only).

        2) The Turbulence section includes

            a) SIGMETs for Turbulence;

            b) AIRMETs for Turbulence and/or Low Level Wind Shear (LLWS);

            c) Forecast of significant turbulence not meeting SIGMET or AIRMET criteria or that is forecast for the period 6 to 12 hours after issuance; and

            d) If no significant turbulence is forecast, NIL SIG will be entered.

        3) Icing section includes

            a) SIGMETs for Icing;

            b) AIRMETs for Icing and freezing precipitation;

            c) Forecast of significant icing not meeting SIGMET or AIRMET criteria or which is forecast for the period 6 to 12 hours after issuance;

            d) Freezing Level; and

            e) If no significant icing is forecast, NIL SIG will be entered followed by the freezing level.

22.4 USING THE PRODUCT

1. Area Forecasts are an invaluable tool when considering the overall weather picture over a regional area.

2. Because the FAs are so similar in content and format only one example of a CONUS FA is provided. To study the other types of FAs available, reference the AWC website listed in Subunit 1.

    a. Additionally, if you are departing from or arriving at an airport when a TAF is not available, an Area Forecast may be the only way for you to get a report on the forecast conditions to exist at the time of your arrival and/or departure.

```
FAUS5 KDFW 030953 (ICAO Communication Header)
FA4W
DFWC FA 030945 (AMD or COR if needed)
SYNOPSIS AND VFR CLDS/WX
SYNOPSIS VALID UNTIL 040400
CLDS/WX VALID UNTIL 032200...OTLK VALID 032200-040400
OK TX AR TN LA MS AL
.
SEE AIRMET SIERRA FOR IFR COND AND MT OBSCN.
TS IMPLY SEV OR GTR TURB SEV ICE LLWS AND IFR CONDS.
NON MSL HGT DENOTED BY AGL OR CIG.
.
SYNOPSIS...HURCN LILI MOVG ONSHORE OVER CENTRAL LA COASTLINE.  SEE LATEST
ADVISORY FM NHC.  QUASI-STNR FRONTAL SYSTEM EXTENDS FM N OH AND CENTRAL IN
ACROSS S IL..SW MO..SW OK INTO SE CORNER OF NM.  BY 04Z...COLD FRONT WILL EXTEND
FM A LOW OVER SERN NE ACROSS CENTRAL KS AND W OK INTO BIG BEND AREA OF SW TX.
.
OK
PANHANDLE/W OK...CIG OVC010.  CLDS LYR TO FL240.
VIS 3-5SM BR.  BECMG 1618 CIG OVC015-025.  WIDELY SCT -SHRA/ISOL EMBD
-TSRA.  CB TOP FL350.  OTLK...MVFR CIG TSRA BR.
ERN OK...AGL SCT-BKN015-025.  TOPS 030-050.  VIS 3-5SM BR.  BECMG
1417 AGL SCT030-050.  OTLK...VFR.
.
NW TX
CIG010.  CLDS LYR TO FL240.  VIS 3-5SM BR.  BECMG 1618 CIG OVC015-025.
WIDELY SCT -SHRA/ISOL EMBD -TSRA.  CB TOP FL350.  OTLK...MVFR CIG TSRA BR.
.
SW TX
AGL SCT040-060.  OTLK...VFR.
.
CENTRAL TX
CIG BKN015-025.  TOP 030-050.  VIS 3-5SM BR.  BECMG 1417 AGL SCT030-050.
OTLK...VFR.
.
E TX
SKC.  BECMG 1316 AGL SCT030-050.  OTLK...VFR.
.
AR
AGL SCT030-050.  SCT-BKN100.  TOP FL200.  BKN CI.  OTLK...MVFR CIG TSRA BR.
.
LA
N LA...AGL SCT-BKN030-050.  BKN100.  TOPS FL240.  ISOL -SHRA.  BECMG 1618
CIG BKN030-050.  WIDELY SCT TSRA/SHRA DEVELOPING.  CB TOP FL400.
OTLK...MVFR CIG TSRA WIND.
S LA...CIG OVC010-020.  CLDS LYR TO FL280.  OCNL RA/+RA...SCT
+TSRA...POSS SEV.  CB TOPS FL450.  SFC WND 14030G50KT.  E SECTIONS...WND
30025G40KT.  WND DIMINISHING TO 20G30KT 19-22Z.
OTLK...MVFR CIG SHRA WND.
.
TN
BKN CI.  OCNL VIS 3-5SM BR TIL 14Z.  OTLK...VFR.
.
MS AL
N AND CENTRAL MS-AL/SE AL..SCT-BKN100.  BKN150.  TOPS FL280.  BECMG 1618
AGL SCT-BKN050 BKN100 OVC150.  OTLK...MVFR CIG TSRA.
S MS/SW AL...AGL SCT-BKN050 BKN100 OVC150.  TOPS FL280.  BECMG 1316 CIG
OVC015-025.  OCNL RA/SCT EMBD TSRA.  CB TOP FL410.  OTLK...MVFR CIG TSRA.
```

END OF STUDY UNIT

STUDY UNIT TWENTY-THREE
TERMINAL AERODROME FORECAST (TAF)

(14 pages of outline)

Please take a few minutes to study each of the concepts listed above and anticipate/imagine what they are and how they relate to the other listed concepts.

23.1 INTRODUCTION

1. The terminal aerodrome forecast (TAF) is a concise statement of the expected meteorological conditions at an airport during a specified period (usually 24 hr.).

   a. The TAF covers a geographic area within a 5-SM radius of the airport's center.

   b. TAFs can be viewed on the National Weather Service (NWS) Aviation Digital Data Service (ADDS) website at http://adds.aviationweather.noaa.gov/tafs/.

2. TAFs are scheduled four times daily for 24-hr. periods beginning at 0000Z, 0600Z, 1200Z, and 1800Z.

   a. Figures 23-1, 23-2, and 23-3 on pages 402, 403, and 404 depict the locations where TAFs are issued.

3. TAFs use the same codes as the METAR reports. See Part III, Study Unit 3, "Aviation Routine Weather Reports (METAR)," beginning on page 223, for a detailed explanation of those codes.

4. All times in a TAF refer to Coordinated Universal Time (UTC).

   a. The term Zulu (Z) may be used to denote UTC.

5. In order for a TAF to be issued for an airport, a minimum of two consecutive, complete METAR (routine) observations (manual or automated), not less than 30 min. apart nor more than 1 hr. apart, is required for that airport.

   a. After a TAF has been issued, the forecaster will use all available weather data sources to maintain the TAF.

   b. However, if during this time a METAR is missing or part of the METAR is missing and the forecaster feels that other weather sources cannot provide the necessary information, the forecaster will discontinue the TAF.

23.2 ELEMENTS

1. A TAF contains the following sequence of elements in the following order (items 1-9). Forecast change indicators (items 10-12) and probability forecast (item 13) are used as appropriate.

Communications Header	Forecast of Meteorological Conditions	Time Elements
1. Type of report	5. Wind	10. Temporary (TEMPO)
2. ICAO station identifier	6. Visibility	11. From (FM)
3. Date and time of origin	7. Significant weather	12. Becoming (BECMG)
4. Valid period date and time	8. Sky condition	13. Probability (PROB)
	9. Wind shear (optional)	

23.3 EXAMPLE OF A TAF

TAF
KOKC 051130Z 051212 14008KT 5SM BR BKN030 WS018/32030KT TEMPO 1316 1 1/2SM BR
   FM1600 16010KT P6SM SKC BECMG 2224 20013G20KT 4SM SHRA OVC020
   PROB40 0006 2SM TSRA OVC008CB=

To aid in the discussion, we have divided the TAF above into the following elements numbered 1. through 13.

TAF	KOKC	051130Z	051212	14008KT	5SM	BR	BKN030	WS018/32030KT
1.	2.	3.	4.	5.	6.	7.	8.	9.

TEMPO 1316 1 1/2SM BR   FM1600 16010KT P6SM SKC
         10.   11.

BECMG 2224 20013G20KT 4SM SHRA OVC020
                12.

PROB40 0006 2SM TSRA OVC008CB=
                13.

1. Routine terminal aerodrome forecast

2. Oklahoma City, OK

3. Forecast prepared on the 5th day at 1130 UTC (or Z)

4. Forecast valid from the 5th day at 1200 UTC until 1200 UTC on the 6th

5. Wind 140° true at 8 kt.

6. Visibility 5 SM

7. Visibility obscured by mist

8. Ceiling 3,000 ft. broken

9. Low-level wind shear at 1,800 ft., wind 320° true at 30 kt.

10. Temporary (spoken as occasional) visibility 1 1/2 SM in mist between 1300 UTC and 1600 UTC

11. From (or after) 1600 UTC, wind 160° true at 10 kt., visibility more than 6 SM, sky clear

12. Becoming (gradual change) wind 200° true at 13 kt., gusts to 20 kt., visibility 4 SM in moderate rain showers, ceiling 2,000 ft. overcast between 2200 UTC and 2400 UTC

13. Probability (40% chance) between 0000 UTC and 0600 UTC of visibility 2 SM, thunderstorm, moderate rain, ceiling 800 ft. overcast, cumulonimbus clouds (the = sign indicates end of forecast)

23.4 TYPE OF REPORT

1. The report type header will always appear as the first element in the TAF.

2. There are two types of TAF issuances:

   a. **TAF** means a routine forecast.
   b. **TAF AMD** means an amended forecast.

      1) An amended forecast is issued when the current TAF no longer adequately describes the ongoing weather or the forecaster feels the TAF is not representative of the current or expected weather.

3. Corrected (COR) or routine delayed (RTD) TAFs are identified only in the communications header which precedes the actual forecast.

   a. A **TAF COR** is issued when a TAF contains typographical or other errors.
   b. A **TAF RTD** is issued for those airports not having a 24-hr. observing schedule. When the first two complete METARs of the day are received, a routine delayed TAF is issued.

      1) After this, the TAF is issued at the normal times.

23.5 ICAO STATION IDENTIFIER

1. The TAF uses the ICAO four-letter station identifier as described in Part III, Study Unit 3, "Aviation Routine Weather Reports (METAR)," beginning on page 223.

   a. EXAMPLE: **KOKC** is the identifier for Will Rogers World Airport in Oklahoma City, OK.

23.6 DATE AND TIME OF ORIGIN

1. This element provides the date and time (UTC) that the forecast is actually prepared.

2. The format is a two-digit date and a four-digit time followed by the letter **Z**.

   a. EXAMPLE: **051130Z** means the TAF was prepared on the 5th day at 1130 UTC (or Z).

3. Routine TAFs are prepared and filed roughly one-half hour prior to the scheduled issuance time.

23.7 VALID PERIOD DATE AND TIME

1. The valid period of the forecast is a two-digit date followed by the two-digit beginning hour and two-digit ending hour in UTC.

   a. EXAMPLE: **051212** means the TAF is valid from the 5th day at 1200 UTC to 1200 UTC on the 6th.

2. Valid periods beginning at 0000 UTC will be indicated as **00**, and valid periods ending at 0000 UTC will be indicated as **24**.

   a. EXAMPLE: **110024** means the TAF is valid from the 11th at 0000 UTC to 0000 UTC on the 12th.

3. In the case of an amended, corrected, or delayed forecast, the valid period may be less than 24 hr.

4. For airports with less than 24-hr. observational coverage for which part-time TAFs are provided, the TAF will be valid until the end of the scheduled forecast even if the observations have ceased before that time.

    a. **AMD NOT SKED** (amendment not scheduled) or **NIL AMD** (no amendment) will be issued after the forecast information.

    b. **AMD NOT SKED AFT (closing time) Z** will be used if the times of the observations are known and judged reliable.

        1) EXAMPLE: **AMD NOT SKED AFT 0300Z** means amendment not scheduled after 0300 UTC.

    c. For the TAFs issued while the location is closed, the word **NIL** (no TAF) will appear in place of the forecast text.

        1) A delayed (RTD) forecast will then be issued for the location after two complete observations are received.

    d. **AMD LTD TO CLD VIS AND WIND** (amendment limited to clouds, visibility, and wind) is used at observation sites that have part-time augmentation. This remark means that there will be amendments only for clouds, visibility, and wind.

        1) There will be no amendments for thunderstorms or freezing/frozen precipitation.

23.8 FORECAST METEOROLOGICAL CONDITIONS

1. This is the body of the TAF.

2. The wind, visibility, and sky condition elements are always included in the initial time group of the forecast. Weather is included only if it is significant to aviation.

3. If a significant, lasting change in any of the elements is expected during the valid period, a new time period with the changes is included.

    a. It should be noted that, with the exception of a FM group (see Subunit 23.15, "From (FM) Group," on page 397), the new time period will include only those elements expected to change; e.g., if a lowering of the visibility is expected but the wind is expected to remain the same, the new time period reflecting the lower visibility would not include a forecast wind.

        1) The forecast wind would remain the same as in the previous time period.

4. Temporary conditions expected during a specific time period are included with that period.

23.9 WIND

1. This element is a five- or six-digit group with the forecast surface wind direction (first three digits) referenced to true north and the average speed (last two digits or three digits if 100 kt. or greater).

2. The abbreviation **KT** is appended to denote the use of knots for wind speed.

3. Wind gusts are denoted by the letter **G** appended to the wind speed, followed by the highest expected gust.

    a. Squalls are forecast in the wind group as gusts **(G)** but must be identified in the significant weather group with the code **SQ**.

4. Variable winds are encoded when it is impossible to forecast a wind direction due to winds associated with convective activity or low wind speeds (3 kt. or less).

    a. Variable wind direction is noted by **VRB** where the three-digit direction usually appears.

5.   A calm wind (0 kt.) is forecast as **00000KT**.

6.   EXAMPLES:

   a.   **14008KT** means wind from 140° (true) at 8 kt.

   b.   **35012G20KT** means wind from 350° (true) at 12 kt. with gusts up to 20 kt.

   c.   **VRB20KT** means wind direction variable at 20 kt.

23.10 VISIBILITY

1.   The expected prevailing visibility is forecast in statute miles with a space and then fractions of statute miles, as needed, with **SM** appended to it.

   a.   EXAMPLE: **2 1/2SM** means visibility is forecast to be two and one-half statute miles.

2.   Sector or variable visibility is not forecast, and the visibility group is omitted if missing.

3.   Forecast visibility greater than 6 SM is coded **P6SM**.

4.   If the prevailing visibility is forecast to be 6 SM or less, one or more weather phenomena (e.g., RA, SN, TS, etc.) must be included.

   a.   Drifting dust **(DRDU)**, drifting sand **(DRSA)**, drifting snow **(DRSN)**, shallow fog **(MIFG)**, partial fog **(PRFG)**, and patchy fog **(BCFG)** may be forecast with a prevailing visibility of greater than or equal to seven statute miles.

5.   If volcanic ash is forecast, the visibility must also be forecast even if it is more than 6 SM.

23.11 SIGNIFICANT WEATHER

1.   The expected weather phenomenon or phenomena are coded in TAF reports using the same format, qualifiers, and phenomena contractions as METAR reports, except **UP** (unknown precipitation).

   a.   See Part III, Study Unit 3, "Aviation Routine Weather Reports (METAR)," beginning on page 223.

2.   Obscurations to vision will be forecast whenever the prevailing visibility is forecast to be 6 SM or less.

   a.   Precipitation and volcanic ash will be forecast regardless of the visibility forecast.

3.   Multiple precipitation elements are encoded in a single group (e.g., **–TSRASN**).

   a.   If more than one type of precipitation is forecast, up to three appropriate precipitation contractions can be combined in a single group (with no spaces) with the predominant type of precipitation being first.

   b.   In this single group, the intensity refers to the total precipitation and can be used with either one or no intensity qualifier, as appropriate.

   c.   Non-precipitation elements are included with a space between them and any precipitation elements.

4.   Intensity is coded with precipitation types, except ice crystals and hail, including those associated with thunderstorms and those of a showery nature **(SH)**.

   a.   If no intensity indicator is present, the intensity is moderate.

   b.   The symbol + indicates heavy intensity.

   c.   The symbol – indicates light intensity.

   d.   In TAFs, the intensity qualifiers (light, moderate, and heavy) refer to the intensity of the precipitation and not to the intensity of any thunderstorms associated with the precipitation.

5. If no significant weather is expected to occur during a specific time period in the forecast, the weather group is omitted for that time period.

    a. If, after a time period in which significant weather has been forecast, a change to a forecast of no significant weather occurs, the contraction **NSW** (no significant weather) will appear as the weather included in becoming (BECMG) or temporary (TEMPO) groups.

        1) NSW will not be used in the initial time period of a TAF or in from (FM) groups.

6. If the forecaster determines that there could be weather that impacts aviation in the vicinity of the airport, the forecaster will include those conditions after the weather group.

    a. The letters **VC** describe conditions that will occur within the vicinity of an airport (5 to 10 SM) and will be used only with FG (fog), SH (showers), or TS (thunderstorm).

7. EXAMPLES:

    a. **−DZ FG** means light drizzle and fog
    b. **+SHRA FG** means heavy rain showers and fog
    c. **TSSNRA** means thunderstorm with moderate snow and rain
    d. **TS −FZRA** means thunderstorms with light freezing rain
    e. **FZRASNPL** means moderate freezing rain, snow, and ice pellets

23.12 SKY CONDITIONS

1. TAF sky conditions use the METAR format as described in Part III, Study Unit 3, "Aviation Routine Weather Reports (METAR)," beginning on page 223, except that cumulonimbus clouds (CB) are the only cloud type forecast in TAFs.

2. When the sky is obscured due to a surface-based phenomenon, vertical visibility (VV) into the obscuration is forecast.

    a. Partial obscurations are not forecast.

3. For aviation purposes, the ceiling is the lowest broken or overcast layer or vertical visibility.

4. EXAMPLES:

    a. **BKN030** means ceiling 3,000 ft. broken.
    b. **VV008** means indefinite ceiling (vertical visibility) 800 ft.

23.13 WIND SHEAR

1. Wind shear is the forecast of nonconvective low-level winds (up to and including 2,000 ft. AGL) and is entered after the sky conditions when wind shear is expected.

    a. Wind shear is only included in the prevailing conditions section. Forecasts of non-convective LLWS are not included in **TEMPO** or **PROB** groups.

    b. The element is omitted if wind shear is not expected to occur.

2. The forecast includes the height of the wind shear followed by the wind direction and wind speed at the indicated height.

3. Wind shear is encoded with the contraction **WS**, followed by a three-digit height solidus (/), and winds at the height indicated in the same format as surface winds. Height is given in hundreds of feet AGL up to and including 2,000 ft.

4. EXAMPLE: **WS018/32030KT** means low-level wind shear at 1,800 ft., wind (at 1,800 ft. AGL) 320° true at 30 kt.

23.14 TIME ELEMENTS

1. Three forecast change indicators are used when a rapid, temporary, or probable change is expected in some or all of the forecast meteorological conditions.

    a. The forecast change indicators are

        1) FM (From)
        2) TEMPO (Temporarily)
        3) PROB (Probability)

    b. Each change indicator marks a time group within the TAF.

23.15 FROM (FM) GROUP

1. The **FM** group is used when a rapid and significant change, usually occurring in less than 1 hour in prevailing conditions, is expected.

    a. Typically, a rapid change of prevailing conditions to more or less a completely new set of conditions is associated with a synoptic feature (i.e., cold or warm front) passing through the terminal area.

2. Appended to the **FM** indicator is the four-digit hour and minute when the change is expected to begin and continue until the next change group or until the end of the current forecast.

3. A **FM** group will always mark the beginning of a new line in a TAF report.

4. Each **FM** group contains all the required elements, i.e., wind, visibility, weather, sky conditions, and wind shear.

    a. Weather and wind shear will be omitted in **FM** groups when they are not significant to aviation.

    b. **FM** groups will not include the contraction **NSW**.

5. EXAMPLE: **FM1600 16010KT P6SM SKC** means the forecast for the hours from 1600 UTC to 2200 UTC (beginning of the next forecast group in the example TAF on page 392), wind 160° true at 10 kt., visibility greater than 6 SM, sky clear.

23.16 TEMPORARY (TEMPO) GROUP

1. The **TEMPO** group is used for temporary fluctuations in wind, visibility, weather, or sky condition that are expected to last for generally less than 1 hour at a time (occasional) and to occur during less than half the time period.

    a. For a TEMPO indicator to be used, there must be a high probability (greater that 50%) of the forecast conditions occurrence.

2. The **TEMPO** indicator is followed by a four-digit group giving the beginning and ending hour of the time period during which the temporary conditions are expected.

3. Only the changing forecast meteorological conditions are included in **TEMPO** groups.

    a. The omitted conditions are carried over from the previous time group.

4. EXAMPLE: **5SM BR BKN030 TEMPO 1316 1 1/2SM BR** means visibility 5 SM in mist, ceiling 3,000 ft. broken with occasional (temporary conditions) visibility 1 1/2 SM in mist between 1300 UTC and 1600 UTC. Note that the sky condition (BKN030) does not change; i.e., only the visibility is forecast to change.

23.17   PROBABILITY (PROB) FORECAST

1.   The **PROB** indicates the chance of thunderstorms or other precipitation events occurring, along with associated weather conditions (wind, visibility, and sky conditions).

   a.   A probability forecast will not be used during the first 6 hr. of a TAF.

2.   Appended to the **PROB** contraction is the probability value.

   a.   At present, only the PROB30 contraction is used on NWS TAFs, indicating a 30-39% probability of the forecast conditions occurrence.

   b.   If the chance is 50% or greater, it is considered a prevailing weather condition and is included in the weather section or the TEMPO change indicator group.

3.   Appended to the **PROB** indicator is a four-digit group giving the beginning and ending hour of the time period during which the precipitation or thunderstorms are expected.

4.   EXAMPLE: **PROB30 0006 2SM TSRA OVC008CB** means that, between 0000 UTC and 0600 UTC, there is a chance (30-39% probability) of visibility 2 SM, thunderstorm with moderate rain, and ceiling 800 ft. overcast with cumulonimbus clouds.

23.18   SAMPLE TAFs

```
TAF
KOMA 010530Z 010606 24009KT P6SM SCT050 BKN250
   BECMG 1214 BKN040 OVC250
   PROB40 1822 25012G18KT 4SM –TSRA BKN030CB
   BECMG 2224 SCT030=
```

TAF	Routine terminal aerodrome forecast
KOMA	Omaha, NE
010530Z	Prepared on the 1st day at 0530 UTC
010606	Forecast valid from 0600 UTC on the 1st until 0600 UTC on the 2nd
24009KT P6SM SCT050 BKN250	Wind 240° at 9 kt., visibility greater than 6 SM, 5,000 ft. scattered, ceiling 25,000 ft. broken
BECMG 1214 BKN040 OVC250	A gradual change to ceiling 4,000 ft. broken, 25,000 ft. overcast between 1200 UTC and 1400 UTC (forecast wind and visibility carried over from previous time group)
PROB40 1822 25012G18KT 4SM –TSRA BKN030CB	Chance (40-49% probability) between 1800 UTC and 2200 UTC of wind 250° at 12 kt., gusts to 18 kt., visibility 4 SM, thunderstorm, light rain, ceiling 3,000 ft. broken cumulonimbus
BECMG 2224 SCT030=	A gradual change to 3,000 ft. scattered between 2200 UTC and 2400 UTC, end of forecast (forecast wind and visibility carried over from previous time group)

```
TAF
KSPI    251730Z 251818 01015KT P6SM BKN050
    PROB40 1819 –RA
    BECMG 1921 33009KT SCT050
    FM0200 VRB04KT P6SM SKC
    PROB30 1115 4SM MIFG=
```

TAF	Routine terminal aerodrome forecast
KSPI	Springfield, IL
251730Z	Prepared on the 25th day at 1730 UTC
251818	Valid from 1800 UTC on the 25th to 1800 UTC on the 26th
01015KT P6SM BKN050	Wind 010° at 15 kt., visibility greater than 6 SM, ceiling 5,000 ft. broken
PROB40 1819 –RA	Chance (40-49% probability) of light rain between 1800 UTC and 1900 UTC
BECMG 1921 33009KT SCT050	A gradual change to wind 330° at 9 kt., 5,000 ft. scattered between 1900 UTC and 2100 UTC (visibility carried over from previous time group)
FM0200 VRB04KT P6SM SKC	After 0200 UTC, wind variable in direction at 4 kt., visibility greater than 6 SM, sky clear
PROB30 1115 4SM MIFG=	Chance (30-39% probability) visibility 4 SM in shallow fog between 1100 UTC and 1500 UTC, end of forecast

```
TAF AMD
KOTH 270740Z 270806 VRB04KT 3SM BR SCT003 OVC015
    TEMPO 1114 1SM –RA OVC005
    FM1400 34014KT 2SM –RA BR SCT005 OVC035
    PROB40 1416 –FZRA
    BECMG 1618 34010KT P6SM BKN040
    BECMG 2301 00000KT NSW SKC=
```

TAF AMD	Amended terminal aerodrome forecast
270740Z	Prepared on the 27th day at 0740 UTC
270806	Valid time from 0800 UTC on the 27th to 0600 UTC on the 28th
VRB04KT 3SM BR SCT003 OVC015	Wind variable in direction at 4 kt., visibility 3 SM in mist, 300 ft. scattered, ceiling 1,500 ft. overcast
TEMPO 1114 1SM RA OVC005	Occasional (temporary) visibility 1 SM in light rain, ceiling 500 ft. overcast between 1100 UTC and 1400 UTC
FM1400 34014KT 2SM –RA BR SCT005 OVC035	From (after) 1400 UTC, wind 340° at 14 kt., visibility 2 SM, light rain, mist, 500 ft. scattered, ceiling 3,500 ft. overcast
PROB40 1416 –FZRA	Chance (40-49% probability) between 1400 UTC and 1600 UTC of light freezing rain
BECMG 1618 34010KT P6SM BKN040	A gradual change to wind 340° at 10 kt., visibility greater than 6 SM, ceiling 4,000 ft. broken between 1600 UTC and 1800 UTC
BECMG 2301 00000KT NSW SKC=	A gradual change to a calm wind, no significant weather, sky clear (forecast visibility carried over from previous time group); these conditions continuing until 0600 UTC, the end of the forecast period

```
TAF AMD
KSEA 161440Z 161512 23012KT P6SM SCT014 OVC020
    TEMPO 1518 5SM –DZ BR BKN012
    BECMG 1820 27008KT BKN022
    BECMG 2123 30010KT SCT025
    BECMG 0406 21012KT OVC015=
```

TAF AMD	Amended terminal aerodrome forecast
KSEA	Seattle-Tacoma, WA
161440Z	Prepared on the 16th day at 1440 UTC
161512	Valid from 1500 UTC on the 16th to 1200 UTC on the 17th
23012KT P6SM SCT014 OVC020	Wind 230° at 12 kt., visibility greater than 6 SM, 1,400 ft. scattered, ceiling 2,000 ft. overcast
TEMPO 1518 5SM –DZ BR BKN012	Occasional (temporary) visibility 5 SM in light drizzle and mist, ceiling 1,200 ft. broken between 1500 UTC and 1800 UTC
BECMG 1820 27008KT BKN022	A gradual change to wind 270° at 8 kt., ceiling 2,200 ft. broken between 1800 UTC and 2000 UTC (visibility carried over from previous time group)
BECMG 2123 30010KT SCT025	A gradual change to wind 300° at 10 kt., 2,500 ft. scattered between 2100 UTC and 2300 UTC (visibility carried over from previous time group)
BECMG 0406 21012KT OVC015=	A gradual change to wind 210° at 12 kt., ceiling 1,600 ft. overcast between 0400 UTC and 0600 UTC (visibility carried over from previous time group), end of forecast

23.19 INTERNATIONAL DIFFERENCES IN METAR/TAF

1. **Altimeter Setting**

    a. In the METAR report, the U.S. reports the altimeter setting in inches of mercury (e.g., A2992), but internationally it will be reported in hectoPascal/millibar (e.g., Q1013).

2. **Wind**

    a. Internationally, wind speed may be reported in knots (KT), kilometers per hour (KMH), or meters per second (MPS).

    b. Appropriate units are indicated in both METAR and TAF.

    c. Wind direction variability is reported only for wind speeds of 3 kt. or less internationally, but wind direction variability is reported for wind speeds up to 6 kt. in the U.S.

3.   **Visibility**

   a.   Internationally, visibility is reported in four digits using meters with the direction of the lowest visibility sector.

   1)   EXAMPLE: **6000SW** means visibility is lowest at 6,000 meters to the southwest.
   2)   International visibility reports also contain a trend code.

      a)   **D** means down.
      b)   **U** means up.
      c)   **N** means no change.
      d)   **V** means variable.

   b.   In the U.S., we use prevailing visibility.

4.   **Wind Shear**

   a.   Low-level wind shear (below 2,000 ft. AGL) not associated with convective activity will appear in TAFs produced only in the U.S. and Canada.

5.   **Other**

   a.   The contraction **CAVOK** (ceiling and visibility OK) replaces visibility, weather, and sky conditions on international METARs and TAFs if

   1)   Visibility is 10 kilometers or more.
   2)   No clouds are below 1,500 meters (5,000 ft.) or below the highest minimum sector altitude, whichever is greater.
   3)   There are no cumulonimbus clouds.
   4)   There are no significant weather phenomena.

   b.   International and U.S. military TAFs also contain forecasts of maximum and minimum temperature, icing, and turbulence.

   1)   The U.S. has no requirement to forecast temperatures in the TAF, and the National Weather Service will continue to forecast icing and turbulence in AIRMETs and SIGMETs.

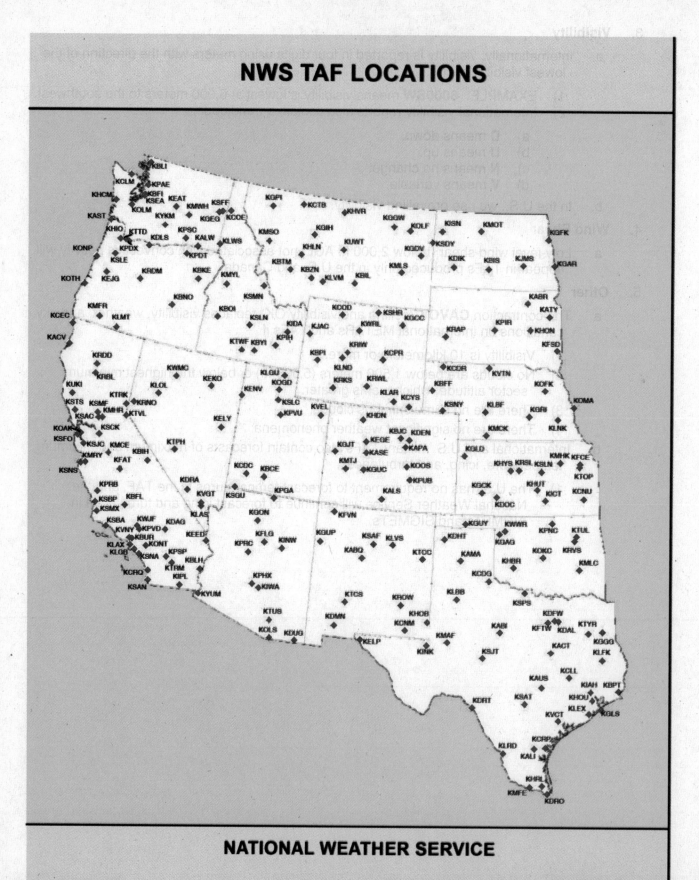

NWS TAF LOCATIONS

NATIONAL WEATHER SERVICE

MIRS GIS GROUP

Figure 23-1. TAF Locations - Western Contiguous United States

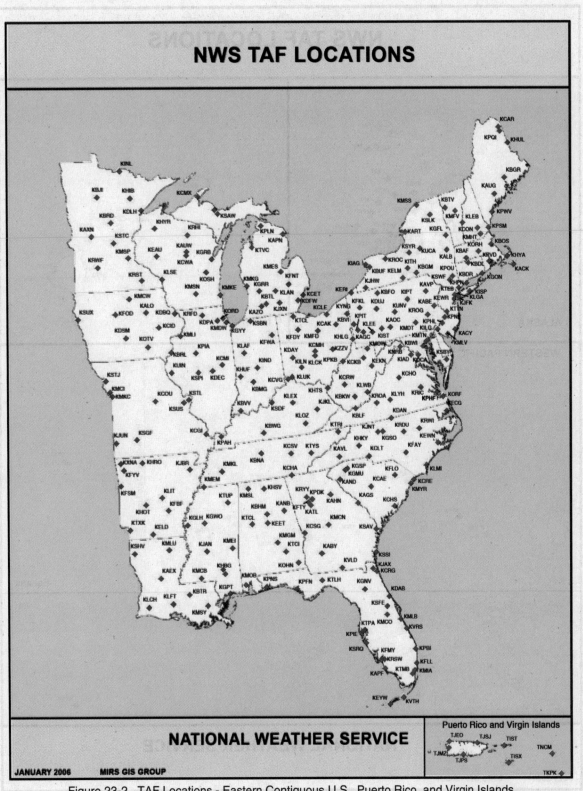

Figure 23-2. TAF Locations - Eastern Contiguous U.S., Puerto Rico, and Virgin Islands

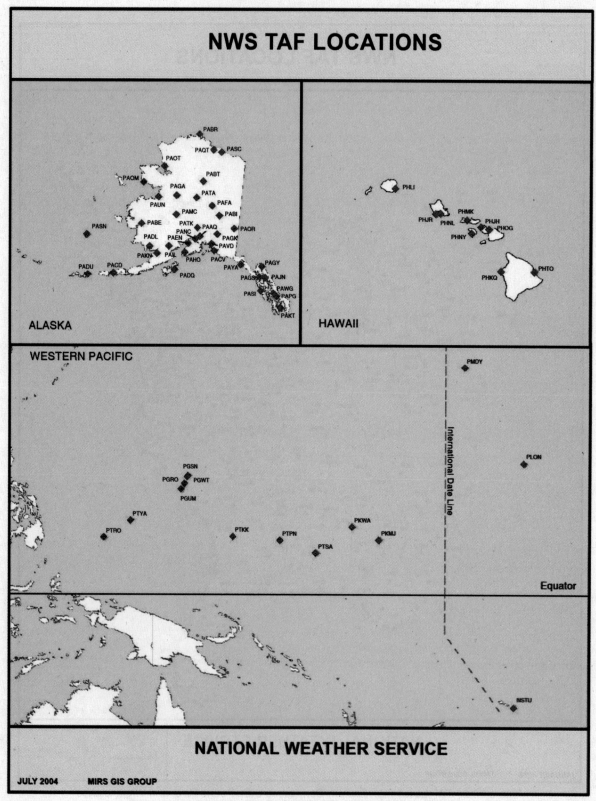

Figure 23-3. TAF Locations - Alaska, Hawaii, and Western Pacific

END OF STUDY UNIT

STUDY UNIT TWENTY-FOUR
INTERNATIONAL AVIATION ROUTE FORECASTS (ROFOR)

(2 pages of outline)

Please take a few minutes to study each of the concepts listed above and anticipate/imagine what they are and how they relate to the other listed concepts.

24.1 PRODUCT DESCRIPTION

1. International Route Forecasts (ROFORs) are prepared and issued several hours in advance of regularly scheduled flights.

    a. The only NWS office which routinely issues ROFORs is the Weather Forecast Office (WFO) in Honolulu in its capacity as a Meteorological Watch Office (MWO) for ICAO.

    b. Reports are created for routes within its area of responsibility that are under-served by conventional aviation forecasts and products.

2. The Route Forecast is an alphanumeric product providing a coded route forecast for regularly scheduled flights or upon request for flights that operate within the National Weather Service Pacific Region WFO in Honolulu or the WFO Guam Area of Responsibility (AOR).

3. The ROFOR is both a routinely scheduled and an upon-request product mostly for low level flights at FL240 or lower.

24.2 ISSUANCE

1. ROFORs are issued for prescribed times, several hours in advance, for regularly scheduled flights.

    a. ROFOR requests for unscheduled flights are prepared as soon as time permits.

2. ROFORs are not amended.

    a. ROFOR corrections are issued as soon as possible when erroneous data has been identified as being transmitted.

24.3 CONTENT

1. ROFORs contain some or all of the following forecast parameters:

    a. Winds and temperatures aloft
    b. Significant en route weather
    c. Weather Synopsis

2. At a minimum, ROFORs include a. and b. above.

    a. They may contain data for multiple altitudes and include TAFs for destination points and/or alternates.

24.4 USING THE PRODUCT

1.   ROFORs are an international product and there is no specific guidance for the symbols used in the report.

   a.   WFO Honolulu produces ROFORs for use by aircraft dispatchers and aircrew personnel, but because they are specially created for individual operations, there is no key or legend to decipher them.

2.   These reports are extremely outdated and barely used at all in day-to-day operations.

   a.   Information on the product is included in this text because of its inclusion in the FAA Advisory Circular.

3.   For your reference, a sample ROFOR is shown below.

   a.   There is no key to understand the first two lines of numeric code, but the weather synopsis uses standard terminology.

Tarawa to Majuro Route
FROC33 PHFO 291510 *(ICAO Communication Header)*

FOR PKMJYMYX
ROFOR VALID 2008 FOR ROUTE NGTA TO PKMJ
01205 4100P08 06010 4140P00 06015 4180M03 07020
01201 4100P08 09015 4140P00 09020 4180M04 10025
SIGWX...ISOL TCU/VIS 5SM SHRA
PKMJ 221120Z 221212 NIL=

END OF STUDY UNIT

STUDY UNIT TWENTY-FIVE
WIND AND TEMPERATURE ALOFT FORECASTS (FB)

(6 pages of outline)

Please take a few minutes to study each of the concepts listed above and anticipate/imagine what they are and how they relate to the other listed concepts.

25.1 PRODUCT DESCRIPTION

1. Wind and Temperature Aloft Forecasts (FB) are computer prepared, alphanumeric forecasts of wind direction, wind speed, and temperature at specified times, altitudes, and locations.

2. Forecasts are based on the North American Mesoscale (NAM) forecast model run.

   a. The altitudes forecast in the Hawaii and western Pacific bulletins are different than those forecast in the Contiguous U.S. and Alaska.

      1) Wind forecasts are not issued for altitudes within 1,500 feet of a location's elevation.

      2) Temperature forecasts are not issued for altitudes within 2,500 feet of a location's elevation.

      3) Forecasts for intermediate levels are determined by interpolation.

   b. The Hawaii and western Pacific bulletins are separated at the 24,000 foot level instead of 39,000 feet because of the additional lower levels.

3.   Table 25-1 contains the altitudes for which winds are forecast.

    a.   Through 12,000 ft., the levels are true altitude, and from 18,000 ft. and above, the levels are pressure altitude.

        1)   Altitudes up to 15,000 feet are referenced to Mean Sea Level (MSL).

        2)   Altitudes at or above 18,000 feet are references to flight levels (FL).

Actual Altitudes (MSL)
1,000 feet*
1,500 feet*
2,000 feet*
3,000 feet
6,000 feet
9,000 feet
12,000 feet
15,000 feet*
Pressure Altitudes (HectoPascals)
18,000 feet (500 HectoPascals)
24,000 feet (400 HectoPascals)
30,000 feet (300 HectoPascals)
34,000 feet (250 HectoPascals)
39,000 feet (200 HectoPascals)
45,000 feet (150 HectoPascals)#
53,000 feet (100 HectoPascals)#
* Hawaii and Western Pacific only.
# Not available for selected locations in the Contiguous U.S.

Table 25-1. Wind and Temperature Aloft Forecast Levels

4.   FBs are available on the Aviation Weather Center (AWC) website at http://aviationweather.gov/products/nws/winds/.

25.2   ISSUANCE

1.   The NWS National Centers for Environmental Prediction (NCEP) produces scheduled Wind and Temperature Aloft Forecasts (FB) four times daily for specified locations in the Continental United States (CONUS), the Hawaiian Islands, Alaska and coastal waters, and the western Pacific Ocean.

    a.   The maps on pages 411 and 412 show the locations where FB data is reported.

    b.   Amendments are not issued to the forecasts.

2.   If the scheduled forecast transmission is delayed, the existing valid forecast based on the earlier 6-hourly data can be used until a new forecast is transmitted.

3.   The table below shows the issuance schedule for FB forecasts.

Model Run	Product Available	6 hour Forecast		12 hour Forecast		24 hour Forecast	
		Valid	For Use	Valid	For Use	Valid	For Use
0000Z	~0200Z	0600Z	0200-0900Z	1200Z	0900-1800Z	0000Z	1800-0600Z
0600Z	~0800Z	1200Z	0800-1500Z	1800Z	1500-0000Z	0600Z	0000-1200Z
1200Z	~1400Z	1800Z	1400-2100Z	0000Z	2100-0600Z	1200Z	0600-1800Z
1800Z	~2000Z	0000Z	2000-0300Z	0600Z	0300-1200Z	1800Z	1200-0000Z

Table 25-2. Wind and Temperature Aloft Forecast (FB) Periods

25.3 FORMAT

1. The product header includes the date and time observations were collected, the forecast valid date and time, and the time period during which the forecast is to be used.

2. Wind direction is indicated in tens of degrees (two digits) with reference to true north and wind speed is given in knots (two digits).

   a. Light and variable wind or wind speeds of less than 5 knots are expressed by **9900**.

   b. Forecast wind speeds of 100 through 199 knots are indicated by subtracting 100 from the speed and adding 50 to the coded direction.

      1) EXAMPLE: A forecast of wind from 250 degrees at 145 knots, is encoded as **7545**.

   c. Forecast wind speeds of 200 knots or greater are indicated as a forecast speed of 199 knots.

      1) EXAMPLE: **7799** is decoded as wind from 270 degrees at 199 knots or greater.

3. Temperature is indicated in degrees Celsius (two digits) and is preceded by the appropriate algebraic sign (+ or −) for the levels from 6,000 through 24,000 feet.

   a. Above 24,000 feet, the sign is omitted since temperatures are always negative at those altitudes.

4. EXAMPLES:

   a. **1312+05** means the wind direction is from 130° (i.e., − southeast), the wind speed is 12 knots, and the temperature is 5°C.

   b. **9900+10** means wind light and variable, temperature +10°.

   c. **7735−07** means the wind direction is from 270° (i.e., west), the wind speed is 135 knots, and the temperature is minus 7°C.

5. **Coding Example**

```
DATA BASED ON 010000Z
VALID 010600Z FOR USE 0500-0900Z.   TEMPS NEG ABV 24000
FT   3000    6000     9000     12000    18000    24000    30000    34000    39000
MKC  9900  1709+06  2018+00  2130-06  2242-18  2361-30  247242  258848  550252
```

   a. Line 1 - **DATA BASED ON 010000Z** - means that the forecast data is based on computer forecasts generated the first day of the month at 0000 UTC.

   b. Line 2 - **VALID 010600Z FOR USE 0500-0900Z.   TEMPS NEG ABV 24000** - means that the valid time of the forecast is the 1st day of the month at 0600 UTC. The forecast winds and temperature are to be used between 0500 and 0900 UTC. Temperatures are negative above 24,000 feet.

   c. Line 3 - **FT 3000 6000 9000 12000 18000 24000 30000 34000 39000** - shows the altitudes analyzed in the report. FT indicates the altitude of the forecast and each number (i.e., 3000) is an altitude.

   d. Line 4 - **MKC 9900 1709+06 2018+00 2130-06 2242-18 2361-30 247242 258848 550252** - shows the location of the forecast and the forecast data. MKC is the station identifier of the forecast. The rest of the data is the winds and temperature aloft forecast for the respective altitudes.

e.   The following table interprets the data for the MKC (Kansas City, MO) FB report.

FT	3000	6000	9000	12000	18000	24000	30000	34000	39000
MKC	9900	1709+06	2018+00	2130−06	2242−18	2361−30	247242	258848	550252

Altitude (feet)	Coded	Wind	Temperature (°C)
3,000 FT	9900	Light and variable	Not forecast
6,000 FT	1709+06	170 degrees at 9 knots	+06 degrees Celsius
9,000 FT	2018+00	200 degrees at 18 knots	Zero degrees Celsius
12,000 FT	2130−06	210 degrees at 30 knots	−06 degrees Celsius
18,000 FT	2242−18	220 degrees at 42 knots	−18 degrees Celsius
24,000 FT	2361−30	230 degrees at 61 knots	−30 degrees Celsius
30,000 FT	247242	240 degrees at 72 knots	−42 degrees Celsius
34,000 FT	258848	250 degrees at 88 knots	−48 degrees Celsius
39,000 FT	550252	250 degrees at 102 knots	−52 degrees Celsius

Table 25-3. Wind and Temperature Aloft Forecast Decoding Examples

25.4   USING THE PRODUCT

1.   Wind and Temperature Aloft Forecasts (FBs) are extremely valuable when planning cross-country flights.

   a.   These forecasts assist pilots in planning for the effects of wind on their true course.

   b.   Pilots can also use FBs to get an idea of where the freezing level is forecast to exist as well as where temperature inversions may occur

2.   The following example of an FB is provided for your reference. Study it to ensure that you understand the data presented.

```
DATA BASED ON 091200Z
VALID 091800Z    FOR USE 1400-2100Z.   TEMPS NEG ABV 24000

FT    3000     6000     9000    12000    18000    24000    30000   34000   39000
ABI          1931+10  1929+10  2024+06  2331-10  2448-23  235239  246348  256056
ABQ                   2213+03  2327-04  2253-17  2263-27  227242  236946  245749
ABR   2017   2312+14  2308+09  2615+02  2724-13  2527-26  273641  274051  274562
AGC (etc.)

FT   45000    53000
ABI  301049   281149
ABQ  235061   244859
ABR  224559   243756
AGC (etc.)
```

Note: 45,000- and 53,000-foot winds are not available for selected locations in the conterminous U.S.

Figure 25-1. Wind and Temperature Aloft Forecast Network - Contiguous U.S.

Figure 25-2. Wind and Temperature Aloft Forecast Network - Alaska

Figure 25-3. Wind and Temperature Aloft Forecast Network - Hawaii

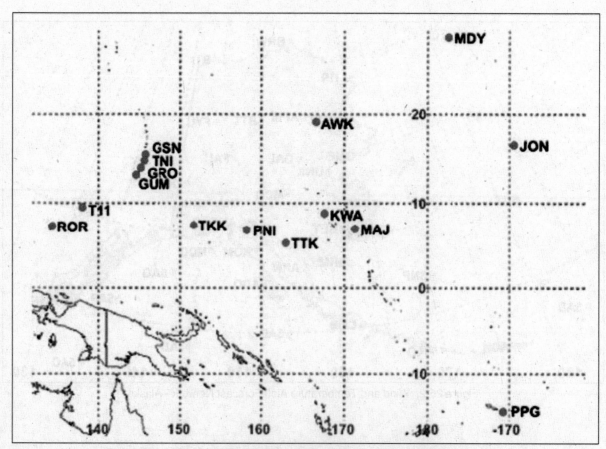

Figure 25-4. Wind and Temperature Aloft Forecast Network - Western Pacific

END OF STUDY UNIT

STUDY UNIT TWENTY-SIX
SHORT-RANGE SURFACE PROGNOSTIC (PROG) CHARTS

(4 pages of outline)

Please take a few minutes to study each of the concepts listed above and anticipate/imagine what they are and how they relate to the other listed concepts.

26.1 PRODUCT DESCRIPTION

1. Short-Range Surface Prognostic (PROG) Charts provide a forecast of surface pressure systems, fronts, and precipitation for a 2-day period.

   a. The forecast area covers the 48-contiguous states, the coastal waters, and portions of Canada and Mexico.

   b. The forecasted conditions are divided into four forecast periods: 12, 24, 36, and 48 hours.

      1) Each chart depicts a "snapshot" of weather elements expected at the specified valid time.

2. PROGs are very similar to surface analysis charts (discussed in Study Unit 8).

   a. All of the symbols depicted on both charts are the same.

   b. The primary difference between the two charts is that PROGs are forecast charts, whereas the surface analysis chart is a "current conditions" chart.

      1) Additionally, the PROG charts do not feature station model plots.

   c. Think of the PROG as a "future" version of the surface analysis chart.

3.   PROGs are produced in color. An example of a PROG is provided below.

Figure 26-1. Surface Prog Chart Example

26.2 ISSUANCE

1.   PROGs are issued by the Hydrometeorological Prediction Center (HPC) in Camp Springs, Maryland.

   a.   The 12- and 24-hour charts are issued four times a day and are termed "Day 1" PROGs.

   b.   The 36- and 48-hour charts are issued twice daily and are termed "Day 2" PROGs.

   c.   The table below explains the product issuance schedule.

	Issuance Time (UTC)			
	~1720	~2310	~0530	~0935
	Valid Time (UTC)			
12-Hour Surface Prog	0000	0600	1200	1800
24-Hour Surface Prog	1200	1800	0000	0600
36-Hour Surface Prog	0000	NA	1200	NA
48-Hour Surface Prog	1200	NA	0000	NA

Table 26.1. Short-Range Surface Prog Charts Schedule

2.   PROGs are available at the Aviation Digital Data Services (ADDS) website at http://adds.aviationweather.noaa.gov/progs/.

26.3 PLOTTED DATA

1. PROGS plot pressure systems, frontal boundaries, and precipitation.

2. **Pressure Systems**

    a. Pressure systems are depicted by pressure centers, troughs, isobars, drylines, tropical waves, tropical storms, and hurricanes using standard symbols.

        1) See the symbol legend below.

Figure 26-2. Surface Prog Chart Symbols

    b. Isobars are denoted by solid, thin, gray lines and labeled with the appropriate pressure in millibars.

    c. The central pressure is plotted near the respective pressure center.

3. **Fronts**

    a. Fronts are depicted to show their forecast position at the chart valid time.

        1) Again, standard chart symbols are used.

    b. Because frontal movement causes significant changes in weather, pressure, and wind, pilots should carefully consider the forecasted frontal depictions and plan their flight accordingly.

4. **Precipitation**

    a. Precipitation areas are enclosed by thick, solid, green lines.

    b. Standard precipitation symbols are used to identify precipitation types.

        1) These symbols are positioned within or adjacent to the associated area of precipitation.

        2) If adjacent to the area, an arrow will point to the area with which they are associated.

    c. A mix of precipitation is indicated by the use of two pertinent symbols separated by a slash.

d. A bold, dashed, gray line is used to separate precipitation within an outlined area with contrasting characteristics.

    1) EXAMPLE: A dashed line would be used to separate an area of snow from an area of rain.

e. Precipitation characteristics are further described by the use of shading.

    1) Shading or lack of shading indicates the expected coverage of the precipitation.

        a) Shaded areas indicate the precipitation is expected to have more than 50% (broken) coverage.

        b) Unshaded areas indicate 30-50% (scattered) coverage.

26.4 USING THE CHART

1. Short-Range Surface Prognostic (PROG) Charts can be used to obtain an overview of the progression of surface weather features during the next 48 hours.

a. The progression of weather is the change in position, size, and intensity of weather with time.

b. Progression analysis is accomplished by comparing charts of observed conditions to the 12-, 24-, 36-, and 48-hour PROGs.

2. PROGs make the comprehension of weather details easier and more meaningful.

a. Pilots should make good use of PROG charts during the planning process, especially if flying over a large distance.

b. PROGs can alert pilots to the need to consider other weather products, such as icing/turbulence advisories, AIRMETs, SIGMETs, and/or weather depiction charts, in order to get an accurate, complete weather picture.

END OF STUDY UNIT

STUDY UNIT TWENTY-SEVEN
LOW-LEVEL SIGNIFICANT WEATHER (SIGWX) CHARTS

(4 pages of outline)

Please take a few minutes to study each of the concepts listed above and anticipate/imagine what they are and how they relate to the other listed concepts.

27.1 PRODUCT DESCRIPTION

1. The Low-Level Significant Weather (SIGWX) Charts provide a forecast of aviation weather hazards.

    a. The charts are primarily intended to be used as guidance products for preflight briefings.

    b. Each chart depicts a "snapshot" of weather expected at the specified valid time.

    c. They are produced in color.

2. The forecast domain covers the 48 contiguous states and the coastal waters for altitudes 24,000 ft. MSL (FL240 or 400 millibars) and below.

3. The figure below is an example of this product.

Figure 27-1. 12-Hour Low-Level SIGWX Chart Example

27.2 ISSUANCE

1. Low-Level SIGWX Charts are issued four times per day by the Aviation Weather Center (AWC) in Kansas City, Missouri.

    a. Two charts are issued: a 12-hour and a 24-hour chart.
    b. Both are available on the AWC website at http://aviationweather.gov/products/swl/.

2. The table below explains the issuance and valid times for each chart release.

	Issuance Time			
	~1720Z	~2310Z	~0530Z	~0935Z
Chart	**Valid Time**			
12-Hour Prog	00Z	06Z	12Z	18Z
24-Hour Prog	12Z	18Z	00Z	06Z

Table 27-1. Low-Level SIGWX Chart Issuance Schedule

27.3 PLOTTED DATA

1. Low-Level SIGWX Charts depict weather flying categories, turbulence, and freezing levels. Icing is not specifically forecast.

    a. See the figure below for the chart symbol legend.

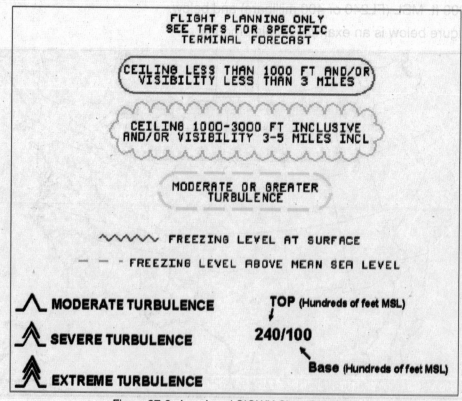

Figure 27-2. Low-Level SIGWX Chart Symbols

2. **Flying Categories**

   a. Instrument Flight Rules (IFR) areas are outlined with a solid, red line.
   b. Marginal Visual Flight Rules (MVFR) areas are outlined with a scalloped, blue line.
   c. Visual Flight Rules (VFR) areas are not depicted.

3. **Turbulence**

   a. Areas of moderate or greater turbulence are enclosed by bold, dashed, yellow lines.
   b. Turbulence intensities are identified by standard symbols, as shown in Figure 27.2.
   c. Turbulence height is depicted by two numbers separated by a solidus (/).

      1) EXAMPLE: An area on the chart with turbulence indicated as **240/100** indicates the turbulence can be expected from the top at FL240 to the base at 10,000 feet MSL.
      2) When the base height is omitted, the turbulence is forecast to reach the surface.

         a) EXAMPLE: An indication of **080/** identifies a turbulence layer from the surface to 8,000 feet MSL.

      3) Turbulence associated with thunderstorms is not depicted on the chart.

   d. The intensity symbols and height information may be located within or adjacent to the forecasted areas of turbulence.

      1) If located adjacent to an area, an arrow will point to the associated area.

4. **Freezing Levels**

   a. If the freezing level is at the surface, it is depicted by a blue, saw-toothed symbol.
   b. Freezing levels above the surface are depicted by fine, green, dashed lines labeled in hundreds of feet MSL beginning at 4,000 feet using 4,000-foot intervals.

      1) If multiple freezing levels exist, these lines are drawn to the highest freezing level.

         a) For example, **80** identifies the 8,000-foot freezing level contour.
         b) The lines are discontinued where they intersect the surface.

   c. The freezing level for locations between lines is determined by interpolation.

      1) For example, the freezing level midway between the 4,000- and 8,000-foot lines is 6,000 feet.

   d. Multiple freezing levels occur when the temperature is zero degrees Celsius at more than one altitude aloft.

      1) Multiple freezing levels can be forecasted on the Low-Level SIGWX Charts in situations where the temperature is below-freezing (negative) at the surface with multiple freezing levels aloft.
      2) On the chart, areas with multiple freezing levels are located on the below-freezing side of the surface freezing level contour and bounded by the 4,000-foot freezing level.
      3) Multiple freezing levels are possible beyond the 4,000-foot freezing level (i.e., below 4,000 feet MSL), but the exact cutoff cannot be determined.

4)   Reference the figure below for examples of various freezing level situations.

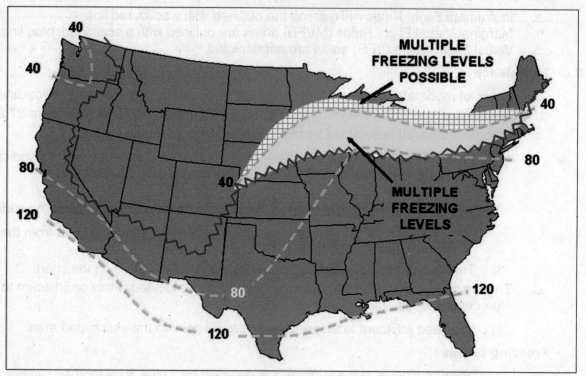

Figure 27-3.   Low-Level SIGWX Chart Multiple Freezing Levels Example

27.4   USING THE CHART

1.   The Low-Level Significant Weather (SIGWX) Charts provide an overview of selected aviation weather hazards up to 24,000 feet MSL (FL240 or 400 millibars) at 12- and 24-hours into the future.

2.   Pilots should use these charts when planning a flight 24 hours or less in advance.

    a.   Pilots can use the information gained from these charts to plot a course that will avoid some of the most common and dangerous weather hazards.

END OF STUDY UNIT

STUDY UNIT TWENTY-EIGHT
MID-LEVEL SIGNIFICANT WEATHER (SIGWX) CHARTS

(8 pages of outline)

Please take a few minutes to study each of the concepts listed above and anticipate/imagine what they are and how they relate to the other listed concepts.

28.1 PRODUCT DESCRIPTION

1. The Mid-Level Significant Weather (SIGWX) Chart provides a forecast of significant en route weather phenomena over a range of flight levels from 10,000 feet MSL to FL450 and associated surface weather features.

    a. The chart depicts a "snapshot" of weather expected at the specified valid time.
    b. It is produced in color.

2. The Mid-Level SIGWX Chart is available on the Aviation Weather Center website at http://aviationweather.gov/products/swm/.

3. The figure below is an example of this product.

Figure 28-1. Mid-Level SIGWX Chart Example

28.2 ISSUANCE

1. The Aviation Weather Center (AWC) in Kansas City, Missouri, has the responsibility as part of the World Area Forecast Center (WAFC), to provide global weather forecasts of significant weather phenomena.

2. The AWC issues a 24-hour Mid-Level SIGWX Chart, four times daily, for the North Atlantic Ocean Region (NAT).

    a. This is the only area covered by the Mid-Level SIGWX Chart

3. The table below explains the issuance and valid times for each chart release.

Issuance Time (UTC)	Valid Time (UTC)
1015	0000
1615	0600
2215	1200
0415	1800

Table 28-1. Mid-level SIGWX Chart Issuance Schedule

28.3 PLOTTED DATA

1. The Mid-Level SIGWX Chart depicts numerous weather elements that can be hazardous to aviation. Each element is discussed below.

2. **Thunderstorms**

    a. The abbreviation **CB** is only included where it refers to the expected occurrence of an area of widespread cumulonimbus clouds, cumulonimbus along a line with little or no space between individual clouds, cumulonimbus embedded in cloud layers, or cumulonimbus concealed by haze.

        1) It does not refer to isolated or scattered cumulonimbus not embedded in cloud layers or concealed by haze.

        2) Each cumulonimbus area is identified with CB and characterized by coverage, bases, and tops.

    b. Coverage is identified as isolated **(ISOL)** meaning less than 1/8th, occasional **(OCNL)** meaning 1/8th to 4/8ths, and frequent **(FRQ)** meaning more than 4/8ths coverage.

        1) Isolated and occasional CBs may be further characterized as **EMBD** if cells are embedded.

        2) The chart does not display isolated or scattered cumulonimbus clouds unless they are embedded in other clouds, haze, or dust.

    c. The vertical extent of cumulonimbus layer is specified by top and base heights.

        1) Bases that extend below 10,000 feet (the lowest altitude limit of the chart) are encoded **XXX**.

    d. Cumulonimbus clouds are depicted by enclosed (red) scalloped lines.

        1) The identification and characterization of each cumulonimbus area appears within or adjacent to the outlined area.

        2) If the identification and characterization is adjacent to an outlined area, an arrow points to the appropriate cumulonimbus area.

3)   See the figure below for an example of thunderstorm depiction on the chart.

Figure 28-2. Mid-Level SIGWX Chart Thunderstorm Examples

e.   On significant weather charts, the inclusion of CB or the thunderstorm symbol Ɽ
should be understood to include all weather phenomena normally associated with
cumulonimbus or thunderstorm, namely, moderate or severe icing, moderate or
severe turbulence, and hail.

3.   **Surface Frontal Positions and Movements**

a.   Surface fronts are depicted using the standard symbols found on the Surface Analysis
Chart.

1)   An arrow identifies the direction of frontal movement with the speed indicated in
knots plotted near the arrow head. The figure below is an example.

Figure 28-3. Mid-Level SIGWX Chart Surface Frontal Position and Movement Example

4.   **Jet Streams**

a.   A jet stream axis with a wind speed of more than 80 knots is identified by a bold
(green) line.

1)   An arrowhead is used to indicate wind direction.

2)   Double-hatched, light green lines positioned along a jet stream axis identify
20-knot wind speed changes.

3)   See the figure below for an example of a jet stream axis as shown on the chart.

Figure 28-4. Mid-Level SIGWX Chart Jet Stream Example

b.   Symbols and altitudes are used to further characterize a jet stream axis.

1)   A standard wind symbol (light green) is placed at each pertinent position to identify wind velocity.

2)   The flight level "FL" in hundreds of feet MSL is placed adjacent to each wind symbol to identify the altitude of the jet stream axis.

c.   Jet stream vertical depth (jet depth) forecasts are included when the maximum speed is 120 knots or more.

1)   **Jet depth** is defined as the vertical depths to the 80-knot wind field above and below the jet stream axis using flight levels.

5.   **Tropopause Heights**

a.   Tropopause heights are plotted at selected locations on the chart.

1)   They are enclosed by rectangles and plotted in hundreds of feet MSL.

2)   Centers of high **(H)** and low **(L)** tropopause heights are enclosed by polygons and plotted in hundreds of feet MSL.

3)   See the figure below for an example of tropopause heights as shown on the chart.

Figure 28-5. Mid-Level SIGWX Chart Tropopause Height Examples

6. **Tropical Cyclones**

    a.   Tropical cyclones are depicted by the appropriate symbol with the storm's name positioned adjacent to the symbol.

        1)   See the figure below for an example of tropical cyclones as shown on the chart.

Figure 28-6. Mid-Level SIGWX Chart Tropical Cyclone Examples

    b.   Cumulonimbus clouds meeting chart criteria are identified and characterized relative to each storm.

7. **Moderate or Severe Icing**

    a.   Areas of moderate or severe icing are depicted by enclosed (red) scalloped lines.

        1)   The identification and characterization of each area appears within or adjacent to the outlined area.

        2)   If the identification and characterization is adjacent to an outlined area, an arrow points to the appropriate area.

        3)   The identification box uses the standard icing symbol.

    b.   The vertical extent of the icing layer is specified by top and base heights.

        1)   Bases which extend below the layer of the chart are identified with **XXX**.

    c.   See the figure below for an example of icing as shown on the chart.

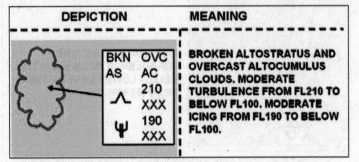

Figure 28-7. Mid-Level SIGWX Chart Icing Examples

8.   **Moderate or Severe Turbulence**

   a.   Areas of moderate or severe turbulence are also depicted by enclosed (red) scalloped lines.

      1)   The identification and characterization of each area appears within or adjacent to the outlined area.

      2)   If the identification and characterization is adjacent to an outlined area, an arrow points to the associated area.

      3)   Standard turbulence symbols are used.

      4)   See the icing figure on the previous page for an example of the general depiction of turbulence as shown on the chart.

      5)   The vertical extent of the turbulence layer is specified by top and base heights.

         a)   A turbulence base which extends below 10,000 feet (the lowest altitude limit on the chart) is encoded **XXX**.

   b.   Forecast areas of moderate or severe turbulence associated with wind shear zones and/or mountain waves are enclosed by bold (yellow) dashed lines.

      1)   Intensities are identified by standard symbols.

      2)   The vertical extent of the turbulence layer is specified by top and base heights.

         a)   A turbulence base which extends below 10,000 feet (the lowest altitude limit on the chart) is encoded **XXX**.

      3)   See the figure below for an example of wind shear and mountain wave turbulence as shown on the chart.

DEPICTION	MEANING
1. $\frac{380}{270}$	**MODERATE TURBULENCE FROM FL380 TO FL270.**
2. $\frac{210}{XXX}$	**MODERATE TO SEVERE TURBULENCE FROM FL210 TO BELOW LOWER LIMIT OF THE PROG (FL100).**

Figure 28-8. Mid-Level SIGWX Chart Turbulence Examples

   c.   Thunderstorm turbulence is not specifically identified because turbulence is implied wherever thunderstorms are present.

9.   **Cloud Coverage and Type**

   a.   Clouds are enclosed within (red) scalloped lines.

      1)   Cloud coverage (non-cumulonimbus) appears within or adjacent to the outlined area.

      2)   Cloud type is also included within or adjacent to the outlined area.

         a)   If the cloud coverage and type is adjacent to an outlined area, an arrow points to the appropriate area.

3)   Reference the figure below for an example of cloud coverage and type as shown on the chart.

Figure 28-9. Mid-Level SIGWX Chart - Example of Moderate or Severe Icing, Moderate or Severe Turbulence (in cloud or in clear air), Clouds, and Cloud Types

b.   The general cloud coverage symbols are listed in the table below.

1)   Cumulonimbus cloud coverage is explained in section 2.b. (page 422) of this subunit.

CODED	MEANING	COVERAGE
SKC	Sky clear	0/8^{ths}
FEW	Few clouds	1/8th to 2/8^{ths}
SCT	Scattered	3/8^{ths} to 4/8^{ths}
BKN	Broken	5/8^{ths} to 7/8^{ths}
OVC	Overcast	8/8^{ths}

Table 28-2. Mid-Level SIGWX Chart Cloud Coverage (Non-cumulonimbus)

c.   The cloud type contractions appear in the table below.

CODED	MEANING
CI	Cirrus
CC	Cirrocumulus
CS	Cirrostratus
AC	Altocumulus
AS	Altostratus
NS	Nimbostratus
SC	Stratocumulus
ST	Stratus
CU	Cumulus
CB	Cumulonimbus

Table 28-3. Mid-Level SIGWX Chart

10. **Volcanic Eruptions**

    a.   Volcanic eruption sites are identified by a (red) trapezoidal symbol.

        1)   The dot on the base of the trapezoid identifies the location of the volcano.

        2)   The name of the volcano and the latitude and longitude are noted adjacent to the symbol.

    b.   The figure below is an example of a volcanic eruption symbol as shown on the chart.

Figure 28-10. Mid-Level SIGWX Chart Volcanic
Eruption Example

11. **Release of Radioactive Materials**

    a.   Radioactive materials in the atmosphere are depicted by the standard radioactive symbol (red) shown below.

Figure 28-11. Mid-Level SIGWX Chart Release of Radioactive Materials Example

    b.   Information on the chart regarding the radioactive material includes the latitude/longitude of the accident site, the date and time of the accident, and a reference to check NOTAMs for further information.

28.4 USING THE CHART

1.   The Mid-Level Significant Weather (SIGWX) Chart is used to determine an overview of selected flying weather conditions between 10,000 feet MSL and FL450.

2.   It can be used by airline dispatchers for flight planning and weather briefings before departure and by flight crew members during flight.

3.   General aviation users may utilize this product to better understand the role of upper-air conditions in influencing the weather near the surface.

    a.   Pilots of high performance airplanes may use this chart regularly for flights within the specified airspace range.

END OF STUDY UNIT

STUDY UNIT TWENTY-NINE
HIGH-LEVEL SIGNIFICANT WEATHER (SIGWX) CHARTS

(6 pages of outline)

Please take a few minutes to study each of the concepts listed above and anticipate/imagine what they are and how they relate to the other listed concepts.

NOTE: This product is essentially the same as the Mid-Level SIGWX Chart discussed in Study Unit 28. This study unit will explain the differences between these two charts. For identical symbol and data reference, you should consult Study Unit 28.

29.1 PRODUCT DESCRIPTION

1. High-Level Significant Weather (SIGWX) Charts provide a forecast of significant en route weather phenomena over a range of flight levels, from FL250 to FL630, and associated surface weather features.

    a. Each chart depicts a "snap-shot" of weather expected at the specified valid time.
    b. It is produced in color.

2. The figure on the next page is an example of this product.

Figure 29-1. High-Level SIGWX Chart Example

29.2 DIFFERENCES WHEN COMPARED TO THE MID-LEVEL SIGWX CHART

1.   All hazards to flight produced on the Mid-Level SIGWX Chart are produced on this chart as well.

    a.   The charts share the same coloration and symbols.

    b.   The items shown on the High-Level SIGWX Charts that are not shown in the Mid-Level SIGWX Chart are detailed below.

2.   **Tropical Cyclones**

    a.   Tropical cyclones are depicted on the Mid-Level SIGWX Chart but, because the Mid-Level Chart covers just the North Atlantic, only the northern hemisphere symbol is used.

    b.   The figure below shows the tropical cyclone symbols for both hemispheres.

Figure 29-2. High-Level SIGWX Chart Tropical Cyclone Examples

    1)   On the actual chart, these symbols are red in color.

    2)   Note that the rain band indications are turned in different directions. This is due to the fact that tropical cyclones rotate in opposite directions in the northern and southern hemispheres.

3.   **Severe Squall Lines**

    a.   Severe squall lines are lines of cumulonimbus clouds (CBs) with 5/8 coverage or greater.

      1)   Cumulonimbus clouds meeting chart criteria are identified and characterized with each squall line.

    b.   They are identified by long dashed (white) lines with each dash separated by a **V**.

    c.   The figure below is an example of what this notation would look like on the chart.

Figure 29-3. High-Level SIGWX Chart Severe Squall Line Example

4.   **Widespread Sandstorms and Dust storms**

    a.   Widespread sandstorms and dust storms are labeled as a red capital letter "S" with a horizontal arrow through the center of it.

    b.   The vertical extent of sand or dust is specified by top and base heights, separated by a horizontal line.

        1)   Sand or dust, which extends below the lower limit of the chart (FL240), is identified with **XXX**.

    c.   The figure below is an example of what this notation would look like on the chart.

Figure 29-4.   High-Level SIGWX Chart Widespread Sandstorm and Dust Storm Example

29.3 ISSUANCE

1.   In accordance with the World Meteorological Organization (WMO) and the World Area Forecast System (WAFS) of the International Civil Aviation Organization (ICAO), High-Level SIGWX forecasts are provided for the en route portion of international flights.

2.   The National Weather Service (NWS) Aviation Weather Center (AWC) in Kansas City, Missouri, provides a suite of SIGWX forecast products for the World Area Forecast Center (WAFC) in Washington, D.C.

    a.   The charts are available for 7 different ICAO areas around the world as defined in the table on the next page.

    b.   The charts are not amended once issued.

ICAO Area	Chart Type	Chart Area	Valid Times (UTC)			
			Issued 1100	Issued 1700	Issued 2300	Issued 0500
A Americas	Mercator		0000	0600	1200	1800
B1 Americas/ Africa	Mercator		0000	0600	1200	1800
F Pacific	Mercator		0000	0600	1200	1800
H N America/ Europe	Polar Stereographic		0000	0600	1200	1800
I N Pacific	Polar Stereographic		0000	0600	1200	1800
J S Pacific	Polar Stereographic		0000	0600	1200	1800
M Pacific	Mercator		0000	0600	1200	1800

Table 29-1. High-Level SIGWX Chart Issuance Schedule - WAFC Washington

3.   The WAFC in London, England, also issues High-Level SIGWX Charts for other geographical areas of the world.

4.   Both Washington and London WAFC charts are available online at http://aviationweather.gov/iffdp/sgwx.shtml.

29.4 USING THE CHART

1. High-Level Significant Weather (SIGWX) Charts are provided for the en route portion of international flights.

2. These products are used directly by airline dispatchers for flight planning and weather briefings before departure and by flight crew members during flight.

   a. Because of the altitude range to which these charts apply, general aviation pilots will gain little if any diagnostic benefit from their use.

END OF STUDY UNIT

STUDY UNIT THIRTY
COLLABORATIVE CONVECTIVE FORECAST PRODUCTS (CCFP)

(5 pages of outline)

Please take a few minutes to study each of the concepts listed above and anticipate/imagine what they are and how they relate to the other listed concepts.

30.1 PRODUCT DESCRIPTION

1. The Collaborative Convective Forecast Product (CCFP) is a graphical, colorized representation of forecast convective occurrence at 2, 4, and 6 hours after the issuance time.

    a. The figure below shows an example of the CCFP.

Figure 30-1. CCFP Example

2. The CCFP is produced from a collaborative effort between public and private meteorologists.

    a. The collaboration occurs between meteorologists from the Aviation Weather Center (AWC), Center Weather Service Units (CWSU), Meteorological Services of Canada (MSC), commercial airlines offices, and other private weather companies.

3.   Convection, for the purposes of the CCFP forecast, is defined as a polygon of at least 3,000 square miles containing all of the following threshold criteria:

  a.   A coverage of at least 25% of echoes with at least 40 dBZ composite reflectivity.

  b.   A coverage of at least 25% of echoes with echo tops of FL250 or greater.

  c.   A forecaster confidence of at least 25 percent.

  d.   All three threshold criteria must be met for any area of convection 3,000 square miles or greater to be included in a CCFP forecast.

     1)   This is defined as the minimum CCFP criteria.

4.   Any area of convection which is forecast to not meet all three of these criteria is not included in a CCFP forecast.

5.   The CCFP is intended to be used as a strategic planning tool for air traffic flow management.

  a.   It aids in the reduction of air traffic delays, reroutes, and cancelations due to significant convection.

  b.   It is not intended to be used for tactical air traffic flow decisions, in the airport terminal environment, or for pilot weather briefing purposes.

6.   The graphical representation is subject to annual revision.

30.2 ISSUANCE

1.   The CCFP is issued by the AWC from March through October for the 48 contiguous states.

2.   Canadian forecasts included on the product are available for southern Ontario and Quebec between April and September.

  a.   This area is roughly from north of Wisconsin extending eastward to north of Maine.

3.   The CCFP is issued every two hours, 11 times per day.

  a.   Issuance times are from 08Z to 04Z during standard time and from 07Z to 03Z during daylight savings time.

4.   The product can be found on the AWC web page at http://aviationweather.gov/products/ccfp.

30.3 PLOTTED DATA

1.   Data graphically displayed on the CCFP consist of

  a.   Coverage of convection within a defined polygon,

  b.   Forecaster confidence of convective occurrence, and

  c.   Forecast movement of the convective areas.

2.   A data block, covered in Subunit 4, displays text information about coverage and confidence as well as forecast echo tops and convective growth information.

3.   **Coverage**

  a.   The convective coverage within the forecast polygon is represented by the amount of fill within the polygon.

     1)   Solid coverage, depicted by solid fill, means 75–100% of the polygon is forecast to contain convection.

     2)   Medium coverage, defined by medium fill, indicates 50–74% of the polygon is forecast to contain convection.

     3)   Sparse coverage, represented by sparse fill, means 25–49% of the polygon is forecast to contain convection.

     4)   The coverage box is colored according to forecaster confidence as explained below.

b. A line of forecast convection, either within a forecast area or alone, is depicted by a solid purple line. For a line of convection to be forecast, it must meet the following criteria:

1) Its length must be at least 100 miles long.
2) The width of the line must be 40 NM wide.
3) 75% of the line must be expected to contain convection.

4. **Confidence**

a. Confidence represents the subjective opinion of the forecasters that the polygon will meet the minimum CCFP criteria.

b. The forecaster's confidence is represented by the color used to depict the polygon.

1) A blue color represents high forecaster confidence (50-100%) that the forecast convection will meet the minimum criteria.

2) A gray color indicates low forecaster confidence (25-49%) that the forecast convection will meet the minimum criteria.

3) See the confidence legend below.

CONFIDENCE

HIGH	LOW
50-100%	25-49%

Figure 30-2. CCFP Forecast Confidence

c. Confidence is not to be associated with probability of occurrence.

5. **Forecast Movement**

a. Forecast movement for each polygon or line is indicated with a blue or gray arrow according to the confidence coloration of the coverage area.

1) The arrow points in the direction of forecast movement.
2) A number at the tip of the arrow represents the speed in knots.
3) See the figure below for an example of forecast movement as shown on the chart.

Figure 30-3. CCFP Forecast Convective Movement

30.4 DATA BLOCKS

1. A data block is located adjacent to every polygon forecast (Figure 30-4 and Figure 30-5).

    a. A thin line connects the data block to the associated forecast area.

    b. Each data block contains information about forecast maximum echo tops **(TOPS)**, convective growth rates **(GWTH)**, forecaster confidence **(CONF)**, and convection coverage **(CRVG)**.

2. See the two figures below for an example of the data block information shown on the chart.

Figure 30-4. CCFP Data Block

TOPS: 370+

GWTH: ++

CONF: HIGH

CVRG: 50 – 74%

Figure 30-5. CCFP Data Block Example

3. **Echo Tops (TOPS)**

    a. The word **TOPS** is used to depict the forecast maximum echo tops, in thousands of feet MSL, specified by three selected layers listed in Table 30-1 below.

FL250–FL310	Flight level 250 to flight level 310
FL310–FL370	Flight level 310 to flight level 370
370+	Above flight level 370

Table 30-1. CCFP Tops

    b. The heights of the forecast echo tops must cover at least 25% of the polygon.

        1) The exact location of the highest echo top within the polygon cannot be determined.

4. **Convective Growth rates (GWTH)**

    a.   The abbreviation **GWTH** is used to depict the forecast average growth rate of the convection as shown in Table 30-2 below.

        1)   The growth rate applies to both the height and aerial coverage of the echoes.

++	Fast positive growth
+	Moderate positive growth
NC	No change in the growth
-	Negative growth

Table 30-2. CCFP Growth

5. **Forecaster Confidence (CONF)**

    a.   The abbreviation **CONF** is used to depict the confidence that the depicted polygon will meet the minimum CCFP criteria as shown in Table 30-3 below.

LOW	25 – 49%
HIGH	50 – 100%

Table 30-3. CCFP Confidence

6. **Convection Coverage (CRVG)**

    a.   The abbreviation **CVRG** is used to depict the forecast convective coverage within the polygon as shown in Table 30-4 below.

        1)   The coverage represents the percentage of the area forecast to be covered by convection.

25 – 49%	Sparse
50 – 74%	Medium
75 – 100%	Solid

Table 30-4. CCFP Coverage

30.5 USING THE CHART

1. The primary strength of the CCFP is that it relies on the vital collaborative efforts between several meteorological units in the private and public sectors.

    a.   The process helps produce the best possible convective forecast to assist in strategic air traffic decision making.

2. The limitation of the CCFP is that it does not include a forecast for all convections.

    a.   If the convection does not meet the threshold criteria, it is not included in the CCFP.

3. The CCFP is not intended to be used as a tactical short-term decision tool.

    a.   It is to be used as a strategic planning tool for air traffic flow management in the 2- to 6-hour forecast period.

4. The product is not intended to be used as a pilot weather briefing tool. It is, however, an excellent source of supplementary information.

END OF STUDY UNIT

STUDY UNIT THIRTY-ONE
NATIONAL CONVECTIVE WEATHER FORECASTS (NCWF)

(4 pages of outline)

Please take a few minutes to study each of the concepts listed above and anticipate/imagine what they are and how they relate to the other listed concepts.

31.1   PRODUCT DESCRIPTION

1.   The National Convective Weather Forecast (NCWF) is a near real-time, high-resolution, color-coded display of current and one-hour extrapolated forecasts of selected hazardous convective conditions for the conterminous United States.

2.   The NCWF is a supplement to, but does not substitute for, the report and forecast information contained within Convective SIGMETs.

3.   The NCWF is intended for use by general aviation, airline dispatchers, and Traffic Management Units.

4.   The image below is an example of the NCWF.

Figure 31-1. NCWF Example

31.2 ISSUANCE

1. The NCWF is issued by the Aviation Weather Center (AWC) and is updated every five minutes.

2. The product is available on the Aviation Digital Data Service (ADDS) web page at http://adds.aviationweather.noaa.gov/convection/java and on the AWC website at http://aviationweather.gov/products/ncwf.

31.3 PLOTTED DATA

1. The NCWF displays current convection hazard fields, one-hour extrapolated forecast polygons, forecast speed and directions, and echo tops.

   a. Previous performance polygons can also be selected for display.

2. **Current Convective Hazard Fields**

   a. The current convective hazard field is a high-resolution display that identifies selected hazards associated with convective precipitation.

   b. The field is created from WSR-88D national reflectivity, echo-top mosaics, and cloud-to-ground lightning data.

      1) WSR-88D radar reflectivity data are filtered to identify locations having significant convective precipitation.

      2) Reflectivity data with echo tops of less than 17,000 feet MSL are eliminated from the data.

         a) This process removes ground clutter and anomalous propagation as well as significantly reduces the amount of stratiform (non-convective) precipitation from the data. Most stratiform precipitation tops are below 17,000 feet.

      3) The filter also removes shallow convection with tops below 17,000 feet.

         a) Shallow convection is often short-lived but can contain conditions hazardous to aviation and may be embedded in stratiform convection.

      4) Frequencies of cloud-to-ground lightning are added to the filtered radar data to provide a more accurate picture of current hazardous convective conditions.

   c. Current convective hazard fields are color-coded according to the convective hazard scale for display on the NCWF.

      1) The convective hazard field scale uses six hazard levels to characterize hazardous convection conditions. The six hazard levels are determined by two factors:

         a) Intensities and maximum tops of WSR-88D reflectivity data
         b) Frequencies of cloud-to-ground lightning

      2) Higher hazard levels are associated with higher radar reflectivity intensities and higher frequencies of lightning strikes.

      3) The six hazard levels are reduced to four color codes for display on the NCWF.

         a) The relationships between the six hazard levels and the four color codes are summarized in the figure on the next page.

NCWF Hazard Scale		
Level	**Color**	**Effect**
6	RED	Thunderstorms may contain any or all
5	RED	of the following: severe turbulence, severe icing,
4	Orange	hail, frequent lightning, tornadoes, and low-level wind shear.
3	Yellow	The risk of hazardous weather generally increases
2	Green	with levels on the NCWF hazard scale
1	Green	

Figure 31-2. NCWF Hazard Scale

3. **One-Hour Extrapolated Forecast Polygons**

   a. One-hour extrapolated forecast polygons are high-resolution polygons outlining areas expected to be filled by selected convective hazard fields in one hour.

      1) Forecasts are provided only for convective hazard scale levels of 3 or higher, but they do not depict specific forecast hazard levels.

   b. Extrapolated forecasts depict new locations for the convective hazard fields based on their past movements.

   c. Extrapolation forecasts do not forecast the development of new convective hazard conditions or the dissipation of existing conditions.

   d. On the NCWF example on page 441, the (light blue) polygon denotes the location of the one-hour forecast convective hazard field.

4. **Forecast Speed and Direction**

   a. Forecast speed and direction are assigned to current convective hazard fields having a one-hour extrapolated forecast.

   b. A line (or arrow on the AWC JavaScript product) is used to depict the direction of movement.

   c. The speed in knots is depicted by the first group of two numbers located near the current convective hazard field

      1) The second group of three numbers identifies echo tops.

   d. Forecast speed and direction is only updated every 10 minutes.

      1) The larger update time interval (compared to five-minute updates for the hazard data) smooths erratic forecast velocities.

      2) EXAMPLE: On the NCWF example on page 441, the forecast direction on the lowest hazard area (depicted by the end of the line opposite the data field) is to the southeast, and the speed is 25 knots.

5. **Echo Tops**

   a. Echo tops are assigned to current convective hazard fields having a one-hour extrapolated forecast.

   b. Echo tops are depicted by a group of three numbers located near the current convective hazard field and are plotted in hundreds of feet MSL.

      1) EXAMPLE: On the NCWF example on page 441, the echo tops for the lowest hazard area are at 45,000 feet MSL.

6. **Previous Performance Polygons**

   a. Previous performance polygons are magenta. (One-hour forecast polygons are light blue.)

      1) They display the previous hour's extrapolated forecast polygons with the current convective hazard fields.

2)   A perfect forecast would have the polygons filled with convective hazard scale levels of 3 or higher.

a)   Levels 1 and 2 would be outside the polygons.

b)   The display of previous performance polygons allows the user to review the accuracy of the previous hour's forecast.

b.   Newly developed convective hazard levels of 3 or higher will not have previous performance polygons because forecasts are only issued for levels of 3 or higher.

1)   The previous hour's data would not have shown these areas as level 3 or higher; thus, they would not appear in a previous performance polygon.

31.4   USING THE CHART

1.   **Service Providers**

a.   The ADDS website allows for the display of all previously discussed attributes of the NCWF.

1)   This site also allows many overlay options, including METARs, TAFs, VORs, ARTCC boundaries, counties, highways, and rivers.

b.   Product animation is possible on the AWC JavaScript image.

2.   **Strengths and Limitations**

a.   Strengths of the NCWF include

1)   Convective hazard fields agree very well with radar and lightning data;
2)   It is updated every five minutes;
3)   It has high-resolution forecasts of convective hazards; and
4)   Long-lived convective precipitation is well forecast.

b.   Limitations of the NCWF include

1)   Initiation, growth, and decay of convective precipitation are not forecast;
2)   Short-lived or embedded convection may not be accurately displayed or forecast;
3)   Low-topped convection that contains little or no lightning may not be depicted;
4)   Erroneous motion vectors are occasionally assigned to storms; and
5)   Convective hazard field scales are not identified within the forecast polygons.

3.   **Uses of the NCWF**

a.   The purpose of the National Convective Weather Forecast (NCWF) is to produce a convective hazard field diagnostic and forecast product based on radar data, echo top mosaics, and lightning data.

b.   The target audience includes the FAA and other government agencies, pilots, airline dispatchers, aviation meteorologists, and other interested aviation users in the general public.

c.   The NCWF is a supplement to, but does not substitute for, the report and forecast information contained in Convective SIGMETs.

1)   This product is a great planning tool, but it is not a primary source of weather information.

END OF STUDY UNIT

STUDY UNIT THIRTY-TWO
CURRENT ICING POTENTIAL (CIP)

(4 pages of outline)

Please take a few minutes to study each of the concepts listed above and anticipate/imagine what they are and how they relate to the other listed concepts.

32.1 PRODUCT DESCRIPTION

1. The Current Icing Potential (CIP) product combines sensor and numerical data to provide an hourly, three-dimensional, colorized diagnosis of the icing environment.

   a. This information is displayed on a suite of 10 graphics, which are available for the 48 contiguous United States, much of Canada and Mexico, and their respective coastal waters. These graphics are

      1) Icing Probability,
      2) Icing Probability – Maximum (Max),
      3) Icing Severity,
      4) Icing Severity – Max,
      5) Icing Severity – Probability > 25%,
      6) Icing Severity – Probability > 25% – Max,
      7) Icing Severity – Probability > 50%,
      8) Icing Severity – Probability > 50% – Max,
      9) Icing Severity plus Supercooled Large Droplets (SLD), and
      10) Icing Severity plus Supercooled Large Droplets (SLD) – Max.

   b. Each graphic is explained in Subunit 3.

2. The CIP products are generated for individual altitudes from 1,000 feet MSL to Flight Level (FL) 300 at intervals of 1,000 feet.

3. The CIP Max products are a composite product which displays information about icing at all altitudes from 1,000 feet MSL to FL300.

   a. Single altitudes are referenced to MSL from 1,000 to 17,000 feet and Flight Levels above 17,000 feet.

   b. The ADDS website allows for access to every other altitude (1,000 ft., 3,000 ft., 5,000 ft., etc.).

      1) All altitudes can be accessed by use of the Flight Path Tool on the ADDS site.

4. Icing PIREPs are plotted on a single altitude graphic if the PIREP is within 1,000 feet of the selected altitude and has been observed within 75 minutes of the chart's valid time.

   a. On the CIP Max graphics, PIREPs for all altitudes (i.e., 1,000 feet MSL to FL300) are displayed.

      1) Negative reports of icing are not plotted on the CIP Max products in an effort to reduce clutter.

   b. The PIREP legend is located on the bottom of each graphic.

5. The CIP product suite is automatically produced with no human modifications.

   a. Information on the graphics is determined from observational data, including WSR-88D radar, satellite, pilot weather reports, surface weather reports, lightning, and computer model output.

6. FAA policy states that the CIP is a supplementary weather product for enhanced situational awareness only and must be used with one or more primary products, such as an AIRMET or SIGMET (see *AIM* 7-1-3).

32.2 ISSUANCE

1. The CIP product suite is issued hourly, 15 minutes after the hour, by the Aviation Weather Center (AWC).

2. The products are available through the Aviation Digital Data Service (ADDS) website at http://adds.aviationweather.noaa.gov/icing/icing_nav.php.

32.3 CHART TYPES AND PLOTTED DATA

1. **Icing Probability**

   a. The Icing Probability product displays the probability of icing at a single altitude. Probabilities range from 0% (no icing expected) to 75% or greater (nearly certain icing).

      1) "Cool" colors represent low probabilities, and "warm" colors represent higher probabilities.

   b. Probabilities do not reach 100% because the data used to determine the probability of icing can not diagnose, with absolute certainty, the presence of icing conditions at any location and altitude.

   c. White regions indicate that the probability of icing is zero.

   d. Brown regions indicate where higher-elevation terrain extends above the altitude of the particular graphic.

2. **Icing Probability – Maximum**

   a. The Icing Probability – Maximum graphic displays the cumulative probability of icing at all altitudes from 1,000 feet MSL to FL300. Probabilities range from 0% (no icing expected) to 75% or greater (nearly certain icing).

   b. The same color scale is used on this product as on the standard Icing Probability graphic.

3. **Icing Severity**

   a. The Icing Severity product depicts, at a single altitude, the intensity of icing expected at locations where the Icing Probability product depicts possible icing.

      1) Icing intensity is displayed using standard icing intensity categories: trace, light, moderate, and heavy.

   b. The lightest blue color represents trace icing. As the blue-color shades become darker, the icing intensity increases.

      1) The darkest blue color represents heavy icing.

   c. White regions indicate where no probability of icing exists and, therefore, no intensity is necessary.

   d. Brown regions indicate where higher-elevation terrain extends above the altitude of the particular graphic.

4. **Icing Severity – Maximum**

   a. The Icing Severity – Maximum product displays the intensity of icing at all altitudes from 1,000 feet MSL to FL300.

   b. The same symbols and coloration are used on the product as on the standard icing severity graphic.

5. **Icing Severity – Probability > 25%**

   a. The Icing Severity – Probability > 25% product depicts, at a single altitude, where a 26 – 100% probability exists for an indicated icing intensity.

   b. All previously mentioned standard symbols and coloration apply to this graphic as well.

      1) Additionally, a gray color is used to mask the intensity pixels where the probability of icing is 25% or less.

6. **Icing Severity – Probability > 25% - Maximum**

   a. The Icing Severity – Probability > 25% - Maximum product depicts, at all altitudes from 1,000 feet MSL to FL300, where the probability of the indicated icing intensity is 26 – 100%.

   b. All data is depicted as described for the standard Icing Severity – Probability > 25% product.

7. **Icing Severity – Probability > 50%**

   a. The Icing Severity – Probability > 50% product depicts, at a single altitude, where the probability of the indicated icing intensity is 51 – 100%.

   b. All previously mentioned standard symbols and coloration apply to this graphic as well.

      1) Additionally, a gray color is used to mask the intensity pixels where the probability of icing is 50% or less.

8. **Icing Severity – Probability > 50% - Maximum**

   a. The Icing Severity – Probability > 50% - Maximum product depicts, at all altitudes from 1,000 feet MSL to FL300, where the probability of the indicated icing intensity is 51 – 100%. Icing intensity is displayed using standard icing intensity categories: trace, light, moderate, and heavy.

   b. All data is depicted as described for the standard Icing Severity – Probability > 50% product.

9. **Icing Severity plus Supercooled Large Droplets (SLD)**

   a. The Icing Severity plus Supercooled Large Droplets (SLD) product depicts, at a single altitude, the intensity of icing expected as well as locations where a threat for SLD exists.

      1) **SLD** is defined as supercooled water droplets larger than 50 micrometers in diameter.

         a) These droplets include freezing drizzle and/or freezing rain aloft.

      2) SLD, which are outside the icing certification envelopes (FAR Part 25 Appendix C), can be particularly hazardous to some aircraft.

   b. Icing intensity is displayed using standard icing intensity categories: trace, light, moderate, and heavy.

   c. All previously mentioned standard symbols and coloration apply to this graphic as well.

      1) Additionally, locations where a threat for SLD exists are depicted with red hatching.

10. **Icing Severity plus Supercooled Large Droplets (SLD) - Maximum**

    a. The Icing Severity plus Supercooled Large Droplets (SLD) product depicts, at all altitudes between 1,000 feet MSL and FL300, the intensity of icing expected as well as locations where a threat for SLD exists.

    b. All data is depicted as described for the standard Icing Severity plus Supercooled Large Droplets (SLD) product.

32.4 USING THE CHART

1. The CIP product suite is updated hourly and provides a diagnostic tool to assist in determining the probability for icing, the intensity of icing, and the threat for SLD.

2. **Limitations**

    a. Actual icing severity may be different than what is depicted on the CIP graphics and plotted PIREPS because

        1) Different aircraft types experience different severities of icing in the same atmospheric environments. Severity definitions are currently pilot-based and thus are a function of the aircraft type, flight phase (takeoff/landing, cruise, etc.), and aircraft configuration as well as the pilot's experience and perception of the icing hazard.

        2) Assessing the amount and drop size of supercooled liquid water (SLW) in the atmosphere is difficult.

        3) The Icing Severity products depict the severity of the meteorological icing environment and not the resultant icing that may occur on the aircraft.

3. **Uses of the Product**

    a. The CIP Icing Probability product can be used to identify the current three-dimensional probability of icing.

    b. The CIP Icing Severity product can be used to determine the intensity of icing.

        1) The CIP Icing Severity – Probability > 25% or Probability > 50% depicts the probability of a given intensity of icing occurring.

    c. The Icing Severity plus SLD product can help in determining the threat of SLD, which is particularly hazardous to some aircraft.

    d. Icing PIREPs are plotted on single altitude graphics if the PIREP is within 1,000 feet of the graphic's altitude and has been observed within 75 minutes of the chart's valid time.

        1) On CIP Max products, PIREPs for all altitudes (i.e., 1,000 feet MSL to FL300) are displayed.

            a) Negative reports of icing are not plotted on the CIP Max product in an effort to reduce clutter.

        2) The PIREP legend is located on the bottom of each graphic.

END OF STUDY UNIT

STUDY UNIT THIRTY-THREE
FORECAST ICING POTENTIAL (FIP)

(2 pages of outline)

Please take a few minutes to study each of the concepts listed above and anticipate/imagine what they are and how they relate to the other listed concepts.

33.1 PRODUCT DESCRIPTION

1. The Forecast Icing Potential (FIP) provides a colorized, three-dimensional forecast of icing potential (or likelihood) using numerical weather prediction model output.

    a. It provides essentially the same data as the Icing Probability chart contained in the Current Icing Potential (CIP) product suite discussed in Study Unit 32.

    b. The difference is that this chart offers a forecast rather than a current look at icing conditions.

2. The FIP product suite is automatically generated, with no human modifications.

3. It may be used as a higher-resolution supplement to AIRMETs and SIGMETs but is not a substitute for them.

    a. It is authorized for operational use only by meteorologists and dispatchers.

        1) Pilots may use this product as a source of supplementary information only.

4. The forecast area covers the 48 contiguous states, much of Canada and Mexico, and their respective coastal waters.

33.2 ISSUANCE

1. The FIP is issued every hour and generates hourly forecasts for 3 hours into the future.

    a. EXAMPLE: Forecasts issued at 1300Z would be valid for 1400Z, 1500Z and 1600Z.

2. Forecasts for 6, 9, and 12 hours in the future are issued every 3 hours, beginning at 00Z.

    a. EXAMPLE: A forecast suite issued at 0300Z would have valid times at 0900Z, 1200Z, and 1500Z, respectively.

3. The product is issued by the Aviation Weather Center (AWC) and is available through the Aviation Digital Data Service (ADDS) website at http://adds.aviationweather.noaa.gov/icing/icing_nav.php.

33.3 PLOTTED DATA

1. The FIP forecasts the likelihood of icing from super-cooled liquid water droplets.

    a. The likelihood field ranges from 0 (no icing) to 100 (icing likely).

2. The scale depicts likelihood of icing using "cool" and "warm" colors, with warmer colors indicating a higher likelihood of icing.

    a. Regions depicted in white indicate zero icing potential according to the CIP.

    b. Brown regions indicate areas of terrain.

3. The scale is not calibrated as a true probability value.

    a. It does, however, have value in pointing out differences in the likelihood of encountering icing at a given location.

        1) EXAMPLE: A value of 70 does not indicate that there is a 70% chance of encountering icing. However, when comparing it to other higher or lower values, it will indicate if there is a greater or lesser likelihood of encountering icing.

4. No information is provided as to the severity of icing, and none should be inferred.

5. FIP output is available for 1,000-foot vertical intervals.

    a. ADDS displays every third level except on the Flight Path Tool, which provides access to all levels.

33.4 USING THE CHART

1. The FIP is primarily used to help determine the likelihood of icing at the specified forecast valid times.

2. **Strengths**

    a. The FIP can be used to help determine the forecast for potential for icing through the entire vertical depth of the atmosphere.

    b. The product is updated hourly.

3. **Limitations**

    a. The product does not display any information about the severity of icing.

    b. The product only displays the forecast potential for icing, not the absolute probability.

    c. It is only approved for operational use by meteorologists and dispatchers.

    d. The product is generated without human modification.

        1) The forecasts are only as accurate as the computer-model output used to create them.

END OF STUDY UNIT

STUDY UNIT THIRTY-FOUR
GRAPHICAL TURBULENCE GUIDANCE (GTG)

(2 pages of outline)

Please take a few minutes to study each of the concepts listed above and anticipate/imagine what they are and how they relate to the other listed concepts.

34.1 PRODUCT DESCRIPTION

1. The Graphical Turbulence Guidance (GTG) product suite provides a color-coded, three-dimensional diagnosis and forecast of Clear Air Turbulence (CAT) potential between FL210 and FL450.

   a. The GTG is created using a combination of computer model output and turbulence observations.

2. When turbulence PIREPs exist, they are plotted on the GTG analysis charts for comparative reference.

3. The GTG product suite, which consists of the GTG Analysis and Forecast and Composite Analysis and Forecast, is automatically generated with no human modifications.

   a. This product may be used as a supplement to AIRMETs and SIGMETs but is not a substitute for them.

   b. It is authorized for operational use only by meteorologists and dispatchers.

4. The GTG is available for the 48-contiguous states, much of Canada and Mexico, and their respective coastal waters.

34.2 ISSUANCE

1. The GTG analysis is issued hourly.

2. The 3-, 6-, 9-, and 12-hour forecasts are issued every three hours beginning at 00Z.

   a. EXAMPLE: A forecast suite issued at 0600Z would have valid times at 0900Z, 1200Z, 1500Z, and 1800Z, respectively.

3. The GTG Analysis and Forecast graphics, along with the Composite product, are issued by the Aviation Weather Center (AWC) and are available through the Aviation Digital Data Service (ADDS) website at http://adds.aviationweather.noaa.gov/turbulence/turb_nav.php.

34.3 PLOTTED DATA

1. **GTG Analysis and Forecast**

   a. The GTG Analysis and Forecast graphics depict the location and intensity of potential Clear Air Turbulence (CAT).

      1) Standard turbulence intensity terminology is used in the legend: light **(LGT)**, moderate **(MDT)**, severe **(SVR)**, and extreme **(Extreme)**.

      2) Lighter colors correspond to lower predicted turbulence intensities, while darker colors correspond to higher predicted turbulence intensities.

b.   The GTG output is available for 1,000-foot vertical intervals between FL200 and FL450.

    1)   The ADDS turbulence page displays every third level starting at FL210 level, while the ADDS Flight Path Tool provides access to all levels.

2.   **GTG Composite Analysis and Forecast**

a.   The GTG Composite product displays the maximum, cumulative intensity of potential turbulence between FL200 and FL450.

    1)   At any given location, the displayed value represents the maximum potential turbulence between FL200 and FL450.

    2)   Single altitude graphics must be examined to determine the altitude of the potential turbulence.

b.   The coloration on this chart is the same as each single altitude graphic.

34.4 USING THE CHART

1.   The GTG provides an hourly, high-resolution analysis and forecast of clear-air turbulence potential at and above FL200.

a.   However, the product is only for turbulence associated with upper level fronts and jet streams, while other known causes of turbulence are not forecast.

2.   **Strengths**

a.   The product is issued hourly.

b.   Turbulence is plotted at a high resolution.

3.   **Limitations**

a.   The accuracy of the analysis is dependent on the number of PIREPs available.

    1)   Typically at night, fewer pilot reports are received, so the accuracy decreases.

b.   The products are only as accurate as the computer model output used to create them.

c.   The product only displays clear air turbulence (CAT) for upper-level fronts and the jet stream. Other known causes of turbulence are not included in the product.

d.   Data and forecasts are only available for FL200 and above.

e.   It is only approved for use by meteorologists and dispatchers.

4.   The Composite product can provide a quick method to determine what the greatest potential of current or forecast turbulence is at a given location.

a.   To determine the turbulence potential at any given altitude, the individual altitude products must be viewed.

5.   The ADDS website allows users to overlay turbulence PIREPs on the single altitude graphics.

a.   For the PIREP to be plotted on the single altitude product, it must be located within 1,000 feet vertically of the altitude and have been reported within 90 minutes of the chart time.

    1)   EXAMPLE: If a user viewed the FL240 GTG product with a valid time of 1400Z, the displayed PIREPs could be located between FL230 and FL250 and reported between 1230Z and 1400Z

END OF STUDY UNIT

STUDY UNIT THIRTY-FIVE
METEOROLOGICAL IMPACT STATEMENT (MIS)

(3 pages of outline)

Please take a few minutes to study each of the concepts listed above and anticipate/imagine what they are and how they relate to the other listed concepts.

35.1 PRODUCT DESCRIPTION

1. A Meteorological Impact Statement (MIS) is an unscheduled flow control and flight operations planning forecast issued by Center Weather Service Units (CWSUs).

2. It is a forecast and briefing product for personnel at Air Route Traffic Control Centers (ARTCCs), Air Traffic Control System Command Center (ATCSCC), Terminal Radar Approach Control Facilities (TRACONS), and Airport Traffic Control Towers (ATCTs) responsible for making flow control-type decisions.

3. A MIS may be tailored to meet the unique requirements of the host ARTCC.

   a. These special requirements will be coordinated between the host ARTCC and the CWSU.

4. **MIS Criteria**

   a. A MIS enables Air Traffic Control (ATC) facility personnel to include the impact of specific weather conditions in their flow control decision-making.

   b. At a minimum, a MIS should be issued when

      1) Any of the following conditions occur, are forecast to occur, and, if previously forecast, are no longer expected:

         a) Conditions meeting convective SIGMET criteria
         b) Icing -- moderate or greater
         c) Turbulence -- moderate or greater
         d) Heavy precipitation
         e) Freezing precipitation
         f) Conditions at or approaching Low IFR
         g) Surface winds/gusts >30 knots
         h) Low Level Wind Shear (surface -- 2,000 feet)
         i) Volcanic ash, dust storms, or sandstorms

      2) In the forecaster's judgment, the conditions listed above, or any others, will adversely impact the flow of air traffic within the ARTCC area of responsibility.

35.2 ISSUANCE AND VALID PERIOD

1. MIS phenomena forecasts use the location reference point identifiers depicted on the Inflight Advisory Plotting Chart (see page 480) and include the height, extent, and movement of the conditions.

2. MIS product issuances are numbered sequentially beginning at midnight local time each day.

3.   The MIS is disseminated and stored as a "replaceable" product.

    a.   Each issuance will contain the details of all pertinent known conditions meeting MIS issuance criteria, including ongoing conditions described in previously issued MISs.

4.   A MIS is valid up to 12 hours after issuance time and details weather conditions expected to adversely impact air traffic flow in the CWSU area of responsibility.

5.   The MIS can be immediately effective for existing conditions when CWSU operations begin or for rapidly deteriorating conditions or it can be effective up to two hours in advance of expected conditions.

6.   The MIS is distributed to ARTCC personnel, including Traffic Management Unit (TMU) personnel.

7.   MISs are available on the Aviation Weather Center (AWC) website at http://aviationweather.gov/products/cwsu/.

35.3 MIS FORMAT

1.   Reference the sample MIS below and the table below it to learn the format of the report.

```
LINE
1 - ZFW MIS 01 VALID 190200-191200
2 - ...FOR ATC PLANNING PURPOSES ONLY...

3 - FROM OKC TO CDS TO GAG TO END TO OKC
4 - LLWS BLO 020 AGL DUE TO LLJ.  CONDS
    GRDLY IPVG AFT 10Z.
```

Figure 35-1. Meteorological Impact Statement (MIS) Example

LINE	CONTENT	DESCRIPTION
1	ZFW MIS 01 VALID 190200-191200	ARTCC identification Product type Issuance number Valid period UTC date/time
2	...FOR ATC PLANNING PURPOSES ONLY...	Product use statement
3	FROM OKC TO CDS TO GAG TO END TO OKC	Phenomenon location
4	LLWS BLO 020 AGL DUE TO LLJ. CONDS GRDLY IPVG AFT 10Z.	Phenomenon description

Table 35-1. Meteorological Impact Statement (MIS) – Decoding

2.   Any remarks such as "SEE CONVECTIVE SIGMET 8W", "NO UPDATES AVBL AFT 0230Z", forecaster initials, and/or facility identifier may be placed at the end of the MIS.

3.   If the phenomenon described in a MIS is no longer expected, a cancelation MIS message may be issued.

    a.   In this situation, the header will not contain an issuance number.

4.   If the phenomenon described in the MIS is expected to continue beyond the operating hours of the CWSU, then the remark "NO UPDATES AFT ttttZ" (where "ttttZ" is the UTC closing time of the CWSU) is added at the end of the text.

35.4 READING THE MIS

1. The following examples and interpretations of MISs are provided to help you decipher MISs on your own.

```
ZOA MIS 01 VALID 041415-041900
...FOR ATC PLANNING PURPOSES ONLY...
FOR SFO BAY AREA
BR/FG WITH CEILING BLW 005 AND VIS OCNL BLW 1SM.
ZOA CWSU
```

Meteorological Impact Statement issued by the Freemont, California CWSU. First MIS issuance of the day, valid from the 4th day of the month at 1415 UTC, to the 4th day of the month at 1900 UTC. For air traffic control planning purposes only. For the San Francisco Bay Area... mist and fog with ceilings below 500 feet MSL and visibility occasionally below 1 statute mile.

```
ZOA MIS 02 VALID 041650
...FOR ATC PLANNING PURPOSES ONLY...
FOR SFO BAY AREA
CNL ZOA MIS 01.   CONDS HAVE IMPRD.
ZOA CWSU
```

Meteorological Impact Statement issued by the Freemont, California CWSU. The second MIS issuance of the day, valid the 4th day of the month at 1650 UTC. For air traffic control planning purposes only. For the San Francisco Bay Area. Cancel Freemont, California Meteorological Impact Statement number 1. Conditions have improved.

```
ZID MIS 03 VALID 041200-042330
...FOR ATC PLANNING PURPOSES ONLY...
FROM IND TO 17WSW APE TO LOZ TO 13NE PXV TO IND
TIL 21Z MOD TURB FL310-390 DUE TO JTST WS.
ZID W OF A LINE FM FWA TO BWG
AFT 18Z OCNL SEV TSGR TOPS TO FL450.  MOV FM 24035KT.  MAX SFC WINDS
60KT.
ZID E OF A LINE FM FWA TO 35SE BKW
MOD MXD ICE IN CLDS/PRECIPITATION 020-120.  CONDS ENDING W OF
A 40S CLE TO 20NE BKW LINE BY 19Z.
ZID CWSU
```

Meteorological Impact Statement issued by the Indianapolis, Indiana CWSU. The third MIS issuance of the day, valid from the 4th day of the month at 1200 UTC to the 4th day of the month at 2130 UTC. For air traffic control planning purposes only. From Indianapolis, Indiana to 17 nautical miles west-southwest of Appleton, Ohio to London, Kentucky to 13 nautical miles northeast of Pocket City, Indiana to Indianapolis, Indiana. Until 21Z, moderate turbulence between flight level 310 and flight level 390 due to jet stream wind shear.

For the Indianapolis ARTCC airspace west of a line from Fort Wayne, Indiana to Bowling Green, Kentucky. After 18Z, occasional severe thunderstorms, hail, tops to flight level 450. Moving from 240 degrees at 35 knots. Maximum surface winds 60 knots.

For the Indianapolis, Indiana ARTCC airspace east of a line from Fort Wayne, Indiana to 35 nautical miles southeast of Beckley, West Virginia. Moderate mixed icing in clouds and precipitation between 2,000 feet to 12,000 feet MSL. Conditions ending west of a line from 40 nautical miles south of Cleveland, Ohio to 20 nautical miles northeast of Beckley, West Virginia by 1900Z.

END OF STUDY UNIT

STUDY UNIT THIRTY-SIX
OTHER WEATHER RELATED INFORMATION

(42 pages of outline)

Please take a few minutes to study each of the concepts listed above and anticipate/imagine what they are and how they relate to the other listed concepts.

36.1 INTRODUCTION

1. This study unit provides other weather-related information that you can use to further understand the weather. Information included covers

    a. ASOS and AWOS locations
    b. Contractions and acronyms
    c. Standard Conversion Table
    d. Density altitude calculation
    e. Internet links
    f. AWC Advisory Plotting Chart – Contiguous U.S.
    g. WSR-88D Weather Radar Network
    h. AWC Geographical Area Designator Map
    i. Present weather symbols
    j. Turbulence and icing intensity depictions

36.2 ASOS AND AWOS LOCATIONS

1. The following 10 graphics show the location and type of ASOS and AWOS stations under the control of the National Weather Service (NWS). The graphics included are

    a. Figure 36-1. ASOS and AWOS Locations – NWS Alaska Region
    b. Figure 36-2. ASOS and AWOS Locations – NWS Pacific Region
    c. Figure 36-3. ASOS and AWOS Locations – NWS Western Region (northern half)
    d. Figure 36-4. ASOS and AWOS Locations – NWS Western Region (southern half)
    e. Figure 36-5. ASOS and AWOS Locations – NWS Central Region (western half)
    f. Figure 36-6. ASOS and AWOS Locations – NWS Central Region (eastern half)
    g. Figure 36-7. ASOS and AWOS Locations – NWS Southern Region (western half)
    h. Figure 36-8. ASOS and AWOS Locations – NWS Southern Region (eastern half)
    i. Figure 36-9. ASOS and AWOS Locations – NWS Eastern Region (northern half)
    j. Figure 36-10. ASOS and AWOS Locations – NWS Eastern Region (southern half)

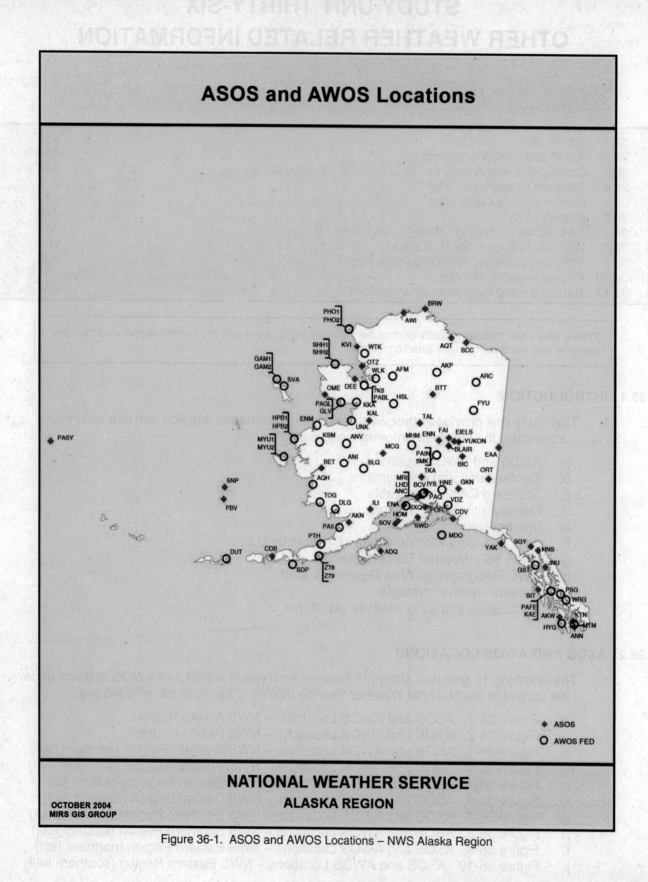

Figure 36-1. ASOS and AWOS Locations – NWS Alaska Region

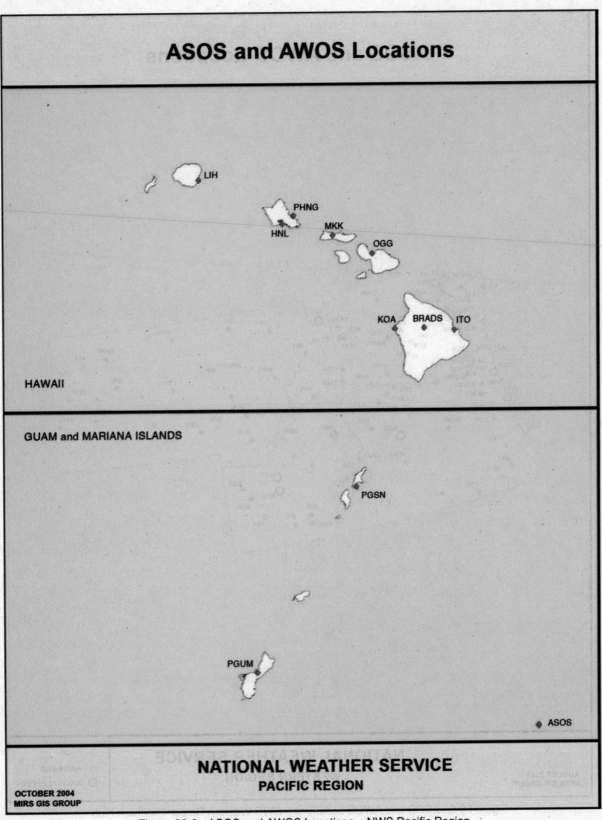

Figure 36-2. ASOS and AWOS Locations – NWS Pacific Region

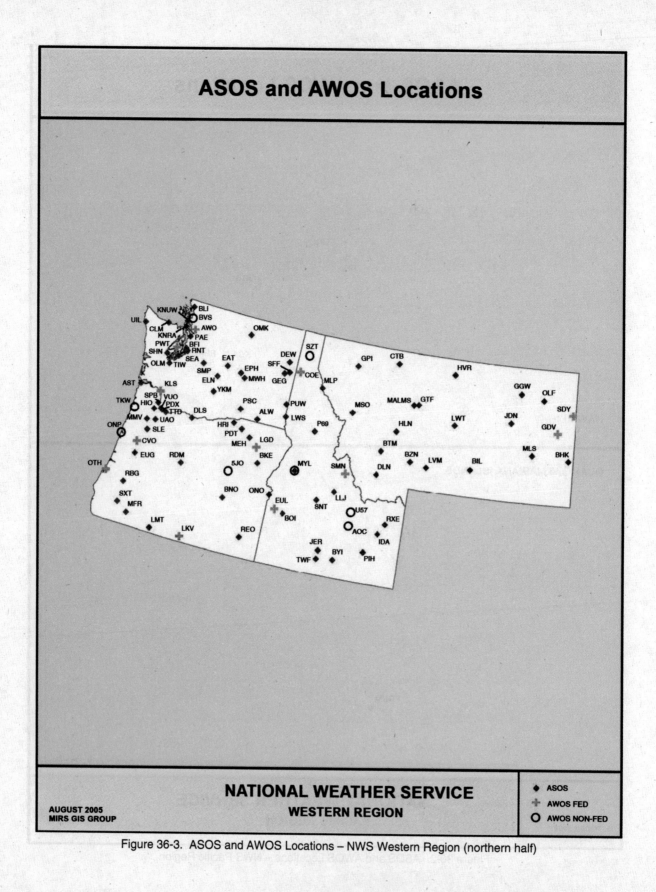

Figure 36-3. ASOS and AWOS Locations – NWS Western Region (northern half)

ASOS and AWOS Locations

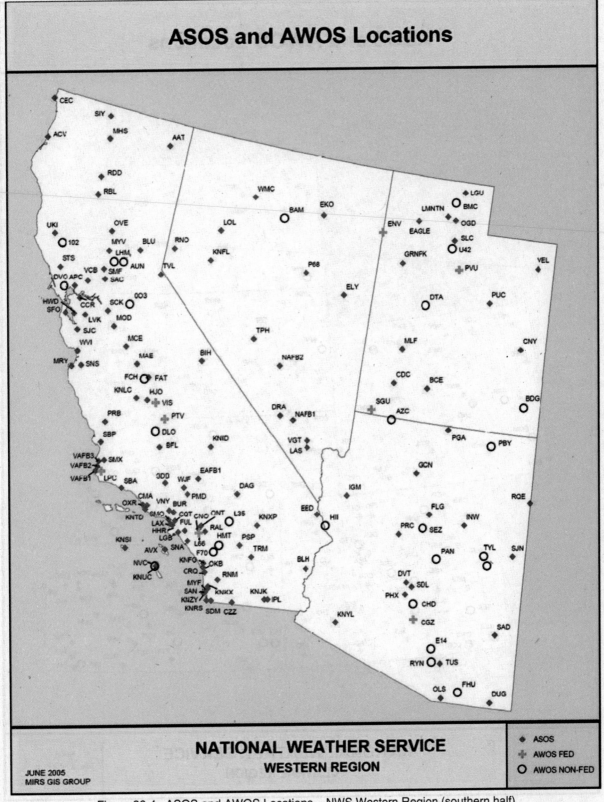

NATIONAL WEATHER SERVICE
WESTERN REGION

JUNE 2005
MIRS GIS GROUP

- ◆ ASOS
- ✚ AWOS FED
- ○ AWOS NON-FED

Figure 36-4. ASOS and AWOS Locations – NWS Western Region (southern half)

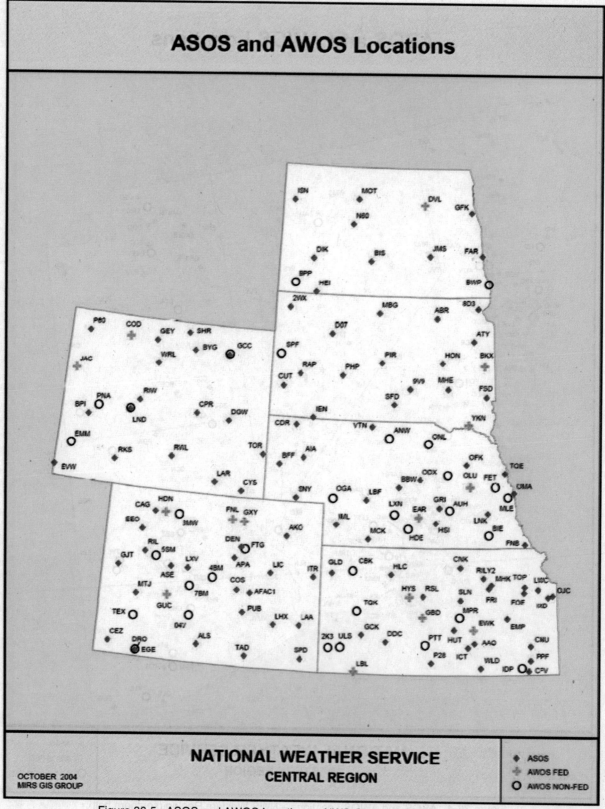

Figure 36-5. ASOS and AWOS Locations – NWS Central Region (western half)

ASOS and AWOS Locations

NATIONAL WEATHER SERVICE
CENTRAL REGION

OCTOBER 2004
MIRS GIS GROUP

◆	ASOS
✛	AWOS FED
○	AWOS NON-FED

Figure 36-6. ASOS and AWOS Locations – NWS Central Region (eastern half)

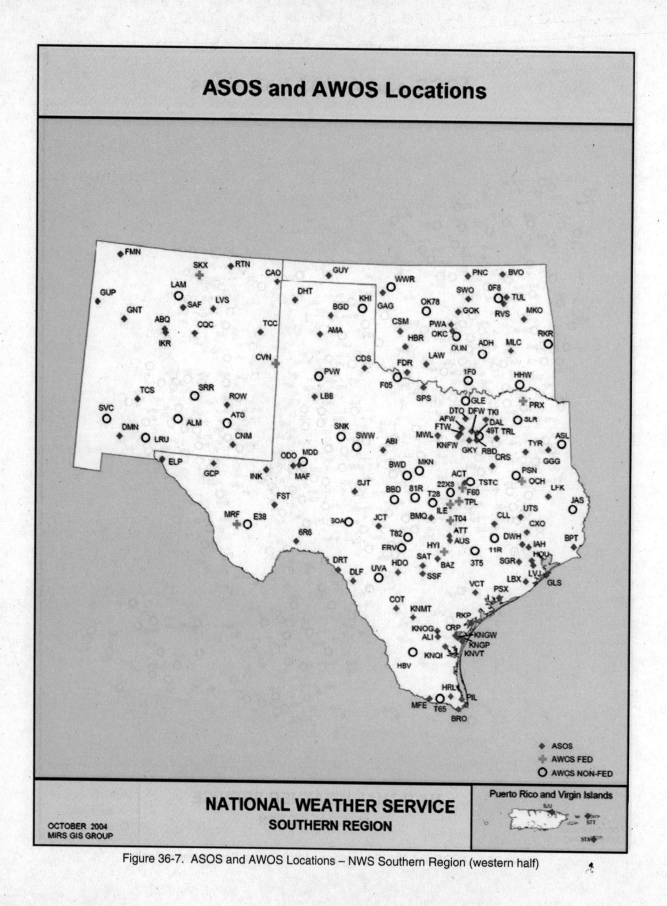

Figure 36-7. ASOS and AWOS Locations – NWS Southern Region (western half)

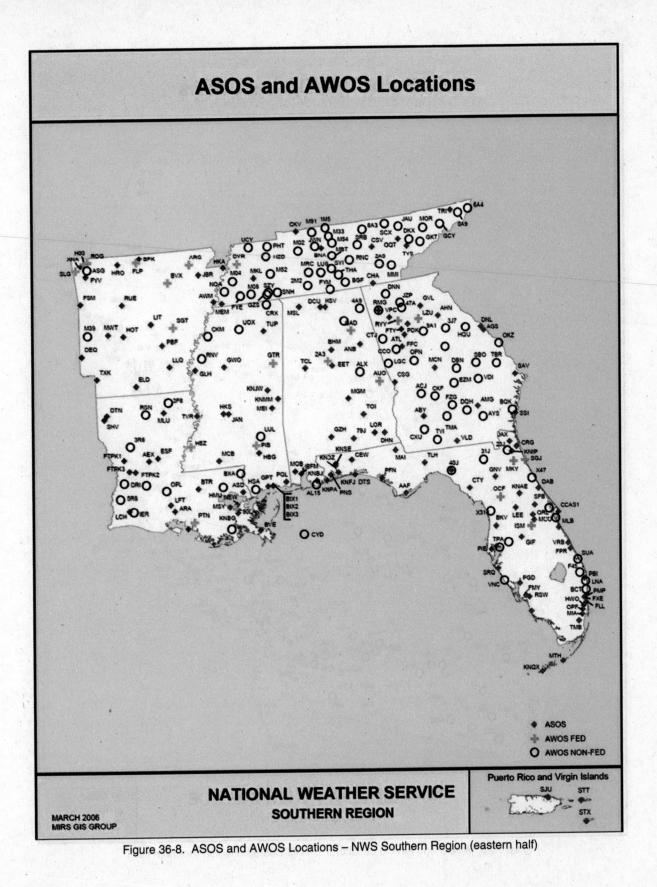

ASOS and AWOS Locations

ASOS
AWOS FED
AWOS NON-FED

NATIONAL WEATHER SERVICE
SOUTHERN REGION

MARCH 2006
MIRS GIS GROUP

Puerto Rico and Virgin Islands

Figure 36-8. ASOS and AWOS Locations – NWS Southern Region (eastern half)

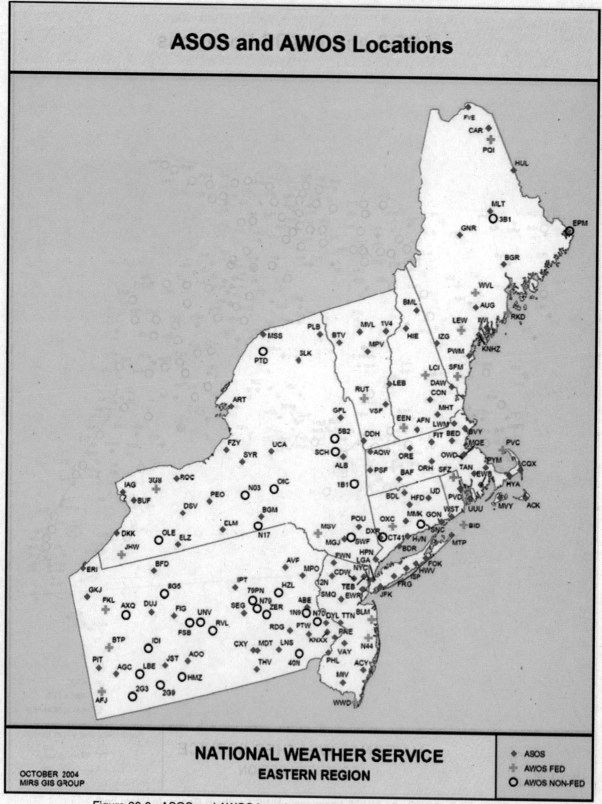

Figure 36-9. ASOS and AWOS Locations – NWS Eastern Region (northern half)

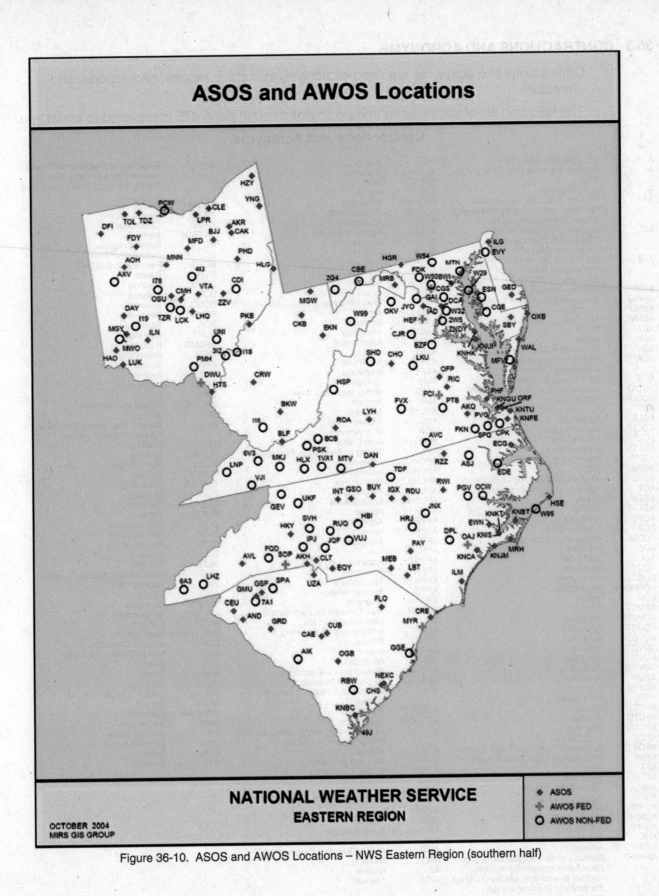

Figure 36-10. ASOS and AWOS Locations – NWS Eastern Region (southern half)

36.3 CONTRACTIONS AND ACRONYMS

1.   Contractions and acronyms are used extensively in surface reports, pilot reports, and forecasts.

2.   The following list of contractions and acronyms through page 475 is provided to assist you.

Contractions and Acronyms

A	Absolute (temperature)	AK	Alaska	B	Beginning of Precipitation (time in minutes) (weather reports only)
A	Alaskan Standard Time (time groups only)	AL	Alabama		
		ALF	Aloft	B	Bering Standard Time (time groups only)
A	Arctic (air mass)	ALG	Along		
AAA	(or AAB, AAC...etc., in sequence) Amended meteorological message (message type designator)	ALGHNY	Allegheny	BACLIN	Baroclinic
		ALQDS	All Quadrants	BAJA	Baja, California
		ALSEC	All Sectors	BASE	Cloud base
A01	Automated Observation with Precipitation Discriminator (rain/snow) (METAR)	ALSTG	Altimeter Setting	BATROP	Barotropic
		ALT	Altitude	BC	British Columbia
		ALTA	Alberta	BC	Patches (METAR)
A02	Automated Observation with Precipitation Discriminator (rain/snow) (METAR)	ALTHO	Although	BCFG	Patchy Fog (METAR)
		ALTM	Altimeter	BCH	Beach
		ALUTN	Aleutian	BCKG	Backing
AAWF	Auxiliary Aviation Weather Facility	ALWF	Actual Wind Factor	BCM	Become
AAWU	Alaska Aviation Weather Unit	AM	Ante Meridiem	BCMG	Becoming
ABNDT	Abundant	AMD	Amend	BCMS	Becomes
ABNML	Abnormal	AMDD	Amended	BDA	Bermuda
ABT	About	AMDG	Amending	BDRY	Boundary
ABV	Above	AMDT	Amendment	BECMG	Becoming
AC	Convective Outlook or Altocumulus	AMP	Amplify	BFDK	Before Dark
ACARS	Aircraft communication and addressing system	AMPG	Amplifying	BFR	Before
		AMPLTD	Amplitude	BGN	Begins
ACC	Altocumulus Castellanus	AMS	Air Mass	BGNG	Beginning
ACCID	Notification of an aircraft accident	AMSL	Above mean sea level	BHND	Behind
ACCUM	Accumulate	AMT	Amount	BINOVC	Breaks in Overcast
ACTF	Aircraft	ANLYS	Analysis	BKN	Broken
ACLT	Accelerate	ANS	Answer	BL...	Blowing (followed by DU = dust, SA = sand or SN = snow)
ACLTD	Accelerated	AOA	At or Above		
ACLTG	Accelerating	AOB	At or Below	BLD	Build
ACLTS	Accelerates	AP	Airport or Anomalous Propagation	BLDG	Building
ACPY	Accompany	APCH	Approach	BLDU	Blowing dust
ACRS	Across	APCHG	Approaching	BLDUP	Buildup
ACSL	Altocumulus Standing Lenticular	APCHS	Approaches	BLKHLS	Black Hills
ACT	Active or activated or activity	APLCN	Appalachian	BLKT	Blanket
ACTV	Active	APLCNS	Appalachians	BLKTG	Blanketing
ACTVTY	Activity	APPR	Appear	BLKTS	Blankets
ACYC	Anticyclone	APPRG	Appearing	BLO	Below Clouds
ADA	Advisory area	APPRS	Appears	BLSA	Blowing sand
ADDN	Addition or additional	APR	Apparent	BLSN	Blowing snow
ADJ	Adjacent	APR	April	BLW	Below
ADL	Additional	APRNT	Apparent	BLZD	Blizzard
ADQT	Adequate	APRNTLY	Apparently	BMS	Basic Meteorological Services
ADQTLY	Adequately	APRX	Approximate	BN	Blowing Sand
ADRNDCK	Adirondack	APRXLY	Approximately	BND	Bound
ADV	Advise	AR	Arkansas	BNDRY	Boundary
ADVCT	Advect	ARFOR	Area Forecast (in aeronautical meteorological code)	BNDRYS	Boundaries
ADVCTD	Advected			BNTH	Beneath
ADVCTG	Advecting	ARL	Air Resources Laboratory	BOOTHEEL	Bootheel
ADVCTN	Advection	ARND	Around	BOVC	Base of Overcast
ADVCTS	Advects	ARPT	Airport	BR	Mist (METAR) or Branch
ADVN	Advance	AS	Altostratus	BRF	Brief
ADVNG	Advancing	ASC	Ascend to or ascending to	BRK	Break
ADVY	Advisory	ASAP	As Soon As Possible	BRKG	Breaking
ADVYS	Advisories	ASOS	Automated Surface Observing System	BRKHIC	Breaks in Higher Clouds
AFC	Area Forecast Center			BRKS	Breaks
AFCT	Affect	ASSOCD	Associated	BRKSHR	Berkshire
AFCTD	Affected	ASSOCN	Association	BRM	Barometer
AFCTG	Affecting	AT...	At (followed by time at which weather change is forecast to occur)	BS	Blowing Snow
AFDK	After Dark			BTL	Between layers
AFOS	Automated Field Operations System	ATLC	Atlantic	BTN	Between
AFSS	Aeronautical Flight Service Station	ATP	At...(time or place)	BYD	Beyond
AFT	After	ATTM	At This Time		
AFTN	Afternoon	ATTN	Attention		
AGL	Above Ground Level	AUG	August		
AGN	Again	AURBO	Aurora Borealis		
AGRD	Agreed	AVBL	Available		
AGRMT	Agreement	AVG	Average		
AGRS	Agrees	AVN	Aviation Model		
AHD	Ahead	AWC	Aviation Weather Center		
AIREP	Air-report	AWP	Aviation Weather Processors		
AIRMET	Airman's Meteorological Information (information concerning en-route weather phenomena which may affect the safety of low-level aircraft operations)	AWT	Awaiting		
		AZ	Arizona		
		AZM	Azimuth		

C	Celsius	CONT	Continue	DKTS	Dakotas
C	Central Standard Time (time groups only)	CONTD	Continued	DLA	Delay or delayed
		CONTDVD	Continental Divide	DLAD	Delayed
		CONTG	Continuing	DLT	Delete
C	Continental (air mass)	CONTLY	Continually	DLTD	Deleted
CA	California	CONTRAILS	Condensation Trails	DLTG	Deleting
CAA	Cold Air Advection	CONTS	Continues	DLY	Daily
CAN	Canada	CONUS	Continental U.S.	DMG	Damage
CAPE	Convective available	COORD	Coordinate	DMGD	Damaged
CARIB	Caribbean	COR	Correction	DMGG	Damaging
CASCDS	Cascades	COT	At the coast	DMNT	Dominant
CAT	Category	COV	Cover or covered or covering	DMSH	Diminish
CAT	Clear air turbulence	CPBL	Capable	DMSHD	Diminished
CAVO	Visibility, cloud and present weather better than prescribed values or conditions	CPC	Climate Prediction Center	DMSHG	Diminishing
		CRC	Circle	DMSHS	Diminishes
		CRCLC	Circulate	DNDFTS	Downdrafts
CAVOK	Cloud and Visibility OK (METAR)	CRCLN	Circulation	DNG	Danger or dangerous
CAVU	Clear or Scattered Clouds and Visibility Greater Than Ten Miles	CRLC	Circulate	DNS	Dense
		CRLN	Circulation	DNSLP	Downslope
CAWS	Common Aviation Weather Sub-system	CRNR	Corner	DNSTRM	Downstream
		CRNRS	Corners	DNWND	Downwind
CB	Cumulonimbus	CRS	Course	DOM	Domestic
CBMAM	Cumulonimbus Mamma	CS	Cirrostratus	DP	Deep
CC	Cirrocumulus	CSDR	Consider	DP	Dew point temperature
CC	Counterclockwise	CSDRBL	Considerable	DPND	Deepened
CCA	(or CCB, CCC...etc., in sequence) Corrected meteorological message	CST	Coast	DPNG	Deepening
		CSTL	Coastal	DPNS	Deepens
CCLDS	Clear of Clouds	CT	Connecticut	DPR	Deeper
CCSL	Cirrocumulus Standing Lenticular	CTGY	Category	DPT	Depth
CDFNT	Cold Front	CTSKLS	Catskills	DR...	Low drifting (followed by DU = dust, SA = sand, or SN = snow
CDN	Coordination	CU	Cumulus		
CFP	Cold Front Passage	CUFRA	Cumulus Fractus	DRFT	Drift
CHARC	Characteristic	CVR	Cover	DRFTD	Drifted
CHC	Chance	CVRD	Covered	DRFTG	Drifting
CHCS	Chances	CVRG	Covering	DRFTS	Drifts
CHG	Change	CVRS	Covers	DRG	During
CHGD	Changed	CWSU	Center Weather Service Units	DRZL	Drizzle
CHGG	Changing	CYC	Cyclonic	DS	Dust Storm (METAR)
CHGS	Changes	CYCLGN	Cyclogenesis	DSCNT	Descent
CHSPK	Chesapeake			DSIPT	Dissipate
CI	Cirrus	D	Downward (tendency in RVR during previous 10 minutes)	DSIPTD	Dissipated
CIG	Ceiling			DSIPTG	Dissipating
CIGS	Ceilings	DABRK	Daybreak	DSIPTN	Dissipation
CIT	Near or over large towns	DALGT	Daylight	DSIPTS	Dissipates
CLA	Clear type of ice formation	DBL	Double	DSND	Descend
CLD	Cloud	DC	District of Columbia	DSNDG	Descending
CLDNS	Cloudiness	DCAVU	Clear or Scattered Clouds and Visibility Greater Than Ten Miles, Remainder of Report Missing (weather reports only)	DSNDS	Descends
CLDS	Clouds			DSNT	Distant
CLKWS	Clockwise			DSTBLZ	Destabilize
CLR	Clear			DSTBLZD	Destabilized
CLRG	Clearing	DCR	Decrease	DSTBLZG	Destabilizing
CLRS	Clears	DCRD	Decreased	DSTBLZN	Destabilization
CLSD	Close or closed or closing	DCRG	Decreasing	DSTBLZS	Destabilizes
CM	Centimeter	DCRGLY	Decreasingly	DSTC	Distance
CMPLX	Complex	DCRS	Decreases	DTG	Date-time group
CNCL	Cancel	DE	Delaware	DTLN	International Dateline
CNCLD	Canceled	DEC	December	DTRT	Deteriorate
CNCLG	Canceling	DEG	Degree	DTRTD	Deteriorated
CNCLS	Cancels	DEGS	Degrees	DTRTG	Deteriorating
CNDN	Canadian	DELMARVA	Delaware-Maryland-Virginia	DTRTS	Deteriorates
CNL	Cancel or cancelled	DFCLT	Difficult	DU	Widespread Dust (METAR)
CNTR	Center	DFCLTY	Difficulty	DUC	Dense upper cloud
CNTRD	Centered	DFNT	Definite	DUR	Duration
CNTRL	Central	DFNTLY	Definitely	DURC	During Climb
CNTY	County	DFRS	Differs	DURD	During Descent
CNTYS	Counties	DGNL	Diagonal	DURG	During
CNVG	Converge	DGNLLY	Diagonally	DURN	Duration
CNVGG	Converging	DIF	Diffuse	DVLP	Develop
CNVGNC	Convergence	DIGG	Digging	DVLPD	Developed
CNVTN	Convection	DIR	Direction	DVLPG	Developing
CNVTV	Convective	DISC	Discontinue	DVLPMT	Development
CNVTVLY	Convectively	DISCD	Discontinued	DVLPS	Develops
CO	Colorado	DISCG	Discontinuing	DVRG	Diverge
COMR	Compare	DISRE	Disregard	DVRGG	Diverging
COMPRD	Compared	DISRED	Disregarded	DVRGNC	Divergence
COMPRG	Comparing	DISREG	Disregarding	DVRGS	Diverges
COMPRS	Compares	DIST	Distance	DVV	Downward Vertical Velocity
COND	Condition			DWNDFTS	Downdrafts
CONFDC	Confidence			DWPNT	Dew Point
CONS	Continuous			DWPNTS	Dew Points
				DZ	Drizzle (METAR)

E	East or eastern longitude	F	Fixed	G	Gust
E	Eastern Standard Time (time groups only)	F	Degrees Fahrenheit	G	Green
		FA	Area Forecast	GA	Georgia
E	Ending of Precipitation (time in minutes) (weather reports only)	FAA	Federal Aviation Administration	GAMET	Area forecast for low level flights
		FAM	Familiar	GEN	General
E	Equatorial (air mass)	FAX	Facsimile transmission	GENLY	Generally
E	Estimated (weather reports only)	FBL	Light (used to indicate the intensity of weather phenomena, interference or static reports, e.g., FBL RA = light rains)	GEO	Geographic
EB	Eastbound			GEOREF	Geographical Reference
EFCT	Effect			GF	Ground Fog
ELEV	Elevation			GFS	Global Forecast System (model)
ELNGT	Elongate	FC	Funnel Cloud (tornado or waterspout)	GICG	Glaze Icing
ELNGTD	Elongated	FCST	Forecast	GLFALSK	Gulf of Alaska
ELSW	Elsewhere	FCSTD	Forecasted	GLFCAL	Gulf of California
EMBD	Embedded in a layer	FCSTG	Forecasting	GLFMEX	Gulf of Mexico
EMBDD	Embedded	FCSTR	Forecaster	GLFSTLAWR	Gulf of St. Lawrence
EMC	Environmental Modeling Center	FCSTS	Forecasts	GND	Ground
EMERG	Emergency	FEB	February	GR	Hail (METAR)
EMSU	Environment Meteorological Support Unit	FEW	1 or 2 Octas (eighths) Cloud Coverage (METAR)	GRAD	Gradient
				GRBNKS	Grand Banks
ENCTR	Encounter	FG	Fog (METAR)	GRDL	Gradual
ENDG	Ending	FIBI	Filed but Impractical to Transmit	GRDLY	Gradually
ENE	East-Northeast	FIG	Figure	GRIB	Processed meteorological data in the form of grid point values expressed in binary form (aeronautical meteorological code)
ENELY	East-Northeasterly	FILG	Filing		
ENERN	East-Northeastern	FINO	Weather Report Will Not be Filed for Transmission		
ENEWD	East-Northeastward				
ENHNC	Enhance	FIR	Flight Information Region	GRT	Great
ENHNCD	Enhanced	FIRAV	First Available	GRTLKS	Great Lakes
ENHNCG	Enhancing	FL	Florida	GRTLY	Greatly
ENHNCMNT	Enhancement	FL	Flight level	GS	Small Hail/Snow Pellets (METAR)
ENHNCS	Enhances	FLD	Field	GSTS	Gusts
ENR	En route	FLDST	Flood Stage	GSTY	Gusty
ENTR	Entire	FLG	Falling	GTS	Global Telecommunications System
EOF	Expected Operations Forecast	FLRY	Flurry		
EQPT	Equipment	FLRYS	Flurries	HAZ	Hazard
ERN	Eastern	FLT	Flight	HCVIS	High Clouds Visible
ERY	Early	FLUC	Fluctuating or fluctuation or fluctuated	HDFRZ	Hard Freeze
ERYR	Earlier	FLW	Follow	HDSVLY	Hudson Valley
ESE	East-Southeast	FLWG	Following	HDWIND	Head Wind
ESELY	East-Southeasterly	FLWIS	Flood Warning Issued	HGT	Height
ESERN	East-Southeastern	FLY	Fly or flying	HI	Hawaii or High
ESEWD	East-Southeastward	FM	From	HIEAT	Highest Temperature Equaled for All Time
ESNTL	Essential	FM...	From (followed by time weather change is forecast to begin)		
EST	Estimate			HIEFM	Highest Temperature Equaled for the Month
ESTAB	Establish	FMT	Format		
ETA	Estimated Time of Arrival or ETA Model	FNCTN	Function	HIER	Higher
		FNT	Front	HIESE	Highest Temperature Equaled So Early
ETC	Et Cetera	FNTGNS	Frontogenesis		
ETD	Estimated time of departure	FNTL	Frontal	HIESL	Highest Temperature Equaled So Late
ETIM	Elapsed Time	FNTLYS	Frontolysis		
EV	Every	FNTS	Fronts	HIFOR	High Level Forecast
EVE	Evening	FORNN	Forenoon	HITMP	Highest Temperature
EWD	Eastward	FPM	Feet per Minute	HIXAT	Highest Temperature Exceeded for All Time
EXC	Except	FQT	Frequent		
EXCLV	Exclusive	FQTLY	Frequently	HIXFM	Highest Temperature Exceeded for the Month
EXCLVLY	Exclusively	FRI	Friday		
EXCP	Except	FRM	Form	HIXSE	Highest Temperature Exceeded So Early
EXP	Expect or expected or expecting	FRMG	Forming		
EXPC	Expect	FRMN	Formation	HIXSL	Highest Temperature Exceeded So Late
EXPCD	Expected	FRNG	Firing		
EXPCG	Expecting	FRONT	Front (relating to weather)	HJ	Sunrise to sunset
EXTD	Extend	FROPA	Frontal Passage	HLDG	Holding
EXTDD	Extended	FROSFC	Frontal Surface	HLF	Half
EXTDG	Extending	FRQ	Frequent	HLSTO	Hailstones
EXTDS	Extends	FRST	Frost	HLTP	Hilltop
EXTN	Extension	FRWF	Forecast Wind Factor	HLYR	Haze Layer Aloft
EXTRAP	Extrapolate	FRZ	Freeze	HN	Sunrise to sunset
EXTRAPD	Extrapolated	FRZG	Freezing	HND	Hundred
EXTRM	Extreme	FRZLVL	Freezing Level	HOL	Holiday
EXTRMLY	Extremely	FRZN	Frozen	HPA	HectoPascal
EXTSV	Extensive	FSS	Field Service Station	HPC	Hydrometeorological Prediction Center
		FST	First	HR	Hour
		FT	Feet (dimensional unit)	HRS	Hours
		FTHR	Further	HRZN	Horizon
		FU	Smoke (METAR)	HTG	Heating
		FULRY	Smoke Layer Aloft	HURCN	Hurricane
		FUOCTY	Smoke over City	HUREP	Hurricane Report
		FVRBL	Favorable	HV	Have
		FWC	Fleet Weather Central	HVY	Heavy
		FWD	Forward	HVYR	Heavier
		FYI	For Your Information	HVYST	Heaviest
		FZ	Supercooled/Freezing (METAR)	HWVR	However
		FZ LVL	Freezing level	HWY	Highway
		FZDZ	Freezing drizzle	HX	High Index
		FZFG	Freezing fog	HYR	Higher
		FZRA	Freezing rain	HZ	Haze (METAR)

IA	Iowa	KFRST	Killing Frost	LTR	Later	
IAO	In and out of clouds	KG	Kilograms	LTST	Latest	
IC	Ice (in PIREPs only)	KLYR	Smoke Layer Aloft	LV	Leaving	
ICAO	International Civil Aviation Organization	KM	Kilometers	LVE	Leave or leaving	
		KMH	Kilometers per hour	LVL	Level	
ICE	Icing	KOCTY	Smoke over City	LVLS	Levels	
ICG	Icing	KPA	Kilopascalsy	LWR	Lower	
ICGIC	Icing in Clouds	KS	Kansas	LWRD	Lowered	
ICGICIP	Icing in Clouds and in Precipitation	KT	Knots	LWRG	Lowering	
ICGIP	Icing in Precipitation	KY	Kentucky	LX	Low Index	
ID	Idaho			LYR	Layer or layered or layers	
IDENT	Identification	L	Left (runway identification)			
IFR	Instrument Flight Rules	LA	Louisiana	M	Maritime (air mass)	
IGA	International general aviation	LABRDR	Labrador	M	Metres (preceded by figures)	
IL	Illinois	LAN	Inland	M	Mach number (followed by figures)	
ILS	Instrument landing system	LAT	Latitude	M	In Temperature Field Means "Minus" or below Zero (METAR)	
IMC	Instrument meteorological conditions	LAWRS	Limited Aviation Weather Reporting Station	M	In RVR Field, Indicates Visibility Less Than Lowest Reportable Sensor Value (e.g., M0600FT)	
IMD	Immediate or immediately	LCL	Local			
IMDT	Immediate	LCLY	Locally	M	Missing (weather reports only)	
IMDTLY	Immediately	LCTD	Located	M	Mountain Standard Time (time groups only)	
IMPL	Impulse	LCTMP	Little Change in Temperature			
IMPLS	Impulses	LCTN	Location	MA	Map Analysis	
IMPR	Improve or improving	LDG	Landing	MA	Massachusetts	
IMPT	Important	LEVEL	Level	MAG	Magnetic	
IMT	Immediate or immediately	LFT	Lift	MAINT	Maintenance	
INC	In cloud	LFTG	Lifting	MAN	Manitoba	
INCL	Include	LGRNG	Long Range	MAR	March	
INCLD	Included	LGT	Light	MAX	Maximum	
INCLG	Including	LGTR	Lighter	MAY	May	
INCLS	Includes	LGWV	Long Wave	MB	Millibars	
INCR	Increase	LI	Lifted Index	MBST	Microburst	
INCRD	Increased	LIFR	Low IFR (weather reports only)	MCD	Mesoscale Discussion	
INCRG	Increasing	LIS	Lifted Indices	MD	Maryland	
INCRGLY	Increasingly	LK	Lake	MDFY	Modify	
INCRS	Increases	LKLY	Likely	MDFYD	Modified	
INDC	Indicate	LKS	Lakes	MDFYG	Modifying	
INDCD	Indicated	LLJ	Low Level Jet	MDL	Model	
INDCG	Indicating	LLWAS	Low-Level Wind Shear Alert System	MDLS	Models	
INDCS	Indicates	LLWS	Low-Level Wind Shear	MDT	Moderate	
INDEF	Indefinite	LMTD	Limited	MDTLY	Moderately	
INFO	Information	LMTG	Limiting	ME	Maine	
INLD	Inland	LMTS	Limits	MED	Medium	
INOP	Inoperative	LN	Line	MEGG	Merging	
INPR	In progress	LO	Low	MESO	Mesoscale	
INSTBY	Instability	LOC	Local or locally or location or located	MET	Meteorological	
INSTR	Instrument	LOEAT	Lowest Temperature Equaled for All Time	METAR	Aviation Routine Weather Report	
INT	Intersectional			METRO	Metropolitan	
INTCNTL	Intercontinental	LOEFM	Lowest Temperature Equaled for the Month	MEX	Mexico	
INTL	International			MHKVLY	Mohawk Valley	
INTMD	Intermediate	LOESE	Lowest Temperature Equaled So Early	MI	Michigan	
INTMT	Intermittent			MI	Shallow (METAR)	
INTMTLY	Intermittently	LOESL	Lowest Temperature Equaled So Late	MID	Middle	
INTR	Interior			MID	Mid-point (related to RVR)	
INTRMTRGN	Intermountain Region	LONG	Longitude	MIDN	Midnight	
INTRP	Interrupt or interruption or interrupted	LONGL	Longitudinal	MIFG	Patches of Shallow Fog Not Deeper Than Two Meters (METAR)	
INTS	Intense	LOTMP	Lowest Temperature			
INTSF	Intensify or intensifying	LOXAT	Lowest Temperature Exceeded for All Time	MIL	Military	
INTSFCN	Intensification			MIN	Minimum	
INTSFY	Intensify	LOXFM	Lowest Temperature Exceeded for the Month	MISG	Missing	
INTSFYD	Intensified			MLTLVL	Melting Level	
INTSFYG	Intensifying	LOXSE	Lowest Temperature Exceeded So Early	MMO	Main Meteorological Office	
INTSFYS	Intensifies			MN	Minnesota	
INTST	Intensity	LOXSL	Lowest Temperature Exceeded So Late	MNLD	Mainland	
INTSTY	Intensity			MNLY	Mainly	
INTVL	Interval	LRG	Large	MNT	Monitor or monitoring or monitored	
INVOF	In Vicinity Of	LRGLY	Largely	MNTN	Maintain	
INVRN	Inversion	LRGR	Larger	MO	Missouri	
IOVC	In Overcast	LRGST	Largest	MOD	Moderate (used to indicate the intensity of weather phenomena, interference or static reports, e.g., moderate rain = MOD RA)	
IP	Ice Pellets	LSR	Loose Snow on Runway			
IPV	Improve	LST	Local Standard Time			
IPVG	Improving	LTD	Limited			
IR	Ice on Runway	LTG	Lightning			
ISA	International standard atmosphere	LTGCC	Lightning Cloud-to-Cloud	MOGR	Moderate or Greater	
ISOL	Isolate	LTGCCCG	Lightning Cloud-to-Cloud Cloud-to-Ground	MON	Monday	
ISOLD	Isolated			MON	Above mountains	
		LTGCG	Lightning Cloud-to-Ground	MONTR	Monitor	
JAN	January	LTGCW	Lightning Cloud-to-Water	MOPS	Minimum operational performance standards	
JCTN	Junction	LTGIC	Lightning in Cloud			
JTST	Jet Stream	LTL	Little	MOV	Move	
JTSTR	Jet Stream	LTLCG	Little Change	MOVD	Moved	
JUL	July					
JUN	June					

MOVG	Moving	NO	Not Available (e.g., SLPNO, RVRNO)	OVC	Overcast
MOVMT	Movement	NOAA	National Oceanic and Atmospheric	OVHD	Overhead
MOVS	Moves		Administration	OVNGT	Overnight
MPH	Miles per Hour	NOPAC	Northern Pacific	OVR	Over
MPS	Meters per second	NORPI	No Pilot Balloon Observation Will Be	OVRN	Overrun
MRG	Medium range		Filed Next Collection Unless Weather	OVRNG	Overrunning
MRGL	Marginal		Changes Significantly	OVTK	Overtake
MRGLLY	Marginally	NOSIG	No significant change (used in	OVTKG	Overtaking
MRNG	Morning		trend-type landing forecasts)	OVTKS	Overtakes
MRTM	Maritime	NOV	November		
MS	Minus	NPRS	Nonpersistent	P	Pacific Standard Time (time group
MS	Mississippi	NR	Near		only)
MSG	Message	NRLY	Nearly	P	Polar (air mass)
MSL	Mean Sea Level	NRN	Northern	P	In RVR Field, Indicates Visibility
MST	Most	NRW	Narrow		Greater Than Highest Reportable
MSTLY	Mostly	NS	Nimbostratus		Sensor Value (e.g., P600FT)
MSTR	Moisture	NS	Nova Scotia	P6SM	Visibility Greater Than 6 Statute Miles
MT	Montana	NSC	No significant cloud		(TAF only)
MTN	Mountain	NSCSWD	No Small Craft or Storm Warning	PA	Pennsylvania
MTNS	Mountains		Being Displayed	PAC	Pacific
MTW	Mountain waves	NSW	No Significant Weather (TAF)	PATWAS	Pacific
MULT	Multiple	NTFY	Notify	PBL	Probable or Planetary Boundary
MULTILVL	Multilevel	NTFYD	Notified		Layer
MVFR	Marginal VFR	NTL	National	PCPN	Precipitation
MWO	Meteorological Watch Office	NV	Nevada	PD	Period
MX	Mixed type of ice formation	NVA	Negative Vorticity Advection	PDMT	Predominant
	(white and clear)	NW	Northwest	PDW	Priority Delayed Weather
MXD	Mixed	NWB	Northwest bound	PEN	Peninsula
		NWD	Northward	PERM	Permanent
N	North or northern latitude	NWLY	Northwesterly	PGTSND	Puget Sound
N	No district tendency (in RVR during	NWRN	Northwestern	PHYS	Physical
	previous 10 minutes)	NWS	National Weather Service	PIBAL	Pilot Balloon Observation
NAB	Not Above	NY	New York	PIREP	Pilot Weather Report
NAM	North American Mesoscale (model)	NXT	Next	PISE	No Pilot Balloon Observation Due to
NAT	North Atlantic				Unfavorable Sea Conditions
NATL	National	OAT	Outside Air Temperature	PISO	No Pilot Balloon Observation Due to
NAV	Navigation	OBND	Outbound		Snow
NB	New Brunswick	OBS	Observation or observe	PIWI	No Pilot Balloon Observation Due to
NB	Northbound	OBSC	Obscure or obscured or obscuring		High, or Gusty, Surface Wind
NBFR	Not before	OCFNT	Occluded Front	PL	Ice Pellets
NBND	Northbound	OCLD	Occlude	PLNS	Plains
NBRHD	Neighborhood	OCLDD	Occluded	PLS	Please
NC	North Carolina	OCLDG	Occluding	PLTO	Plateau
NC	No change	OCLDS	Occludes	PLVL	Present level
NCEP	National Centers for Environmental	OCLN	Occlusion	PLW	Plow (snow)
	Prediction	OCNL	Occasional or occasionally	PM	Postmeridian
NCO	NCEP Central Operations	OCR	Occur	PNHDL	Panhandle
NCWX	No Change in Weather	OCRD	Occurred	PO	Dust/Sand Whirls (METAR)
ND	North Dakota	OCRG	Occurring	POS	Positive
NE	Northeast	OCRS	Occurs	POSLY	Positively
NE	Nebraska	OCT	October	POSS	Possible
NEB	Northeast bound	OFC	Office	PPI	Plan position indicator
NEC	Necessary	OFP	Occluded Frontal Passage	PPINA	Radar Weather Report Not Available
NEG	Negative or No	OFSHR	Offshore	PPINE	Radar Weather Report No Echoes
NEGLY	Negatively	OH	Ohio		Observed
NELY	Northeasterly	OHD	Overhead	PPINO	Radar Weather Report Equipment
NERN	Northeastern	OK	Oklahoma or we agree or it is correct		Inoperative Due to Breakdown
NEW ENG	New England	OMTNS	Over Mountains	PPIOK	Radar Weather Report Equipment
NEWD	Northeastward	ONSHR	On Shore		Operation Resumed
NFLD	Newfoundland	ONT	Ontario	PPIOM	Radar Weather Report Equipment
NGM	Nested Grid Model	OPA	Opaque, white type of ice formation		Inoperative Due to Maintenance
NGT	Night	OPC	Ocean Prediction Center	PPSN	Present Position
NH	New Hampshire	OPN	Open or opening or opened	PR	Partial (METAR)
NHC	National Hurricane Center	OPR	Operator or operate or operative	PRBL	Probable
NIL	None		or operating or operational	PRBLTY	Probability
NJ	New Jersey	OR	Oregon	PRBLY	Probably
NL	No Layers	ORGPHC	Orographic	PRECD	Precede
NLT	Not Later Than	ORIG	Original	PRECDD	Preceded
NLY	Northerly	OSV	Ocean Station Vessel	PRECDG	Preceding
NM	New Mexico	OTAS	On Top and Smooth	PRECDS	Precedes
NM	Nautical miles	OTLK	Outlook	PRES	Pressure
NMBR	Number	OTP	On Top	PRESFR	Pressure Falling Rapidly
NMBRS	Numbers	OTR	Other	PRESRR	Pressure Rising Rapidly
NML	Normal	OTRW	Otherwise	PRFG	Aerodrome partially covered by fog
NMRS	Numerous	OUBD	Outbound	PRI	Primary
NNE	North-Northeast	OUTFLO	Outflow	PRIM	Primary
NNELY	North-Northeasterly			PRIN	Principal
NNERN	North-Northeastern			PRIND	Present Indications Are
NNEWD	North-Northeastward			PRJMP	Pressure Jump
NNNN	End of Message				
NNW	North-Northwest				
NNWLY	North-Northwesterly				
NNWRN	North-Northwestern				
NNWWD	North-Northwestward				
NNNN	End of message				

PROB30	Probability 30 Percent (TAF)	RCD	Radar Cloud Detection Report	RPRT	Report
PROB40	Probability 40 Percent (TAF)	RCDNA	Radar Cloud Detection Report Not Available	RPRTD	Reported
PROB	Probability			RPRTG	Reporting
PROC	Procedure	RCDNE	Radar Cloud Detection Report No Echoes Observed	RPRTS	Reports
PROD	Produce			RPT	Repeat
PRODG	Producing	RCDNO	Radar Cloud Detection Inoperative Due to Breakdown Until	RPTG	Repeating
PROG	Prognosis or Prognostic or Forecast			RPTS	Repeats
PROGD	Forecasted	RCDOM	Radar Cloud Detection Inoperative Due to Maintenance Until	RQMNTS	Requirements
PROGS	Forecasts			RQR	Require
PRSNT	Present	RCH	Reach	RQRD	Required
PRSNTLY	Presently	RCHD	Reached	RQRG	Requiring
PRST	Persist	RCHG	Reaching	RQRS	Requires
PRSTNC	Persistence	RCHS	Reaches	RRA	(or RRB, RRC...etc., in sequence)
PRSTS	Persists	RCKY	Rocky		Delayed meteorological message (message type designator)
PRSTNT	Persistent	RCKYS	Rockies		
PRVD	Provide	RCMD	Recommend	RSG	Rising
PRVDD	Provided	RCMDD	Recommended	RSN	Reason
PRVDG	Providing	RCMDG	Recommending	RSNG	Reasoning
PRVDS	Provides	RCMDS	Recommends	RSNS	Reasons
PS	Plus	RCRD	Record	RSTR	Restrict
PSBL	Possible	RCRDS	Records	RSTRD	Restricted
PSBLTY	Possibility	RCV	Receive	RSTRG	Restricting
PSBLY	Possibly	RCVD	Received	RSTRS	Restricts
PSG	Passage	RCVG	Receiving	RTD	Delayed (used to indicate delayed meteorological message; message type designator)
PSG	Passing	RCVS	Receives		
PSN	Position	RDC	Reduce		
PSND	Positioned	RDG	Ridge	RTE	Route
PSR	Primary surveillance radar	RDGG	Ridging	RTN	Return or returned or returning
PTCHY	Patchy	RDL	Radial	RTRN	Return
PTLY	Partly	RDVLP	Redevelop	RTRND	Returned
PTNL	Potential	RDVLPG	Redeveloping	RTRNG	Returning
PTNLY	Potentially	RDVLPMT	Redevelopment	RTRNS	Returns
PTNS	Portions	RDWND	Radar Dome Wind	RTS	Return to service
PUGET	Puget Sound	RE	Regard	RUC	Rapid Update Cycle (model)
PVA	Positive Vorticity Advection	RE...	Recent (used to qualify weather phenomena, e.g., RERA = recent rain	RUF	Rough
PVL	Prevail			RUFLY	Roughly
PVLD	Prevailed	REC	Receive or receiver	RVR	Runway visual range
PVLG	Prevailing	RECON	Reconnaissance	RVS	Revise
PVLS	Prevails	REF	Reference	RVSD	Revised
PVLT	Prevalent	REP	Report or reporting or reporting point	RVSG	Revising
PWB	Pilot Weather Briefing	REPL	Replace	RVSS	Revises
PWR	Power	REPLD	Replaced	RWY	Runway
PY	Spray (METAR)	REPLG	Replacing	S	South or southern latitude
QFE	Atmospheric pressure at aerodrome elevation	REPLS	Replaces	SA	Sand (METAR)
		REQ	Request	SAB	Satellite Analysis Branch
QN	Question	REQS	Requests	SAP	As soon as possible
QNH	Altimeter sub-scale setting to obtain elevation when on the ground	REQSTD	Requested	SAPRS	Standards and Recommended Practices (ICAO)
		RES	Reserve		
QSTNRY	Quasistationary	RESP	Response	SASK	Saskatchewan
QTR	Quarter	RESTR	Restrict	SAT	Saturday
QUAD	Quadrant	RGD	Ragged	SATFY	Satisfactory
QUE	Quebec	RGL	Regional Model	SB	Southbound
		RGLR	Regular	SBSD	Subside
R	Rain (Radar Weather Report)	RGN	Region	SBSDD	Subsided
R	Runway (used in RVR measurement)	RGNS	Regions	SBSDNC	Subsidence
R	Right (runway identification)	RGT	Right	SBSDS	Subsides
R	Rain (U.S. Weather Radar Reports)	RH	Relative Humidity	SC	South Carolina or Stratocumulus
RA	Rain (METAR)	RI	Rhode Island	SCND	Second
RABA	No RAWIN Obs., No Balloons Available	RIOGD	Rio Grande	SCNDRY	Secondary
		RITE	Right (direction of turn)	SCSL	Stratocumulus Standing Lenticular
RABAL	Radiosonde Balloon Wind Data	RLBL	Reliable	SCT	Scatter
RABAR	Radiosonde Balloon Release	RLTV	Relative	SCTD	Scattered
RACO	No RAWIN Obs., Communications Out	RLTVLY	Relatively	SCTR	Sector
		RMK	Remark	SD/ROB	Radar Weather Report
RADAT	Radiosonde Additional Data	RMN	Remain	SD	South Dakota
RADNO	Report Missing Account Radio Failure	RMND	Remained	SE	Southeast
		RMNDR	Remainder	SEB	Southeast bound
RAFC	Regional area forecast centre	RMNG	Remaining	SEC	Second
RAFI	Radiosonde Observation Not Filed	RMNS	Remains	SECT	Sector
RAFRZ	Radiosonde Observation Freezing Levels	RNFL	Rainfall	SELS	Severe Local Storms
		ROBEPS	Radar Operating Below Prescribed Standard	SELY	Southeasterly
RAG	Ragged			SEP	September
RAHE	No RAWIN Obs., No Gas Available	ROFOR	Route forecast (in aeronautical meteorological code)	SEPN	Separation
RAICG	Radiosonde Observation Icing			SEQ	Sequence
RAOB	Radiosonde Observation	ROT	Rotate	SER	Service or servicing or served
RAVU	Radiosonde Analysis and Verification Unit	ROTD	Rotated	SERN	Southeastern
		ROTG	Rotating	SEV	Severe
RAWE	No RAWIN Obs., Unfavorable Weather	ROTS	Rotates	SEWD	Southeastward
		RPD	Rapid	SFC	Surface
RAWI	No RAWIN Obs., High and Gusty Winds	RPDLY	Rapidly	SFERICS	Atmospherics
		RPLC	Replace	SG	Snow Grains (METAR)
RAWIN	Upper Winds Obs. (by radio methods)	RPLCD	Replaced	SGFNT	Significant
		RPLCG	Replacing	SGFNTLY	Significantly
		RPLCS	Replaces		

SGD	Solar-Geophysical Data	SRNDG	Surrounding	THKNG	Thickening
SH...	Showers (followed by RA = rain,	SRNDS	Surrounds	THKNS	Thickness
	SN = snow, PL = ice pellets,	SRY	Secondary	THKR	Thicker
	GR = hail and/or snow pellets or	SS	Sandstorm (METAR)	THKST	Thickest
	combinations thereof, e.g., SHRASN =	SS	Sunset	THN	Thin
	showers of rain and snow)	SSE	South-Southeast	THNG	Thinning
SHFT	Shift	SSELY	South-Southeasterly	THNR	Thinner
SHFTD	Shifted	SSERN	South-Southeastern	THNST	Thinnest
SHFTG	Shifting	SSEWD	South-Southeastward	THR	Threshold
SHFTS	Shifts	SSW	South-Southwest	THRFTR	Thereafter
SHLD	Shield	SSWLY	South-Southwesterly	THRU	Through
SHLW	Shallow	SSWRN	South-Southwestern	THRUT	Throughout
SHRT	Short	SSWWD	South-Southwestward	THSD	Thousand
SHRTLY	Shortly	ST	Stratus	THTN	Threaten
SHRTWV	Shortwave	STAGN	Stagnation	THTND	Threatened
SHUD	Should	STBL	Stable	THTNG	Threatening
SHWR	Shower	STBLTY	Stability	THTNS	Threatens
SIERNEV	Sierra Nevada	STD	Standard	THU	Thursday
SIG	Signature	STDY	Steady	TKOF	Takeoff
SIGMET	Significant Meteorological	STF	Stratiform	TL...	Till (followed by time by which
	Information	STFR	Stratus Fractus		weather change is forecast to end)
SIGWX	Significant weather	STG	Strong	TMW	Tomorrow
SIMUL	Simultaneous	STGLY	Strongly	TN	Tennessee
SIR	Snow and Ice on Runway	STGR	Stronger	TNDCY	Tendency
SKC	Sky Clear	STGST	Strongest	TNDCYS	Tendencies
SKED	Schedule	STM	Storm	TNGT	Tonight
SLD	Solid	STMS	Storms	TNTV	Tentative
SLGT	Slight	STN	Station	TNTVLY	Tentatively
SLGTLY	Slightly	STNR	Stationary	TO	To...(place)
SLO	Slow	STNRY	Stationary	TOC	Top of climb
SLOLY	Slowly	STS	Status	TOP	Cloud Top
SLOR	Slower	SUB	Substitute	TOPS	Tops
SLP	Slope	SUBTRPCL	Subtropical	TOVC	Top of Overcast
SLP	Sea Level Pressure (e.g., 1013.2	SUF	Sufficient	TPC	Tropical Prediction Center
	reported as 132)	SUFLY	Sufficiently	TPG	Topping
SLPG	Sloping	SUG	Suggest	TR	Track
SLR	Slush on Runway	SUGG	Suggesting	TRBL	Trouble
SLT	Sleet	SUGS	Suggests	TRIB	Tributary
SLW	Slow	SUN	Sunday	TRKG	Tracking
SLY	Southerly	SUP	Supply	TRML	Terminal
SM	Statute Mile(s)	SUPG	Supplying	TRMT	Terminate
SMK	Smoke	SUPR	Superior	TRMTD	Terminated
SML	Small	SUPSD	Supersede	TRMTG	Terminating
SMLR	Smaller	SUPSDG	Superseding	TRMTS	Terminates
SMRY	Summary	SUPSDS	Supersedes	TRNSP	Transport
SMTH	Smooth	SVC	Service message	TRNSPG	Transporting
SMTHR	Smoother	SVG	Serving	TROF	Trough
SMTHST	Smoothest	SVR	Severe	TROFS	Troughs
SMTM	Sometime	SVRL	Several	TROP	Tropopause
SMWHT	Somewhat	SW	Southwest	TRPCD	Tropical Continental Air Mass
SN	Snow (METAR)	SWB	Southwest bound	TRPCL	Tropical
SNBNK	Snowbank	SWD	Southward	TRPLYR	Trapping Layer
SNFLK	Snowflake	SWLG	Swelling	TRRN	Terrain
SNGL	Single	SWLY	Southwesterly	TRSN	Transition
SNOINCR	Snow Increase	SWRN	Southwestern	TS	Thunderstorm
SNOINCRG	Snow Increasing	SWWD	Southwestward	TS...	Thunderstorm (followed by RA = rain,
SNST	Sunset	SX	Stability Index		SN = snow, PL = ice pellets, GR = hail,
SNW	Snow	SXN	Section		GS = small hail and/or snow pellets or
SNWFL	Snowfall	SYNOP	Synoptic		combinations thereof, e.g., TSRASN =
SOP	Standard Operating Procedure	SYNS	Synopsis		thunderstorm with rain and snow)
SP	Station Pressure	SYS	System	TSFR	Transfer
SPC	Storm Prediction Center			TSFRD	Transferred
SPCLY	Especially	T	Temperature	TSFRG	Transferring
SPD	Speed	T	Trace	TSFRS	Transfers
SPECI	Special Report (METAR)	T	Tropical (air mass)	TSHWR	Thundershower (non METAR)
SPECIAL	Special meteorological report	TAF	Aviation Terminal Forecast	TSNT	Transient
	(in abbreviated plain language)	TAIL	Tail wind	TSQLS	Thundersqualls (non METAR)
SPKL	Sprinkle	TB	Turbulence (PIREPs only)	TSTM	Thunderstorm (non METAR)
SPLNS	Southern Plains	TC	Tropical Cyclone	TUE	Tuesday
SPRD	Spread	TCNTL	Transcontinental	TURB	Turbulence
SPRDG	Spreading	TCU	Towering Cumulus	TURBT	Turbulent
SPRDS	Spreads	TDA	Today	TWD	Toward
SPRL	Spiral	TDO	Tornado	TWDS	Towards
SQ	Squall (METAR)	TEMP	Temperature	TWI	Twilight
SQAL	Squall	TEMPO	Temporary Changes Expected	TWR	Aerodrome control tower or aerodrome
SQL	Squall Line		(between 2-digit beginning hour and		control
SR	Sunrise		2-digit ending hour)	TWRG	Towering
SRG	Short range	TEND	Trend forecast	TX	Texas
SRN	Southern	THD	Thunderhead (non METAR)	TYP	Type of aircraft
SRND	Surround	THDR	Thunder (non METAR)	TYPH	Typhoon
SRNDD	Surrounded	THK	Thick		

U	Upward (tendency in RVR during previous 10 minutes)
UA	Pilot Weather Reports
UAG	Upper Atmosphere Geophysics
UDDF	Up and Down Drafts
UFN	Until further notice
UNA	Unable
UNAVBL	Unavailable
UNEC	Unnecessary
UNKN	Unknown
UNL	Unlimited
UNREL	Unreliable
UNRELBL	Unreliable
UNRSTD	Unrestricted
UNSATFY	Unsatisfactory
UNSBL	Unseasonable
UNSTBL	Unstable
UNSTDY	Unsteady
UNSTL	Unsettle
UNSTLD	Unsettled
UNUSBL	Unusable
UP	Unknown Precipitation (automated observations)
UPDFTS	Updrafts
UPR	Upper
UPSLP	Upslope
UPSTRM	Upstream
URG	Urgent
USBL	Usable
UT	Utah
UTC	Coordinated Universal Time
UVV	Upward Vertical Velocity
UWNDS	Upper Winds
V	Varies (wind direction and RVR)
V	Variable (weather reports only)
VA	Virginia
VA	Volcanic Ash (METAR)
VAAC	Volcanic Ash Advisory Center
VAAS	Volcanic Ash Advisory Statement
VAL	Valley
VARN	Variation
VC	Vicinity
VCOT	VFR Conditions on Top
VCTR	Vector
VER	Vertical
VFR	Visual Flight Rules
VFY	Verify
VFYD	Verified
VFYG	Verifying
VFYS	Verifies
VIS	Visibility
VLCTY	Velocity
VLCTYS	Velocities
VLNT	Violent
VLNTLY	Violently
VLY	Valley
VMC	Visual Meteorological Conditions
VOL	Volume
VOLMT	Meteorological information for aircraft in flight
VORT	Vorticity
VR	Veer
VRB	Variable Wind Direction When Speed Is Less Than or Equal to 6 Knots
VRBL	Variable
VRG	Veering
VRISL	Vancouver Island, BC
VRS	Veers
VRT	Vertical motion
VRT MOTN	Vertical Motion
VRY	Very
VSB	Visible
VSBY	Visibility
VSBYDR	Visibility Decreasing Rapidly
VSBYIR	Visibility Increasing Rapidly
VT	Vermont
VV	Vertical Velocity
VV	Vertical Visibility (indefinite ceiling) (METAR)

Abbrev	Meaning
W	Warm (air mass)
W	West or western longitude
WA	AIRMET
WA	Washington
WAA	Warm Air Advection
WAFC	World area forecast centre
WAFS	World Area Forecast System
WB	Westbound
WBND	Westbound
WDC-1	World Data Centers in Western Europe
WDC-2	World Data Centers Throughout Rest of World
WDI	Wind direction indicator
WDLY	Widely
WDSPR	Widespread
WDSPRD	Widespread
WEA	Weather
WED	Wednesday
WEF	With effect from or effective from
WFO	Weather Forecast Office
WFP	Warm front passage
WFSO	Weather Forecast Service Office
WFP	Warm Front Passage
WI	Wisconsin
WI	Within
WIBIS	Will Be Issued
WID	Width
WIE	With immediate effect or effective immediately
WINT	Winter
WINTEM	Forecast upper wind and temperature for aviation
WK	Weak
WKDAY	Weekday
WKEND	Weekend
WKN	Weaken
WKNG	Weakening
WKNS	Weakens
WKR	Weaker
WKST	Weakest
WL	Will
WLY	Westerly
WND	Wind
WNDS	Winds
WNW	West-Northwest
WNWLY	West-Northwesterly
WNWRN	West-Northwestern
WNWWD	West-Northwestward
WO	Without
WPLTO	Western Plateau
WR	Wet Runway
WRM	Warm
WRMFNT	Warm Front
WRMFNTL	Warm Frontal
WRMG	Warming
WRMR	Warmer
WRMST	Warmest
WRN	Western
WRNG	Warning
WRS	Worse
WS	Wind Shear
WS	SIGMET
WSFO	Weather Service Forecast Office
WSHFT	Wind Shift
WSOM	Weather Service Operations Manual
WSPD	Wind speed
WSR	Wet Snow on Runway
WSTCH	Wasatch Range
WSW	West-Southwest
WSWLY	West-Southwesterly
WSWRN	West-Southwestern
WSWWD	West-Southwestward
WTR	Water
WTSPT	Waterspout
WUD	Would
WV	Wave
WV	West Virginia
WVS	Waves
WW	Severe Weather Watch
WWD	Westward
WWW	World wide web
WX	Weather
WXCON	Weather Reconnaissance Flight Pilot Report
WY	Wyoming

Abbrev	Meaning
X	Cross
XCP	Except
XNG	Crossing
XPC	Expect
XPCD	Expected
XPCG	Expecting
XPCS	Expects
XPLOS	Explosive
XS	Atmospherics
XTND	Extend
XTNDD	Extended
XTNDG	Extending
XTRM	Extreme
XTRMLY	Extremely
Y	Yukon Standard Time (time groups only)
YDA	Yesterday
YKN	Yukon
YLSTN	Yellowstone
Z	Coordinated Universal Time (in meteorological messages)
ZI	Zonal Index
ZI	Zone of Interior
ZN	Zone
ZNS	Zones

36.4 STANDARD CONVERSION TABLE

This table can be used as a quick reference for conversion between metric and English units.

Figure 36-11. Standard Conversion Table

36.5 DENSITY ALTITUDE CALCULATION

1. Use the graph below to find density altitude either on the ground or aloft.

    a. Set the aircraft's altimeter to 29.92 in.; it now indicates pressure altitude.
    b. Read the outside air temperature.
    c. Enter the graph at the pressure altitude and move horizontally to the temperature.
    d. Read the density altitude from the sloping lines.

2. **Examples of Density Altitude**

    a. Density altitude in flight. Pressure altitude is 9,500 ft., and the temperature is –8°C. Find 9,500 ft. on the left of the graph and move to –8°C. Density altitude is 9,000 ft., as marked by the dot labeled 1 on Figure 36-12.

    b. Density altitude for takeoff. Pressure altitude is 4,950 ft., and the temperature is 97°F. Enter the graph at 4,950 ft. and move across to 97°F. Density altitude is 8,200 ft. as marked by the dot labeled 2 on Figure 36-12. Note that, in the warm air, density altitude is considerably higher than pressure altitude.

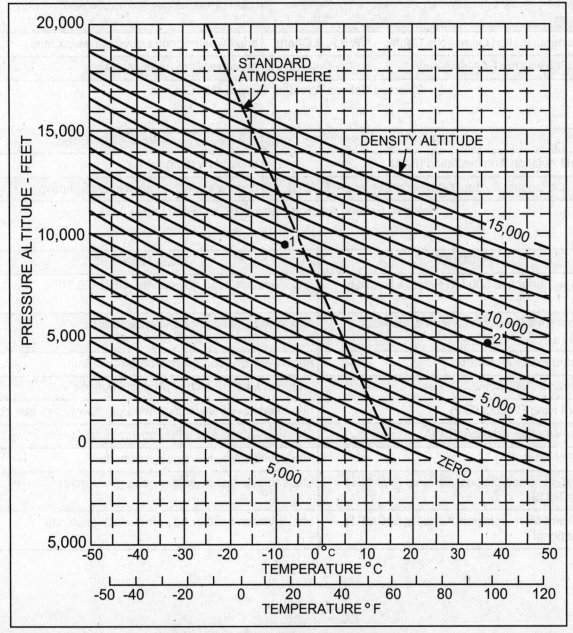

Figure 36-12. Density Altitude Computation Chart

36.6 INTERNET LINKS

SITE	WEB ADDRESS
National Weather Service (NWS)	http://weather.gov/
Aviation Digital Data Service (ADDS)	http://adds.aviationweather.noaa.gov/
Aviation Weather Center (AWC)	http://aviationweather.gov
Hydrometeorological Prediction Center (HPC)	http://www.hpc.ncep.noaa.gov/
Storm Prediction Center (SPC)	http://spc.noaa.gov/
Tropical Predication Center (TPC)	http://www.nhc.noaa.gov/
Alaska Aviation Weather Unit (AAWU)	http://aawu.arh.noaa.gov
Center Weather Service Units (CWSU)	http://aviationweather.gov/products/cwsu/
Weather Forecast Offices (WFO)	http://www.srh.noaa.gov/
Weather Forecast Office (WFO) Honolulu, HI – Aviation Products	http://prh.noaa.gov/hnl/pages/aviation.php
Telecommunication Operations Center – NWS Fax Charts	http://weather.noaa.gov/fax/nwsfax.html
NWS Office at the FAA Academy	http://www.srh.noaa.gov/faa/

Selected National Weather Service (NWS) Links

SITE	WEB ADDRESS
Federal Aviation Administration (FAA)	http://www.faa.gov/
Air Traffic Control System Command Center (ATCSCC)	http://www.fly.faa.gov/flyfaa/usmap.jsp

Selected Federal Aviation Administration (FAA) Links

PRODUCT	WEB ADDRESS
Average Surface to 500 MB Relative Humidity Chart	http://weather.noaa.gov/pub/fax/QRUA00.TIF
Collaborative Convective Weather Forecast (CFP)	http://aviationweather.gov/products/ccfp/
Constant Pressure Charts	http://weather.noaa.gov/fax/barotrop.shtml
Convective Outlooks	http://www.spc.noaa.gov/products/outlook/
Current Icing Product (CIP)	http://adds.aviationweather.noaa.gov/icing/icing_nav.php
Center Weather Advisory (CWA)	http://www.aviationweather.gov/products/cwsu/
Area Forecast (FA)	http://aviationweather.gov/products/fa/
Significant Meteorological Advisory (SIGMET) – US (CONUS)	http://adds.aviationweather.noaa.gov/airmets/
Significant Meteorological Advisory (SIGMET) – International	http://aviationweather.gov/products/sigmets/intl/

Airmen's Meteorological Advisory (AIRMET)	http://adds.aviationweather.noaa.gov/airmets/
Forecast Icing Potential (FIP)	http://adds.aviationweather.noaa.gov/icing/icing_nav.php
Freezing Level Graphics	http://adds.aviationweather.noaa.gov/icing/frzg_nav.php
High Level SIGWX Charts	http://aviationweather.gov/products/swh
Lifted Index (LI) Analysis Chart	http://weather.noaa.gov/pub/fax/QXUA00.TIF
Low Level SIGWX Charts	http://aviationweather.gov/products/swl
Mid Level SIGWX Charts	http://aviationweather.gov/products/swm
Meteorological Impact Statement (MIS)	http://aviationweather.gov/products/cwsu
National Convective Weather Forecast (NCWF)	http://adds.aviationweather.noaa.gov/convection/java/ https://adds.aviationweather.noaa.gov/convection/java/?appletsize=large http://aviationweather.gov/products/ncwf/
Pilot Weather Report	http://adds.aviationweather.noaa.gov/pireps/
Radar Summary Chart	http://weather.noaa.gov/pub/fax/QAUA00.TIF
Aviation Routine Weather Report (METAR) / Selected Special Weather Report (SPECI)	http://adds.aviationweather.noaa.gov/metars/
Surface Analysis Charts	http://www.hpc.ncep.noaa.gov/html/sfc2.shtml http://www.hpc.ncep.noaa.gov/html/avnsfc.shtml http://www.opc.ncep.noaa.gov/ http://www.nhc.noaa.gov/marine_forecasts.shtml http://www.opc.ncep.noaa.gov/UA.shtml
Short Range Surface Prog Chart	http://adds.aviationweather.noaa.gov/progs/
Strike Probabilities of Tropical Cyclone Conditions (SPF)	http://www.nhc.noaa.gov/
Terminal Aerodrome Forecast (TAF)	http://adds.aviationweather.gov/tafs/
Aviation Tropical Cyclone Advisory (TCP)	http://www.nhc.noaa.gov/
Tropical Cyclone Public Advisory (TCP)	http://www.nhc.noaa.gov/
Volcanic Ash Advisory Statement (VAAS)	http://aviationweather.gov/iffdp/volt.shtml
Volcanic Ash Forecast Transport and Dispersion (VAFTAD) Chart	http://aviationweather.gov/iffdp/volc.shtml
Watch Notification Messages	http://www.spc.noaa.gov/products/watch/
Weather Depiction Chart	http://weather.noaa.gov/pub/fax/QGUA00.TIF
Wind and Temperature Aloft Forecast Graphics	http://adds.aviationweather.noaa.gov/winds/
Wind and Temperature Aloft Forecasts (FB) Text	http://aviationweather.gov/products/nws/winds/

Selected Links to Aviation Weather Products

36.7   AWC ADVISORY PLOTTING CHART – CONTIGUOUS U.S.

Figure 36-13.   AWC Advisory Plotting Chart – Contiguous U.S.

NOTE: The content of this subunit does not have an obvious usefulness for pilots. FAA Advisory Circular 00-45F contains this information because it is written to train National Weather Service employees, air traffic controllers, and employees of other aviation fields that require a knowledge of aviation weather services. This material exists in our reorganization of the FAA Advisory Circular to assist the professionals and students in other disciplines of aviation.

STID	NAME	ST	CO	LAT/LON (100's)		LAT/LON (deg min)		
ABI	ABILENE	TX	US	3248	−9986	32	29	−99	52
ABQ	ALBUQUERQUE	NM	US	3504	−10682	35	02	−106	49
ABR	ABERDEEN	SD	US	4542	−9837	45	25	−98	22
ABY	ALBANY	GA	US	3165	−8430	31	39	−84	18
ACK	NANTUCKET	MA	US	4128	−7003	41	17	−70	02
ACT	WACO	TX	US	3166	−9727	31	40	−97	16
ADM	ARDMORE	OK	US	3421	−9717	34	13	−97	10
AEX	ALEXANDRIA	LA	US	3126	−9250	31	16	−92	30
AIR	BELLAIRE	OH	US	4002	−8082	40	01	−80	49
AKO	AKRON	CO	US	4016	−10318	40	10	−103	11
ALB	ALBANY	NY	US	4275	−7380	42	45	−73	48
ALS	ALAMOSA	CO	US	3735	−10582	37	21	−105	49
AMA	AMARILLO	TX	US	3529	−10164	35	17	−101	38
AMG	ALMA	GA	US	3154	−8251	31	32	−82	31
ANW	AINSWORTH	NE	US	4257	−9999	42	34	−99	59
APE	APPLETON	OH	US	4015	−8259	40	09	−82	35
ARG	WALNUT_RIDGE	AR	US	3611	−9095	36	07	−90	57
ASP	OSCODA	MI	US	4445	−8339	44	27	−83	23
ATL	ATLANTA	GA	US	3363	−8444	33	38	−84	26
AUS	AUSTIN	TX	US	3030	−9770	30	18	−97	42
BAE	MILWAUKEE	WI	US	4312	−8828	43	07	−88	17
BAM	BATTLE_MOUNTAIN	NV	US	4057	−11692	40	34	−116	55
BCE	BRYCE_CANYON	UT	US	3769	−11230	37	41	−112	18
BDF	BRADFORD	IL	US	4116	−8959	41	10	−89	35
BDL	WINSOR_LOCKS	CT	US	4194	−7269	41	56	−72	41
BFF	SCOTTSBLUFF	NE	US	4189	−10348	41	53	−103	29
BGR	BANGOR	ME	US	4484	−6887	44	50	−68	52
BIL	BILLINGS	MT	US	4581	−10863	45	49	−108	38
BIS	BISMARK	ND	US	4677	−10067	46	46	−100	40
BJI	BEMIDJI	MN	US	4758	−9502	47	35	−95	01
BKE	BAKER	OR	US	4484	−11781	44	50	−117	49
BKW	BECKLEY	WV	US	3778	−8112	37	47	−81	07
BLI	BELLINGHAM	WA	US	4895	−12258	48	57	−122	35
BNA	NASHVILLE	TN	US	3614	−8668	36	08	−86	41
BOI	BOISE	ID	US	4355	−11619	43	33	−116	11
BOS	BOSTON	MA	US	4236	−7099	42	22	−70	59
BOY	BOYSEN_RESV.	WY	US	4346	−10830	43	28	−108	18
BPI	BIG_PINEY	WY	US	4258	−11011	42	35	−110	07
BRD	BRAINERD	MN	US	4635	−9403	46	21	−94	02
BRO	BROWNSVILLE	TX	US	2592	−9738	25	55	−97	23
BTR	BATON_ROUGE	LA	US	3048	−9130	30	29	−91	18
BTY	BEATTY	NV	US	3680	−11675	36	48	−116	45
BUF	BUFFALO	NY	US	4293	−7865	42	56	−78	39
BUM	BUTLER	MO	US	3827	−9449	38	16	−94	29
BVL	BONNEVILLE	UT	US	4073	−11376	40	44	−113	46
BVT	LAFAYETTE	IN	US	4056	−8707	40	34	−87	04
BWG	BOWLING GREEN	KY	US	3693	−8644	36	56	−86	26
BZA	YUMA	AZ	US	3277	−11460	32	46	−114	36
CAE	COLUMBIA	SC	US	3386	−8105	33	52	−81	03
CDS	CHILDRESS	TX	US	3437	−10028	34	22	−100	17
CEW	CRESTVIEW	FL	US	3083	−8668	30	50	−86	41
CHE	HAYDEN	CO	US	4052	−10731	40	31	−107	19
CHS	CHARLESTON	SC	US	3289	−8004	32	53	−80	02
CIM	CIMARRON	NM	US	3649	−10487	36	29	−104	52
CLE	CLEVELAND	OH	US	4142	−8185	41	25	−81	51
CLT	CHARLOTTE	NC	US	3522	−8093	35	13	−80	56
CON	CONCORD	NH	US	4322	−7158	43	13	−71	35
COU	COLUMBIA	MO	US	3882	−9222	38	49	−92	13
CRG	JACKSONVILLE	FL	US	3034	−8151	30	20	−81	31
CRP	CORPUS_CHRISTI	TX	US	2790	−9745	27	54	−97	27
CSN	CASSANOVA	VA	US	3864	−7787	38	38	−77	52
CTY	CROSS_CITY	FL	US	2960	−8305	29	36	−83	03
CVG	COVINGTON	KY	US	3902	−8470	39	01	−84	42
CYN	COYLE	NJ	US	3982	−7443	39	49	−74	26
CYS	CHEYENNE	WY	US	4121	−10477	41	13	−104	46

CZI	CRAZY_WOMAN	WY	US	4400	−10644	44	00	−106	26
CZG	FRESNO	CA	US	3688	−11982	36	53	−119	49
DBL	EAGLE	CO	US	3944	−10690	39	26	−106	54
DBQ	DUBUQUE	IA	US	4240	−9071	42	24	−90	43
DBS	DUBOIS	ID	US	4409	−11221	44	05	−112	13
DCA	WASHINGTON	DC	US	3886	−7704	38	52	−77	02
DDY	CASPER	WY	US	4309	−10628	43	05	−106	17
DEC	DECATUR	IL	US	3974	−8886	39	44	−88	52
DEN	DENVER	CO	US	3981	−10466	39	49	−104	40
DFW	DALLAS-FT_WORTH	TX	US	3287	−9703	32	52	−97	02
DIK	DICKINSIN	ND	US	4686	−10277	46	52	−102	46
DLF	LAUGHLIN_AFB	TX	US	2936	−10077	29	22	−100	46
DLH	DULUTH	MN	US	4680	−9220	46	48	−92	12
DLL	DELLS	WI	US	4355	−8976	43	33	−89	46
DLN	DILLON	MT	US	4525	−11255	45	15	−112	33
DMN	DEMING	NM	US	3228	−10760	32	17	−107	36
DNJ	MC_CALL	ID	US	4477	−11621	44	46	−116	13
DPR	DUPREE	SD	US	4508	−10172	45	05	−101	43
DRK	PRESCOTT	AZ	US	3470	−11248	34	42	−112	29
DSD	REDMOND	OR	US	4425	−12130	44	15	−121	18
DSM	DES_MOINES	IA	US	4144	−9365	41	26	−93	39
DTA	DELTA	UT	US	3930	−11251	39	18	−112	31
DVC	DOVE_CREEK	CO	US	3781	−10893	37	49	−108	56
DXO	DETROIT	MI	US	4221	−8337	42	13	−83	22
DYR	DYERSBURG	TN	US	3602	−8932	36	01	−89	19
EAU	EAU_CLAIRE	WI	US	4490	−9148	44	54	−91	29
ECG	ELIZABETH_CITY	NC	US	3625	−7618	36	15	−76	11
ECK	PECK	MI	US	4326	−8272	43	16	−82	43
EED	NEEDLES	CA	US	3477	−11447	34	46	−114	28
EHF	BAKERSFIELD	CA	US	3548	−11910	35	29	−119	06
EIC	SHREVEPORT	LA	US	3277	−9381	32	46	−93	49
EKN	ELKINS	WV	US	3892	−8010	38	55	−80	06
ELD	EL_DORADO	AR	US	3326	−9274	33	16	−92	44
ELP	EL_PASO	TX	US	3182	−10628	31	49	−106	17
ELY	ELY	NV	US	3930	−11485	39	18	−114	51
EMI	WESTMINSTER	MD	US	3950	−7698	39	30	−76	59
END	VANCE_AFB	OK	US	3635	−9792	36	21	−97	55
ENE	KENNEBUNK	ME	US	4343	−7061	43	26	−70	37
ENI	UKIAH	CA	US	3905	−12327	39	03	−123	16
EPH	EPHRATA	WA	US	4738	−11942	47	23	−119	25
ERI	ERIE	PA	US	4202	−8030	42	01	−80	18
ETX	EAST_TEXAS	PA	US	4058	−7568	40	35	−75	41
EUG	EUGENE	OR	US	4412	−12322	44	07	−123	13
EWC	ELLWOOD_CITY	PA	US	4083	−8021	40	50	−80	13
EYW	KEY_WEST	FL	US	2459	−8180	24	35	−81	48
FAM	FARMINGTON	MO	US	3767	−9023	37	40	−90	14
FAR	FARGO	ND	US	4675	−9685	46	45	−96	51
FCA	KALISPELL	MT	US	4821	−11418	48	13	−114	11
FLO	FLORENCE	SC	US	3423	−7966	34	14	−79	40
FMG	RENO	NV	US	3953	−11966	39	32	−119	40
FMN	FARMINGTON	NM	US	3675	−10810	36	45	−108	06
FMY	FT_MEYERS	FL	US	2658	−8187	26	35	−81	52
FNT	FLINT	MI	US	4297	−8374	42	58	−83	44
FOD	FT_DODGE	IA	US	4261	−9429	42	37	−94	17
FOT	FORTUNA	CA	US	4067	−12423	40	40	−124	14
FSD	SIOUX_FALLS	SD	US	4365	−9678	43	39	−96	47
FSM	FT_SMITH	AR	US	3538	−9427	35	23	−94	16
FST	FT_STOCKTON	TX	US	3095	−10298	30	57	−102	59
FWA	FT_WAYNE	IN	US	4098	−8519	40	59	−85	11
GAG	GAGE	OK	US	3634	−9988	36	20	−99	53
GCK	GARDEN_CITY	KS	US	3792	−10073	37	55	−100	44
GEG	SPOKANE	WA	US	4756	−11763	47	34	−117	38
GFK	GRAND_FORKS	ND	US	4795	−9719	47	57	−97	11
GGG	LONGVIEW	TX	US	3242	−9475	32	25	−94	45
GGW	GLASGOW	MT	US	4822	−10663	48	13	−106	38
GIJ	NILES	MI	US	4177	−8632	41	46	−86	19

GLD	GOODLAND	KS	US	3939	−10169	39	23	−101	41
GQO	CHATTANOOGA	TN	US	3496	−8515	34	58	−85	09
GRB	GREEN_BAY	WI	US	4456	−8819	44	34	−88	11
GRR	GRAND_RAPIDS	MI	US	4279	−8550	42	47	−85	30
GSO	GREENSBORO	NC	US	3605	−7998	36	03	−79	59
GTF	GREAT_FALLS	MT	US	4745	−11141	47	27	−111	25
HAR	HARRISBURG	PA	US	4023	−7702	40	14	−77	01
HBU	GUNNISON	CO	US	3845	−10704	38	27	−107	02
HEC	HECTOR	CA	US	3480	−11646	34	48	−116	28
HLC	HILL_CITY	KS	US	3926	−10023	39	16	−100	14
HLN	HELENA	MT	US	4661	−11195	46	37	−111	57
HMV	HOLSTON_MOUNTAIN	TN	US	3644	−8213	36	26	−82	08
HNK	HANCOCK	NY	US	4206	−7532	42	04	−75	19
HNN	HENDERSON	WV	US	3875	−8203	38	45	−82	02
HQM	HOQUIAM	WA	US	4695	−12415	46	57	−124	09
HTO	EAST_HAMPTON	NY	US	4092	−7232	40	55	−72	19
HUL	HOULTON	ME	US	4604	−6783	46	02	−67	50
HVE	HANKSVILLE	UT	US	3842	−11070	38	25	−110	42
HVR	HAVRE	MT	US	4854	−10977	48	32	−109	46
IAH	HOUSTON_INTERNATIONAL	TX	US	2996	−9535	29	58	−95	21
ICT	WICHITA	KS	US	3775	−9758	37	45	−97	35
IGB	BIGBEE	MS	US	3348	−8852	33	29	−88	31
ILC	WILSON_CREEK	NV	US	3825	−11439	38	15	−114	23
ILM	WILMINGTON	NC	US	3435	−7787	34	21	−77	52
IND	INDIANAPOLIS	IN	US	3981	−8637	39	49	−86	22
INK	WINK	TX	US	3187	−10324	31	52	−103	14
INL	INTERNATIONAL_FALLS	MN	US	4857	−9340	48	34	−93	24
INW	WINSLOW	AZ	US	3506	−11080	35	04	−110	48
IOW	IOWA_CITY	IA	US	4152	−9161	41	31	−91	37
IRK	KIRKSVILLE	MO	US	4014	−9259	40	08	−92	35
IRQ	COLLIERS	SC	US	3371	−8216	33	43	−82	10
ISN	WILLISTON	ND	US	4818	−10363	48	11	−103	38
JAC	JACKSON	WY	US	4362	−11073	43	37	−110	44
JAN	JACKSON	MS	US	3251	−9017	32	31	−90	10
JCT	JUNCTION	TX	US	3060	−9982	30	36	−99	49
JFK	NEW_YORK/JF_KENNEDY	NY	US	4063	−7377	40	38	−73	46
JHW	JAMESTOWN	NY	US	4219	−7912	42	11	−79	07
JNC	GRAND_JUNCTION	CO	US	3906	−10879	39	04	−108	47
JOT	JOLIET	IL	US	4155	−8832	41	33	−88	19
JST	JOHNSTOWN	PA	US	4032	−7883	40	19	−78	50
LAA	LAMAR	CO	US	3820	−10269	38	12	−102	41
LAR	LARAMIE	WY	US	4133	−10572	41	20	−105	43
LAS	LAS_VEGAS	NV	US	3608	−11516	36	05	−115	10
LAX	LOS_ANGELES_INTL	CA	US	3393	−11843	33	56	−118	26
LBB	LUBBOCK_INTERNATIONAL	TX	US	3370	−10192	33	42	−101	55
LBF	NORTH_PLATTE	NE	US	4113	−10072	41	08	−100	43
LBL	LIBERAL	KS	US	3704	−10097	37	02	−100	58
LCH	LAKE_CHARLES	LA	US	3014	−9311	30	08	−93	07
LEV	GRAND_ISLE	LA	US	2918	−9010	29	11	−90	06
LFK	LUFKIN	TX	US	3116	−9472	31	10	−94	43
LGC	LA_GRANGE	GA	US	3305	−8521	33	03	−85	13
LIT	LITTLE_ROCK	AR	US	3468	−9218	34	41	−92	11
LKT	SALMON	ID	US	4502	−11408	45	01	−114	05
LKV	LAKEVIEW	OR	US	4249	−12051	42	29	−120	31
LOU	LOUISVILLE	KY	US	3810	−8558	38	06	−85	35
LOZ	LONDON	KY	US	3703	−8412	37	02	−84	07
LRD	LAREDO	TX	US	2748	−9942	27	29	−99	25
LVS	LAS_VEGAS	NM	US	3566	−10514	35	40	−105	08
LWT	LEWISTOWN	MT	US	4705	−10961	47	03	−109	37
LYH	LYNCHBURG	VA	US	3725	−7923	37	15	−79	14
MAF	MIDLAND	TX	US	3202	−10218	32	01	−102	11
MBS	SAGINAW	MI	US	4353	−8408	43	32	−84	05
MCB	MC_COMB	MS	US	3130	−9026	31	18	−90	16
MCK	MC_COOK	NE	US	4020	−10059	40	12	−100	35
MCN	MACON	GA	US	3269	−8365	32	41	−83	39
MCW	MASON_CITY	IA	US	4309	−9333	43	05	−93	20

MEI	MERIDIAN	MS	US	3238	−8880	32	23	−88	48
MEM	MEMPHIS	TN	US	3506	−8998	35	04	−89	59
MGM	MONTGOMERY	AL	US	3222	−8632	32	13	−86	19
MIA	MIAMI	FL	US	2580	−8030	25	48	−80	18
MKC	KANSAS_CITY	MO	US	3928	−9459	39	17	−94	35
MKG	MUSKEGON	MI	US	4317	−8604	43	10	−86	02
MLC	MC_CALESTER	OK	US	3485	−9578	34	51	−95	47
MLD	MALAD_CITY	ID	US	4220	−11245	42	12	−112	27
MLP	MULLAN_PASS	ID	US	4746	−11565	47	28	−115	39
MLS	MILES_CITY	MT	US	4638	−10595	46	23	−105	57
MLT	MILLINOCKET	ME	US	4558	−6852	45	35	−68	31
MLU	MONROE	LA	US	3252	−9203	32	31	−92	02
MOD	MODESTO	CA	US	3763	−12096	37	38	−120	58
MOT	MINOT	ND	CA	4826	−10129	48	16	−101	17
MPV	MONTPELIER	VT	US	4422	−7257	44	13	−72	34
MQT	MARQUETTE	MI	US	4653	−8759	46	32	−87	35
MRF	MARFA	TX	US	3030	−10395	30	18	−103	57
MSL	MUSCLE_SHOALS	AL	US	3470	−8748	34	42	−87	29
MSP	MINNEAPOLIS	MN	US	4488	−9323	44	53	−93	14
MSS	MASSENA	NY	US	4491	−7472	44	55	−74	43
MSY	NEW_ORLEANS	LA	US	3000	−9027	30	00	−90	16
MTU	MYTON	UT	US	4015	−11013	40	09	−110	08
MZB	MISSION_BAY	CA	US	3278	−11723	32	47	−117	14
OAK	OAKLAND	CA	US	3773	−12222	37	44	−122	13
OAL	COALDALE	NV	US	3800	−11777	38	00	−117	46
OBH	WOLBACH	NE	US	4138	−9835	41	23	−98	21
OCS	ROCKSPRINGS	WY	US	4159	−10902	41	35	−109	01
ODF	TOCCOA	GA	US	3470	−8330	34	42	−83	18
ODI	NODINE	MN	US	4391	−9147	43	55	−91	28
OED	MEDFORD	OR	US	4248	−12291	42	29	−122	55
OKC	OKLAHOMA_CITY	OK	US	3536	−9761	35	22	−97	37
OMN	ORMOND_BEACH	FL	US	2930	−8111	29	18	−81	07
ONL	ONEILL	NE	US	4247	−9869	42	28	−98	41
ONP	NEWPORT	OR	US	4458	−12406	44	35	−124	04
ORD	O'HARE_INTERNATIONAL	IL	US	4198	−8790	41	59	−87	54
ORF	NORFOLK	VA	US	3689	−7620	36	53	−76	12
ORL	ORLANDO	FL	US	2854	−8134	28	32	−81	20
OSW	OSWEGO	KS	US	3715	−9520	37	09	−95	12
OVR	OMAHA	NE	US	4117	−9574	41	10	−95	44
PBI	WEST_PALM_BEACH	FL	US	2668	−8009	26	41	−80	05
PDT	PENDLETON	OR	US	4570	−11894	45	42	−118	56
PDX	PORTLAND	OR	US	4558	−12260	45	35	−122	36
PGS	PEACH_SPRINGS	AZ	US	3562	−11354	35	37	−113	32
PHX	PHOENIX	AZ	US	3343	−11202	33	26	−112	01
PIE	SAINT_PETERSBURG	FL	US	2791	−8268	27	55	−82	41
PIH	POCATELLO	ID	US	4287	−11265	42	52	−112	39
PIR	PIERRE	SD	US	4440	−10017	44	24	−100	10
PLB	PLATTSBURGH	NY	US	4469	−7352	44	41	−73	31
PMM	PULLMAN	MI	US	4247	−8611	42	28	−86	07
PQI	PRESQUE_ISLE	ME	US	4677	−6809	46	46	−68	05
PSB	PHILLIPSBURG	PA	US	4092	−7799	40	55	−77	59
PSK	DUBLIN	VA	US	3709	−8071	37	05	−80	43
PSX	PALACIOS	TX	US	2876	−9631	28	46	−96	19
PUB	PUEBLO	CO	US	3829	−10443	38	17	−104	26
PVD	PROVIDENCE	RI	US	4172	−7143	41	43	−71	26
PWE	PAWNEE_CITY	NE	US	4020	−9621	40	12	−96	13
PXV	POCKET_CITY	IN	US	3793	−8776	37	56	−87	46
PYE	POINT_REYES	CA	US	3808	−12287	38	05	−122	52
RAP	RAPID_CITY	SD	US	4398	−10301	43	59	−103	01
RBL	RED_BLUFF	CA	US	4010	−12224	40	06	−122	14
RDU	RALEIGH-DURHAM	NC	US	3587	−7878	35	52	−78	47
REO	ROME	OR	US	4259	−11787	42	35	−117	52
RHI	RHINELANDER	WI	US	4563	−8945	45	38	−89	27
RIC	RICHMOND	VA	US	3750	−7732	37	30	−77	19
ROD	ROSEWOOD	OH	US	4029	−8404	40	17	−84	02
ROW	ROSWELL	NM	US	3334	−10462	33	20	−104	37

RWF	REDWWOD-FALLS	MN	US	4447	−9513	44	28	−95	08
RZC	RAZORBACK	AR	US	3625	−9412	36	15	−94	07
RZS	SANTA BARBARA	CA	US	3451	−11977	34	31	−119	46
SAC	SACRAMENTO	CA	US	3844	−12155	38	26	−121	33
SAT	SAN_ANTONIO	TX	US	2964	−9846	29	38	−98	28
SAV	SAVANNAH	GA	US	3216	−8111	32	10	−81	07
SAX	SPARTA	NJ	US	4107	−7454	41	04	−74	32
SBY	SALISBURY	MD	US	3835	−7552	38	21	−75	31
SEA	SEATTLE	WA	US	4744	−12231	47	26	−122	19
SGF	SPRINGFIELD	MO	US	3736	−9333	37	22	−93	20
SHR	SHERIDAN	WY	US	4484	−10706	44	50	−107	04
SIE	SEA_ISLE	NJ	US	3910	−7480	39	06	−74	48
SJI	SEMMNES	AL	US	3073	−8836	30	44	−88	22
SJN	ST JOHNS	AZ	US	3442	−10914	34	25	−109	08
SJT	SAN_ANGELO	TX	US	3138	−10046	31	23	−100	28
SLC	SALT_LAKE_CITY	UT	US	4085	−11198	40	51	−111	59
SLN	SALINA	KS	US	3893	−9762	38	56	−97	37
SLT	SLATE_RUN	PA	US	4151	−7797	41	31	−77	58
SNS	SALINAS	CA	US	3666	−12160	36	40	−121	36
SNY	SIDNEY	NE	US	4110	−10298	41	06	−102	59
SPA	SPARTANBURG	SC	US	3503	−8193	35	02	−81	56
SPS	WICHITA_FALLS	TX	US	3399	−9859	33	59	−98	35
SQS	SIDON	MS	US	3346	−9028	33	28	−90	17
SRQ	SARASOTA	FL	US	2740	−8255	27	24	−82	33
SSM	SAULT_STE_MARIE	MI	US	4641	−8431	46	25	−84	19
SSO	SAN_SIMON	AZ	US	3227	−10926	32	16	−109	16
STL	ST_LOUIS	MO	US	3886	−9048	38	52	−90	29
SYR	SYRACUSE	NY	US	4316	−7620	43	10	−76	12
TBC	TUBA_CITY	AZ	US	3612	−11127	36	07	−111	16
TBE	TOBE	CO	US	3727	−10360	37	16	−103	36
TCC	TUCUMCARI	NM	US	3518	−10360	35	11	−103	36
TCS	TRUTH_OR_CONSEQUENCES	NM	US	3328	−10728	33	17	−107	17
TLH	TALLAHASSEE	FL	US	3056	−8437	30	34	−84	22
TOU	NEAH_BAY	WA	US	4830	−12463	48	18	−124	38
TRM	THERMAL	CA	US	3363	−11616	33	38	−116	10
TTH	TERRE_HAUTE	IN	US	3949	−8725	39	29	−87	15
TUL	TULSA	OK	US	3620	−9579	36	12	−95	47
TUS	TUCSON	AZ	US	3210	−11092	32	06	−110	55
TVC	TRAVERSE_CITY	MI	US	4467	−8555	44	40	−85	33
TWF	TWIN_FALLS	ID	US	4248	−11449	42	29	−114	29
TXK	TEXARKANA	AR	US	3351	−9407	33	31	−94	04
TXO	TEXICO	TX	US	3450	−10284	34	30	−102	50
UIN	QUINCY	IL	US	3985	−9128	39	51	−91	17
VRB	VERO_BEACH	FL	US	2768	−8049	27	41	−80	29
VUZ	VULCAN	AL	US	3367	−8690	33	40	−86	54
VXV	KNOXVILLE	TN	US	3590	−8389	35	54	−83	53
YDC	PRINCETON	BC	CN	4947	−12052	49	28	−120	31
YKM	YAKIMA	WA	US	4657	−12045	46	34	−120	27
YOW	OTTAWA	ON	CN	4532	−7567	45	19	−75	40
YQB	QUEBEC	QB	CN	4680	−7138	46	48	−71	23
YQL	LETHBRIDGE	AB	CN	4963	−11280	49	38	−112	48
YQT	THUNDER_BAY	ON	CN	4837	−8932	48	22	−89	19
YQV	YORKTON	SA	CN	5127	−10247	51	16	−102	28
YSC	SHERBROOKE	QB	CN	4543	−7168	45	26	−71	41
YSJ	ST_JOHN	NB	CN	4532	−6588	45	19	−65	53
YVV	WIARTON	ON	CN	4475	−8110	44	45	−81	06
YWG	WINNIPEG	MB	CN	4990	−9723	49	54	−97	14
YXC	CRANBROOK	BC	CN	4960	−11578	49	36	−115	47
YXH	MEDICINE_HAT	AB	CN	5002	−11072	50	01	−110	43
YYN	SWIFT_CURRENT	SA	CN	5028	−10768	50	17	−107	41
YYZ	TORONTO	ON	CN	4367	−7963	43	40	−79	38

36.8 WSR-88D WEATHER RADAR NETWORK

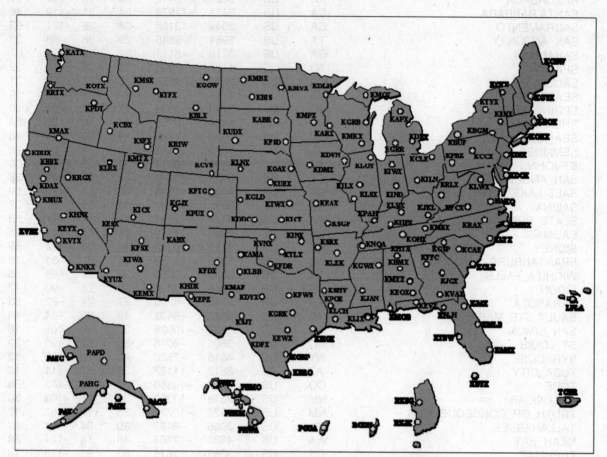

Figure 36-14. WSR-88D Weather Radar Network Sites

Table 36-1. WSR-88D Weather Radar Network

ICAO	NEXRAD SITENAME	CITY	COUNTY	STATE	AGENCY	ELEVATION
KABR	Aberdeen	Aberdeen	Brown	SD	NWS	396.85m (1302.49 ft)
KABX	Albuquerque	Albuquerque	Bernalillo	NM	NWS	1789.18 m (5869.42 ft)
KAKQ	Norfolk	Wakefield	Sussex	VA	NWS	34.14 m (111.55 ft)
KAMA	Amarillo	Amarillo	Potter	TX	NWS	1093.32 m (3585.96 ft)
KAMX	Miami	Miami	Dade	FL	NWS	4.27 m (13.12 ft)
KAPX	Northcentral Lower Michigan	Gaylord	Alpena	MI	NWS	446.23 m (1463.25 ft)
KARX	La Crosse	La Crosse	La Crosse	WI	NWS	388.92 m (1276.25 ft)
KATX	Seattle	Everett	Island	WA	NWS	150.57 m (495.41 ft)
KBBX	Beale AFB	Oroville	Butte	CA	AFWA	52.73 m (173.88 ft)
KBGM	Binghamton	Binghamton	Broome	NY	NWS	489.51 m (1607.61 ft)
KBHX	Eureka (Bunker Hill)	Eureka	Humboldt	CA	NWS	732.13 m (2401.57 ft)
KBIS	Bismarck	Bismarck	Burleigh	ND	NWS	505.36 m (1656.82 ft)
KBLX	Billings	Billings	Yellowstone	MT	NWS	1096.67 m (3599.08 ft)
KBMX	Birmingham	Alabaster	Shelby	AL	NWS	196.6 m (646.33 ft)
KBOX	Boston	Taunton	Bristol	MA	NWS	35.97 m (118.11 ft)
KBRO	Brownsville	Brownsville	Cameron	TX	NWS	7.01 m (22.97 ft)
KBUF	Buffalo	Buffalo	Erie	NY	NWS	211.23 m (692.26 ft)
KBYX	Key West	Boca Chica Key	Monroe	FL	NWS	2.44 m (6.56 ft)
KCAE	Columbia	West Columbia	Lexington	SC	NWS	70.41 m (229.66 ft)
KCBW	Caribou	Houlton	Aroostook	ME	NWS	227.38 m (744.75 ft)
KCBX	Boise	Boise	Ada	ID	NWS	932.99 m (3061.02 ft)

ICAO	NEXRAD SITENAME	CITY	COUNTY	STATE	AGENCY	ELEVATION
KCCX	State College	State College	Centre	PA	NWS	733.04 m (2404.86 ft)
KCLE	Cleveland	Cleveland	Cuyahoga	OH	NWS	232.56 m (764.44 ft)
KCLX	Charleston, SC	Grays	Beaufort	SC	NWS	29.57 m (98.43 ft)
KCRP	Corpus Christi	Corpus Christi	Nueces	TX	NWS	13.72 m (45.93 ft)
KCXX	Burlington	Colchester	Chittenden	VT	NWS	96.62 m (318.24 ft)
KCYS	Cheyenne	Cheyenne	Laramie	WY	NWS	1867.81 m (6128.61 ft)
KDAX	Sacramento	Davis	Yolo	CA	NWS	9.14 m (29.53 ft)
KDDC	Dodge City	Dodge City	Ford	KS	NWS	789.43 m (2588.58 ft)
KDFX	Laughlin AFB	Bracketville	Kinney	TX	AFWA	344.73 m (1131.89 ft)
KDGX	Jackson/Brandon, MS	Brandon	Rankin	MS	NWS	150.92 m (495.41 ft)
KDIX	Philadelphia	Fort Dix	Burlington	NJ	NWS	45.42 m (147.64 ft)
KDLH	Duluth	Duluth	St. Louis	MN	NWS	435.25 m (1427.17 ft)
KDMX	Des Moines	Johnston	Polk	IA	NWS	299.01 m (980.97 ft)
KDOX	Dover AFB	Ellendale State Forest	Sussex	DE	AFWA	15.24 m (49.21 ft)
KDTX	Detroit	White Lake	Oakland	MI	NWS	326.75 m (1072.83 ft)
KDVN	Quad Cities	Davenport	Scott	IA	NWS	229.82 m (754.59 ft)
KDYX	Dyess AFB	Moran	Shackelford	TX	AFWA	462.38 m (1515.75 ft)
KEAX	Pleasant Hill	Pleasant Hill	Cass	MO	NWS	303.28 m (994.09 ft)
KEMX	Tuscon	Tucson	Pima	AZ	NWS	1586.48 m (5203.41 ft)
KENX	Albany	East Berne	Albany	NY	NWS	556.56 m (1827.43 ft)
KEOX	Ft Rucker	Echo	Dale	AL	AFWA	132.28 m (433.07 ft)
KEPZ	El Paso	Santa Teresa	Dona Ana	NM	NWS	1250.9 m (4104.33 ft)

ICAO	NEXRAD SITENAME	CITY	COUNTY	STATE	AGENCY	ELEVATION
KESX	Las Vegas	Las Vegas	Clark	NV	NWS	1483.46 m (4865.49 ft)
KEVX	Eglin AFB	Red Bay	Walton	FL	AFWA	42.67 m (141.08 ft)
KEWX	Austin/San Antonio	New Braunfels	Comal	TX	NWS	192.94 m (633.2 ft)
KEYX	Edwards AFB	Boron	San Bernadino	CA	AFWA	840.33 m (2755.91 ft)
KFCX	Roanoke	Roanoke	Floyd	VA	NWS	874.17 m (2867.45 ft)
KFDR	Altus AFB	Frederick	Tillman	OK	AFWA	386.18 m (1266.4 ft)
KFDX	Cannon AFB	Field	Curry	NM	AFWA	1417.32 m (4648.95 ft)
KFFC	Atlanta	Peachtree City	Fayette	GA	NWS	261.52 m (859.58 ft)
KFSD	Sioux Falls	Sioux Falls	Minnehaha	SD	NWS	435.86 m (1430.45 ft)
KFSX	Flagstaff	Flagstaff	Coconino	AZ	NWS	2260.7 m (7417.98 ft)
KFTG	Denver	Front Range	Arapahoe	CO	NWS	1675.49 m (5495.41 ft)
KFWS	Dallas/Ft Worth	Fort Worth	Tarrant	TX	NWS	208.18 m (682.41 ft)
KGGW	Glasgow	Glasgow	Valley	MT	NWS	693.72 m (2276.9 ft)
KGJX	Grand Junction	Grand Junction	Mesa	CO	NWS	3045.26 m (9990.16 ft)
KGLD	Goodland	Goodland	Sherman	KS	NWS	1112.82 m (3651.57 ft)
KGRB	Green Bay	Green Bay	Brown	WI	NWS	207.87 m (682.41 ft)
KGRK	Ft Hood	Granger	Bell	TX	AFWA	163.98 m (538.06 ft)
KGRR	Grand Rapids	Grand Rapids	Kent	MI	NWS	237.13 m (777.56 ft)
KGSP	Greer	Greer	Spartanburg	SC	NWS	286.51 m (941.6 ft)
KGWX	Columbus AFB	Greenwood Springs	Monroe	MS	AFWA	145.08 m (475.72 ft)
KGYX	Portland, ME	Gray	Cumberland	ME	NWS	124.66 m (410.1 ft)
KHDX	Holloman AFB	Ruidoso	Dona Ana	NM	AFWA	1286.87 m (4222.24 ft)

ICAO	NEXRAD SITENAME	CITY	COUNTY	STATE	AGENCY	ELEVATION
KHGX	Houston	Dickinson	Galveston	TX	NWS	5.49 m (16.4 ft)
KHNX	San Joaquin Valley	Hanford	Kings	CA	NWS	74.07 m (242.78 ft)
KHPX	Ft Campbell	Trenton	Todd	KY	AFWA	175.56 m (577.43 ft)
KHTX	Northeast Alabama	Hytop	Jackson	AL	NWS	537.06 m (1761.81 ft)
KICT	Wichita	Wichita	Sedgwick	KS	NWS	406.91 m (1335.3 ft)
KICX	Cedar City	Cedar City	Iron	UT	NWS	3230.88 m (10600.39 ft)
KILN	Cincinnati	Wilmington	Clinton	OH	NWS	321.87 m (1056.43 ft)
KILX	Lincoln	Lincoln	Logan	IL	NWS	177.39 m (580.71 ft)
KIND	Indianapolis	Indianapolis	Marion	IN	NWS	240.79 m (790.68 ft)
KINX	Tulsa	Inola	Rogers	OK	NWS	203.61 m (669.29 ft)
KIWA	Phoenix	Phoenix	Maricopa	AZ	NWS	412.39 m (1351.71 ft)
KIWX	Northern Indiana	North Webster	Kosciusko	IN	NWS	292.3 m (958.01 ft)
KJAX	Jacksonville	Jacksonville	Duval	FL	NWS	10.06 m (32.81 ft)
KJGX	Robins AFB	Jeffersonville	Twiggs	GA	AFWA	158.8 m (521.65 ft)
KJKL	Jackson, KY	Jackson	Breathitt	KY	NWS	415.75 m (1364.83 ft)
KLBB	Lubbock	Lubbock	Lubbock	TX	NWS	993.34 m (3257.87 ft)
KLCH	Lake Charles	Lake Charles	Calcasieu	LA	NWS	3.96 m (13.12 ft)
KLIX	Slidell	Slidell	St Tammany	LA	NWS	7.32 m (22.97 ft)
KLNX	North Platte	North Platte	Logan	NE	NWS	905.26 m (2969.16 ft)
KLOT	Chicago	Romeoville	Will	IL	NWS	202.08 m (662.73 ft)
KLRX	Elko	Elko	Lander	NV	NWS	2055.57 m (6745.41 ft)
KLSX	St Louis	Weldon Spring	St Charles	MO	NWS	185.32 m (606.96 ft)

ICAO	NEXRAD SITENAME	CITY	COUNTY	STATE	AGENCY	ELEVATION
KLTX	Wilmington	Shallotte	Brunswick	NC	NWS	19.51 m (65.62 ft)
KLVX	Louisville	Fort Knox	Hardin	KY	NWS	219.15 m (718.5 ft)
KLWX	Sterling	Sterling	Loudoun	VA	NWS	82.91 m (272.31 ft)
KLZK	Little Rock	North Little Rock	Pulaski	AR	NWS	173.13 m (567.59 ft)
KMAF	Midland/ Odessa	Midland	Midland	TX	NWS	874.17 m (2867.45 ft)
KMAX	Medford	Medford	Jackson	OR	NWS	2289.96 m (7513.12 ft)
KMBX	Minot AFB	Deering	McHenry	ND	AFWA	455.07 m (1492.78 ft)
KMHX	Morehead City	Newport	Carteret	NC	NWS	9.45 m (29.53 ft)
KMKX	Milwaukee	Dousman	Waukesha	WI	NWS	292 m (958.01 ft)
KMLB	Melbourne	Melbourne	Brevard	FL	NWS	10.67 m (36.09 ft)
KMOB	Mobile	Mobile	Mobile	AL	NWS	63.4 m (206.69 ft)
KMPX	Minneapolis	Chanhassen	Carver	MN	NWS	288.34 m (944.88 ft)
KMQT	Marquette	Negaunee	Marquette	MI	NWS	430.07 m (1410.76 ft)
KMRX	Knoxville	Morristown	Hamblen	TN	NWS	407.52 m (1338.58 ft)
KMSX	Missoula	Missoula	Missoula	MT	NWS	2394.2 m (7854.33 ft)
KMTX	Salt Lake City	Salt Lake City	Salt Lake	UT	NWS	1969.01 m (6459.97 ft)
KMUX	San Francisco	Los Gatos	Santa Clara	CA	NWS	1057.35 m (3467.85 ft)
KMVX	Fargo/Grand Forks	Grand Forks	Traill	ND	NWS	300.53 m (987.53 ft)
KMXX	Maxwell AFB	Carrville	Tallapoosa	AL	AFWA	121.92 m (400.26 ft)
KNKX	San Diego	San Diego	San Diego	CA	NWS	291.08 m (954.72 ft)
KNQA	Memphis	Millington	Shelby	TN	NWS	85.95 m (282.15 ft)
KOAX	Omaha	Valley	Douglas	NE	NWS	349.91 m (1148.29 ft)

ICAO	NEXRAD SITENAME	CITY	COUNTY	STATE	AGENCY	ELEVATION
KOHX	Nashville	Old Hickory	Wilson	TN	NWS	176.48 m (577.43 ft)
KOKX	Brookhaven	Upton	Suffolk	NY	NWS	25.91 m (85.3 ft)
KOTX	Spokane	Spokane	Spokane	WA	NWS	726.64 m (2385.17 ft)
KPAH	Paducah	Paducah	McCracken	KY	NWS	119.48 m (390.42 ft)
KPBZ	Pittsburgh	Coraopolis	Allegheny	PA	NWS	361.19 m (1184.38 ft)
KPDT	Pendleton	Pendleton	Umatilla	OR	NWS	461.77 m (1515.75 ft)
KPOE	Ft Polk	Ft Polk	Vernon	LA	AFWA	124.36 m (406.82 ft)
KPUX	Pueblo	Pueblo	Pueblo	CO	NWS	1599.9 m (5249.34 ft)
KRAX	Raleigh/ Durham	Clayton	Wake	NC	NWS	106.07 m (347.77 ft)
KRGX	Reno	Nixon	Washoe	NV	NWS	2529.54 m (8300.52 ft)
KRIW	Riverton/ Lander	Riverton	Fremont	WY	NWS	1697.13 m (5567.59 ft)
KRLX	Charleston, WV	Charleston	Kanawha	WV	NWS	329.18 m (1079.4 ft)
KRTX	Portland, OR	Portland	Washington	OR	NWS	479.15 m (1571.52 ft)
KSFX	Pocatello	Springfield	Bingham	ID	NWS	1363.68 m (4475.07 ft)
KSGF	Springfield	Springfield	Greene	MO	NWS	389.53 m (1279.53 ft)
KSHV	Shreveport	Shreveport	Caddo	LA	NWS	83.21 m (272.31 ft)
KSJT	San Angelo	San Angelo	Tom Green	TX	NWS	576.07 m (1889.76 ft)
KSOX	Santa Ana Mountains	Santa Ana Mountains	Orange	CA	NWS	927 m (3041.34 ft)
KSRX	Western Arkansas	Chaffee Ridge	Sebastian	AR	NWS	195.07 m (639.76 ft)
KTBW	Tampa	Ruskin	Hillsborough	FL	NWS	12.5 m (39.37 ft)
KTFX	Great Falls	Great Falls	Cascade	MT	NWS	1132.03 m (3713.91 ft)
KTLH	Tallahassee	Tallahassee	Leon	FL	NWS	19.2 m (62.34 ft)

ICAO	NEXRAD SITENAME	CITY	COUNTY	STATE	AGENCY	ELEVATION
KTLX	Norman	Midwest City	Oklahoma	OK	NWS	369.72 m (1213.91 ft)
KTWX	Topeka	Topeka	Wabaunsee	KS	NWS	416.66 m (1368.11 ft)
KTYX	Ft Drum	Montague	Lewis	NY	AFWA	562.66 m (1847.11 ft)
KUDX	Rapid City	New Underwood	Pennington	SD	NWS	919.28 m (3015.09 ft)
KUEX	Grand Island	Blue Hill	Webster	NE	NWS	602.28 m (1975.07 ft)
KVAX	Moody AFB	South Stockton	Lanier	GA	AFWA	54.25 m (177.17 ft)
KVBX	Vandenberg AFB	Orcutt	Santa Barbara	CA	AFWA	372.77 m (1223.75 ft)
KVNX	Vance AFB	Cherokee	Alfalfa	OK	AFWA	368.81 m (1210.63 ft)
KVTX	Los Angeles	Los Angeles	Ventura	CA	NWS	830.88 m (2726.38 ft)
KVWX	Evansville, IN (Non- NEXRAD)	Owensville	Gibson	IN	NWS	155.75 m (511.81 ft)
KYUX	Yuma	Yuma	Pima	AZ	NWS	53.04 m (173.88 ft)
LPLA	Lajes AB	Santa Barbara	N/A	AZO RES	AFWA	1016.2 m (3333.33 ft)
PABC	Bethel FAA	Bethel	N/A	AK	FAA	49.07 m (160.76 ft)
PACG	Sitka FAA	Biorka Island	N/A	AK	FAA	63.09 m (206.69 ft)
PAEC	Nome FAA	Nome	N/A	AK	FAA	17.68 m (59.06 ft)
PAHG	Anchorage FAA	Kenai	N/A	AK	FAA	73.76 m (242.78 ft)
PAIH	Middleton Island	Middleton Island	N/A	AK	FAA	20.42 m (65.62 ft)
PAKC	King Salmon FAA	King Salmon	N/A	AK	FAA	19.2 m (62.34 ft)
PAPD	Fairbanks FAA	Fairbanks	N/A	AK	FAA	790.35 m (2591.86 ft)
PGUA	Andersen AFB	Andersen AFB	N/A	GUAM	AFWA	80.47 m (262.47 ft)
PHKI	South Kauai FAA	South Kauai	Kauai	HI	FAA	54.56 m (180.45 ft)
PHKM	Kamuela/ Kohala Apt	Kamuela	Hawaii	HI	FAA	1161.9 m (3812.34 ft)

ICAO	NEXRAD SITENAME	CITY	COUNTY	STATE	AGENCY	ELEVATION
PHMO	Molokai FAA	Molokai	Molokai	HI	FAA	415.44 m (1361.55 ft)
PHWA	South Shore FAA	Naalehu	Hawaii	HI	FAA	420.62 m (1381.23 ft)
RKJK	Kunsan AB	Kunsan Ab	N/A	KOREA	AFWA	23.77 m (78.74 ft)
RKSG	Camp Humphreys	Camp Humphreys	N/A	KOREA	AFWA	15.85 m (52.49 ft)
RODN	Kadena AB	Kadena Ab	N/A	JAPAN	AFWA	66.45 m (216.54 ft)
TJUA	San Juan FAA	San Juan	N/A	PR	FAA	851.61 m (2795.28 ft)

36.9 AWC GEOGRAPHICAL AREA DESIGNATOR MAP

Figure 36-15. AWC Geographical Area Designator Map

36.10 PRESENT WEATHER SYMBOLS

	0	1	2	3	4	5	6	7	8	9
00	Cloud development not observed or not observable during past hour	Clouds generally dissolving or becoming less developed during past hour	State of sky on the whole unchanged during past hour	Clouds generally forming or developing during past hour	Visibility reduced by smoke	Haze	Widespread dust in suspension in the air, not raised by wind, at time of obo	Dust or sand raised by wind, at time of obo	Well developed dust devil(s) within past hour	Duststorm or sandstorm within sight of station during past hour
10	Light fog	Patches of shallow fog at station not deeper than 6 feet on land	More or less continuous shallow fog at station not deeper than 6 feet on land	Lightning visible, no thunder heard	Precipitation within sight, but not reaching the ground	Precipitation within sight, reaching ground, but distant from station	Precipitation within sight, reaching the ground, near to but not at station	Thunder heard but no precipitation at the station	Squall(s) within sight during past hour	Funnel clouds(s) within sight during past hour
20	Drizzle (not freezing, not showers) during past hour, not at time of obo	Rain (not freezing, not showers) during past hour, not at time of obo	Snow (not falling as showers) during past hour, not at time of obo	Rain and snow (not falling as showers) during past hour, not at time of obo	Freezing drizzle or rain (not showers) during past hour, not at time of obo	Showers of rain during past hour, but not at time of obo	Showers of snow, or of rain and snow during past hour, but not at time of obo	Showers of hail, or of hail and rain during past hour, but not at time of obo	Fog during past hour, but not at time of obo	Thunderstorm (with or without precip) during past hour, but not at time of obo
30	Slight or moderate duststorm or sandstorm, has decreased during past hour	Slight or moderate duststorm or sandstorm, no appreciable change during past hour	Slight or moderate duststorm or sandstorm, has increased during past hour	Severe duststorm or sandstorm, has decreased during past hour	Severe duststorm or sandstorm, no appreciable change during past hour	Severe duststorm or sandstorm, has increased during past hour	Slight or moderate drifting snow, generally low	Heavy drifting snow, generally low	Slight or moderate drifting snow, generally high	Heavy drifting snow, generally high
40	Fog at distance at time of obo but not at station during past hour	Fog in patches	Fog, sky discernible, has become thinner during past hour	Fog, sky not discernible, has become thinner during past hour	Fog, sky discernible, no appreciable change during past hour	Fog, sky not discernible, no appreciable change during past hour	Fog, sky discernible, has begun or become thicker during past hour	Fog, sky not discernible, has begun or become thicker during past hour	Fog, depositing rime, sky discernible	Fog, depositing rime, sky not discernible
50	Intermittent drizzle (not freezing), slight at time of obo	Continuous drizzle (not freezing), slight at time of obo	Intermittent drizzle (not freezing), moderate at time of obo	Continuous drizzle (not freezing), moderate at time of obo	Intermittent drizzle (not freezing), thick at time of obo	Continuous drizzle (not freezing), thick at time of obo	Slight freezing drizzle	Moderate or thick freezing drizzle	Drizzle and rain, slight	Drizzle and rain, moderate or heavy
60	Intermittent rain (not freezing), slight at time of obo	Continuous rain (not freezing), slight at time of obo	Intermittent rain (not freezing), moderate at time of obo	ontinuous rain (not freezing), moderate at time of obo	Intermittent rain (not freezing), heavy at time of obo	Continuous rain (not freezing), heavy at time of obo	Slight freezing rain	Moderate or heavy freezing rain	Rain or drizzle and snow, slight	Rain or drizzle and snow, moderate or heavy
70	Intermittent fall of snowflakes, slight at time of obo	Continuous fall of snowflakes, slight at time of obo	Intermittent fall of snowflakes, moderate at time of obo	Continuous fall of snowflakes, moderate at time of obo	Intermittent fall of snowflakes, heavy at time of obo	Continuous fall of snowflakes, heavy at time of obo	Ice needles (with or without fog)	Granular snow (with or without fog)	Isolated starlike snow crystals (with or without fog)	Ice pellets (sleet, U.S definition)
80	Slight rain shower(s)	Moderate or heavy rain shower(s)	Violent rain shower(s)	Slight shower(s) of rain and snow mixed	Moderate or heavy shower(s) of rain and snow mixed	Slight snow shower(s)	Moderate or heavy snow shower(s)	Slight shower(s) of soft or small hail, with or without rain, and/or snow	Moderate or heavy shower(s) of soft or small hail, with or without rain and/or snow	Slight shower(s) of hail, with or without rain and/or rain snow, not assoc with thunder
90	Moderate or heavy shower(s) of hail and/or rain/snow, not associated with thunder	Slight rain at time of obo; thunderstorm during past hour not at time of obo	Moderate or heavy rain at time of obo; TS during past hour not at time of obo	Slight snow and/or rain/hail at time of obo; TS during past hour not at time of obo	Moderate or heavy snow and/or rain/hail at time of obo; TS past hour not at obo time	Slight or moderate thunderstorm without hail but with rain and/or snow at obo time	Slight or moderate thunderstorm with hail at time of obo	Heavy thunderstorm without hail but with rain and/or snow at time of obo	Thunderstorm combined with duststorm or sandstorm at time of obo	Heavy thunderstorm with hail at time of obo

Figure 36-16. Present Weather Symbols with Text Explanation

Watching of METAR present weather text to symbol in table below is not necessarily endorsed by the National Weather Service or the World Meteorological Organization. Blue numbers in upper-left corner of white boxes indicate the priority for plotting in the event more than one symbol is possible (symbols in grey boxes have no corresponding METAR present weather text). Graphical representation of METARs using this table fond at http://adds.aviationweather.gov

	0	1	2	3	4	5	6	7	8	9
00					FU VA	H2	DU	SA BLSA VCBLSA BLDU VCBLDU BLPY	PO VCPO	VCSS VCDS
10	BR		MIFG	VCTS	VIRGA		VCSH	TS	SQ	FC +FC
20										
30		SS DRSA DS DRDU			+SS +05		BLSN VCBLSN		DRSN	
40	VCFG	BCFG			PRFO	FG				FZFG
50		-DZ	DZ	+DZ	-FZDZ	FZDZ +FZDZ	DZ -RA -DZ RA -DZ -RA			DZ RA +DZ RA DZ +RA +DZ+RA
60			RA			-FZRA	FZRA +FZRA	RA -SN -RA SN -DZ -SN -DZ SN	RA SN DZ SN +RA SN +DZ SN RA +SN DZ +SN +RA+SN +DZ+SN	
70		-SN		SN	+SN	UP	SG	IC	PL PE SHPL SHPE	
80	-SH -SHRA	SH +SH SHRA +SHRA		-SHRA SN -SHSN RA -SHRA -SN -SHSN -RA	SHRA SN SHSN RA +SHRA SN +SHSN RA	-SHSN	SHSN +SHSN	-GS -SHGS	GS SHGS +GS +SHGS	-GR -SHGR
90	GR SDGR +GR +SHGR				TSRA TSSN TSPL	TSGR TSGS	+TSRA +TSSN +TSPL	any TS and any SA or DU	+TSGS -TSGR	

Figure 36-17. Present Weather Symbols with Corresponding METAR/SPECI Present Weather Code

36.11 TURBULENCE AND ICING INTENSITY DEPICTIONS

Turbulence Intensity

Intensity	Aircraft Reaction	Symbol
Light	Loose objects in aircraft remain at rest.	
Moderate	Unsecured objects are dislodged. Occupants feel definite strains against seat belts and shoulder straps.	
Severe	Occupants thrown violently against seat belts. Momentary loss of aircraft control. Unsecured objects tossed about.	
Extreme	Aircraft is tossed violently about, impossible to control. May cause structural damage.	

Figure 36-18. Turbulence Intensity

Icing Intensity

Intensity	Aircraft Reaction	Symbol
Trace	Ice becomes perceptible. Rate of accumulation slightly greater than sublimation. Deicing/anti-icing equipment is not used unless encountered for an extended period of time (over 1 hour).	
Light	The rate of accumulation may create a problem if flight is prolonged in this environment (over 1 hour). Occasional use of deicing/anti-icing equipment removes or prevents accumulation. It does not present a problem if this equipment is used.	
Moderate	The rate of accumulation is such that even short encounters become potentially hazardous, and use of deicing/anti-icing equipment or diversion is necessary.	
Severe	The rate of accumulation is such that deicing/anti-icing equipment fails to reduce or control the hazard. Immediate diversion is necessary.	

Figure 36-19. Icing Intensity

END OF STUDY UNIT

APPENDIX A
FAA GLOSSARY OF WEATHER TERMS

The following glossary of weather terms is taken from AC 00-6A *Aviation Weather*.

A

absolute instability–A state of a layer within the atmosphere in which the vertical distribution of temperature is such that an air parcel, if given an upward or downward push, will move away from its initial level without further outside force being applied.

absolute temperature scale–*See* Kelvin Temperature Scale.

absolute vorticity–*See* vorticity.

adiabatic process–The process by which fixed relationships are maintained during changes in temperature, volume, and pressure in a body of air without heat being added or removed from the body.

advection–The horizontal transport of air or atmospheric properties. In meteorology, sometimes referred to as the horizontal component of *convection*.

advection fog–Fog resulting from the transport of warm, humid air over a cold surface.

air density–The mass density of the air in terms of weight per unit volume.

air mass–In meteorology, an extensive body of air within which the conditions of temperature and moisture in a horizontal plane are essentially uniform.

air mass classification–A system used to identify and to characterize the different *air masses* according to a basic scheme. The system most commonly used classifies air masses primarily according to the thermal properties of their *source regions*: "tropical" (T); "polar" (P); and "Arctic" or "Antarctic" (A). They are further classified according to moisture characteristics as "continental" (c) or "maritime" (m).

air parcel–*See* parcel.

albedo–The ratio of the amount of electromagnetic *radiation* reflected by a body to the amount incident upon it, commonly expressed in percentage; in meteorology, usually used in reference to *insolation* (solar radiation); i.e., the albedo of wet sand is 9, meaning that about 9% of the incident insolation is reflected; albedoes of other surfaces range upward to 80–85 for fresh snow cover; average albedo for the Earth and its atmosphere has been calculated to range from 35 to 43.

altimeter–An instrument which determines the altitude of an object with respect to a fixed level. *See* pressure altimeter.

altimeter setting–The value to which the scale of a *pressure altimeter* is set so as to read true altitude at field elevation.

altimeter setting indicator–A precision *aneroid barometer* calibrated to indicate directly the altimeter setting.

altitude–Height expressed in units of distance above a reference plane, usually above mean seal level or above ground.

  (1) **corrected altitude**–Indicated altitude of an aircraft altimeter corrected for the temperature of the column of air below the aircraft, the correction being based on the estimated departure of existing temperature from standard atmospheric temperature; an approximation of true altitude.

  (2) **density altitude**–The altitude in the standard atmosphere at which the air has the same density as the air at the point in question. An aircraft will have the same performance characteristics as it would have in a standard atmosphere at this altitude.

  (3) **indicated altitude**–The altitude above mean sea level indicated on a *pressure altimeter* set at current local *altimeter setting*.

  (4) **pressure altitude**–The altitude in the standard atmosphere at which the pressure is the same as at the point in question. Since an altimeter operates solely on pressure, this is the uncorrected altitude indicated by an altimeter set at standard sea level pressure of 29.92 inches or 1013 millibars.

  (5) **radar altitude**–The altitude of an aircraft determined by radar-type radio altimeter; thus the actual distance from the nearest terrain or water feature encompassed by the downward directed radar beam. For all practical purposes, it is the "actual" distance above a ground or inland water surface or the true altitude above an ocean surface.

  (6) **true altitude**–The exact distance above mean sea level.

altocumulus–White or gray layers or patches of cloud, often with a waved appearance; cloud elements appear as rounded masses or rolls; composed mostly of liquid water droplets which may be supercooled; may contain ice crystals at subfreezing temperatures.

altocumulus castellanus–A species of middle cloud of which at least a fraction of its upper part presents some vertically developed, cumuliform protuberances (some of which are taller than they are wide, as castles) and which give the cloud a crenelated or turreted appearance; especially evident when seen from the side; elements usually have a common base arranged in lines. This cloud indicates instability and turbulence at the altitudes of occurrence.

anemometer–An instrument for measuring *wind* **speed**.

aneroid barometer–A *barometer* which operates on the principle of having changing atmospheric pressure bend a metallic surface, which, in turn, moves a pointer across a scale graduated in units of pressure.

angel–In radar meteorology, an *echo* caused by physical phenomena not discernible to the eye; they have been observed when abnormally strong temperature and/or moisture *gradients* were known to exist; sometimes attributed to insects or birds flying in the radar beam.

anomalous propagation (sometimes called AP)–In radar meteorology, the greater than normal bending of the radar beam such that *echoes* are received from ground *targets* at distances greater than normal *ground clutter*.

anticyclone–An area of high atmospheric pressure which has a closed circulation that is anticyclonic, i.e., as viewed from above, the circulation is clockwise in the Northern Hemisphere, counterclockwise in the Southern Hemisphere, undefined at the Equator.

anvil cloud–Popular name given to the top portion of a *cumulonimbus* cloud having an anvil-like form.

APOB–A *sounding* made by an aircraft.

Arctic air–An air mass with characteristics developed mostly in winter over Arctic surface of ice and snow. Arctic air extends to great heights, and the surface temperatures are basically, but not always, lower than those of *polar air*.

Arctic front–The surface of discontinuity between very cold (Arctic) air flowing directly from the Arctic region and another less cold and, consequently, less dense air mass.

astronomical twilight–*See* twilight.

atmosphere–The mass of air surrounding the Earth.

atmospheric pressure (also called barometric pressure)–The pressure exerted by the atmosphere as a consequence of gravitational attraction exerted upon the "column" of air lying directly above the point in question.

atmospherics–Disturbing effects produced in radio receiving apparatus by atmospheric electrical phenomena such as an electrical storm. Static.

attenuation–In radar meteorology, any process which reduces power density in radar signals.

(1) **precipitation attenuation**–Reduction of power density because of absorption or reflection of energy by precipitation.

(2) **range attenuation**–Reduction of radar power density because of distance from the antenna. It occurs in the outgoing beam at a rate proportional to $1/range^2$. The return signal is also attenuated at the same rate.

aurora–A luminous, radiant emission over middle and high latitudes confined to the thin air of high altitudes and centered over the Earth's magnetic poles. Called "aurora borealis" (northern lights) or "aurora australis" according to its occurrence in the Northern or Southern Hemisphere, respectively.

B

backing–Shifting of the wind in a counterclockwise direction with respect to either space or time; opposite of *veering*. Commonly used by meteorologists to refer to a cyclonic shift (counterclockwise in the Northern Hemisphere and clockwise in the Southern Hemisphere).

backscatter–Pertaining to radar, the energy reflected or scattered by a *target*; an *echo*.

banner cloud (also called cloud banner)–A banner-like cloud streaming off from a mountain peak.

barograph–A continuous-recording *barometer*.

barometer–An instrument for measuring the pressure of the atmosphere; the two principle types are *mercurial* and *aneroid*.

barometric altimeter–*See* pressure altimeter.

barometric pressure–Same as *atmospheric pressure*.

barometric tendency–The change of barometric pressure within a specified period of time. In aviation weather observations, routinely determined periodically, usually for a 3-hour period.

beam resolution–*See* resolution.

Beaufort scale–A scale of wind speeds.

black blizzard–Same as *duststorm*.

blizzard–A severe weather condition characterized by low temperatures and strong winds bearing a great amount of snow, either falling or picked up from the ground.

blowing dust–A type of *lithometeor* composed of dust particles picked up locally from the surface and blown about in clouds or sheets.

blowing sand–A type of *lithometeor* composed of sand picked up locally from the surface and blown about in clouds or sheets.

blowing snow–A type of *hydrometeor* composed of snow picked up from the surface by the wind and carried to a height of 6 feet or more.

blowing spray–A type of *hydrometeor* composed of water particles picked up by the wind from the surface of a large body of water.

bright band–In radar meteorology, a narrow, intense *echo* on the *range-height indicator* scope resulting from water-covered ice particles of high reflectivity at the melting level.

Buys Ballot's law–If an observer in the Northern Hemisphere stands with his back to the wind, lower pressure is to his left.

C

calm–The absence of wind or of apparent motion of the air.

cap cloud (also called cloud cap)–A standing or stationary cap-like cloud crowning a mountain summit.

ceiling–In meteorology in the U.S., (1) the height above the surface of the base of the lowest layer of clouds or *obscuring phenomena* aloft that hides more than half of the sky, or (2) the *vertical visibility* into an *obscuration*. *See* summation principle.

ceiling balloon–A small balloon used to determine the height of a cloud base or the extent of vertical visibility.

ceiling light–An instrument which projects a vertical light beam onto the base of a cloud or into surface-based obscuring phenomena; used at night in conjunction with a *clinometer* to determine the height of the cloud base or as an aid in estimating the vertical visibility.

ceilometer–A cloud-height measuring system. It projects light on the cloud, detects the reflection by a photoelectric cell, and determines height by triangulation.

Celsius temperature scale (abbreviated C)–A temperature scale with zero degrees as the melting of pure ice and 100 degrees as the boiling point of pure water at standard sea level atmospheric pressure.

Centigrade temperature scale–Same as *Celsius temperature scale*.

chaff–Pertaining to radar, (1) short, fine strips of metallic foil dropped from aircraft, usually by military forces, specifically for the purpose of jamming radar; (2) applied loosely to *echoes* resulting from chaff.

change of state–In meteorology, the transformation of water from one form, i.e., solid (ice), liquid, or gaseous (water vapor), to any other form. There are six possible transformations designated by the five terms following:

(1) **condensation**–The change of water vapor to liquid water.

(2) **evaporation**–The change of liquid water to water vapor.

(3) **freezing**–The change of liquid water to ice.

(4) **melting**–The change of ice to liquid water.

(5) **sublimation**–The change of (a) ice to water vapor or (b) water vapor to ice. *See* latent heat.

Chinook–A warm, dry *foehn* wind blowing down the eastern slopes of the Rocky Mountains over the adjacent plans in the U.S. and Canada.

cirriform–All species and varieties of *cirrus*, *cirrocumulus*, and *cirrostratus* clouds; descriptive of clouds composed mostly or entirely of small ice crystals, usually transparent and white; often producing *halo* phenomena not observed with other clouds forms. Average height ranges upward from 20,000 feet in middle latitudes.

cirrocumulus–A *cirriform* cloud appearing as a thin sheet of small white puffs resembling flakes or patches of cotton without shadows; sometimes confused with *altocumulus*.

cirrostratus–A *cirriform* cloud appearing as a whitish veil, usually fibrous, sometimes smooth; often produces *halo* phenomena; may totally cover the sky.

cirrus–A *cirriform* cloud in the form of thin, white featherlike clouds in patches or narrow bands; have a fibrous and/or silky sheen; large ice crystals often trail downward a considerable vertical distance in fibrous, slanted, or irregularly curved wisps called mares' tails.

civil twilight–*See* twilight.

clear air turbulence (abbreviated CAT)–Turbulence encountered in air where no clouds are present; more popularly applied to high level turbulence associated with *wind shear*.

clear icing (or clear ice)–Generally, the formation of a layer or mass of ice which is relatively transparent because of its homogeneous structure and small number and size of air spaces; used commonly as synonymous with *glaze*, particularly with respect to aircraft icing. Compare with *rime icing*. Factors which favor clear icing are large drop size, such as those found in *cumuliform* clouds, rapid accretion of supercooled water, and slow dissipation of *latent heat* of fusion.

climate–The statistical collective of the weather conditions of a point or area during a specified interval of time (usually several decades); may be expressed in a variety of ways.

climatology–The study of *climate*.

clinometer–An instrument used in weather observing for measuring angles of inclination; it is used in conjunction with a *ceiling light* to determine cloud height at night.

cloud bank–Generally, a fairly well-defined mass of cloud observed at a distance; it covers an appreciable portion of the horizon sky, but does not extend overhead.

cloudburst–In popular terminology, any sudden and heavy fall of *rain*, almost always of the *shower* type.

cloud cap–*See* cap cloud.

cloud detection radar–A vertically directed radar to detect cloud bases and tops.

cold front–Any non-occluded *front* which moves in such a way that colder air replaces warmer air.

condensation–*See* change of state.

condensation level–The height at which a rising *parcel* or layer of air would become saturated if lifted adiabatically.

condensation nuclei–Small particles in the air on which water vapor condenses or sublimates.

condensation trail (or contrail) (also called a vapor trail)–A cloud-like streamer frequently observed to form behind aircraft flying in clear, cold, humid air.

conditionally unstable air–Unsaturated air that will become unstable on the condition it becomes saturated. *See* instability.

conduction–The transfer of heat by molecular action through a substance or from one substance in contact with another; transfer is always from warmer to colder temperature.

constant pressure chart–A chart of a constant pressure surface; may contain analyses of height, wind, temperature, humidity, and/or other elements.

continental polar air–*See* polar air.

continental tropical air–*See* tropical air.

contour–In meteorology, (1) a line of equal height on a constant pressure chart; analogous to contours on a relief map; (2) in radar meteorology, a line on a radar scope of equal *echo* intensity.

contouring circuit–On weather radar, a circuit which displays multiple contours of *echo* intensity simultaneously on the *plan position indicator* or *range-height indicator* scope. *See* contour (2).

contrail–Contraction for *condensation trail*.

convection–(1) In general, mass motions within a fluid resulting in transport and mixing of the properties of that fluid. (2) In meteorology, atmospheric motions that are predominantly vertical, resulting in vertical transport and mixing of atmospheric properties; distinguished from *advection*.

convective cloud–*See* cumuliform.

convective condensation level (abbreviated CCL)–The lowest level at which condensation will occur as a result of *convection* due to surface heating. When condensation occurs at this level, the layer between the surface and the CCL will be thoroughly mixed, temperature *lapse rate* will be dry adiabatic, and *mixing ratio* will be constant.

convective instability–The state of an unsaturated layer of air whose *lapse rates* of temperature and moisture are such that when lifted adiabatically until the layer becomes saturated, convection is spontaneous.

convergence–The condition that exists when the distribution of winds within a given area is such that there is a net horizontal inflow of air into the area. In convergence at lower levels, the removal of the resulting excess is accomplished by an upward movement of air; consequently, areas of low-level convergent winds are regions favorable to the occurrence of clouds and precipitation. Compare with *divergence*.

Coriolis force–A deflective force resulting from Earth's rotation; it acts to the right of wind direction in the Northern Hemisphere and to the left in the Southern Hemisphere.

corona–A prismatically colored circle or area of a circle with the sun or moon at its center; coloration is from blue inside to red outside (opposite that of a *halo*); varies in size (much smaller) as opposed to the fixed diameter of the halo; characteristic of clouds composed of water droplets and valuable in differentiating between middle and cirriform clouds.

corposant–*See* St. Elmo's Fire.

corrected altitude (approximation of true altitude)–*See* altitude.

cumuliform–A term descriptive of all convective clouds exhibiting vertical development in contrast to the horizontally extended *stratiform* types.

cumulonimbus–A cumuliform cloud type; it is heavy and dense, with considerable vertical extent in the form of massive towers; often with tops in the shape of an *anvil* or massive plume; under the base of cumulonimbus, which often is very dark, there frequently exists *virga*, precipitation and low ragged clouds (*scud*), either merged with it or not; frequently accompanied by lightning, thunder, and sometimes hail; occasionally produces a tornado or a waterspout; the ultimate manifestation of the growth of a cumulus cloud, occasionally extending well into the stratosphere.

cumulonimbus mamma–A *cumulonimbus* cloud having hanging protuberances, like pouches, festoons, or udders, on the under side of the cloud; usually indicative of severe turbulence.

cumulus–A cloud in the form of individual detached domes or towers which are usually dense and well defined; develops vertically in the form of rising mounds of which the bulging upper part often resembles a cauliflower; the sunlit parts of these clouds are mostly brilliant white; their bases are relatively dark and nearly horizontal.

cumulus fractus–*See* fractus.

cyclogenesis–Any development or strengthening of cyclonic circulation in the atmosphere.

cyclone–(1) An area of low atmospheric pressure which has a closed circulation that is cyclonic, i.e., as viewed from above, the circulation is counterclockwise in the Northern Hemisphere, clockwise in the Southern Hemisphere, undefined at the Equator. Because cyclonic circulation and relatively low atmospheric pressure usually coexist, in common practice the terms cyclone and low are used interchangeably. Also, because cyclones often are accompanied by inclement (sometimes destructive) weather, they are frequently referred to simply as storms. (2) Frequently misused to denote a *tornado*. (3) In the Indian Ocean, a *tropical cyclone* of hurricane or typhoon force.

D

deepening–A decrease in the central pressure of a pressure system; usually applied to a *low* rather than to a *high*, although technically, it is acceptable in either sense.

density–(1) The ratio of the mass of any substance to the volume it occupies–weight per unit volume. (2) The ratio of any quantity to the volume or area it occupies, i.e., population per unit area, *power density*.

density altitude–*See* altitude.

depression–In meteorology, an area of low pressure; a *low* or *trough*. This is usually applied to a certain stage in the development of a *tropical cyclone*, to migratory lows and troughs, and to upper-level lows and troughs that are only weakly developed.

dew–Water condensed onto grass and other objects near the ground, the temperatures of which have fallen below the initial dew point temperature of the surface air, but is still above freezing. Compare with *frost*.

dew point (or dew-point temperature)–The temperature to which a sample of air must be cooled, while the *mixing ratio* and barometric pressure remain constant, in order to attain saturation with respect to water.

discontinuity–A zone with comparatively rapid transition of one or more meteorological elements.

disturbance–In meteorology, applied rather loosely: (1) any low pressure or cyclone, but usually one that is relatively small in size; (2) an area where weather, wind, pressure, etc., show signs of cyclonic development; (3) any deviation in flow or pressure that is associated with a disturbed state of the weather, i.e., cloudiness and precipitation; and (4) any individual circulatory system within the primary circulation of the atmosphere.

diurnal–Daily, especially pertaining to a cycle completed within a 24-hour period, and which recurs every 24 hours.

divergence–The condition that exists when the distribution of winds within a given area is such that there is a net horizontal flow of air outward from the region. In divergence at lower levels, the resulting deficit is compensated for by subsidence of air from aloft; consequently the air is heated and the relative humidity lowered making divergence a warming and drying process. Low-level divergent regions are areas unfavorable to the occurrence of clouds and precipitation. The opposite of *convergence*.

doldrums–The equatorial belt of calm or light and variable winds between the two tradewind belts. Compare *intertropical convergence zone*.

downdraft–A relative small scale downward current of air; often observed on the lee side of large objects restricting the smooth flow of the air or in precipitation areas in or near *cumuliform* clouds.

drifting snow–A type of *hydrometeor* composed of snow particles picked up from the surface, but carried to a height of less than 6 feet.

drizzle–A form of *precipitation*. Very small water drops that appear to float with the air currents while falling in an irregular path (unlike *rain*, which falls in a comparatively straight path, and unlike *fog* droplets which remain suspended in the air).

dropsonde–A *radiosonde* dropped by parachute from an aircraft to obtain *soundings* (measurements) of the atmosphere below.

dry adiabatic lapse rate–The rate of decrease of temperature with height when unsaturated air is lifted adiabatically (due to expansion as it is lifted to lower pressure). *See* adiabatic process.

dry bulb–A name given to an ordinary thermometer used to determine temperature of the air; also used as a contraction for *dry-bulb temperature*. Compare *wet bulb*.

dry-bulb temperature–The temperature of the air.

dust–A type of *lithometeor* composed of small earthen particles suspended in the atmosphere.

dust devil–A small, vigorous *whirlwind*, usually of short duration, rendered visible by dust, sand, and debris picked up from the ground.

duster–Same as *duststorm*.

duststorm (also called duster, black blizzard)–An unusual, frequently severe weather condition characterized by strong winds and dust-filled air over an extensive area.

D-value–Departure of true altitude from pressure altitude (*see* altitude); obtained by algebraically subtracting true altitude from pressure altitude; thus it may be plus or minus. On a constant pressure chart, the difference between actual height and *standard atmospheric* height of a constant pressure surface.

E

echo–In radar, (1) the energy reflected or scattered by a *target*; (2) the radar scope presentation of the return from a target.

eddy–A local irregularity of wind in a larger scale wind flow. Small scale eddies produce turbulent conditions.

estimated ceiling–A ceiling classification applied when the ceiling height has been estimated by the observer or has been determined by some other method; but, because of the specified limits of time, distance, or precipitation conditions, a more descriptive classification cannot be applied.

evaporation–*See* change of state.

extratropical low (sometimes called extratropical cyclone, extratropical storm)–Any *cyclone* that is not a *tropical cyclone*, usually referring to the migratory frontal cyclones of middle and high latitudes.

eye–The roughly circular area of calm or relatively light winds and comparatively fair weather at the center of a well-developed *tropical cyclone*. A *wall cloud* marks the outer boundary of the eye.

F

Fahrenheit temperature scale (abbreviated F)–A temperature scale with 32 degrees as the melting point of pure ice and 212 degrees as the boiling point of pure water at standard sea level atmospheric pressure (29.92 inches or 1013.2 millibars).

Fall wind–A cold wind blowing downslope. Fall wind differs from *foehn* in that the air is initially cold enough to remain relatively cold despite compressional heating during descent.

filling–An increase in the central pressure of a pressure system; opposite of *deepening*; more commonly applied to a low rather than a high.

first gust–The leading edge of the spreading downdraft, *plow wind*, from an approaching thunderstorm.

flow line–A *streamline*.

foehn–A warm, dry downward slope; the warmness and dryness being due to adiabatic compression upon descent; characteristic of mountainous regions. *See* adiabatic process, Chinook, Santa Ana.

fog–A *hydrometeor* consisting of numerous minute water droplets and based at the surface; droplets are small enough to be suspended in the Earth's atmosphere indefinitely. (Unlike *drizzle*, it does not fall to the surface; differs from cloud only in that a cloud is not based at the surface; distinguished from haze by its wetness and gray color.)

fractus–Clouds in the form of irregular shreds, appearing as if torn; have a clearly ragged appearance; applies only to stratus and cumulus, i.e., *cumulus* fractus and *stratus* fractus.

freezing–*See* change of state.

freezing level–A level in the atmosphere at which the temperature is 0°C (32°F).

front–A surface, interface, or transition zone of discontinuity between two adjacent *air masses* of different densities; more simply the boundary between two different air masses. *See* frontal zone.

frontal zone–A *front* or zone with a marked increase of density gradient; used to denote that fronts are not truly a "surface" of discontinuity but rather a "zone" of rapid transition of meteorological elements.

frontogenesis–The initial formation of a *front* or *frontal zone*.

frontolysis–The dissipation of a *front*.

frost (also hoarfrost)–Ice crystal deposits formed by sublimation when temperature and dew point are below freezing.

funnel cloud–A *tornado* cloud or *vortex* cloud extending downward from the parent cloud but not reaching the ground.

G

glaze–A coating of ice, generally clear and smooth, formed by freezing of supercooled water on a surface. *See* clear icing.

gradient–In meteorology, a horizontal decrease in value per unit distance of a parameter in the direction of maximum decrease; most commonly used with pressure, temperature, and moisture.

ground clutter–Pertaining to radar, a cluster of *echoes*, generally at short range, reflected from ground *targets*.

ground fog–In the United States, a *fog* that conceals less than 0.6 of the sky and is not contiguous with the base of clouds.

gust–A sudden brief increase in wind; according to U.S. weather observing practice, gusts are reported when the variation in wind speed between peaks and lulls is at least 10 knots.

H

hail–A form of *precipitation* composed of balls or irregular lumps of ice, always produced by convective clouds which are nearly always *cumulonimbus*.

halo–A prismatically colored or whitish circle or arcs of a circle with the sun or moon at its center; coloration, if not white, is from red inside to blue outside (opposite that of a *corona*); fixed in size with an angular diameter or 22° (common) or 46° (rare); characteristic of clouds composed of ice crystals; valuable in differentiating between *cirriform* and forms of lower clouds.

haze–A type of *lithometeor* composed of fine dust or salt particles dispersed through a portion of the atmosphere; particles are so small they cannot be felt or individually seen with the naked eye (as compared with the larger particles of *dust*), but diminish the visibility; distinguished from *fog* by its bluish or yellowish tinge.

high–An area of high barometric pressure, with its attendant system of winds; an *anticyclone*. Also high pressure system.

hoar frost–*See* frost.

humidity–Water vapor content of the air; may be expressed as *specific humidity*, *relative humidity*, or *mixing ratio*.

hurricane–A *tropical cyclone* in the Western Hemisphere with winds in excess of 65 knots or 120 km/h.

hydrometeor–A general term for particles of liquid water or ice such as rain, fog, frost, etc., formed by modification of water vapor in the atmosphere; also water or ice particles lifted from the earth by the wind such as sea spray or blowing snow.

hygrograph–The record produced by a continuous-recording *hygrometer*.

hygrometer–An instrument for measuring the water vapor content of the air.

I

ice crystals–A type of *precipitation* composed of unbranched crystals in the form of needles, columns, or plates; usually having a very slight downward motion, may fall from a cloudless sky.

ice fog–A type of fog composed of minute suspended particles of ice; occurs at very low temperatures and may cause *halo* phenomena.

ice needles–A form of *ice crystals*.

ice pellets–Small, transparent or translucent, round or irregularly shaped pellets of ice. They may be (1) hard grains that rebound on striking a hard surface or (2) pellets of snow encased in ice.

icing–In general, any deposit of ice forming on an object. *See* clear icing, rime icing, glaze.

indefinite ceiling–A ceiling classification denoting *vertical visibility* into a surface based obscuration.

indicated altitude–*See* altitude.

insolation–Incoming solar *radiation* falling upon the Earth and its atmosphere.

instability–A general term to indicate various states of the atmosphere in which spontaneous *convection* will occur when prescribed criteria are met; indicative of turbulence. *See* absolute instability, conditionally unstable air, convective instability.

intertropical convergence zone–The boundary zone between the trade wind system of the Northern and Southern Hemispheres; it is characterized in maritime climates by showery precipitation with cumulonimbus clouds sometimes extending to great heights.

inversion–An increase in temperature with height–a reversal of the normal decrease with height in the *troposphere*; may also be applied to other meteorological properties.

isobar–A line of equal or constant barometric pressure.

iso echo–In radar circuitry, a circuit that reverses a signal strength above a specified intensity level, thus causing a void on the scope in the most intense portion of an echo when maximum intensity is greater than the specified level.

isoheight–On a weather chart, a line of equal height; same as *contour* (1).

isoline–A line of equal value if a variable quantity, i.e., an isoline of temperature is an *isotherm*, etc. *See* isobar, isotach, etc.

isoshear–A line of equal *wind shear*.

isotach–A line of equal or constant wind speed.

isotherm–A line of equal or constant temperature.

isothermal–Of equal or constant temperature, with respect to either space or time; more commonly, temperature with height; a zero *lapse rate*.

J

jet stream–A quasi-horizontal stream of winds 50 knots or more concentrated within a narrow band embedded in the westerlies in the high *troposphere*.

K

katabatic wind–Any wind blowing downslope. *See* fall wind, foehn.

Kelvin temperature scale (abbreviated K)–A temperature scale with zero degrees equal to the temperature at which all molecular motion ceases, i.e., absolute zero (0°K = –273°C); the Kelvin degree is identical to the Celsius degree; hence at standard sea level pressure, the melting point is 273°K and the boiling point 373°K.

knot–A unit of speed equal to one nautical mile per hour.

L

land breeze–A coastal breeze blowing from land to sea, caused by temperature difference when the sea surface is warmer than the adjacent land. Therefore, it usually blows at night and alternates with a *sea breeze*, which blows in the opposite direction by day.

lapse rate–The rate of decrease of an atmospheric variable with height; commonly refers to decrease of temperature with height.

latent heat–The amount of heat absorbed (converted to kinetic energy) during the processes of change of liquid water to water vapor, ice to water vapor, or ice to liquid water; or the amount released during the reverse processes. Four basic classifications are:

(1) **latent heat of condensation**–Heat released during change of water vapor to water.

(2) **latent heat of fusion**–Heat released during change of water to ice or the amount absorbed in change of ice to water.

(3) **latent heat of sublimation**–Heat released during change of water vapor to ice or the amount absorbed in the change of ice to water vapor.

(4) **latent heat of vaporization**–Heat absorbed in the change of ice to water to water vapor; the negative of latent heat of condensation.

layer–In reference to sky cover, clouds or other obscuring phenomena whose bases are approximately at the same level. The layer may be continuous or composed of detached elements. The term "layer" does not imply that a clear space exists between the layers or that the clouds or *obscuring phenomena* composing them are of the same type.

lee wave–Any stationary wave disturbance caused by a barrier in a fluid flow. In the atmosphere when sufficient moisture is present, this wave will be evidenced by *lenticular clouds* to the lee of mountain barriers; also called *mountain wave* or *standing wave*.

lenticular cloud (or lenticularis)–A species of cloud whose elements have the form of more or less isolated, generally smooth lenses or almonds. These clouds appear most often in formations of orographic origin, the result of *lee waves*, in which case they remain nearly stationary with respect to the terrain (standing cloud), but they also occur in regions without marked orography.

level of free convection (abbreviated LFC)–The level at which a *parcel* of air lifted dry-adiabatically until saturated and moist-adiabatically thereafter would become warmer than its surroundings in a conditionally unstable atmosphere. *See* conditional instability and adiabatic process.

lifting condensation level (abbreviated LCL)–The level at which a *parcel* of unsaturated air lifted dry-adiabatically would become saturated. Compare *level of free convection* and *convective condensation level*.

lightning–Generally, any and all forms of visible electrical discharge produced by a *thunderstorm*.

lithometeor–The general term for dry particles suspended in the atmosphere such as dust, haze, smoke, and sand.

low–An area of low barometric pressure, with its attendant system of winds. Also called a barometric depression or *cyclone*.

M

mammato cumulus–Obsolete. *See* cumulonimbus mamma.

mare's tail–*See* cirrus.

maritime polar air (abbreviated mP)–*See* polar air.

maritime tropical air (abbreviated mT)–*See* tropical air.

maximum wind axis–On a constant pressure chart, a line denoting the axis of maximum wind speeds at that constant pressure surface.

mean sea level–The average height of the surface of the sea for all stages of tide; used as reference for elevations throughout the U.S.

measured ceiling–A ceiling classification applied when the ceiling value has been determined by instruments or the known heights of unobscured portions of objects, other than natural landmarks.

melting–*See* change of state.

mercurial barometer–A *barometer* in which pressure is determined by balancing air pressure against the weight of a column of mercury in an evacuated glass tube.

meteorological visibility–In U.S. observing practice, a main category of *visibility* which includes the subcategories of *prevailing visibility* and *runway visibility*. Meteorological visibility is a measure of horizontal visibility near the Earth's surface, based on sighting of objects in the daytime or unfocused lights of moderate intensity at night. Compare *slant visibility*, *runway visual range*, *vertical visibility*. *See* surface visibility, tower visibility, and sector visibility.

meteorology–The science of *atmosphere*.

microbarograph–An aneroid *barograph* designed to record atmospheric pressure changes of very small magnitudes.

millibar (abbreviated mb.)–An internationally used unit of pressure equal to 1,000 dynes per square centimeter. It is convenient of reporting *atmospheric pressure*.

mist–A popular expression for drizzle or heavy fog.

mixing ratio–The ratio by weight of the amount of water vapor in a volume of air to the amount of dry air; usually expressed as grams per kilogram (g/kg).

moist-adiabatic lapse rate–*See* saturated-adiabatic lapse rate.

moisture–An all-inclusive term denoting water in any or all of its three states.

monsoon–A wind that in summer blows from sea to a continental interior, bringing copious rain, and in winter blows from the interior to the sea, resulting in sustained dry weather.

mountain wave–A *standing wave* or *lee wave* to the lee of a mountain barrier.

N

nautical twilight–*See* twilight.

negative vorticity–*See* vorticity.

nimbostratus–A principal cloud type, gray colored, often dark, the appearance of which is rendered diffuse by more or less continuously falling rain or snow, which in most cases reaches the ground. It is thick enough throughout to blot out the sun.

noctilucent clouds–Clouds of unknown composition which occur at great heights, probably around 75 to 90 kilometers. They resemble thin *cirrus*, but usually with a bluish or silverish color, although sometimes orange to red, standing out against a dark night sky. Rarely observed.

normal–In meteorology, the value of an element averaged for a given location over a period of years and recognized as a standard.

numerical forecasting–*See* numerical weather prediction.

numerical weather prediction–Forecasting by digital computers solving mathematical equations; used extensively in weather services throughout the world.

O

obscuration–Denotes sky hidden by surface-based *obscuring phenomena* and *vertical visibility* restricted overhead.

obscuring phenomena–Any *hydrometeor* or *lithometeor* other than clouds; may be surface based or aloft.

occluded front (commonly called occlusion, also called frontal occlusion)–A composite of two fronts as a *cold front* overtakes a *warm front* or *quasi-stationary front*.

occlusion–Same as *occluded front*.

orographic–Of, pertaining to, or caused by mountains as in orographic clouds, orographic lift, or orographic precipitation.

ozone–An unstable form of oxygen; heaviest concentrations are in the stratosphere; corrosive to some metals; absorbs most ultraviolet solar radiation

P

parcel–A small volume of air, small enough to contain uniform distribution of its meteorological properties, and large enough to remain relatively self-contained and respond to all meteorological processes. No specific dimensions have been defined, however, the order of magnitude of 1 cubic foot has been suggested.

partial obscuration–A designation of sky cover when part of the sky is hidden by surface based *obscuring phenomena*.

pilot balloon–A small free-lift balloon used to determine the speed and direction of winds in the upper air.

pilot balloon observation (commonly called PIBAL)–A method of winds-aloft observation by visually tracking a *pilot balloon*.

plan position indicator (PPI) scope–A radar indicator scope displaying range and azimuth of *targets* in polar coordinates.

plow wind–The spreading downdraft of a *thunderstorm*; a strong, straight-line wind in advance of the storm. *See* first gust.

polar air–An air mass with characteristics developed over high latitudes, especially within the subpolar highs. Continental polar air (cP) has cold surface temperatures, low moisture content, and, especially in its source regions, has great stability in the lower layers. It is shallow in comparison with *Arctic air*. Maritime polar (mP) initially possesses similar properties to those of continental polar air, but in passing over warmer water it becomes unstable with a higher moisture content. Compare *tropical air*.

polar front–The semipermanent, semicontinuous *front* separating air masses of tropical and polar origins.

positive vorticity–*See* vorticity.

power density–In radar meteorology the amount of radiated energy per unit cross sectional area in the radar beam.

precipitation–Any or all forms of water particles, whether liquid or solid, that fall from the atmosphere and reach the surface. It is a major class of *hydrometeor*, distinguished from cloud and *virga* in that it must reach the surface.

precipitation attenuation–*See* attenuation.

pressure–*See* atmospheric pressure.

pressure altimeter–An *aneroid barometer* with a scale graduated in altitude instead of pressure using *standard atmospheric* pressure-height relationships; shows indicated altitude (not necessarily true altitude); may be set to measure altitude (indicated) from any arbitrarily chosen level. *See* altimeter setting, altitude.

pressure altitude–*See* altitude.

pressure gradient–The rate of decrease of pressure per unit distance at a fixed time.

pressure jump–A sudden, significant increase in *station pressure*.

pressure tendency–*See* barometric tendency.

prevailing easterlies–The broad current or pattern of persistent easterly winds in the Tropics and in polar regions.

prevailing visibility–In the U.S., the greatest horizontal visibility which is equaled or exceeded throughout half of the horizon circle; it need not be a continuous half.

prevailing westerlies–The dominant west-to-east motion of the atmosphere, centered over middle latitudes of both hemispheres.

prevailing wind–Direction from which the wind blows most frequently.

prognostic chart (contracted PROG)–A chart of expected or forecast conditions.

pseudo-adiabatic lapse rate–*See* saturated-adiabatic lapse rate.

psychrometer–An instrument consisting of a *wet-bulb* and a *dry-bulb* thermometer for measuring wet-bulb and dry-bulb temperature; used to determine water vapor content of the air.

pulse–Pertaining to radar, a brief burst of electromagnetic radiation emitted by the radar; of very short time duration. *See* pulse length.

pulse length–Pertaining to radar, the dimension of a radar pulse; may be expressed as the time duration or the length in linear units. Linear dimension is equal to time duration multiplied by the speed of propagation (approximately the speed of light).

Q

quasi-stationary front (commonly called stationary front)–A *front* which is stationary or nearly so; conventionally, a front which is moving at a speed of less than 5 knots is generally considered to be quasi-stationary.

R

RADAR (contraction for radio detection and ranging)–An electronic instrument used for the detection and ranging of distant objects of such composition that they scatter or reflect radio energy. Since *hydrometeors* can scatter radio energy, *weather radars*, operating on certain frequency bands, can detect the presence of precipitation, clouds, or both.

radar altitude–*See* altitude.

radar beam–The focused energy radiated by radar similar to a flashlight or searchlight beam.

radar echo–*See* echo.

radarsonde observation–A *rawinsonde observation* in which winds are determined by radar tracking a balloon-borne target.

radiation–The emission of energy by a medium and transferred, either through free space or another medium, in the form of electromagnetic waves.

radiation fog–*Fog* characteristically resulting when radiational cooling of the Earth's surface lowers the air temperature near the ground to or below its initial dew point on calm, clear nights.

radiosonde–A balloon-borne instrument for measuring pressure, temperature, and humidity aloft. Radiosonde observation–a *sounding* made by the instrument.

rain–A form of *precipitation*; drops are larger than *drizzle* and fall in relatively straight, although not necessarily vertical, paths as compared to drizzle which falls in irregular paths.

rain shower–*See* shower.

range attenuation–*See* attenuation.

range-height indicator (RHI) scope–A radar indicator scope displaying a vertical cross section of *targets* along a selected azimuth.

range resolution–*See* resolution.

RAOB–A *radiosonde observation*.

rawin–A *rawinsonde observation*.

rawinsonde observation–A combined winds aloft and radiosonde observation. Winds are determined by tracking the *radiosonde* by radio direction finder or radar.

refraction–In radar, bending of the radar beam by variations in atmospheric density, water vapor content, and temperature.

(1) **normal refraction**–Refraction of the radar beam under normal atmospheric conditions; normal radius of curvature of the beam is about 4 times the radius of curvature of the Earth.

(2) **subrefraction**–Less than normal bending of the radar beam resulting from abnormal vertical gradients of temperature and/or water vapor.

(3) **superrefraction**–More than normal bending of the radar beam resulting from abnormal vertical gradients of temperature and/or water vapor.

relative humidity–The ratio of existing amount of water vapor in the air at a given temperature to the maximum amount that could exist at that temperature; usually expressed in percent.

relative vorticity–*See* vorticity.

remote scope–In radar meteorology a "slave" scope remoted from weather *radar*.

resolution–Pertaining to radar, the ability of radar to show discrete *targets* separately, i.e., the better the resolution, the closer two targets can be to each other, and still be detected as separate targets.

(1) **beam resolution**–The ability of radar to distinguish between targets at approximately the same range but at different azimuths.

(2) **range resolution**–The ability of radar to distinguish between targets on the same azimuth but at different ranges.

ridge (also called ridge line)–In meteorology, an elongated area of relatively high atmospheric pressure; usually associated with and most clearly identified as an area of maximum anticyclonic curvature of the wind flow (*isobars, contours, or streamlines*).

rime icing (or rime ice)–The formation of a white or milky and opaque granular deposit of ice formed by the rapid freezing of supercooled water droplets as they impinge upon an exposed aircraft.

rocketsonde–A type of *radiosonde* launched by a rocket and making its measurements during a parachute descent; capable of obtaining *soundings* to a much greater height than possible by balloon or aircraft.

roll cloud (sometimes improperly called rotor cloud)–A dense and horizontal roll-shaped accessory cloud located on the lower leading edge of a *cumulonimbus* or less often, a rapidly developing *cumulus*; indicative of turbulence.

rotor cloud (sometimes improperly called *roll cloud*)–A turbulent cloud formation found in the lee of some large mountain barriers, the air in the cloud rotates around an axis parallel to the range; indicative of possible violent turbulence.

runway temperature–The temperature of the air just above a runway, ideally at engine and/or wing height, used in the determination of density *altitude*; useful at airports when critical values of density altitude prevail.

runway visibility–The *meteorological visibility* along an identified runway determined from a specified point on the runway; may be determined by a *transmissometer* or by an observer.

runway visible range–An instrumentally derived horizontal distance a pilot should see down the runway from the approach end; based on either the sighting of high intensity runway lights or on the visual contrast of other objects, whichever yields the greatest visual range.

S

St. Elmo's Fire (also called corposant)–A luminous brush discharge of electricity from protruding objects, such as masts and yardarms of ships, aircraft, lightning rods, steeples, etc., occurring in stormy weather.

Santa Ana–A hot, dry, *foehn* wind, generally from the northeast or east, occurring west of the Sierra Nevada Mountains especially in the pass and river valley near Santa Ana, California.

saturated adiabatic lapse rate–The rate of decrease of temperature with height as saturated air is lifted with no gain or loss of heat from outside sources; varies with temperature, being greatest at low temperatures. *See* adiabatic process and dry-adiabatic lapse rate.

saturation–The condition of the atmosphere when actual *water vapor* present is the maximum possible at existing temperature.

scud–Small detached masses of stratus *fractus* clouds below a layer of higher clouds, usually *nimbostratus*.

sea breeze–A coastal breeze blowing from sea to land, caused by the temperature difference when the land surface is warmer than the sea surface. Compare *land breeze*.

sea fog–A type of *advection fog* formed when air that has been lying over a warm surface is transported over a colder water surface.

sea level pressure—The *atmospheric pressure* at *mean sea level*, either directly measured by stations at sea level or empirically determined from the *station pressure* and temperature by stations not at sea level; used as a common reference for analyses of surface pressure patterns.

sea smoke—Same as *steam fog*.

sector visibility—*Meteorological visibility* within a specified sector of the horizon circle.

sensitivity time control—A radar circuit designed to correct for range *attenuation* so that echo intensity on the scope is proportional to reflectivity of the *target* regardless of range.

shear—*See* wind shear.

shower—*Precipitation* from a *cumuliform* cloud; characterized by the suddenness of beginning and ending, by the rapid change of intensity, and usually by rapid change in the appearance of the sky; showery precipitation may be in the form of rain, ice pellets, or snow.

slant visibility—For an airborne observer, the distance at which he can see and distinguish objects on the ground.

sleet—*See* ice pellets.

smog—A mixture of *smoke* and *fog*.

smoke—A restriction to visibility resulting from combustion.

snow—Precipitation composed of white or translucent ice crystals, chiefly in complex branched hexagonal form.

snow flurry—Popular term for snow *shower*, particularly of a very light and brief nature.

snow grains—*Precipitation* of very small, white opaque grains of ice, similar in structure to *snow* crystals. The grains are fairly flat or elongated, with diameters generally less than 0.04 inch (1 mm.).

snow pellets—*Precipitation* consisting of white, opaque approximately round (sometimes conical) ice particles having a snow-like structure, and about 0.08 to 0.2 inch in diameter; crisp and easily crushed, differing in this respect from snow *grains*; rebound from a hard surface and often break up.

snow shower—*See* shower.

solar radiation—The total electromagnetic *radiation* emitted by the sun. *See* insolation.

sounding—In meteorology, an upper-air observation; a *radiosonde* observation.

source region—An extensive area of the Earth's surface characterized by relatively uniform surface conditions where large masses of air remain long enough to take on characteristic temperature and moisture properties imparted by that surface.

specific humidity—The ratio by weight of *water vapor* in a sample of air to the combined weight of water vapor and dry air. Compare *mixing ratio*.

squall—A sudden increase in wind speed by at least 15 knots to a peak of 20 knots or more and lasting for at least one minute. Essential difference between a *gust* and a squall is the duration of the peak speed.

squall line—Any nonfrontal line or narrow bank of active *thunderstorms* (with or without *squalls*).

stability—A state of the atmosphere in which the vertical distribution of temperature is such that a *parcel* will resist displacement from its initial level. (*See also* instability.)

standard atmosphere—A hypothetical atmosphere based on climatological averages comprised of numerous physical constants of which the most important are:

(1) A surface *temperature* of 59°F (15°C) and a surface pressure of 29.92 inches of mercury (1013.2 millibars) at sea level;

(2) A *lapse rate* in the troposphere of 6.5°C per kilometer (approximately 2°C per 1,000 feet);

(3) A *tropopause* of 11 kilometers (approximately 36,000 feet) with a temperature of −56.5°C; and

(4) An *isothermal* lapse rate in the stratosphere to an altitude of 24 kilometers (approximately 80,000 feet).

standing cloud (standing lenticular altocumulus)—*See* lenticular cloud.

standing wave—A wave that remains stationary in a moving fluid. In aviation operations it is used most commonly to refer to a *lee wave* or *mountain wave*.

station pressure—The actual *atmospheric pressure* at the observing station.

stationary front—Same as *quasi-stationary front*.

steam fog—Fog formed when cold air moves over relatively warm water or wet ground.

storm detection radar—A weather radar designed to detect *hydrometeors* of precipitation size; used primarily to detect storms with large drops or hailstones as opposed to clouds and light precipitation of small drop size.

stratiform—Descriptive of clouds of extensive horizontal development, as contrasted to vertically developed *cumuliform* clouds; characteristic of stable air and, therefore, composed of small water droplets.

stratocumulus—A low cloud, predominantly *stratiform* in gray and/or whitish patches or layers, may or may not merge; elements are tessellated, rounded, or roll-shaped with relatively flat tops.

stratosphere—The atmospheric layer above the tropopause, average altitude of base and top, 7 and 22 miles respectively; characterized by a slight average increase of temperature from base to top and is very stable; also characterized by low moisture content and absence of clouds.

stratus—A low, gray cloud layer or sheet with a fairly uniform base; sometimes appears in ragged patches; seldom produces precipitation but may produce *drizzle* or *snow grains*. A *stratiform* cloud.

stratus fractus—*See* fractus.

streamline—In meteorology, a line whose tangent is the wind direction at any point along the line. A flowline.

sublimation—*See* change of state.

subrefraction—*See* refraction.

subsidence—A descending motion of air in the atmosphere over a rather broad area; usually associated with *divergence*.

summation principle—The principle states that the cover assigned to a layer is equal to the summation of the sky cover of the lowest layer plus the additional coverage at all successively higher layers up to and including the layer in question. Thus, no layer can be assigned a sky cover less than a lower layer, and no sky cover can be greater than 1.0 (10/10).

superadiabatic lapse rate—A *lapse rate* greater than the *dry-adiabatic lapse rate*. See *absolute instability*.

supercooled water—Liquid water at temperatures colder than freezing.

superrefraction—*See* refraction.

surface inversion–An *inversion* with its base at the surface, often caused by cooling of the air near the surface as a result of *terrestrial radiation*, especially at night.

surface visibility–Visibility observed from eye-level above the ground.

synoptic chart–A chart, such as the familiar weather map, which depicts the distribution of meteorological conditions over an area at a given time.

T

target–In radar, any of the many types of objects detected by radar.

temperature–In general, the degree of hotness or coldness as measured on some definite temperature scale by means of any of various types of thermometers.

temperature inversion–*See* inversion.

terrestrial radiation–The total infrared *radiation* emitted by the Earth and its atmosphere.

theodolite–An optical instrument which, in meteorology, is used principally to observe the motion of a *pilot balloon*.

thermograph–A continuous-recording *thermometer*.

thunderstorm–In general, a local storm invariably produced by a *cumulonimbus* cloud, and always accompanied by lightning and thunder.

tornado (sometimes called cyclone, twister)–A violently rotating column of air, pendant from a cumulonimbus cloud, and nearly always observable as "funnel-shaped." It is the most destructive of all small-scale atmospheric phenomena.

tower visibility–*Prevailing visibility* determined from the control tower.

towering cumulus–A rapidly growing *cumulus* in which height exceeds width.

trade winds–Prevailing, almost continuous winds blowing with an easterly component from the subtropical high pressure belts toward the *intertropical convergence zone*; northeast in the Northern Hemisphere, southeast in the Southern Hemisphere.

transmissometer–An instrument system which shows the transmissivity of light through the atmosphere. Transmissivity may be translated either automatically or manually into *visibility* and/or *runway visual range*.

tropical air–An air mass with characteristics developed over low latitudes. Maritime tropical air (mT), the principle type, is produced over the tropical and subtropical seas; very warm and humid. Continental tropical (cT) is produced over subtropical arid regions and is hot and very dry. Compare *polar air*.

tropical cyclone–A general term for a *cyclone* that originates over tropical oceans. By international agreement, tropical cyclones have been classified according to their intensity, as follows:

(1) **tropical depression**–winds up to 34 knots (64 km/h);

(2) **tropical storm**–winds of 35 to 64 knots (65 to 119 km/h);

(3) **hurricane or typhoon**–winds of 65 knots or higher (190 km/h).

tropical depression–*See* tropical cyclone.

tropical storm–*See* tropical cyclone.

tropopause–The transition zone between the *troposphere* and *stratosphere*, usually characterized by an abrupt change of *lapse rate*.

troposphere–That portion of the *atmosphere* from the Earth's surface to the *tropopause*; that is, the lowest 10 to 20 kilometers of the atmosphere. The troposphere is characterized by decreasing temperature with height, and by appreciable water vapor.

trough (also called trough line)–In meteorology, an elongated area of relatively low atmospheric pressure; usually associated with and most clearly identified as an area of maximum cyclonic curvature of the wind flow (*isobars*, *contours*, or *streamlines*); compare with *ridge*.

true altitude–*See* altitude.

true wind direction–The direction, with respect to true north, from which the wind is blowing.

turbulence–In meteorology, any irregular or disturbed flow in the atmosphere.

twilight–The intervals of incomplete darkness following sunset and preceding sunrise. The time at which evening twilight ends or morning twilight begins is determined by arbitrary convention, and several kinds of twilight have been defined and used; most commonly civil, nautical, and astronomical twilight.

(1) **Astronomical Twilight**–The period of time before sunrise and after sunset when the sun is not more than 18° below the horizon.

(2) **Civil Twilight**–The period of time before sunrise and after sunset when the sun is not more than 6° below the horizon.

(3) **Nautical Twilight**–The period of time before sunrise and after sunset when the sun is not more than 12° below the horizon.

twister–In the United States, a colloquial term for *tornado*.

typhoon–A *tropical cyclone* in the Eastern Hemisphere with winds in excess of 65 knots (120 km/h).

U

undercast–A cloud *layer* of ten-tenths (1.0) coverage (to the nearest tenth) as viewed from an observation point above the layer.

unlimited ceiling–A clear sky or a sky cover that does not meet the criteria for a *ceiling*.

unstable–*See* instability.

updraft–A localized upward current of air.

upper front–A *front* aloft not extending to the Earth's surface.

upslope fog–Fog formed when air flows upward over rising terrain and is, consequently, adiabatically cooled to or below its initial *dew point*.

V

vapor pressure–In meteorology, the pressure of water vapor in the atmosphere. Vapor pressure is that part of the total atmospheric pressure due to water vapor and is independent of the other atmospheric gases or vapors.

vapor trail–Same as *condensation trail*.

veering–Shifting of the wind in a clockwise direction with respect to either space or time; opposite of *backing*. Commonly used by meteorologists to refer to an anticyclonic shift (clockwise in the Northern Hemisphere and counterclockwise in the Southern Hemisphere).

vertical visibility–The distance one can see upward into a surface based *obscuration*; or the maximum height from which a pilot in flight can recognize the ground through a surface based obscuration.

virga–Water or ice particles falling from a cloud, usually in wisps or streaks, and evaporating before reaching the ground.

visibility–The greatest distance one can see and identify prominent objects.

visual range–*See* runway visual range.

vortex–In meteorology, any rotary flow in the atmosphere.

vorticity–Turning of the atmosphere. Vorticity may be imbedded in the total flow and not readily identified by a flow pattern.

(a) **absolute vorticity**–the rotation of the Earth imparts vorticity to the atmosphere; absolute vorticity is the combined vorticity due to this rotation and vorticity due to circulation relative to the Earth (relative vorticity).

(b) **negative vorticity**–vorticity caused by anticyclonic turning; it is associated with downward motion of the air.

(c) **positive vorticity**–vorticity caused by cyclonic turning; it is associated with upward motion of the air.

(d) **relative vorticity**–vorticity of the air relative to the Earth, disregarding the component of vorticity resulting from Earth's rotation.

W

wake turbulence–*Turbulence* found to the rear of a solid body in motion relative to a fluid. In aviation terminology, the turbulence caused by a moving aircraft.

wall cloud–The well-defined bank of vertically developed clouds having a wall-like appearance which form the outer boundary of the *eye* of a well-developed *tropical cyclone*.

warm front–Any non-occluded *front* which moves in such a way that warmer air replaced colder air.

warm sector–The area covered by warm air at the surface and bounded by the *warm front* and *cold front* of a *wave cyclone*.

water equivalent–The depth of water that would result from the melting of snow or ice.

water vapor–Water in the invisible gaseous form.

waterspout–*See* tornado.

wave cyclone–A *cyclone* which forms and moves along a front. The circulation about the cyclone center tends to produce wavelike deformation of the front.

weather–The state of the *atmosphere*, mainly with respect to its effects on life and human activities; refers to instantaneous conditions or short-term changes as opposed to *climate*.

weather radar–Radar specifically designed for observing weather. *See* cloud detection radar and storm detection radar.

weather vane–A *wind vane*.

wedge–Same as *ridge*.

wet bulb–Contraction of either *wet-bulb temperature* or *wet-bulb thermometer*.

wet-bulb temperature–The lowest *temperature* that can be obtained on a wet-bulb thermometer in any given sample of air, by evaporation of water (or ice) from the muslin wick; used in computing *dew point* and *relative humidity*.

wet-bulb thermometer–A thermometer with a muslin-covered bulb used to measure wet-bulb temperature.

whirlwind–A small, rotating column of air; may be visible as a dust devil.

willy-willy–A *tropical cyclone* of hurricane strength near Australia.

wind–Air in motion relative to the surface of the earth; generally used to denote horizontal movement.

wind direction–The direction from which wind is blowing

wind shear–The rate of change of *wind velocity* (direction and/or speed) per unit distance; conventionally expressed as vertical or horizontal wind shear.

wind speed–Rate of wind movement in distance per unit time.

wind vane–An instrument to indicate wind direction.

wind velocity–A vector term to include both *wind direction* and *wind speed*.

X-Y-Z

zonal wind–A west wind; the westerly component of a wind. Conventionally used to describe large-scale flow that is neither cyclonic nor anticyclonic.

END OF APPENDIX

APPENDIX B
THE WEATHER CHANNEL

THE WEATHER CHANNEL

1. The Weather Channel (TWC) is the only all-weather network on cable television that broadcasts local, regional, national, and international (mostly limited to Europe) weather reports and forecasts 24 hr. a day, 7 days a week.

   a. TWC began broadcasting in May 1982, and today it is available to over 63 million cable subscribers.

2. TWC's diversified programming is designed to meet everyone's weather needs.

3. TWC employs more than 67 staff meteorologists who analyze information from the NWS and other sources to produce local reports and forecasts for the entire nation.

   a. These forecasts are those made by the staff at TWC, not by the NWS.

4. TWC produces over 2,000 computer-generated graphics each day to display current and forecast weather conditions. These graphics help make the presentation more viewer-friendly.

   a. Local radar reports and surface observations are updated hourly, and sometimes more often.

   b. With this information, current surface analysis charts are also reviewed and updated hourly.

5.   Regularly scheduled programs of interest to pilots are shown in the table below.

    a.   TWC also provides a variety of specialty and seasonal programming.

TIME (IN MINUTES PAST THE HOUR)	PROGRAM TITLE	DESCRIPTION
EARLY MORNING 5-1pmET, 2-10amPT		
:00	WeatherScope	A look at the day's national weather
:10/:40 (only at 7:10, 7:40 M-F; 9-10, 9:40 S-S)	Weather coverage	National and regional roundup for the day
:14 (during hours of 5, 6, and 7 o'clock ET)	Aviation Weather	Report of weather information of interest to pilots
:20	5-day Planner	Tells impact of upcoming weather on travelers
:30	WeatherScope	A look at the day's national weather
:42 (except 7:42 M-F & 9:42 S-S)	International Weather	Conditions across Europe
:50	This Morning's Weather	Day's weather with seasonal weather update plus outlook
MID-DAY 1pm-5pmET, 10am-2pmPT		
:00 (all other times)	WeatherScope	Forecast of national weather
:20	5-day Planner	Tells impact of upcoming weather on travelers
:30	WeatherScope	Forecast of national weather
:42	International Weather	Conditions across Europe and at 3:42 pm in Australia
:50	This Afternoon's Weather	Day's weather with seasonal weather update plus outlook
LATE DAY/EVENING 5pm-1amET, 2pm-10pmPT		
:10/:40 (at 9:10, 9:40 only)	Weather coverage	National weather report
:20	5-day Planner	Tells impact of upcoming weather on travel
:42	International Weather	Conditions across Europe
:47	This Evening's Weather	Day's weather with seasonal weather update plus outlook
NIGHT 1am-5amET, 10pm-2amPT		
:00 & :30 (at 1amET/10pmPT only)	Pacific/International	West Coast weather, international cities
:01 (all hours starting & after 2amET/ 11pmPT)	Good Morning Forecast	Weather forecast for day ahead with traveler's update
:12 (all hours after 2amET/11pmPT)	Pacific Regional Forecast	Provides Pacific coastal states with forecast
:20	5-day Planner	Tells impact of upcoming weather on travel
:15 (all hours after 2amET/11pmPT)	Satellite Review	National and regional satellite views with animation
:25 (at 1:25amET/11:25pmPT only)	Alaska/Hawaii Update	Provides Pacific weather with forecast for Alaska and Hawaii
:31 (all hours after 2amET/11pmPT)	Good Morning Forecast	Weather forecast for day ahead with traveler's update
:42	International Weather	Conditions across Europe and in Australia
:44 (all hours after 2amET/11pmPT)	Pacific Regional Forecast	Provides Pacific coastal states with forecast
:50	This Morning's Weather	Seasonal weather/storm update along with forecast for the day

LOCAL WEATHER

1. TWC has developed a computerized system called the **Weather Star**, which allows TWC to broadcast different local reports simultaneously to 1,200 weather zones around the country.

    a. The Weather Star system allows each cable system to receive local surface observations automatically from the nearest observation site.

        1) This information normally appears at the bottom of the TV screen during other presentations.

    b. The Weather Star system also provides the current and forecast conditions for each weather zone.

        1) These forecasts are shown six times per hour (or every 10 min.) at 8, 18, 28, 38, 48, and 58 min. past the hour.

    c. The part that is of interest to most pilots is the local radar image, which is also transmitted on the Weather Star system.

2. The radar presentations are enhanced versions of the raw radar images provided by NWS.

    a. TWC uses a process that eliminates ground clutter and other false echoes.

        1) This cleanup allows accurate radar imaging and contouring.

    b. These enhancements make TWC's radar image very useful in preflight planning.

        1) Radar shows the movement of the echoes over the last 90 min. to provide you with more information.

USING THE WEATHER CHANNEL

1. TWC presents "Aviation Weather" in the morning at 5:14, 6:14, and 7:14 ET daily and constantly updates the surface charts and radar imagery.

2. TWC is an excellent source to complement your weather briefing from an FSS specialist and provide you with a visual presentation of the weather, which is currently impossible by telephone.

INTERNET SITE

1.   TWC has a site on the Internet that contains, among a vast amount of weather information, various aviation-related charts. These aviation charts are the

    a.   Jet stream

        1)   Current-day location of the jet stream(s) over North America
        2)   Forecast location of the jet stream(s) over North America

    b.   Winds aloft observations (based on radiosonde data)

        1)   5,000 ft.
        2)   10,000 ft.
        3)   34,000 ft.

    c.   National airport overview

        1)   This chart depicts airports reporting either IFR or MVFR and also shows areas of precipitation. Check the time on the chart.

2.   In addition to these aviation-related charts, you can select specific cities for forecasts. These forecasts also include access to local and regional radar images and satellite images.

3.   The site address is http://www.weather.com.

4.   Remember, this information will give you a background to use when you receive your official weather briefing from an FSS or through DUATS.

    a.   The more information you have, the more informed you are when making a "go/no go" decision.

END OF APPENDIX

APPENDIX C
AUTOMATED FLIGHT SERVICE STATIONS

FLIGHT SERVICE STATIONS (FSSs)

Flight Service Stations (FSSs) are air traffic facilities that provide a variety of services to pilots.

1. Automated FSSs (AFSSs) have replaced most of the older FSSs, usually with one AFSS per state.

    a. Nonautomated FSSs were at a large number of airports around the country.

    b. The same services are available at AFSSs that were available at the FSSs but with a much faster and more complete dissemination of information nationwide.

2. AFSS personnel are responsible for providing emergency, inflight, and preflight services.

    a. Emergency situations are those in which life or property is in danger and include

        1) VFR search and rescue services
        2) Assistance to lost aircraft and other aircraft in emergency situations

    b. Inflight services are those provided to or affecting aircraft in flight or operating on the airport surface.

        1) NAVAID monitoring and restoration
        2) Local Airport Advisories (LAA)
        3) Delivery of ATC clearances, advisories, or requests
        4) Issuance of military flight advisory messages
        5) En Route Flight Advisory Service (EFAS) or Flight Watch
        6) Issuance of NOTAMs
        7) Transcribed or live weather broadcasts
        8) Weather observations
        9) PIREPs
        10) Radio pilot briefings

    c. Preflight services are those provided prior to actual departure, usually by telephone.

        1) Pilot briefings
        2) Flight plan filing and processing
        3) Aircraft operational reservations

TRANSCRIBED OR LIVE BROADCASTS

1. A variety of reports and forecasts are broadcast over selected VOR and NDB frequencies.

2. Unscheduled broadcasts are made upon receipt of special weather reports, PIREPs, NOTAMs, weather advisories, radar reports, military training route data, alert notices, and other information considered necessary to enhance safety and efficiency of flight.

3. Transcribed weather broadcasts (TWEBs) are broadcast continuously over selected NDB and VOR frequencies.

    a. A TWEB is weather information presented in a route-of-flight format.

4. The Pilot's Automatic Telephone Weather Answering Service (PATWAS) is provided by nonautomated FSSs and is a recorded telephone briefing service with the forecast for the local area, usually within a 50-NM radius of the station.

    a. A few selected stations also include route forecasts similar to the TWEB.

5. The Telephone Information Briefing Service (TIBS) is provided by AFSSs and furnishes weather and/or aeronautical information for a variety of routes and/or areas.

    a. TIBS may provide any of the following:

        1) Area and/or route briefings

            a) METARs
            b) TAFs
            c) Winds aloft

        2) Airspace procedures
        3) Special announcements

    b. A pilot who calls an AFSS by touch-tone telephone can select from different TIBS briefing areas and/or routes.

        1) The information contained in a TIBS is the same as in a standard briefing.

6. Scheduled weather broadcasts are made at H+15 in Alaska only and include surface reports from a number of airports in the vicinity of the station.

7. The Hazardous Inflight Weather Advisory Service (HIWAS) is a continuous broadcast service of inflight weather advisories, i.e., SIGMETs, convective SIGMETs, AIRMETs, CWAs, and AWWs over selected VORs.

PILOT BRIEFING

1. AFSSs are equipped with computer terminals and graphic displays that can generate or display any desired report, forecast, chart, and/or satellite imagery.

2. A preflight briefing may be any one of the following types:

    a. A standard briefing is a summary and interpretation of all available data concerning an intended flight.

    b. An abbreviated briefing is intended to supplement mass disseminated data (e.g., TWEB, TIBS, etc.), update a previous briefing, or provide the pilot with only specifically requested information.

    c. An outlook briefing is provided when the proposed departure is 6 hr. or more from the time of the briefing.

INFLIGHT SERVICES

1. AFSSs provide services to aircraft on a "first come, first served" basis, except for the following, which receive priority:

    a. Aircraft in distress
    b. Lifeguard (air ambulance) aircraft
    c. Search and rescue aircraft

2. The following types of radio communications are generally made by AFSSs:

    a. Authorized transmission of messages necessary for ATC or safety
    b. Routine radio contacts, e.g., inflight briefings
    c. ATC clearances, advisories, and requests
    d. Flight progress reports upon receipt of pilot position reports

3. AFSSs regularly monitor NAVAIDs within their area for proper operation.

    a. When a malfunction is indicated or reported by several aircraft, the AFSS attempts to restore the NAVAID or discontinue its use and issue an appropriate NOTAM.

4. A Local Airport Advisory (LAA) is a terminal service provided by an FSS physically located on an airport without an operating control tower.

    a. LAA provides information to arriving and departing aircraft concerning wind direction and speed, favored runway, altimeter setting, pertinent known traffic, and pertinent known field conditions.

        1) This information is advisory in nature and is not an ATC clearance.

    b. LAA may also provide control of airport lighting, e.g., rotating beacon, runway lights, etc., after dark and at times of reduced visibility.

    c. If Class D or E airspace exists at the surface of an airport served by an LAA, the FSS there may assist a pilot in obtaining a special VFR clearance, when appropriate.

5. The En Route Flight Advisory Service (EFAS), or Flight Watch, provides en route aircraft with timely and pertinent weather data tailored to a specific altitude and route using the most current available information.

    a. Briefings are intended to apply to the en route phase of flight (i.e., between climbout and descent to land).

    b. When conditions dictate, information is provided on weather for alternate routes and/or altitudes.

    c. EFAS may not be used for inflight services, i.e., flight plan filing, position reporting, or full route (preflight) briefing.

    d. PIREPs are solicited from pilots who contact Flight Watch.

EMERGENCY SERVICES

1. An emergency can be either a distress or an urgent situation.

   a. Distress is a condition of being threatened by serious and/or imminent danger and of requiring immediate assistance.

   b. Urgency is a condition of being concerned about safety and of requiring timely but not immediate assistance, i.e., a potential distress condition.

2. FSSs may provide assistance to aircraft in emergency situations by

   a. Assisting in orienting a lost pilot

   b. Coordinating communications between the aircraft, ATC, and search and rescue crews, as appropriate

   c. Monitoring frequencies 121.5 and 243.0 for emergency radio calls and ELT signals

3. The Direction Finder Service (DF Steer) allows an appropriately equipped FSS to determine an aircraft's bearing from the station using the two-way VHF radio communication transmitter on board the aircraft.

   a. Under emergency conditions when a standard instrument approach cannot be executed, an FSS can provide DF guidance and instrument approach service.

4. Using VOR or ADF facilities as appropriate to the aircraft's equipment, an FSS can assist a pilot in determining his/her position and provide guidance to the airport if desired.

FLIGHT DATA

1. FSSs accept domestic and international IFR, VFR, and DVFR flight plans and forward the flight plan data to the appropriate agencies.

2. Data from IFR flight plans are transmitted to the ARTCC as part of the IFR flight plan proposal.

   a. Search and rescue information from the flight plan is retained in the FSS and is available upon request.

3. VFR flight plans are forwarded to the FSSs serving the departure and the destination points.

   a. When an aircraft on a VFR flight plan changes destination, the FSS will forward a notification to the original and the new destination stations.

   b. When an aircraft changes its ETA, the information is passed by FSS to the destination station.

4. Military flight plans are handled by FSSs in much the same way as civilian flight plans.

5. For security control of air traffic, flight data and position reports from DVFR and IFR aircraft operating within an ADIZ are forwarded by FSS to ARTCC.

6. FSSs disseminate law enforcement alert messages, stolen aircraft summaries, and aircraft lookout alerts within FSS facilities and offices but not to the general public.

7. FSSs coordinate all pertinent information received from pilots prior to and during parachute jumping activity with other affected ATC facilities.

INTERNATIONAL OPERATIONS

1. AFSSs record and relay flight plans to and from Canada and Mexico to the appropriate stations.

    a. When the pilot requests Customs flight notification service (by including ADCUS in the remarks), the FSS will notify the appropriate Customs office.

        1) This service is available at airports so indicated in the *A/FD*.

    b. Round-robin flight plans to Mexico cannot be accepted.

2. AFSSs also relay International Civil Aeronautics Organization (ICAO) messages in four categories.

    a. Distress or urgency messages, or other messages concerning known or suspected emergencies, such as radio communications failures

    b. Movement and control

        1) Flight plans, amendments, and cancelations
        2) Clearances and flow control
        3) Requests and position reports

    c. Flight information

        1) Traffic information
        2) Weather information
        3) NOTAMs

    d. Technical messages

SEARCH AND RESCUE (SAR) OPERATIONS

1. An aircraft on a VFR or DVFR flight plan is considered to be overdue when it fails to arrive 30 min. after its ETA and communications or location cannot be established.

    a. An aircraft not on a flight plan is considered to be overdue when it is reported to be at least 1 hr. late at its destination.

    b. In either case, the actions taken by an FSS are the same.

2. As soon as a VFR aircraft becomes overdue, the destination FSS will attempt to locate the aircraft by checking all adjacent flight plan area airports.

    a. Appropriate approach control and ARTCC facilities are also checked.

    b. If these measures do not locate the aircraft, a request is made for SAR information from the departure FSS.

    c. The departure FSS then checks locally for any information about the aircraft.

        1) If the aircraft is located, a notification is sent to the destination FSS.
        2) If not, all SAR information from the flight plan is sent, including any remarks that may be pertinent to the search.

3. If the aircraft has not been located within 30 min. after it becomes overdue, an Information Request (INREQ) is sent to all FSSs, Flight Watch stations, and ARTCCs along the route, as well as the Rescue Coordination Center (RCC).

    a. Upon receipt of an INREQ, a facility will check its records and all area airports along the proposed route of flight.

4.   If the aircraft is not located within 1 hr. after transmission of the INREQ, an Alert Notice (ALNOT) is transmitted to all facilities within the search area.

   a.   The search area is normally 50 mi. on either side of the proposed route of flight from the last reported position to the destination.

   b.   Upon receipt of an ALNOT, each station within the search area conducts a search of airports within the area that were not checked previously.

   c.   ALNOTs are also broadcast over VOR and NDB voice-capable frequencies.

5.   When lake, island, mountain, or swamp reporting service programs have been established and a pilot requests the service, the FSS will establish contact every 10 min. with the aircraft while it is crossing the hazardous area.

   a.   If contact with the aircraft is lost for more than 15 min., Search and Rescue is notified.

   b.   Hazardous Area Reporting Service and chart depictions are published in the *AIM*.

AVIATION WEATHER SERVICES

1.   Aviation routine weather reports (METAR, SPECI) are filed at scheduled and unscheduled intervals with stations having sending capability for dissemination.

2.   FSSs actively solicit PIREPs when one or more of the following conditions are reported or forecast:

   a.   Ceilings at or below 5,000 ft.
   b.   Visibilities 5 SM or less
   c.   Thunderstorms and related phenomena
   d.   Turbulence of moderate degree or greater
   e.   Icing of light degree or greater
   f.   Wind shear

3.   Radar weather reports (SD/ROB) are collected by the National Center Operations (NCO) in Washington, D.C., and transmitted to FSSs.

4.   Winds and temperature aloft forecasts (FB) are computer-prepared and issued by the NCO to FSSs.

5.   Terminal aerodrome forecasts (TAF) for selected U.S. airports are prepared by National Weather Forecast Offices and forwarded for distribution.

6.   Area forecasts (FA) are issued by the Aviation Weather Center in Kansas City, MO, and disseminated to all FSSs.

7.   Severe weather forecasts are filed by the NWS and distributed to all FSSs.

8.   SIGMETs and AIRMETs are issued by the Aviation Weather Center in Kansas City, MO, to provide notice of potentially hazardous weather conditions.

9.   The TWEB and synopsis for selected routes are prepared by National Weather Forecast Offices and distributed to the appropriate FSSs.

10.   A Meteorological Impact Statement (MIS) is an unscheduled planning forecast intended for ARTCC specialists responsible for making flow control-related decisions.

   a.   It enables these specialists to include the impact of expected weather conditions in making such decisions.

11.   A Center Weather Advisory (CWA) is issued by the Central Weather Service Unit to reflect adverse weather conditions in existence at the time of issuance or conditions beginning within the next 2 hr.

USING THE AFSS

1. A universal toll-free number has been established for AFSSs throughout the country.

    a. When you dial (800) WX-BRIEF [(800) 992-7433], you are automatically switched to the AFSS that serves your area.

        1) You are answered by a recording giving instructions for both touch-tone and rotary dial telephones.

        2) Touch-tone users can elect to talk to a briefer or select any of the direct-access services, e.g., TIBS or "fast-file" flight plan filing.

        3) If you are using a rotary or pulse dial telephone, you will be switched automatically to a briefer.

    b. So that your preflight briefing can be tailored to your needs, give the briefer the following information:

        1) Your qualifications, e.g., student, private, commercial, and whether instrument rated

        2) The type of flight, either VFR or IFR

        3) The aircraft's registration number or your name if you do not know the registration number

        4) The aircraft type

        5) Your departure point

        6) Your proposed route of flight

        7) Your destination

        8) Your proposed flight altitude(s)

        9) Your estimated time of departure (ETD)

        10) Your estimated time en route (ETE)

    c. At a minimum, a **standard briefing** should include the following information in sequence:

        1) **Adverse conditions** -- significant meteorological and aeronautical information that might influence you to alter your proposed route of flight or even cancel your flight entirely. Expect the briefer to emphasize conditions that are particularly significant, e.g., low-level wind shear, embedded thunderstorms, reported icing, or frontal zones.

        2) **VFR flight not recommended** -- a statement issued when, in the briefer's judgment, a proposed VFR flight is jeopardized by conditions present or forecast, surface or aloft. The briefer will describe the conditions and affected locations, and announce, "VFR flight is not recommended."

            a) This is advisory in nature.

            b) You are responsible for making a final decision as to whether the flight can be conducted safely.

        3) **Synopsis** -- a brief statement describing the type, location, and movement of weather systems and/or air masses that may affect the proposed flight

        4) **Current conditions** -- a summary from all available sources of reported weather conditions applicable to the flight

            a) This summary is omitted if the proposed time of departure is over 2 hr. later, unless you request it.

5) **En route forecast** -- a summary of forecast conditions for the proposed route presented in logical order, i.e., departure/climbout, en route, and descent

6) **Destination forecast** -- a forecast of any significant changes within 1 hr. before and after the ETA at the planned destination

7) **Winds aloft** -- a summary of forecast winds aloft for the proposed route and altitude

8) **NOTAMs** -- information from any NOTAM (D) or NOTAM (L) pertinent to the proposed flight, and pertinent FDC NOTAMs within approximately 400 mi. of the FSS providing the briefing

   a) NOTAM (D) and FDC NOTAMs that have been published in the *Notices to Airmen Publication* are not included, unless requested by you.

9) **ATC delays** -- any known ATC delays and flow control advisories that might affect the proposed flight

10) The following may be obtained on your request:

   a) Information on military training routes (MTR) and military operations area (MOA) activity within the flight plan area and a 100-NM extension around the flight plan area

   b) Approximate density altitude data

   c) Information regarding such items as air traffic services and rules, customs/immigration procedures, ADIZ rules, etc.

   d) LORAN-C NOTAMs

   e) GPS NOTAMs

   f) Other assistance as required

d. Request an **abbreviated briefing** when you need to supplement mass disseminated data (e.g., weather channel or TIBS), update a previous briefing, or ask for only one or two specific items.

1) Provide the briefer with appropriate background information, the time you received the previous information, and/or the specific items needed.

2) The briefer can then limit the briefing to the information that you have not received and/or to changes in conditions since your previous briefing.

   a) To the extent possible, the briefing will be given in the same sequence as a standard briefing.

3) If you request only one or two specific items, the briefer will advise you if adverse conditions are present or forecast.

   a) Details on these conditions will be provided at your request.

e. You should request an **outlook briefing** whenever your proposed time of departure is 6 hr. or more from the time of the briefing.

1) The briefer will provide available forecast data applicable to the proposed flight for planning purposes only.

2) You should obtain a standard briefing prior to departure in order to obtain such items as current conditions, updated forecasts, winds aloft, and NOTAMs.

2. To provide inflight services, such as weather updates, filing a flight plan, etc., a number of sources exist.

   a. Transcribed weather broadcasts, such as TWEB or HIWAS, are available on certain VOR and NDB frequencies, as indicated in the identifier boxes on your navigational charts.

      1) To hear such a broadcast, listen on the appropriate frequency through your VOR or ADF receiver.

   b. To obtain current weather along your route of flight or to file a PIREP, contact Flight Watch (i.e., EFAS) on 122.0 MHz below FL 180 and as published at and above FL 180.

   c. For weather outlooks and to file, activate, or extend a flight plan, contact the nearest FSS.

      1) Use the frequency shown on your navigational chart atop the identifier box of the VOR nearest you.

3. Following any briefing, feel free to ask for any information that you or the briefer may have missed.

   a. It helps to save your questions until the briefing has been completed.

   b. This enables the briefer to present the information in a logical sequence and reduces the chance of important items being overlooked.

VISITING THE AFSS

1. You should visit an AFSS and tour the facility. A visit is an excellent way for you to learn what services are available and how you can best use them.

   a. AFSSs are open 24 hr., but usually the best time to visit is during normal business hours.

   b. You do not need to call ahead, but you may want to so you do not visit during a normal peak time or when staffing is reduced.

2. Your tour will be given by a specialist and usually begins at a telephone briefing station.

   a. The specialist is able to call up the various weather reports and forecasts for the departure, en route, and destination phases of a flight.

   b. Various charts (e.g., surface analysis chart) and a sequence of satellite images (either NOAA or GOES) can be displayed on another monitor.

   c. Here, also, the specialist will input the data for a flight plan. The specialist can also view information on aircraft that have already filed, either departing from or arriving in the AFSS's area.

3.   You will also see the radio communication station used to contact aircraft.

    a.   Here you will learn why it is very important that you identify the frequency on which you are transmitting and your aircraft's location.

        1)   Remember that most states have only one AFSS, so it is important for the specialist to know where you are in order to select the proper remote transmitter to talk to you.

    b.   At these positions, the specialist can provide the same services as those positions that answer incoming telephone calls, in addition to accepting PIREPs.

    c.   At a separate station will be the specialist who provides the En Route Flight Advisory Service (EFAS) for aircraft en route.

4.   As you tour the facility, you may also observe the other services provided at the AFSS. These may include the VHF direction finding (VHF/DF) equipment to help lost pilots and information on how weather observations are taken.

5.   By touring the AFSS and talking with specialists, you will gain a better understanding of how the AFSS supports pilot operations.

    a.   By understanding the strengths and weaknesses of the AFSS, you can maximize the services provided by the AFSS, and you can provide assistance (e.g., by making a PIREP).

KAVOURAS WEATHER GRAPHICS

1.   A company in Minneapolis called Kavouras is the FAA's contractor to provide weather graphics to AFSSs. It provides both hardware and software.

2.   The capability of each computer console includes four graphics menus:

    a.   Current menu -- analysis charts
    b.   Forecast menu -- forecast charts
    c.   Satellite menu -- satellite imagery
    d.   Radar menu -- radar data

3.   A final menu provides maps, charts, etc., that are produced at the specific request of a particular AFSS, e.g., Bahamas maps for Florida AFSSs.

4.   A paragraph on each chart follows.

    a.   Current Menu (Analysis Charts)

        1)   Weather depiction.

            a)   The Weather Depiction Analysis is a contoured and shaded depiction of MVFR and IFR areas. This chart gives the user a general overview of the country in terms of ceiling and visibility. Major synoptic features, such as highs, lows, and fronts, are included to aid in interpreting the chart. Individual station data and models are not shown on this chart. The Weather Depiction Analysis is quite valuable in assessing the large-scale picture in the vicinity of a route of flight; however, the latest surface observations at the destination airport must also be checked.

2) North American surface.

    a) The North American Surface Analysis depicts isobars, high and low pressure centers, and fronts. Individual station data and station models are not shown. The analysis depicts synoptic features -- those of fairly large scale. The placement of frontal features is determined by the Kavouras meteorologist using computer-generated surface plots which are hand analyzed every 2 to 3 hr. Before any features are placed, they are compared to the previous 3-hourly position and also to recent trends noticed over the last 12 hr.

3) National radar summary.

    a) The National Radar Summary Analysis is a composite of 211 National Weather Service, military, and ARTCC radars. The chart depicts precipitation areas using the standard VIP scale of six intensity levels. Echo top data, movement, and "Out for Maintenance" and "Not Available" sites are also included.

VIP Level	Contour Color	Intensity Level
1	Light green	Light
2	Dark green	Moderate
3	Light yellow	Heavy
4	Dark yellow	Very heavy
5	Light red	Intense
6	Dark red	Extreme

    b) The actual altitude of these levels varies significantly with season and latitude. All levels are lower in winter and in northern latitudes since the atmosphere is colder and more compact (denser).

4) Upper air (850, 700, 500 mb/hPa).

    a) Upper-air charts at 850, 700, and 500 mb/hPa display height contours in decameters, temperature in degrees Celsius, and relative moisture content. The following table gives an approximate relationship between millibar/hectoPascal level and altitude:

Pressure (mb/hPa)	Altitude (ft.)
500	18,000
700	10,000
850	5,000

5) Upper air (300, 200 mb/hPa).

    a) Upper-air charts at 300 mb/hPa and 200 mb display height contours in decameters and wind speeds in knots. The 300-mb/hPa level is at approximately 30,000 ft., and 200 mb/hPa is at approximately 39,000 ft. The exact altitude of these levels varies significantly with season and latitude.

6) Freezing level.

a) The freezing level chart displays the height of the lowest freezing level in thousands of feet above the surface. Data are derived from NWS balloon soundings, taken twice daily at 0000Z and 1200Z. The map is computer-generated, with a contour color of red and an interval of 4,000 ft.

7) Lifted Index/K Index.

a) The Lifted Index/K Index chart is a measure of atmospheric stability. Data are derived from National Weather Service radiosondes launched at 0000Z and 1200Z. Two values are displayed for every radiosonde site. The top value is the Lifted Index, with negative values indicating an unstable atmosphere and positive values indicating a more stable atmosphere. The lower value is the K Index. The larger this number, the greater the likelihood of precipitation.

8) Precipitable water.

a) Precipitable water is a measure of the amount of liquid water in a vertical column of air. This chart displays a contoured analysis of precipitable water, which can be correlated with precipitation total. Higher values indicate the atmosphere is holding a greater amount of moisture and imply that more significant precipitation is possible from the air mass, given that other conditions are favorable.

9) Average relative humidity (SFC -- 500 mb/hPa).

a) The Surface to 500 mb/hPa Relative Humidity Chart gives the average humidity in the lower 18,000 ft. of the atmosphere. Relative humidity values are contoured every 10% in red.

10) Winds aloft (FL 040, FL 140, FL 240, FL 340).

a) Winds aloft charts are an analysis of wind flow at various levels in the atmosphere. Data are displayed using the conventional wind barb format. The data are derived from NWS radiosondes, with the analysis computer-generated. Barbs are yellow and temperatures are black for FL 240 and FL 340 (temperatures are not reported for FL 040 and FL 140).

b. Forecast Menu (Forecast Charts)

1) North American surface.

a) The North American Surface Forecast depicts high- and low-pressure centers, fronts, and precipitation. The chart depicts synoptic features, those of fairly large scale. Therefore, weak pressure centers and features produced by terrain are generally ignored.

2) Low-level significant weather.

a) Low-level significant weather forecasts display important weather features from the surface to 24,000 ft. Freezing levels, shaded regions of MVFR and IFR, and turbulence are provided.

3) Winds/temperatures aloft (FB winds).

   a) Forecast winds aloft are generated twice daily by the National Weather Service in Suitland, Maryland. Forecasts are available for 12-, 24-, 36-, and 48-hr. time periods. At this time, only the 12-hr. chart (actually the 9- to 18-hr. forecast) is displayed since it is the most pertinent and often the most accurate. These data are reproduced without any changes by Kavouras, Inc. Wind data are displayed using the conventional wind barb format in yellow. Forecast temperatures are shown in degrees Celsius and colored black.

FL 390	.. approximately 200 mb/hPa
FL 340	.. approximately 250 mb/hPa
FL 300	.. approximately 300 mb/hPa
FL 240	.. approximately 400 mb/hPa
FL 180	.. approximately 500 mb/hPa
FL 120	.. approximately 650 mb/hPa
FL 090	.. approximately 700 mb/hPa
FL 060	.. approximately 800 mb/hPa

4) U.S. high-level significant weather.

   a) High-level significant weather forecasts cover events occurring at levels above 24,000 ft. Forecasts are available four times daily, covering a 6-hr. time period (3 hr. either side of 0000Z and 1200Z). Each chart displays jet stream axes with altitude and wind maximums, tropopause heights, areas of broken thunderstorm coverage, areas of moderate or greater turbulence, and surface fronts.

5) 36-hour thickness/sea-level pressure.

   a) This forecast gives a depiction of how the atmosphere will look 36 hr. in the future. Sea-level pressure is depicted, along with frontal features. The thickness of the lower half (approximately) of the atmosphere is also displayed.

c. GOES Menu (GOES Satellite Imagery)

1) GOES (Geostationary Operational Environmental Satellite) imagery is available to AFSSs every half hour. Kavouras receives the data directly from the satellite via its communications facility in Minneapolis. The transmission schedule is dictated partly by NOAA and partly by Kavouras.

d. Radar Menu (NWS Radar Data)

1) National radar composite.

   a) The national radar composite, consisting of the National Weather Service WSR-88D radars, is available at 5-min. intervals. This composite is assembled at Kavouras's central processing facility in Minneapolis. Option 1 displays the animation of the most recent images. Option 6 displays the latest image received by the system. The ANIMATE UP and DOWN keys can be used to change the speed of the animation loop when option 1 is chosen or to single step through the images when option 6 is chosen.

2) Regional radar composite.

a) Twenty regional radar composites are assembled and transmitted every 5 min. Each AFSS facility will receive one region, likely one which correlates with the most air traffic handled by the facility. Each region is about the size of five or six states and gives the advantage of seeing high resolution radar data on a larger basemap.

3) Single-site radar imagery.

a) Data from two single-site radars can be combined and either animated or viewed singly. The options are either to have one radar site with two ranges or to have two individual radar sites with one range from each. It is up to the AFSS facility to choose whether two radar sites or two ranges from a single site are needed.

END OF APPENDIX

APPENDIX D
DIRECT USER ACCESS TERMINAL SERVICE (DUATS)

DUATS INTRODUCTION

The FAA's Direct User Access Terminal Service (DUATS) is a computerized weather briefing and flight planning system that provides pilots with the most up-to-date and reliable briefing information possible.

1. DUATS may be accessed via the Internet or by a direct connection through a toll-free 800 telephone number. There are no usage fees for the basic service.

    a. Our discussion will focus on the Internet-based versions of DUATS.

2. The service is provided under contract from the FAA by two companies, Data Transformation Corporation (DTC) and Computer Science Corporation (CSC).

3. You should try both DTC and CSC DUATS before deciding which one you will use regularly.

    a. Choosing the service that you are the most comfortable with is a personal decision.
    b. You, of course, may also use both systems.

4. Both systems are being upgraded continuously.

ACCESSING DUATS

To access DUATS, you need a personal computer with an Internet connection.

1. DUATS services are available at the following websites:

    a. DTC is at www.duat.com
    b. CSC is at www.duats.com

2. Both services also offer customer assistance lines that are open 24 hr. a day.

    a. DTC's help line is (800) 243-3828.
    b. CSC's help line is (800) 345-3828.

SIGNING UP

Once you establish a connection to one of the DUATS websites, both systems require you to complete a sign-up procedure that confirms your authorization to use the system. You will be asked to enter your access code and password, as shown below.

1. Only medically current pilots, student pilots, balloonists, ultralight and glider pilots, flight instructors, ground instructors, and aircraft dispatchers are authorized by the FAA to access DUATS.

2. If you do not have an access code and a password and you are an authorized user, register as a new user by choosing "Register" on DTC's site, or "New User Registration" on CSC's site. Follow the instructions, and DUATS will assign you an access code (which you can change if you wish) and ask you to choose a password.

    a. Your access code and password must then be used in all subsequent DUATS briefings.

STORING YOUR AIRCRAFT PROFILE

After signing onto DUATS, or anytime during a briefing, you can store a profile of your aircraft that will be retained permanently in the DUATS.

1. This aircraft profile consists of search and rescue information, such as aircraft registration number, type of aircraft, aircraft color, etc.

    a. The profile also includes flight planning information, such as fuel flow, true airspeed, and climb/descent rate.

2. When you use DUATS to file a flight plan, this information is entered automatically in the appropriate spaces unless you wish to change it.

DUATS MAIN MENU

The DUATS main menu allows you to access a weather briefing, plan a flight, and use various other options.

DTC's Main Menu Options

CSC's Main Menu Options

```
                    DUAT MENU

            Weather Briefings
              Graphical TFRs
              Route Briefing
              Area Briefing
              State Briefing
              Specific Locations
              Weather Graphics
              Interactive Overlays
            Flight Plans
              File Domestic
              File ICAO
              Close VFR
              Flight Plan Status
              Amend/Cancel FP
            Planning Tools
              Flight Planner
              Flight Log
              Special Airspace
              ATC Advisories
            Aeronautical Data
              Airport Info and Approach Plates
              Sectional Charts
              Decode Location ID
              Encode Location ID
            My DUAT
              Stored Routes
              Stored Requests
              User Profiles
```

```
                 DUATS MAIN MENU

            Flight Restrictions
            GPS RAIM Prediction
            Weather Briefing
            Weather Graphics
            Flight Planner
            Airport Diagrams
            FAA Flight Plan Filing
            Stored Routes
            Encode and Decode Contractions
            Personal Profile Management
            Help
            Golden Eagle and Cirrus Programs
            Feedback
            Sign Off
```

1. You are allowed 30 min. to use the FAA functions, after which the system terminates your briefing automatically.

    a. If you have not completed your briefing by that time, you must sign back on and begin again.

WEATHER BRIEFING

DTC's weather briefing options are incorporated into the main menu, while CSC's weather briefing options are shown on a separate Weather Briefing Menu.

CSC's Weather Briefing Menu

```
            Standard Briefing
            (Drop-down Menu)
              – Low Altitude
              – High Altitude
              – Area
            Outlook Briefing
            (Drop-down Menu)
              – Route
              – Area
            Abbreviated Briefing
            (Drop-down Menu)
              – Route
              – Location
              – State/Collective
              – Defined Radius
```

1. Both DUATS services offer similar weather briefing options.

    a. The route options are used to retrieve weather products along a proposed route of flight.

        1) You are required to enter your departure point, time of departure, altitude, destination, route of flight, and estimated time en route.

    b. The "specific location" and "location" options are used to retrieve weather information for a particular location.

        1) You are prompted for one or more location identifiers and your time of departure.

    c. The abbreviated weather options allow you to request specific weather products from specified weather reporting locations.

        1) State collectives (as part of an abbreviated briefing) allow you to request weather products by state.

2. As with an FSS briefer, DUATS allows you the option of a standard, an abbreviated, or an outlook briefing.

    a. Selecting a route or local briefing provides you with a standard briefing, including all the reports and forecasts commonly provided by a briefer.

    b. Abbreviated weather briefings provide the report types you request for selected locations.

    c. Requesting weather information more than 6 hr. in advance of your proposed time of departure provides you with an outlook briefing.

3. The weather data presented are normally displayed in the standard FAA abbreviated format and in UTC, unless you request the expanded (plain English) version and local time zone.

  a. EXAMPLES:

   1) Standard format:

   METAR KLAL 011454Z 19004 8SM SCT040 OVC120 21/16 A3014

   2) Expanded format (CSC DUATS):

   LAKELAND FL (LAKELAND LINDER REGIONAL) [LAL] ROUTINE OBSERVATIONS AT 9:54 A.M. EST: WIND 190 AT 4, VISIBILITY 8 MILES, 4,000 SCATTERED, CEILING 12,000 OVERCAST, TEMPERATURE 21, DEWPOINT 16, ALTIMETER 30.14

FLIGHT PLAN FILING

The flight plan options are used to file, amend, cancel, or close flight plans. DTC's flight plan options are incorporated into the main menu, while CSC's flight plan options are shown on a separate FAA flight plan menu.

CSC's Flight Plan Menu

File
(Drop-down Menu)
  – Domestic
  – ICAO
Display
(view, cancel, or modify flight plan)
Close
(Close VFR flight plan)

1. Note that, if you have not previously entered your access code and password, the system will not allow you to file or amend any flight plan information.

2. When filing a flight plan, you may use any previously stored data on your aircraft or enter all the values individually.

    a. After you complete all of the flight data prompts, your entire flight plan will be visible, and you should take this opportunity to look for any errors or changes you wish to make.

Filing DC ADIZ Flight Plans

File FAA Domestic Flight Plan

1. Type
2. Aircraft Identification
3. Aircraft Type / Special Equipment   Number of Aircraft 1   ☐ Heavy
4. True Airspeed (KTS)
5. Departure Point
6. Proposed Departure Time
7. Cruising Altitude
8. Route of Flight   Click to check for preferred routes
9. Destination
10. Est. Time Enroute (HHMM)
11. Remarks
12. Fuel on Board (HHMM)
13. Alternate Airport
14. Pilot Name and Address:
Phone:
Aircraft Home Base:
15. Number Aboard
16. Color of Aircraft
17. Destination Contact (optional)
Name:
Phone:

[File This Flight Plan] [Reset Form] [Cancel and Return to Main Menu]

Note: The pilot name cannot be changed here. To file a flight plan with a different Pilot in Command, list the PIC's name in the *remarks* section or log in to DUATS using that pilot's access code.

    b. When all the fields are correct, click the appropriate button to file your flight plan.

        1) DUATS will then display the ARTCC or FSS to which your flight plan will be sent and the time it will be transmitted.

        2) Up to the time it is sent, you can amend or cancel with DUATS service.

        3) After it is sent, you must contact an FSS.

3. To amend or cancel a flight plan you filed with DUATS, you must enter the aircraft ID number used in the flight plan.

    a. If you attempt to amend or cancel your flight plan after it is forwarded, you are advised to contact the appropriate FSS.

4. DTC's ATC Advisories option (found on the Main Menu) provides current advisories issued by the Air Traffic Control Systems Command Center.

5. DTC's Aircraft Info option and CSC's Aircraft Profile option allow you to store or modify any data contained in your aircraft profiles.

    a. This data may be used when requesting a weather briefing, filing a flight plan, or creating a flight log.

6. DTC's Flight Log and CSC's Flight Planner both create a navigation log of a proposed flight based on your estimated departure time, airspeed, and the forecast winds aloft at your proposed altitude.

   a. To plan a flight, you must supply DUATS with certain information.

      1) Departure point
      2) Destination
      3) Departure time
      4) Route selection
      5) Aircraft performance information
      6) Cruise altitude

   b. You may input your own route or allow DUATS to generate one of its own.

      1) CSC will generate one of the following routes at your request:

         a) Low-altitude airway auto-routing selects the shortest path from your origin to the destination using Victor airways.

            i)   This selection is available both with and without appropriate DPs and STARs.

            ii) This selection may not be possible for certain airports that are very remote from any navigational facility.

         b) Jet route auto-routing selects the shortest path from your origin to the destination using jet routes.

            i)   You will be prompted for departure and arrival routings (e.g., DPs or STARs).

         c) VOR-direct auto-routing is similar to low-altitude airway auto-routing.

         d) Direct routing for LORAN.

         e) Direct routing for RNAV.

         f) User-selected routing.

   c. Once you select one of the routing options, DUATS computes and displays the optimal route, along with the distance along the route.

      1) Note that DUATS does NOT take into account obstacles, terrain, controlled airspace, and special-use airspace.

      2) You must verify the suggested route against your charts to see that it can be flown safely.

   d. DTC's DUATS generates a flight log as shown below, complete with forecast winds aloft and heading and groundspeed computations.

DTC's Flight Log

——> Data Transformation's Flight Log <——
Altitude--7000 Ft   Air Speed--150 Knots   Departure Time--2200Z

LEG	MAG CRS	MAG HDG	GND SPD	DIST (NM)	ETE (MIN)	WIND	ATE
GNV ARPT	217	225	138	9	0+04	276/023	____
GNV VORTAC	162	170	157	25	0+09	276/023	____
OCF VORTAC	171	179	160	72	0+27	290/024	____
LAL VORTAC	153	160	166	77	0+28	290/024	____
LBV VORTAC	157	163	160	61	0+23	284/018	____
XING V035	109	110	167	19	0+07	284/018	____
CURVE	087	085	167	19	0+07	284/018	____
MIA ARPT	TOTAL			282	1+45		

YOUR ETA = 2345Z

e. CSC will prompt you for your aircraft's climb, cruise, and descent airspeeds; climb and descent rates; and fuel consumption rates throughout and then generate the following flight log. Other flight log formats are available in the Modify Flight Planner Profile Menu.

CSC's Flight Log

From: KGNV -- Gainesville FL
To: KMIA -- Miami FL
Time: Fri Feb 26 22:00 (UTC)

Routing options selected: Automatic low altitude airway.
Flight plan route:
     KGNV OCF V295 BAIRN V267 GREMM KMIA
Flight totals: fuel: 30 gallons, time: 1:37, distance 265.7 nm.

Ident Type/Morse Code Name or Fix/radial/dist Latitude Longitude Alt.	Route Winds Temp	Mag Crs Hdg	KTS TAS GS	Fuel Time Dist	Fuel Time Dist
1. KGNV Apt. Gainesville FL 29:41:24 82:16:18 2					0.0 0:00 266
	Direct 291/15 + 16C	 179 184	 130 136	4.8 0:14 31	
2. OCF --- -.- ..-. d113.7 Ocala 29:10:39 82:13:35 70					4.8 0:14 235
	V295 284/24 + 10C	 132 136	 155 176	6.1 0:20 60	
3. ORL --- .-. .-.. d112.2 Orlando 28:32:34 81:20:06 70					10.9 0:34 175
	V295 284/24 + 10C	 165 172	 155 166	4.1 0:14 38	
4. BAIRN Int. ORLr162/37 VRBr300 27:56:53 81:06:54 70					15.0 0:48 137
	V267 284/24 + 10C	 165 173	 155 166	8.0 0:26 73	
5. PHK .-. .... -.- d115.4 Pahokee 26:46:58 80:41:29 70					23.0 1:14 64
	V267 277/17 + 13C	 158 164	 161 169	4.3 0:15 41	
6. GREMM Int. PHKr155/41 MIAr020 26:09:57 80:22:36 40					27.3 1:29 23
	Direct 263/17 + 17C	 171 177	 170 171	2.4 0:08 23	
7. KMIA Apt. Miami FL 25:47:35 80:17:25 0					29.7 1:37 0

NOTE: Fuel calculations do not include required reserves.
Flight totals: fuel: 30 gallons, time: 1:37, distance 265.7 nm.
Average groundspeed 165 knots.
Great circle distance is 256.4 nm -- this route is 4% longer.

7.   DTC's Special Use Airspace selection provides you with information on alert areas, MOAs, prohibited areas, restricted areas, and warning areas within 5 NM of your route of flight.

8.   CSC's Flight Planning System Operating Instructions document gives complete user-friendly directions on how to use the Flight Planner option.

ENCODE AND DECODE FUNCTIONS

The encode and decode functions are used to find the identifier for a known location and to receive information on NAVAIDs and airports for any valid location identifier, respectively.

1.   In the encode function, all locations that use the name you enter are shown.

DTC's Encode Function

2.   In the decode function, information concerning a given identifier or contraction is provided.

CSC's Encode/Decode Function

3.   At any field that requires entry of a location identifier, both DTC and CSC allow you to retrieve encode/decode information.

END OF APPENDIX

APPENDIX E
AVIATION WEATHER RESOURCES ON THE INTERNET

1. In recent years, an explosion of data has been available on the Internet, and much of it is of interest to pilots, especially aviation weather. By careful use of this seemingly endless, constantly changing resource, any pilot with access to an Internet connection can obtain current official and unofficial aviation weather products.

    a. There are many excellent sources of weather information on the Internet.

        1) Some sites provide aviation weather data free of charge to the user. These sites are normally sponsored by commercial vendors, and their billboard commercials are placed around the site. If you are in the market for any of the advertised products, your support of these companies, with a mention that you saw their ads on the Internet, will help continue this free service to all users.

        2) Other sites require one to sign up for membership, generally at no cost, but user demographic data are often gathered for marketing purposes.

        3) Other sites provide aviation weather data to subscribers for a monthly subscription fee, typically about $10.

    b. Once you have assembled a list of favorite websites, you will be able to get the weather information you need quickly.

    c. By having multiple sites available, you can have backups for those times when technical problems with a particular site may make it unavailable.

2. **Sites.** The following is a list of nine selected aviation-weather-related Internet sites and their URLs that will serve to get you started in using the Internet as a quick, practical, inexpensive source of aviation weather data. These sites represent just the tip of the iceberg and are representative of the hundreds of sites available. Also, you will want to try typing weather or aviation weather in your search engine to see how many sites are listed for you to explore.

a.   **Gleim Publications.** www.gleim.com/aviation/ -- contains several links to other aviation and aviation weather sites on the Internet, plus other information about Gleim aviation products.

b. **Gleim Aviation Weather.** www.gleim.com/aviation/weather/ -- contains links to National Weather Service radar images as well as METAR/TAF reports by airport, winds aloft, and area forecast reports. It's an easy, one-stop aviation weather information resource.

c. **Landings.** www.landings.com -- a very large site with many different aviation links. The Aviation Weather Information sources section has over 100 different links, including information (e.g., key to ASOS Weather Observations) and current data (e.g., convective SIGMETs from NWS/NOAA). This Internet site is very popular with pilots.

d. **AVweb.** www.avweb.com -- another very large, popular site with many aviation links, including aviation weather sources worldwide. The AVweb site requires membership but no fee. Membership includes a weekly aviation news summary (very interesting and informative) emailed to the user every Monday morning.

e. **Aircraft Owners and Pilots Association (AOPA).** www.aopa.org -- a superb aviation site with many aviation databases and an excellent source of aviation weather data, including text products (e.g., METARs and TAFs) and charts. You must be an AOPA member to access the databases and weather links since they are in the members-only section.

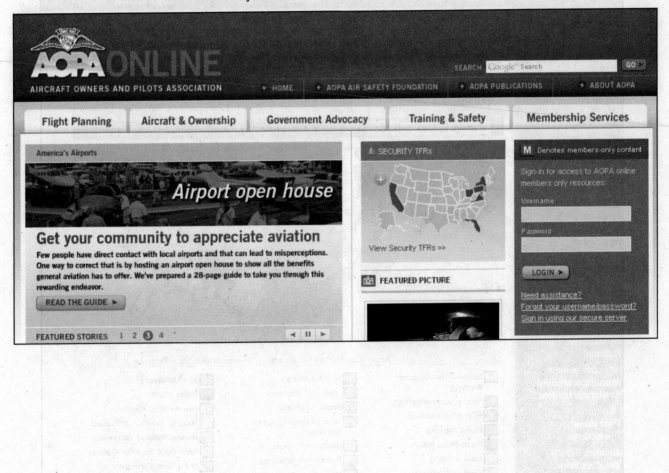

f.   **National Weather Service.** www.nws.noaa.gov -- official aviation weather products, including text products and charts that are available in several different formats. It is a great site with many products that are not normally seen.

g.   **Aviation Weather Center products.** www.aviationweather.gov -- official products themselves, such as AIRMETs, TAFs, winds aloft forecasts, etc., and excellent descriptions of the products. New products at the site include satellite pictures from GOES-8 and 9 with aviation flight conditions (IFR, MVFR, and VFR) and sky cover overlaid, and National Radar with tops and convective SIGMETs overlaid, updated twice hourly.

h.   **Intellicast.** www.intellicast.com -- superb WSR-88D NexRad (Doppler radar) color radar summary graphics of the entire U.S. and individual parts of the country (e.g., Jacksonville Radar Summary). The graphics show precipitation returns, tops, movement, etc.

i.   **Tropical Prediction Center.** www.nhc.noaa.gov -- the best color tropical cyclone graphics available, including histories and current storm movement predictions.

END OF APPENDIX

INDEX

AUTHORS' RECOMMENDATIONS

The Experimental Aircraft Association, Inc. is a very successful and effective nonprofit organization that represents and serves those of us interested in flying, in general, and in sport aviation, in particular. We personally invite you to enjoy becoming a member. Visit their website at www.eaa.org.

Types of EAA Memberships:

$40 - Individual (plus choice of *EAA Sport Aviation Magazine* or *EAA Sport Pilot Magazine*) - add a second magazine subscription for $20

$50 - Individual Plus Spouse (extends all benefits to member's spouse, except for an additional EAA magazine subscription)

$10 - Student (for those age 17 or under; includes Student Membership kit & access to student members-only website)

$975 - Lifetime

Write: EAA Aviation Center
3000 Poberezny Rd.
Oshkosh, Wisconsin 54902

Call: (920) 426-4800
(800) JOIN-EAA
Email: membership@eaa.org

The annual EAA Oshkosh AirVenture is an unbelievable aviation spectacular with over 10,000 airplanes at one airport! Virtually everything aviation-oriented you can imagine! Plan to spend at least 1 day (not everything can be seen in a day) in Oshkosh (100 miles northwest of Milwaukee).

Convention dates: 2008 -- July 28 through August 3
2009 -- July 27 through August 2
2010 -- July 26 through August 1

The annual Sun 'n Fun EAA Fly-In is also highly recommended. It is held at the Lakeland, FL (KLAL) airport (between Orlando and Tampa). Visit the Sun 'n Fun website at www.sun-n-fun.org.

Convention dates: 2009 -- April 21 through April 26
2010 -- April 13 through April 18
2011 -- April 5 through April 10

BE-A-PILOT: INTRODUCTORY FLIGHT

Be-A-Pilot is an industry-sponsored marketing program designed to inspire people to "Stop dreaming, start flying." Be-A-Pilot has sought flight schools to participate in the program and offers a $99 introductory flight certificate that can be redeemed at a participating flight school.

The goal of this program is to encourage people to experience their dreams of flying through an introductory flight and to begin taking flying lessons. For more information, you can visit the Be-A-Pilot home page at www.beapilot.com or call 1-888-BE-A-PILOT.

AIRCRAFT OWNERS AND PILOTS ASSOCIATION

AOPA is the largest, most influential aviation association in the world, with more than 415,000 members--two thirds of all pilots in the United States. AOPA's most important contribution to the world's most accessible, safest, least expensive, friendliest, easiest-to-use general aviation environment is their lobbying on our behalf at the federal, state, and local levels. AOPA also provides legal services, advice, and other assistance to the aviation community.

We recommend that you become an AOPA member, which costs only $39 annually. To join, call 1-800-USA-AOPA or visit the AOPA website at www.aopa.org.

Gleim's Complete Pilot Kits

Sport Pilot	$199.95 _____
Private Pilot	$249.95 _____
Instrument Pilot	$249.95 _____
Commercial Pilot	$174.95 _____
Instrument/Commercial Pilot	$341.95 _____
Sport Pilot Flight Instructor	$174.95 _____
Flight/Ground Instructor	$174.95 _____
ATP	$189.95 _____

Also Available:

Flight Engineer Test Prep CD-Rom .... $59.95 _____

Shipping (nonrefundable): **$20 per kit** ...... $ _____
(Alaska and Hawaii please call for shipping price)
Add applicable sales tax for shipments within the state of Florida. ...... $ _____
For orders outside the United States, please visit our website at
www.gleim.com/aviation/products.php to place your order. ...... TOTAL $ _____

Reference Materials and Other Accessories Available by Contacting Gleim.

TOLL FREE: 800.874.5346 INTERNET: gleim.com	LOCAL: 352.375.0772 FAX: 352.375.6940 E-MAIL: sales@gleim.com	Gleim Publications, Inc. P.O. Box 12848 Gainesville, FL 32604

NAME (please print) _____

ADDRESS _____ Apt. _____
(street address required for UPS)

_____

CITY _____ STATE ____ ZIP _____

____ MC/VISA/DISC ____ Check/M.O. Daytime Telephone (____) ___ - ___

Credit Card # _____ - _____ - _____ - _____

Exp. ___/___ Signature _____
Mo./Yr.

E-mail Address _____

1. We process and ship orders daily, within one business day, over 99.8% of the time. Call by 4PM Eastern for same-day service!
2. Please PHOTOCOPY this order form for others.
3. No CODs. Orders from individuals must be prepaid. Volume orders may be purchased on account.
4. Gleim Publications, Inc. guarantees the immediate refund of all resalable texts and unopened software and audios if returned within 30 days. Applies only to items purchased direct from Gleim Publications, Inc. Our shipping charge is nonrefundable.
5. Components of specially priced package deals are nonreturnable.
   Prices subject to change without notice.
   0508

552

Please forward your suggestions, corrections, and comments concerning typographical errors, etc., to **Irvin N. Gleim • c/o Gleim Publications, Inc. • P.O. Box 12848 • University Station • Gainesville, Florida • 32604.** Please include your name and address so we can properly thank you for your interest.

1. _____

2. _____

3. _____

4. _____

5. _____

6. _____

7. _____

8. _____

9. _____

10. _____

11. _____

12. _____

13. _____

14. _____

15. _____

16. _____

17. _____

18. _____

Remember, for superior service: Mail, email, or fax questions about our materials.
Telephone questions about orders, prices, shipments, or payments.

Name: _____

Address: _____

City/State/Zip: _____

Telephone: Home: _____   Work: _____   Fax: _____

Email: _____